# DIRECTORY OF BRITISH FOSSILIFEROUS LOCALITIES

PALAEONTOGRAPHICAL  SOCIETY

DIRECTORY  OF

# BRITISH

# FOSSILIFEROUS  LOCALITIES

LONDON

1954

Reprinted with the permission of the Palaeontographical Society, London


JOHNSON REPRINT CORPORATION
111 Fifth Avenue, New York, N. Y. 10003

JOHNSON REPRINT COMPANY LTD.
Berkeley Square House, London, W. 1

*Published in* 1954 *by the*
*Palaeontographical Society,*
*Burlington House, London,*
*W.* 1.

First reprinting, 1966, Johnson Reprint Corporation

Printed in the United States of America

*To the Amateur Palaeontologist*

THE Palaeontographical Society was founded in 1847 for the purpose of publishing annual volumes of monographs on British fossils. The founders included professional and amateur geologists, the latter those, no less distinguished, who studied the subject solely for the love of it. Throughout the history of the Society such co-operation has continued, the enthusiasm of the amateurs blending with the experience of the professionals to the added benefit of the science. Amateurs have written some of the Society's most celebrated monographs, and have always taken a very active share in the guidance of the Society's affairs.

When the Council of the Society came to consider measures for the celebration of its centenary in 1947, the restrictions consequent on the aftermath of war forced it to abandon many desirable plans. It was felt that tribute was due to the twin sources of the Society's continuing vitality : for the professional palaeontologists the Society instituted a series of supplements to early monographs, many of which needed but a revision of nomenclature to give topicality to the original research ; to their amateur colleagues it offers this Directory of British Fossiliferous Localities to serve as a guide to the fossil-collecting opportunities of this country, and to provide references to scientific literature. Many amateurs have helped in the compilation of the book ; it is hoped that they will find their reward in its usefulness and in the recruitment, through it, of new enthusiasts to their ranks.

## Acknowledgements

THIS Directory was made possible, first, by those many geologists and palaeontologists who contributed the information incorporated in its pages and, secondly, by those members of the Palaeontographical Society who sorted and compiled the material so collected, typed the manuscript, edited it, read the proofs and supervised it through to publication. The Council of the Society is indeed indebted to all these for their invaluable assistance so freely given.

Although this work was substantially ready for the press at the time of the Centenary of the Society, financial stringency made publication at that time impossible. The Society's Rules do not permit the diversion of its normal income from the publication of monographs, and the President and Council of the Society sought for aid elsewhere. They have received £100 from the Directors of the Anglo-Iranian Oil Company Limited, £100 from the Directors of the Burmah Oil Company Limited, and £150 from the Council of the British Association for the Advancement of Science (Bernard Hobson Bequest). They offer their warmest thanks for this generous support, as a consequence of which they are able to offer the book at less than the cost of production and at a price which, it is hoped, will be within the means of all who enjoy collecting fossils.

List of contributors : W. J. Arkell, P. G. H. Boswell, Miss A. Brading, A. Bray, A. G. Brighton, O. M. B. Bulman, E. St. J. Burton, A. J. Butler, P. J. Channon, F. W. Cope, Hugh Curtis, A. G. Davis, H. R. Dudley, C. Edmonds, Miss G. L. Elles, G. F. Elliott, W. D. Evans, W. G. Fearnsides, J. Fowler, C. T. A. Gaster, E. Greenly, R. Kay Gresswell, T. F. Grimsdale, H. L. Hawkins, W. P. Hedley, H. G. Hickling, W. Hopkins, R. G. S. Hudson, J. W. Jackson, T. A. Jones, G. A. Kellaway, P. E. Kent, W. B. R. King, W. D. Lang, H. P. Lewis, A. Ludford, R. V. Melville, G. H. Mitchell, E. W. J. Moore, L. R. Moore, E. Neaverson, K. P. Oakley, C. D. Ovey, D. E. Owen, T. Pain, D. Parkinson, L. G. Peirson, R. W. Pocock, J. Pringle, L. Richardson, J. A. Robbie, J. E. Sainty, J. Shirley, H. E. P. Spencer, J. V. Stephens, C. J. Stubblefield, J. H. Taylor, D. G. Titcomb, C. T. Trechmann, Sir Arthur Trueman, W. D. Ware, F. B. A. Welch, T. H. Whitehead, W. F. Whittard, H. B. Whittington, E. Williams-Mitchell, L. J. Wills, V. Wilson, Henry Woods, C. W. Wright, J. Wright, A. Wrigley.

# CONTENTS

# INTRODUCTION

THIS Directory has been prepared with the twofold object of extending interest in the study of palaeontology, and of providing a field handbook in which much information on fossil localities, disseminated throughout the geological literature of past years, is made easily accessible. It is hoped that the Directory will not only be of use to those, especially overseas visitors, seeking information on unfamiliar territory, but that it will also encourage workers to take an interest in the geology of their home districts.

Palaeontology has a scientific history of some 150 years. The classical contributions to the subject were directed to making known the characteristic fossils of particular geological formations, and to establishing the zoological relationships of groups of fossils and forging their links with the creatures of to-day. The main outlines of the pictures based on these studies are now firmly drawn, although much detail remains to be filled in : to do so use is now made of studies of variation in communities of fossils (believed to correspond more or less closely to the populations studied by zoologists), and of inferences about the conditions of life of the fossil-forming organisms. Search is still made for direct evidence of evolution by the collecting of stratigraphical sequences of fossils showing continuous morphological change : described examples of such " lineages " are few, and of these some are disputed.

Fossil-collecting can be a rewarding hobby when pursued for its own sake, but it has far greater interest when applied to some particular problem, and in this connection the advice of specialists should be sought : they are few in most fields of study, but their help is seldom withheld from serious collectors. Approach to them may be made through University geological departments, through the British Museum (Natural History) or the Geological Survey and Museum, or through local museums and natural history societies. It is no more than a fair return for such help that collections of scientific value should finally find a home, either by gift or bequest, in a responsible museum : many important discoveries first made by, and properly credited to, amateurs have been wasted by the disappearance of their collections. Valuable guidance in the methods of collecting and keeping fossils can be found in the pamphlet *Instructions to Collectors, No. 11, Fossils and Minerals* published by the British Museum (Natural History), price 3*d*.

Finally, it cannot be too strongly stated that many of the localities mentioned in this book are on private land, and that permission should always be asked before visiting them. In the interests of other workers and in courtesy to the owner, every care should be taken to avoid damage to the exposure and its surroundings.

Since the compilation of this directory in 1947 there has been considerable publication amplifying information on previously recorded fossil localities and giving details of new ones. With very few exceptions, neither this information nor references to the papers in which it was published are included in this Directory.

Users of the book are asked to co-operate by notifying the Society of any additions or corrections which ought to be made in subsequent editions of the Directory. This information, which will be most helpful if given in the form used in this Directory, should be sent to The Secretary, Palaeontographical Society, Geological Survey and Museum, London, S.W. 7.

*The Arrangement of the Directory*

The localities are grouped in alphabetical order of counties under the headings, England, Wales and Scotland, the Isles of Wight and Man being treated individually, and the Scottish Isles grouped with their respective counties. Within each county-group, the localities are listed, alphabetically, by reference to the nearest village or town.

The position of the locality and the type of exposure is followed by the geological facts, which include some indication of the kinds of fossils to be found, with mention of items of outstanding interest. The references which follow are detailed in the " *Lists of Works Referred to* " which will be found after the locality-lists of each country. Map references are given to the current 1-inch sheets of the Geological Survey and Ordnance Survey *New Popular Edition* maps. An attempt has been made to include localities of importance in the history of British geology, where the location is known.

## Stratigraphical Divisions

Geological time is divided into Eras. Each era comprises a number of Periods, each of which is the time-equivalent of, and bears the same name as one of the Systems in which the sedimentary rocks of the earth's crust are grouped. The names of the Systems are the same over the whole of the earth's surface, and they are recognized internationally. Space forbids discussion of the basis of the stratigraphical classification of rocks, but each System " may perhaps be defined as a consecutive series of strata formed during the prevalence of certain generic forms of life throughout a large part of the earth's surface " : in other words the basis is primarily palaeontological. Each System comprises a number of Series which may be of local or regional significance. Each Series is sub-divided into Formations, Beds etc. and Zones ; tables of these can be found in the *Handbook of the Geology of Great Britain* (London, 1929), by J. W. Evans and C. J. Stubblefield, and in many of the papers named in the " *Lists of Works Referred to* " in this book. The relative positions of many of the stratigraphical names used in this book are as follows :—

SYSTEM

HOLOCENE

PLEISTOCENE

PLIOCENE   -   -   *Leda myalis* Bed
                  Cromer Forest Bed
                  Weybourne Crag
                  Chillesford Beds
                  Norwich Crag
                  Red Crag
                  Coralline Crag
                  St. Erth Beds
                  Lenham Beds

MIOCENE   -   -   (not definitely recognized in Britain)

OLIGOCENE   -   -   Hamstead Beds
                    Bembridge Beds
                    Osborne Beds
                    Headon Beds

EOCENE   -   -   Barton Beds
                 Bracklesham Beds
                 Bagshot Beds
                 London Clay
                 Woolwich and Reading Beds
                 Thanet Beds

| | | |
|---|---|---|
| CRETACEOUS | - - | Upper, Middle, and Lower Chalk |

Lower Cretaceous
  S. and E. England—
    Gault and Upper Greensand
    Lower Greensand
    Wealden

  N.E. England—
    Red Chalk
    Speeton Clay of Yorkshire

JURASSIC    - - Purbeck Beds
    Portland Beds
    Kimmeridge Clay
    Corallian Beds and Ampthill Clay
    Oxford Clay and Kellaways Beds
    Cornbrash (Upper and Lower)
    Great Oolite Series
    Inferior Oolite Series
    Lias (Upper, Middle and Lower)

TRIASSIC    - - Rhaetic Beds
    Keuper Series
    Bunter Series

PERMIAN    - - Permian Marls
    Magnesian Limestone

CARBONIFEROUS - - Coal Measures
    Millstone Grit Series
    Carboniferous Limestone Series

DEVONIAN    - - Old Red Sandstone *or*
    Upper Devonian
    Middle Devonian
    Lower Devonian (including part of the Downton
      Series)

SILURIAN    - - Downton Series (part)
    Ludlow Series
    Wenlock Series
    Llandovery Series

ORDOVICIAN    - - Ashgill Series
    Caradoc Series
    Llandeilo Series
    Llanvirn Series
    Arenig Series

CAMBRIAN    - - Upper Cambrian (including Tremadoc Series)
    Middle Cambrian
    Lower Cambrian

# DIRECTORY OF BRITISH
# FOSSILIFEROUS LOCALITIES

## ENGLAND

### BEDFORDSHIRE

**Leighton Buzzard.** Monday's Hill Pit, 2 miles N.E. of town, on N.W. side of road which meets road from Heath and Reach to Watling Street. 21 Acre Pit, immediately S. of this, is often referred to but is now filled in.

Cretaceous, Lower Greensand (Shenley Limestone lenticles at junction of Leighton Sands and Gault). Abundant brachiopods, with molluscs, echinoderms, crustacea, etc.

Lamplugh, G. W. and Walker, J. F. 1903, with geol. map. Lamplugh, G. W. 1922, with topog. map.

Geol. Surv. O.S. 46 N.W. ; Ord. New Pop. 146.

**Leighton Buzzard.** Arnold's Pit (formerly Pratt's Pit) immediately N.E. of Billington Crossing (Leighton-Dunstable railway line and Leighton-Hemel Hempstead road).

Cretaceous, Lower Greensand and Gault, gritty clays with four nodulebands in *tardefurcata* and *mammillatum* zones, with many casts of ammonites, gastropods and lamellibranchs.

Lamplugh, G. W. 1922, p. 35 with topog. map. Wright, C. W. and E. V. 1947.

Geol. Surv. O.S. 46 S.W. ; Ord. New Pop. 146.

**Leighton Buzzard.** Chamberlain Barn Pit, 1000 yds. N. of 5-way crossroads at E. end of town.

Cretaceous, Gault, gritty brown clays of *tardefurcata*, *mammillatum* and (?) lower *dentatus* zones, resting on current-bedded sands and containing nodules with ammonites, lamellibranchs, etc.

Lamplugh, G. W. 1922, p. 30 with topog. map ; Wright, C. W. and E. V. 1947.

Geol. Surv. O.S. 46 N.W. ; Ord. New Pop. 146.

**Leighton Buzzard.** Harris's Pit, Shenley Hill, *c.* ½ mile E. of Shenley House.

Cretaceous, nodule-bed at base of Upper Gault with many ammonites. Shenley Limestone lenticles visible.

Lamplugh, G. W. 1922, p. 7 with topog. map.

Geol. Surv. O.S. 46 N.W. ; Ord. New Pop. 146.

### BERKSHIRE

**Bracknell.** Brickyards ½ mile and 1 mile W. of railway station, at Down Mill and Amen Corner, S. of Wokingham road.

Eocene, London Clay with many gastropods and lamellibranchs. Good for studying succession of London Clay faunas.

Wrigley, A. 1922, pp. 79-80.

Geol. Surv. N.S. 269 ; Ord. New Pop. 169.

B

**Cothill,** on by-road from Marcham to Oxford *via* Boar's Hill.   Cothill and Dry Sandford quarries, ¼ mile E. and beside road ¼ mile S.W. of Cothill school.

Jurassic, Corallian Beds (Lower Calcareous Grit and Berkshire Oolites) with many ammonites and gastropods (*Natica*-band).  *Cf.* Marcham, Sheepstead Farm Quarry.

Arkell, W. J. 1936, pp. 156-159 ; 1947a, p. 80.   Pringle, J. and others 1926, p. 48.

Geol. Surv. Oxford Special ; Ord. New Pop. 158.

**Cumnor.**  Rockley (Bradley Farm) Quarry, beside Swindon road, 250 yds. W. of Bradley Farm, Cumnor.

Jurassic, Corallian Beds : Coral Rag with many corals and reef-dwelling molluscs ; shell-bed ; Lower Calcareous Grit with a bed of gastropods (*Natica*).

Arkell, W. J. 1927, p. 77 ; 1947a, p. 80.   Pringle, J. and others 1926, p. 49.

Geol. Surv. Oxford Special ; Ord. New Pop. 158.

**Cumnor.**  Chawley Brickwords (disused) on S. side of Oxford-Swindon road ¾ mile E. of church.

Jurassic, Kimmeridge Clay, capped by Cretaceous, Lower Greensand and Gault which are channelled by Pleistocene deposits.  Ammonites and many saurian bones in Kimmeridge Clay.

Arkell, W. J. 1947a, p. 106.   Pringle, J. and others 1926, p. 68.

Geol. Surv. Oxford Special ; Ord. New Pop. 158.

**Faringdon.**  Little Coxwell Pit on E. side of road to Fernham, 500 yds. S. of junction with road to Swindon.   Permission must be obtained from Coxwell Lodge.

Cretaceous, Lower Greensand (yellow sponge-gravel) with many sponges (*Raphidonema*, etc.), bryozoa, brachiopods, sea-urchins and lamellibranchs. Many derived Jurassic fossils.

Arkell, W. J. 1947a, pp. 155-160, with geol. map.   White, H. J. O. 1910a, p. 216.

Geol. Surv. O.S. 34 ; Ord. New Pop. 158.

**Faringdon.**  Faringdon Pit, S. of reservoir on W. side of Sands Lane 600 yds. S. of junction with road passing railway station.   Worked intermittently, but also used as refuse-dump.

Cretaceous, Lower Greensand (red and yellow sponge-gravel).   Fossils and literature as for Little Coxwell Pit.

Geol. Surv. O.S. 13 ; Ord. New Pop. 158.

**Faringdon.**  Wicklesham Pit, approached by unfenced track running E. from Sands Lane opposite reservoir.

Cretaceous, Lower Greensand (red sponge-gravel).   Fossils and literature as for Little Coxwell Pit.   Large *Nautilus* abundant and ammonites very rare.

Geol. Surv. O.S. 13 ; Ord. New Pop. 158.

**Kingsclere,** 6 miles S.E. of Newbury.   Stream bank by culvert 2½ miles N.E. of Kingsclere and ½ mile S.W. of Fairoak.

Eocene, London Clay, with many molluscs, including the gastropod *Turritella*, confined to very few London Clay localities.

Whitaker, W. 1872, p. 280.

Geol. Surv. N.S. 284 ; Ord. New Pop. 168.

**Kingston Bagpuize.**  Lamb Inn Quarry (disused), S. of Oxford-Swindon road ¼ mile W. of Lamb and Flag Inn, opposite turning to Hinton Waldrist.

Jurassic, Corallian Beds (Berkshire Oolite Series) with *Trigonia* and other lamellibranchs and many ammonites.

Arkell, W. J. 1927, pp. 95-97 ; 1947a, p. 87.   Pringle, J. and others 1926, p. 43.

Geol. Surv. Oxford Special ; Ord. New Pop. 158.

**Marcham.** Sheepstead Farm Quarry, ⅞ mile N.N.E. of church.

Jurassic, Corallian Beds (Lower Calcareous Grit and Berkshire Oolite Series) with perfect *Trigonia* and other lamellibranchs and sea-urchins (*Nucleolites, Pygaster*).

Arkell, W. J. 1927, pp. 92-94 ; 1936, p. 160 ; 1947a, p. 88. Pringle, J. and others 1926, p. 46.

Geol. Surv. Oxford Special ; Ord. New Pop. 158.

**Reading.** Grovelands Pit (Messrs. S. E. Collier Ltd.), 200 yds. W. of works in Water Road, 1¼ miles W. of Reading West station.

Eocene, London Clay basement bed with molluscs, worm-tubes, etc., in tabular masses of indurated sand.

Hawkins, H. L. 1946, p. 165.

Geol. Surv. N.S. 268 ; Ord. New Pop. 159.

**Shellingford.** Crossroads Quarry, ½ mile N.E. of church.

Jurassic, Corallian Beds (Berkshire Oolite Series and Coral Rag) with many corals and reef-dwelling molluscs ; sea-urchins in Urchin Marls.

Arkell, W. J. 1927, p. 103 ; 1939b, pp. 490-493, with geol. map ; 1947a, p. 87.

Geol. Surv. O.S. 13 ; Ord. New Pop. 158.

**Sparsholt,** 3½ miles W. of Wantage. Small pit on N. side of Childrey-Lambourn road near Sincombe Farm, 1 mile S. of Sparsholt at top of hill.

Cretaceous, Upper Chalk (*planus* zone, Chalk Rock), with many ammonites, gastropods, lamellibranchs and brachiopods.

Arkell, W. J. 1947a, p. 178.

Geol. Surv. O.S. 13 ; Ord. New Pop. 158.

**Stanford-in-the-Vale.** Pit by road to Pusey, 1¼ miles N.N.E. of Stanford Church.

Jurassic, Corallian Beds (Pusey Flags, Highworth Grit and Coral Rag) with many lamellibranchs ; a few ammonites in Pusey Flags.

Arkell, W. J. 1939b, p. 493, with geol. map ; 1947a, p. 86.

Geol. Surv. O.S. 13 ; Ord. New Pop. 158.

**Wokingham.** Large deep brickyard in outskirts of town at Fishponds, *c.* ½ mile S.W. of Wokingham station.

Eocene, London Clay, with three distinct faunal horizons.

Wrigley, A. 1925, pp. 452-455.

Geol. Surv. N.S. 268 ; Ord. New Pop. 169.

# BUCKINGHAMSHIRE

**Aylesbury.** Webster and Cannon's brickpit behind No. 134 Cambridge Street (Bierton Road), *c.* ⅜ mile N.E. of Market Place. Section in good condition though disused.

Jurassic, Kimmeridge Clay (Hartwell Clay capped by Portland Lydite Bed), with ammonites of the *pallasioides* zone, gastropods, lamellibranchs, crustacea, etc. Many foraminifera in the clay.

Sherlock, R. L. and others 1922b, pp. 4, 7.

Geol. Surv. N.S. 238 ; Ord. New Pop. 159.

**Boarstall,** 6 miles S.E. of Bicester. Disused pits 250 yds. S.E. of Old Arngrove Farm.

Jurassic, Corallian Beds, Arngrove Stone ; a rock composed of globular spicules of the siliceous sponge *Rhaxella.* Small ammonites and lamellibranchs also occur.

Arkell, W. J. 1947a, pp. 95-98, with geol. map. Davies, A. M. 1907, pp. 37-43.

Geol. Surv. Oxford Special ; Ord. New Pop. 146.

**Charndon,** 6½ miles S.S.W. of Buckingham. Calvert Brickworks S.W. of Calvert station, midway between Charndon and Steeple Claydon.
Jurassic, lower and middle Oxford Clay with abundant crushed ammonites (*Kosmoceras*) and other fossils.
Arkell, W. J. 1933a, p. 350 and pl. xv.
Geol. Surv. O.S. 45 N.E.-S.E. ; Ord. New Pop. 146.

**Cheddington,** 8 miles E.N.E. of Aylesbury. Disused pit on West End Hill, ⅞ mile S.W. of church.
Cretaceous, Lower Chalk (Chalk Marl, *varians* zone), about 10 ft. seen above talus, with many ammonites, lamellibranchs, brachiopods, sea-urchins, etc.
Oakley, K. P. 1936, p. 39. Sherlock, R. L. and others 1922b, p. 15.
Geol. Surv. N.S. 238 ; Ord. New Pop. 146.

**Hartwell,** 2 miles S.W. of Aylesbury. Quarry 200 yds. N.W. of Bugle Inn and ⅜ mile S.W. of Hartwell House.
Jurassic, Portland Beds, with giant ammonites (as in wall of Hartwell Park), and gastropods, lamellibranchs and crustacea ; Purbeck Beds at top with ostracods, land-snails and turtle-plates.
Arkell, W. J. 1947a, p. 126. Davies, A. M. 1934, p. 104.
Geol. Surv. N.S. 255 ; Ord. New Pop. 146.

**Latimer.** Disused pit on S. side of road running S.E. from Chesham to Chenies, ¼ mile S.E. of Blackwell Hall Farm.
Cretaceous, Upper Chalk (*planus* zone, Chalk Rock). Ammonites, gastropods, lamellibranchs, brachiopods, sea-urchins and sponges in weathered blocks.
Sherlock, R. L. and others 1922a, p. 13. Lea, F. A. 1939.
Geol. Surv. N.S. 255 ; Ord. New Pop. 159.

**Marlow.** Old pit ¼ mile E. of Blount's Farm, 1¼ miles N.W. of Marlow station.
Cretaceous, Upper Chalk (*planus* zone, Chalk Rock) with many ammonites, gastropods, sponges, etc. The best bed lies in the roots of a tree on the S. side of the pit.
Sherlock, R. L. and others 1922a, pp. 17, 49.
Geol. Surv. N.S. 255 ; Ord. New Pop. 159.

**Westcott,** 6½ miles W.N.W. of Aylesbury. Woodham Brickpit, N.E. of Akeman Street station (L.N.E.R.).
Jurassic, Oxford Clay (*athleta, lamberti* and *mariae* zones), with many well-preserved ammonites.
Arkell, W. J. 1939a, p. 135 ; 1947a, p. 74.
Geol. Surv. O.S. 45 S.E. ; Ord. New Pop. 146.

## CAMBRIDGESHIRE

**Barnwell,** Cambridge. Barnwell station gravelpit (now refuse dump) on N. side of Newmarket road by railway bridge.
Pleistocene gravels and sands with plant-beds (*Betula nana*) and shells (*Columella columella*) indicating a cold climate.
Marr, J. E. 1920, p. 236, with topog. map.
Geol. Surv. O.S. 51 S.W. ; Ord. New Pop. 148.

**Barrington,** 6 miles S.W. of Cambridge. Large cement-works ½ mile N. of the church.
Cretaceous, Gault, Cambridge Greensand and Lower Chalk. The best exposure of Cambridge Greensand, though fossils are scarce.
Reed, F. R. C. 1897 .p. 95.
Geol. Surv. O.S. 51 S.W. ; Ord. New Pop. 148.

**Barrington.** Old chalkpit at W. end of village, 1 mile S.W. of church. Access not allowed.

Pleistocene gravels (overlying Chalk). Famous for *Hippopotamus* and other mammals.

Marr, J. E. 1920, p. 229, with topog. map.
Geol. Surv. O.S. 51 S.W. ; Ord. New Pop. 148.

**Elsworth,** 8½ miles N.W. of Cambridge. Small exposures in banks of stream and temporary excavations in village.

Jurassic, Corallian Beds, Elsworth Rock, with small ammonites and many other fossils.

Arkell, W. J. 1937a. Reed, F. R. C. 1897, p. 15.
Geol. Surv. N.S. 187 ; Ord. New Pop. 134.

**Westley Waterless,** 5 miles S.S.W. of Newmarket. Old pit in wood 300 yds. S.W. of Underwood Hall.

Cretaceous, Upper Chalk (*planus* zone, Chalk Rock), with ammonites, gastropods and many other fossils.

White, H. J. O. 1932, p. 38.
Geol. Surv. N.S. 205 ; Ord. New Pop. 135.

**Weston Colville,** 7 miles S.S.W. of Newmarket. Pit in fork of roads 1 mile W.N.W. of village.

Cretaceous, Upper Chalk (*planus* zone), with the sea-urchin *Micraster* common.

White, H. J. O. 1932, p. 39.
Geol. Surv. N.S. 205 ; Ord. New Pop. 148.

**Wicken,** 2 miles S.W. of Soham. Upware old North Pit, 1 mile N.E. of new bridge over river, now much overgrown.

Jurassic, Corallian Beds (oolitic facies) with many sea-urchins.

Reed, F. R. C. 1897, p. 29. Roberts, T. 1892, p. 56.
Geol. Surv. O.S. 51 N.W. ; Ord. New Pop. 135.

**Wicken.** Upware Bridge Pit, immediately S.E. of new bridge on Streatham-Wicken road.

Jurassic, Corallian Beds, reef-facies with abundant corals.

Arkell, W. J. 1937b, p. 380. Reed, F. R. C. 1897, p. 29.
Geol. Surv. O.S. 51 N.W. ; Ord. New Pop. 135.

**Wicken.** Upware South Pit, on W. side of drove-road ½ mile N. of Upware Inn.

Jurassic, Corallian Beds (coral rag with many coral masses) ; Cretaceous, Lower Greensand (mostly quarried away), with some phosphatized fossils.

Keeping, W. 1883. Reed, F. R. C. 1897, p. 61.
Geol. Surv. O.S. 51 N.W. ; Ord. New Pop. 135.

**Wood Ditton,** 3 miles S. of Newmarket. Roadside pit ½ mile N. of village. Cretaceous, Upper Chalk (" Top Rock " with green-coated nodules and the sea-urchin *Micraster* at junction of *planus* and *cortestudinarium* zones).

Brighton, A. G. 1928, p. 371.
Geol. Surv. O.S. 51 S.E. ; Ord. New Pop. 135.


# CHESHIRE

**Astbury,** 2 miles S.W. of Congleton. Quarry on S. side of Mow Lane, Congleton Edge, 1000 yds. S.W. of Horseshoe Inn and 2¼ miles S.E. of Astbury.

Carboniferous, Millstone Grit, *Homoceras proteum* band, with goniatites, brachiopods, etc., in ironstone nodules and a limy bed at S. end of quarry.

Gibson, W. and others 1905, p. 24.
Geol. Surv. N.S. 110 ; Ord. New Pop. 110.

**Dukinfield,** between Stalybridge and Ashton-under-Lyne. Section on E. bank of R. Tame, 150 yds. S.W. of Dukinfield station.

Carboniferous, Coal Measures (*similis-pulchra* zone, Dukinfield Marine Band), with goniatites, nautiloids, fish, etc.

Tonks, L. H. and others 1931, pp. 147-149.

Geol. Surv. N.S. 85 ; Ord. New Pop. 102.

**Higher Bebington** (Wirral). Storeton Quarry, *c.* ½ mile S.W. of Higher Bebington church.

Triassic, Keuper Beds. Saurian footprints are exposed from time to time in a three-foot bed 120 ft. above base of Keuper.

Wedd, C. B. and others 1923, pp. 87-88.

Geol. Surv. N.S. 96 ; Ord. New Pop. 100.

**Neston,** 11 miles N.W. of Chester. Tips of old Wirral Colliery, ¾ mile S. of village.

Carboniferous, Coal Measures (shales and ironstone nodules from roof of Six-Feet Seam at base of *modiolaris* zone), with non-marine lamellibranchs (*Carbonicola, Anthraconaia, Naiadites*).

Wood, A. 1937, p. 7.

Geol. Surv. N.S. 96 ; Ord. New Pop. 109.

**Pott Shrigley,** 1 mile N. of Bollington. Stream-section on N. side of Pott Shrigley-Charleshead road, *c.* 700 yds. W. of Bakestonedale Farm. Best locality a few yards upstream from road.

Carboniferous, Coal Measures (Bullion Mine Marine Band, *c.* 2 ft.) with goniatites and lamellibranchs.

Geol. Surv. O.S. 81 N.W. ; Ord. New Pop. 101.

**Thurstaston** (Wirral). Section in dingle known as The Dungeon, *c.* 1000 yds. S.E. of Thurstaston Church, between Hooton—West Kirby and Chester—West Kirby roads.

Triassic, Keuper Waterstones with plant fragments.

Wedd, C. B. and others 1923, p. 92.

Geol. Surv. N.S. 96 ; Ord. New Pop. 100 and 109.

# CORNWALL

**Bude.** Small cliff at N. end of bathing-pool.

Carboniferous, Culm Measures (Bude Sandstone) with fish and arthropods in large earthy nodules in shales.

Arber, E. A. N. 1904, p. 291.

Geol. Surv. O.S. 29 ; Ord. New Pop. 174.

**Bude.** Cliffs 700 yds. N. of Phillips Point, 1¾ miles S.S.W. of Bude.

Carboniferous, Culm Measures (Bude Sandstone and shales), with drifted plant remains—flattened in shales, casts in sandstone.

Arber, E. A. N. 1904, p. 291.

Geol. Surv. O.S. 29 ; Ord. New Pop. 174.

**Crackington Haven,** 9 miles N.N.E. of Camelford. Base of cliff at Alder Strand and Southern Door, 1½ miles S.W. of Crackington Haven.

Carboniferous, slates of Millstone Grit age with goniatites in siliceous nodules.

Owen, D. E. 1934, p. 459, with geol. map.

Geol. Surv. O.S. 29 ; Ord. New Pop. 174.

**St. Erth,** 4 miles S.S.E. of St. Ives. Old claypits on E. side of St. Erth village and immediately N.W. of vicarage.

Pliocene, St. Erth Beds. Many molluscs and plants formerly found in a clay now covered by head and no longer visible.

Reid, C. and Flett, J. S. 1907, pp. 71-74.

Geol. Surv. N.S. 351/358 ; Ord. New Pop. 189.

**St. Gennys,** 9 miles N.N.E. of Camelford. Foreshore and base of cliff in Thorn's Beach, 400 yds. N. of church.

Carboniferous, slates of Millstone Grit age with goniatites ; flattened impressions and pyritized casts in shales, uncrushed in siliceous nodules. Lamellibranchs also occur.

Owen D. E. 1934, pp. 451–471, with geol. map.

Geol. Surv. O.S. 29 ; Ord. New Pop. 174.

# CUMBERLAND

**Bassenthwaite Halls,** 7½ miles E. of Cockermouth. Scree on White Horse, 1330 yds. E. 38° S. of Barkbeth, 1 mile S.E. of Bassenthwaite Halls.

Ordovician, Arenig, Skiddaw Slates, grey-blue slates with tuning-fork and tetragraptid graptolites of the *extensus* zone and the crustacean *Caryocaris*.

Elles, G. L. 1933.

Geol. Surv. O.S. 101 N.E. ; Ord. New Pop. 82.

**Bassenthwaite Halls.** Screes on Great Knott : (*a*) on S. side, 1400 yds. E. 2° S. and (*b*) at E. end below crag 1500 yds. E. 2° S. of Dyke Nook, 1½ miles S. of Bassenthwaite Halls.

Ordovician, Arenig, Skiddaw Slates with graptolites (*Didymograptus* and *Tetragraptus*) of *extensus* zone.

Elles, G. L. 1933.

Geol. Surv. O.S. 101 N.E. ; Ord. New Pop. 82.

**Bassenthwaite Halls.** Scree on S. side of Randel Crag, 820 yds. W. 18° N. of Skiddaw Man triangulation point 3053.

Ordovician, Arenig, Skiddaw Slates with graptolites (*Didymograptus*) of base of *hirundo* and ( ?) top of *extensus* zones.

Elles, G. L. 1933.

Geol. Surv. O.S. 101 S.E. ; Ord. New Pop. 82.

**Bassenthwaite Halls.** Scree on N. side of Randel Crag, 540 yds. W. 27° N. of Skiddaw Man triangulation point 3053.

Ordovician, Arenig, Skiddaw Slates with didymograptid graptolites of the *hirundo* zone.

Elles, G. L. 1933.

Geol. Surv. O.S. 101 S.E. ; Ord. New Pop. 82.

**Bigrigg,** on Egremont-Whitehaven road. Cutting of disused mineral line 320 yds. S.E. of Park House, Bigrigg, on W. side of Springfield Road.

Carboniferous, Millstone Grit, black and chocolate shales, with goniatites (*Gastrioceras cumbriense*) and lamellibranchs.

Eastwood, T. and others 1931, p. 111.

Geol. Surv. N.S. 28 ; Ord. New Pop. 82.

**Bigrigg.** Old opencast working on E. side of Springfield Road just S. of bridge over Pallaflat mineral line.

Carboniferous Limestone Series (First Limestone) with corals (*Aulophyllum*) and brachiopods (giganteid productids).

Eastwood, T. and others 1931, p. 84.

Geol. Surv. N.S. 28 ; Ord. New Pop. 82.

**Bigrigg.** Old opencast working 100 yds. N.E. of Langhorne Farm on W. side of main road S. of turning to Cleator about ⅓ mile S. of Bigrigg.

Carboniferous Limestone Series (First Limestone 40 ft., shales and sandstones 12 ft., Orebank Sandstone 70 ft.) with corals (*Aulophyllum, Lonsdaleia*) and brachiopods (giganteid productids).

Eastwood, T. and others 1931, pp. 83–84.

Geol. Surv. N.S. 28 ; Ord. New Pop. 82.

**Bigrigg.**  Cutting of Pallaflat mineral railway, E. and W. of bridge carrying Egremont-Whitehaven road, S. of Bigrigg.

Carboniferous, Millstone Grit, black and chocolate shales with interbedded sandstones and fireclays, overlain by rough grit.   Type-locality of the goniatite *Gastrioceras cumbriense.*

Eastwood, T. and others 1931, p. 111.

Geol. Surv. N.S. 28 ;  Ord. New Pop. 82.

**Bigrigg,** see Woodend.

**Bolton Low Houses,** 12 miles N.E. of Cockermouth.  Pow Gill ; sections 120 to 185 yds. N. by W. of bridge at Pow Bank, 1¾ miles S.E. of Bolton Low Houses.

Carboniferous, Hensingham Group, shales with brachiopods, lamellibranchs, gastropods, nautiloids (*Tylonautilus nodiferus*) and goniatites (*Anthracoceras glabrum*).

Geol. Surv. O.S. 101 N.E. ;  Ord. New Pop. 82.

**Bolton Low Houses.**  Pow Gill, section on left bank, 190-200 yds. above Parson Bridge, ¼ mile N. of Bolton Low Houses.

Carboniferous, Coal Measures, marine band in Whitehaven Sandstone with goniatites (*Homoceratoides*, *Anthracoceras*) which suggest correlation with Mansfield Marine Band in Yorkshire.

Geol. Surv. O.S. 101 N.E. ;  Ord. New Pop. 82.

**Bothel,** 6 miles N.E. of Cockermouth.  Disused quarry, Wharrels Hill, ¼ mile S.W. of village.

Carboniferous Limestone Series (dark and light grey limestones at base of Fourth Limestone) with corals (*Lonsdaleia*) and brachiopods (*Linoproductus* and *Davidsonina* [*Cyrtina*] *septosa*).

Geol. Surv. O.S. 101 N.E. ;  Ord. New Pop. 82.

**Bothel.**  Quarry at Threapland Bridge, 2 miles S.W. of village.

Carboniferous Limestone Series, Fourth Limestone, 60 ft. seen, with corals and brachiopods in the *Davidsonina* [*Cyrtina*] *septosa* band.

Geol. Surv. O.S. 101 N.E. ;  Ord. New Pop. 82.

**Caldbeck,** 7 miles S.E. of Wigton.  Quarry at Brocklebank, 1250 yds. E. 25° N. of Hilltop, 2½ miles N.W. of Caldbeck.

Carboniferous Limestone Series (Great Limestone) with corals (*Diphyphyllum, Lonsdaleia*) and brachiopods (giganteid productids).

Geol. Surv. O.S. 101 N.E. ;  Ord. New Pop. 82.

**Caldbeck.**  Drygill Beck Head, 3¼ miles S. of Caldbeck church.

Ordovician, Caradoc (Drygill Shales) with brachiopods and trilobites.

Geol. Surv. O.S. 101 N.E. ;  Ord. New Pop. 82.

**Cleator.**  Old opencast working 100 yds. N.W. of R.C. church, ¼ mile N.E. of The Flosh, Cleator, and S.W. of Todholes House, Cleator Moor.

Carboniferous Limestone Series (Seventh Limestone, 40 ft.) with corals and brachiopods ;  teeth of the fish *Psephodus magnus* occur.

Eastwood, T. and others 1931, p. 86.

Geol. Surv. N.S. 28 ;  Ord. New Pop. 82.

**Cleator.**  Old opencast working 500 yds. N. of the village and 300 yds. N.W. of The Flosh.

Carboniferous Limestone Series (Seventh Limestone with corals and brachiopods ;  *Chonetes* shale with brachiopods ;  Fifth Limestone with the brachiopod *Cancrinella undata*).

Eastwood, T. and others 1931, p. 85.

Geol. Surv. N.S. 28 ;  Ord. New Pop. 82.

**Cleator Moor.**  Disused quarry with limekiln S.E. of Birks Farm, 1200 yds. N.E. of Cleator Moor crossroads.

Carboniferous Limestone Series (First Limestone, *c.* 20 ft.) with corals

(*Lonsdaleia*) and giganteid productids and smaller brachiopods
Eastwood, T. and others 1931, p. 87.
Geol. Surv. N.S. 28 ; Ord. New Pop. 82.

**Distington,** 4 miles N.E. of Whitehaven. Barfs Quarry (disused), 200 yds.
N.W. of village.
Carboniferous Limestone Series (First Limestone, *c.* 50 ft.), with corals
(*Dibunophyllum, Lonsdaleia*) and *Gigantoproductus.*
Eastwood, T. and others 1931, p. 94.
Geol. Surv. N.S. 28 ; Ord. New Pop. 82.

**Distington.** Barfs Silica Works, long quarry midway between Distington
and High Harrington railway stations, at junction of three roads 1 mile N.W.
of Distington Church.
Carboniferous, Hensingham Group, with the brachiopod *Schizophoria
resupinata* abundant.
Eastwood, T. and others 1931, pp. 104-105.
Geol. Surv. N.S. 28 ; Ord. New Pop. 82.

**Frizington,** 5 miles N.E. of Egremont. Frizington Parks Quarry (dis-
used), N.E. of Scalelands Farm, 1 mile S.S.E. of Frizington Church.
Carboniferous Limestone Series, limestones and thin shales near top of
Seventh Limestone. The corals *Syringopora* near the top and *Nematophyllum
minus* lower down ; small productids near the base ; gastropods in dark
limestone.
Eastwood, T. and others 1931, p. 87.
Geol. Surv. N.S. 28 ; Ord. New Pop. 82.

**Frizington.** Yeathouse Quarries, E. of Yeathouse railway station, ½ mile
E. of Frizington.
Carboniferous Limestone Series, from base of series to top of Fourth
Limestone in a series of quarries and cuttings. Ostracods occur in basal beds
in railway cutting ; the coral *Syringopora* at top of Seventh Limestone ;
giganteid brachiopods in Sixth Limestone ; algal (*Girvanella*) and brachiopod
(*Davidsonina* [*Cyrtina*] *septosa*) bands in Fourth Limestone, with the coral
*Orionastraea.*
Eastwood, T. and others 1931, p. 88.
Geol. Surv. N.S. 28 ; Ord. New Pop. 82.

**Frizington.** Eskett Quarry, E. of Winder hamlet.
Carboniferous Limestone Series (from base of Fourth Limestone to top of
*junceum*-beds. The sponge *Erythrospongia lithodes* occurs in a band between
*Saccammina*- and *junceum*-bed.) Corals (type-locality of *Orionastraea edmondsi*
and *Nemistium edmondsi*) and brachiopods.
Eastwood, T. and others 1931, pp. 88-89.
Geol. Surv. N.S. 28 ; Ord. New Pop. 82.

**Hensingham,** 1¼ miles S.E. of Whitehaven. Quarries E. of the town and
near Overend Farm.
Carboniferous Limestone Series, First, Second and Fourth Limestones with
corals (*Lonsdaleia*) and giganteid brachiopods.
Eastwood, T. and others 1931, p. 93.
Geol. Surv. N.S. 28 ; Ord. New Pop. 82.

**Hensingham.** Stream section, Snebro Gill, continuation of Bedlam Gill
on W. side of Main Street.
Carboniferous, thin limestones and shales of Hensingham Group, with
sponge-remains, zaphrentid corals, productid brachiopods, lamellibranchs,
gastropods (*Bellerophon*), nautiloids and trilobites.
Eastwood, T. and others 1931, p. 100.
Geol. Surv. N.S. 28 ; Ord. New Pop. 82.

**Hensingham.** Chapel House Gill, 50 yds. N. of Chapel House Farm,
½ mile S. of Hensingham Church.

Carboniferous, shales and sandstones of Hensingham Group near small waterfall, yielding abundant small productid brachiopods.
Eastwood, T. and others 1931, pp. 100-101.
Geol. Surv. N.S. 28 ; Ord. New Pop. 82.

**Hensingham.** Section in Bedlam Gill *c.* 250 yds. W. of crossroads at Richmond Hill.
Carboniferous, Millstone Grit, black shales with goniatites (*Gastrioceras*), gastropods, lamellibranchs and brachiopods.
Eastwood, T. and others 1931, p. 112.
Geol. Surv. N.S. 28 ; Ord. New Pop. 82.

**Keswick.** Screes on E. and S. sides of Barf Hill, ¼ mile W. of Swan Hotel, which is 3 miles N.W. of town on S.W. side of Bassenthwaite Lake.
Ordovician, Arenig, Skiddaw Slates with many graptolites (*Bryograptus*, *Dichograptus*, *Didymograptus*, *Phyllograptus*, *Tetragraptus*).
Elles, G. L. 1898, pp. 463-539.
Geol. Surv. O.S. 101 S.E. ; Ord. New Pop. 82.

**Keswick.** Scree on N. side of Outerside, 3¼ miles W.S.W. of town.
Ordovician, Arenig, Skiddaw Slates, with the graptolites *Didymograptus*, *Glyptograptus* and *Tetragraptus*, also the crustacean *Caryocaris*.
Elles, G. L. 1898, pp. 463-539.
Geol. Surv. O.S. 101 S.E. ; Ord. New Pop. 82.

**Keswick,** see Portinscale.

**Kirkcambeck,** 5 miles N. of Brampton. Cam Beck, 900 yds. N.E. of Kirkcambeck Church.
Carboniferous Limestone Series, Cementstone Series (Cambeck Beds) with the calcareous alga *Mitcheldeania gregaria* (now called *Garwoodia*).
Garwood, E. J. 1931, p. 118, with geol. map.
Geol. Surv. O.S. 106 N.W. ; Ord. New Pop. 76.

**Kirkland,** 6 miles E. of Whitehaven. Old quarry in Thistle Gill, leading to Stockhow Hall Quarries, W. of village on road to Rowrah.
Carboniferous Limestone Series (Seventh Limestone, 60 ft.), with the coral *Syringopora* in a band near the top and gastropods in the middle. Some calcite-mudstones.
Eastwood, T. and others 1931, p. 90.
Geol. Surv. N.S. 28 ; Ord. New Pop. 82.

**Kirkland.** Kelton Head Quarries (disused).
Carboniferous Limestone Series (Fourth Limestone in cutting leading to quarry ; Third, Second and First Limestone in railway cutting), with corals (*Chaetetes*), brachiopods (including *Davidsonina* [*Cyrtina*] *septosa* band) and algae (*Girvanella*-bed).
Eastwood, T. and others 1931, p. 90.
Geol. Surv. N.S. 28 ; Ord. New Pop. 82.

**Kirkland.** Stockhow Hall Quarry.
Carboniferous Limestone Series (Seventh, Sixth and Fifth Limestones) with corals (*Lonsdaleia*) and brachiopods (the productids *Linoproductus* and *Gigantoproductus*).
Eastwood, T. and others 1931, pp. 89-90.
Geol. Surv. N.S. 28 ; Ord. New Pop. 82.

**Kirksanton,** on Millom-Ravenglass road. Disused quarry 50 yds. N.W. of brewery.
Carboniferous Limestone Series, 14 ft. seen with corals (*Michelinia grandis*) and brachiopods indicating a low horizon.
Geol. Surv. O.S. 98 S.W. ; Ord. New Pop. 88.

**Lamplugh,** 6¼ miles S.E. of Cockermouth.    Quarry N. of village near Scalesmoor Farm.

Carboniferous Limestone Series (Fifth Limestone, 30 ft. seen), with corals (*Palaeosmilia* and *Lonsdaleia*) and brachiopods.

Eastwood, T. and others 1931, p. 90.

Geol. Surv. N.S. 28 ; Ord. New Pop. 82.

**Millom.**  Quarry near Hodbarrow Point, 1¼ miles S.E. of Millom station.

Carboniferous Limestone Series with brachiopods (*Linoproductus* and *Punctospirifer*), corals and gastropods.

Geol. Surv. O.S. 98 S.W. ; Ord. New Pop. 88.

**Moota House,** *c.* 3½ miles N.E. of Cockermouth.    Quarries on Moota Hill, N.W. of Moota House.

Carboniferous Limestone Series (Fifth and Fourth Limestones), with corals, brachiopods (*Gigantoproductus*) and algae (*Girvanella*-band exposed near top of hill).

Geol. Surv. O.S. 101 N.E. ; Ord. New Pop. 82.

**Mungrisdale,** 2 miles N. of Penrith road at 8th milestone from Keswick. Small crags and scree 250 yds. E. of Hazelhurst, ¾ mile S. of village.

Ordovician, Arenig, Skiddaw Slates, with graptolites of the *extensus* zone, including *Didymograptus protobifidus*.

Elles, G. L. 1933.

Geol. Surv. O.S. 101 S.E. ; Ord. New Pop. 83.

**Mungrisdale.**  Roadside section 440 yds. N. by E. of Hazelhurst, ¾ mile S. of village.

Ordovician, Llanvirn, Skiddaw Slates, with graptolites of base of *bifidus* zone in one inch of dark slate.

Elles, G. L. 1933, p. 94.

Geol. Surv. O.S. 101 S.E. ; Ord. New Pop. 83.

**Mungrisdale.**  Quarry 150 yds. N. 13° W. of church.

Ordovician, Arenig, Skiddaw Slates with graptolites (*Didymograptus* and *Tetragraptus*) of the *extensus* zone.

Geol. Surv. O.S. 101 N.E. ; Ord. New Pop. 83.

**Pardshaw,** 4 miles S.W. of Cockermouth.    Pardshaw Crags and quarries W. of village.

Carboniferous Limestone Series (Fifth Limestone at crags ; Fourth Limestone farther west) with brachiopods (*Davidsonina* [*Cyrtina*] *septosa* and *Daviesiella* cf. *comoides* bands) and algae (*Girvanella*-band in quarry).

Eastwood, T. and others 1931, p. 92.

Geol. Surv. N.S. 28 ; Ord. New Pop. 82.

**Penton,** 7 miles N.E. of Longtown. " Jockie's Sike," an unnamed tributary to left bank of R. Liddel, crossing railway (L.N.E.R., Edinburgh-Carlisle) near milepost 83, E. of Ridding's Junction.    Localitites 38-41 of Barrett and Richey, 1945.

Carboniferous, Coal Measures, barren red measures of *tenuis* zone, with non-marine lamellibranchs (*Anthraconauta*), very rare crustacea (*Estheriella reumauxi*) and insect-wings at the base of shale-groups, with plants in higher beds of same shales.

Barrett, H. H. and Richey, J. E. 1945.

Geol. Surv. O.S. 106 N.W. ; Ord. New Pop. 76.

**Portinscale,** 1 mile W. of Keswick.    Hodgson How Quarry, N. side of Keswick-Cockermouth road.

Ordovician, Arenig, Skiddaw Slates, with the graptolites *Dichograptus, Tetragraptus* and rare *Didymograptus*.   Type-locality of *Azygograptus lapworthi*.

Elles, G. L. 1898, pp. 513-514.

Geol. Surv. O.S. 101 S.E. ; Ord. New Pop. 82.

**Raughtonhead,** 7 miles S.S.W. of Carlisle. Left bank of R. Roe, 900 yds. E. 12° S. of church.
Upper Carboniferous red-stained mudstones with the crustacean *Leaia tricarinata.*
Geol. Surv. O.S. 101 N.E. ; Ord. New Pop. 83.

**Rowrah.** Large quarries S.S.E. of village.
Carboniferous Limestone Series (from base of Fourth to top of First Limestone) with abundant corals and brachiopods.
Eastwood, T. and others 1931, p. 90.
Geol. Surv. N.S. 28 ; Ord. New Pop. 82.

**St. Bees.** Cliff-section 100 yds. N. of Barrowmouth Wood, between Whitehaven and St. Bees Head.
Permian, Magnesian Limestone with lamellibranchs.
Geol. Surv. N.S. 28 ; Ord. New Pop. 82.

**Wilton,** near Egremont. Disused quarry 2 miles E. of Egremont.
Carboniferous Limestone Series (Seventh Limestone, about 120 ft. of reddish-grey limestone with thin shales and cherts) with corals (*Syringopora*-band and *Caninia*) and brachiopods (*Linoproductus*) ; fish remains near the top.
Eastwood, T. and others 1931, pp. 92-93.
Geol. Surv. N.S. 28 ; Ord. New Pop. 82.

**Woodend,** Bigrigg. Clints Quarries, W. of Egremont-Cleator road, S. of Woodend station.
Carboniferous Limestone Series (Third and Fourth Limestones, 260 ft., with thin shales) with corals, brachiopods, algae (*Girvanella*-band about 80 ft. from base) and foraminifera (abundant *Saccamminopsis* near top).
Eastwood, T. and others 1931, p. 80.
Geol. Surv. N.S. 28 ; Ord. New Pop. 82.

**Woodend.** Disused mineral railway cutting 50 yds. W. of Woodend Mill.
Carboniferous Limestone Series (Fifth Limestone, 40 ft.), with corals (*Lonsdaleia*) and brachiopods (*Chonetes* in white limestone in upper beds).
Eastwood, T. and others 1931, p. 80.
Geol. Surv. N.S. 28 ; Ord. New Pop. 82.

# DERBYSHIRE

**Bamford.** Stream-section, Swint Clough, W. of Alport Castles Farm, Alportdale. (Alportdale joins Ashop Dale 9 miles E. of Glossop on Sheffield road). Localities 20-24 of Hudson and Cotton, 1943.
Carboniferous, Millstone Grit (Edale Shales and Mam Tor Sandstone, $R_1$ subzone) with abundant goniatites, crushed in shales, uncrushed in bullions.
Bisat, W. S. and Hudson, R. G. S. 1943, p. 389. Hudson and Cotton, G. 1943, p. 148, with topog. map.
Geol. Surv. O.S. 81 N.E. ; Ord. New Pop. 111.

**Bradbourne,** 5 miles N.E. of Ashbourne. Disused quarry S.E. of Haven Hill, ¼ mile S.W. of Bank Top Farm, S. of Bradbourne.
Carboniferous Limestone Series ($S_2D_1$ subzones) with zaphrentid corals fairly common.
Sibly, T. F. 1908, p. 61.
Geol. Surv. O.S. 72 N.E. ; Ord. New Pop. 111.

**Bradwell.** Morton's Quarry, W. side of Bradwell Dale.
Carboniferous Limestone Series ($D_2$ and $B_2$ subzones) with corals (*Orionastraea placenta*) and brachiopods in bedded limestone, and brachiopods in overlying knoll-reef limestone.
Shirley, J. and Horsfield, E. L. 1940, p. 288, with geol. map.
Geol. Surv. O.S. 81 N.E. ; Ord. New Pop. 111.

**Burbage,** 1 mile S.W. of Buxton. Stream-section on S. side of Maccles-field road *c.* 1200 yds. S.W. of Canholes and 150 yds. S.E. of Toad Rock. Locality 13 of Cope, 1946a.
Carboniferous, Millstone Grit, 1 ft. marine shale with goniatites (*Reticuloceras reticulatum* mut. *superbilingue*, R₂ subzone).
Cope, F. W. 1946a, p. 171.
Geol. Surv. O.S. 81 S. W. ; Ord. New Pop. 111.

**Castleton.** Jack Bank Quarry, between Earle's Quarry and Pindale, on 900 ft. contour.
Carboniferous Limestone Series (P zone, knoll-reef limestones), with brachiopods and occasional goniatites.
Shirley, J. and Horsfield, E. L. 1940, p. 283, with geol. map.
Geol. Surv. O.S. 81 N.E. ; Ord. New Pop. 111.

**Castleton.** Cow Low Nick, between Castleton and the Winnatts at about the 1100 ft. contour.
Carboniferous Limestone Series (B zone, knoll-reef limestones), with abundant goniatites and brachiopods.
Shirley, J. and Horsfield, E. L. 1940, p. 278, with geol. map.
Geol. Surv. O.S. 81 N.E. ; Ord. New Pop. 111.

**Castleton.** Landslip at base of Mam Tor, W. of Castleton.
Carboniferous, Millstone Grit (Edale Shales and underlying Mam Tor Sandstone, H and lower R zones), with goniatites in bullions.
Jackson, J. W. 1927, pp. 23-25.
Geol. Surv. O.S. 81 N.E. ; Ord. New Pop. 111.

**Castleton.** Middle Hill and Peakshill, 1¾ miles W. of Castleton church.
Carboniferous Limestone Series (B₂ subzone, knoll-reef limestones) with brachiopods, goniatites and corals.
Parkinson, D. 1943, p. 126. Shirley, J. and Horsfield, E. L. 1940, p. 278, with geol. map.
Geol. Surv. O.S. 81 N.E. ; Ord. New Pop. 111.

**Castleton.** Treak (Tray) Cliff, 1 mile W. of Castleton church.
Carboniferous Limestone Series (B₂ subzone, knoll-reef limestones) with brachiopods and molluscs.
Jackson, J. W. 1927, p. 25, with geol. map.
Geol. Surv. O.S. 81 N.E. ; Ord. New Pop. 111.

**Castleton.** Old quarries 350 yds. N.E. of the summit of Eldon Hill, 3 miles S.W. of Castleton.
Carboniferous Limestone Series (D₁ subzone) with corals and brachiopods of the *Davidsonina* [*Cyrtina*] *septosa* band.
Shirley, J. and Horsfield, E. L. 1940, p. 275.
Geol. Surv. O.S. 81 N.E. ; Ord. New Pop. 111.

**Castleton,** see also Hope.

**Creswell.** Caves of Pin Hole, Robin Hood and Mother Grundy's Parlour, 3 miles S.W. of Worksop.
Middle and Upper Pleistocene deposits with Palaeolithic flint-implements and bones of mammoth, woolly rhinoceros, lion, bison, etc. ; Hippopotamus at Mother Grundy's parlour.
Dawkins, W. B. 1880, pp. 175-187.
Geol. Surv. N.S. 100 ; Ord. New Pop. 112.

**Earl Sterndale.** Parkhouse Hill, ¾ mile W. of Earl Sterndale church and 1½ miles N. of Longnor (Staffs).
Carboniferous Limestone Series (D zone, knoll-reef limestones) with brachiopods and molluscs.
Jackson, J. W. 1922, p. 468.
Geol. Surv. O.S. 81 S.E. ; Ord. New Pop. 111.

**Edale,** River section N. of Barber Booth viaduct, *c.* 1 mile S.W. of Edale church.
Carboniferous, Millstone Grit ($E_1$ subzone), shales with molluscs (*Posidonia membranacea*) and obscure goniatites.
Jackson, J. W. 1927, pp. 29-30.
Geol. Surv. O.S. 81 N.E. ; Ord. New Pop. 111.

**Edale.** River section W. of Edale Mill, ¼ mile S.E. of Edale church.
Carboniferous, Millstone Grit ($E_2$ subzone), with goniatites (*Eumorphoceras bisulcatum,* etc.), brachiopods and trilobites.
Jackson, J. W. 1927, p. 27.
Geol. Surv. O.S. 81 N.E. ; Ord. New Pop. 111.

**Hope.** Quarry on S.E. side of Pin Dale, 1 mile S.W. of Hope church.
Carboniferous Limestone Series ($D_1$-$D_2$ zone), cherty above, with algae (*Girvanella*) at base ; and rolled corals (clisiophyllids and *Lithostrotion*) in massive limestone 50 ft. down.
Jackson, J. W. 1941b, p. 239.   Shirley, J. and Horsfield, E. L. 1940, p. 284.
Geol. Surv. O.S. 81 N.E. ; Ord. New Pop. 111.

**Hope.** Nun Low, *c.* 1 miles S. of Hope church.
Carboniferous Limestone ($B_2$ subzone, reef-limestones), with volcanic tuff, and molluscs and brachiopods.
Shirley, J. and Horsfield, E. L. 1940, p. 282, with geol. map.
Geol. Surv. O.S. 81 N.E. ; Ord. New Pop. 111.

**Hope.** Earle's Shale Quarry, S. of Hope, on E. side of Pin Dale.
Carboniferous, Millstone Grit (H and lower R zones), with goniatites in bullions.
Geol. Surv. O.S. 81 N.E. ; Ord. New Pop. 111.

**Kingsterndale,** 3 miles E. of Buxton.   Cliff and roadside section at foot of Topley Pike at confluence of Deep Dale with Wye Dale.
Carboniferous Limestone Series ($S_2$ subzone, fine grey and black limestones) with many brachiopods (*Daviesiella llangollensis*).
Cope, F. W. 1943, p. 207.   Jackson, J. W. 1922, p. 461.
Geol. Surv. O.S. 81 S.E. ; Ord. New Pop. 111.

**Kingsterndale.** Small disused quarry on W. side of Cunning Dale, *c.* 300 yds. N.W. of Ashwood Dale works and 1000 yds. W.N.W. of Pictor Hall.
Carboniferous Limestone Series ($S_2$ subzone) with the brachiopod *Daviesiella derbiensis* (type-locality).
Cope, F. W. 1943, p. 208.
Geol. Surv. O.S. 81 S.E. ; Ord. New Pop. 111.

**Little Longstone,** 3½ miles N.W. of Bakewell.   Limestone stacks at Hobs House, S. side of Monsal Dale, about 400 yds. N. of summit of Fin Cop and 1000 yds. W.S.W. of Monsal Head Hotel.
Carboniferous Limestone Series (upper $D_2$ subzone, grey limestones with chert) with clisiophyllid corals in thick and well-defined bands.
Cope, F. W. 1936a, p. 140, with sketch-maps.
Geol. Surv. O.S. 81 S.E. ; Ord. New Pop. 111.

**Little Longstone.** Bluff known as White Cliff on N. side of R. Wye about 150 yds. N. of Netherdale Farm and 500 yds. N.W. of Monsal Head Hotel.
Carboniferous Limestone, $D_2$ subzone, with a band of the coral *Lonsdaleia.*
Sibly, T. F. 1908, p. 41.   Smith, S. 1915, p. 244, pl. 18.
Geol. Surv. O.S. 81 S.E. ; Ord. New Pop. 111.

**Litton Mill,** 1 mile E. of Tideswell.   Small scars on hillside immediately S. of main L.M.S. line about 700 yds. W. of W. mouth of Litton Tunnel and 800 yds. S.W. of Littonslack Farm.

Carboniferous Limestone, lower part of D$_2$ subzone. Perhaps Martin's type-locality for the brachiopod *Gigantoproductus giganteus*.
Cope, F. W. 1937, p. 181.
Geol. Surv. O.S. 81 S.E. ; Ord. New Pop. 111.

**Matlock.** Cawdor Quarry, at N. end of town, adjoining railway station.
Carboniferous Limestone (upper D$_2$ subzone) with corals ; overlain by dark limestones and shales with zaphrentid corals, brachiopods, goniatites and trilobites.
Geol. Surv. O.S. 82 S.W. ; Ord. New Pop. 111.

**Miller's Dale.** Large disused quarry (Miller's Dale Limeworks), on S. side of dale at railway station.
Carboniferous Limestone (D$_2$ subzone). Many brachiopods and corals occur in thin-bedded black limestones with chert (overlying some 120 ft. of barren white limestone), especially to E. of footpath from Miller's Dale to Priestcliffe.
Cope, F. W. 1937, p. 182.
Geol. Surv. O.S. 81 S.E. ; Ord. New Pop. 111.

**Overseal,** 6 miles S.E. of Burton-on-Trent. Robinson and Dowler's Claypit (western pit), 700 yds. N. 7° E. of Overseal church.
Carboniferous, Coal Measures (*similis-pulchra* zone, Overseal Marine Band), with brachiopods (*Crurithyris*) in nodules and *Lingula* in blue shales.
Mitchell, G. H. and Stubblefield, C. J. 1941b, p. 19.
Geol. Surv. N.S. 155 ; Ord. New Pop. 120.

**Peak Dale,** 3½ miles N.E. of Buxton. Cutting on E. side of mineral line at Longsiding Works, Great Rocks Dale, 300 yds. N. of Buxton Bridge and 1300 yds. S.E. of Peak Dale.
Carboniferous Limestone (D$_1$ subzone) with a well-marked band of the brachiopod *Davidsonina* [*Cyrtina*] *septosa*.
Cope, F. W. 1936b, p. 48.
Geol. Surv. O.S. 81 N.E. ; Ord. New Pop. 111.

**Sparrowpit,** 1½ miles E. of Chapel-en-le-Frith. Quarry on N.W. side of Eldon Hill, 1¾ miles E.N.E. of Sparrowpit on S.E. side of road to Castleton.
Carboniferous Limestone (upper D$_1$ subzone), knoll-reef limestones with brachiopods (*Davidsonina* [*Cyrtina*] *septosa*) and corals (*Lithostrotion, Dibunophyllum*).
Parkinson, D. 1943, p. 124. Shirley, J. and Horsfield, E. L. 1940, p. 275, with geol. map.
Geol. Surv. O.S. 81 N.E. ; Ord. New Pop. 111.

**Sparrowpit.** Barmoor Quarry, about ½ mile S.S.W. of village.
Carboniferous Limestone, including a limestone-conglomerate with com-minuted shells and many fish-teeth (*Psammodus rugosus, Psephodus magnus*).
Davis, J. W. 1886, p. 148. Jackson, J. W. 1908, p. 309.
Geol. Surv. O.S. 81 N.E. ; Ord. New Pop. 111.

**Stony Middleton,** 5 miles N. of Bakewell. Coombs Dale, ½ mile S. of village.
Carboniferous Limestone (D$_2$ subzone) with corals (*Orionastraea*, etc.) and brachiopods.
Shirley, J. and Horsfield, E. L. 1940, p. 295, with geol. map.
Geol. Surv. O.S. 81 S.E. ; Ord. New Pop. 111.

**Stony Middleton.** Middleton Dale, westward from village.
Carboniferous Limestone (D$_2$ subzone). Corals (*Orionastraea placenta*) and brachiopods in bedded limestones, succeeded by knoll-reef limestones with many brachiopods.
Shirley, J. and Horsfield, E. L. 1940, p. 294, with geol. map.
Geol. Surv. O.S. 81 N.E. ; Ord. New Pop. 111.

**Taddington,** 6 miles E. of Buxton.    Limestone scars at Tadwell Gate and Five Wells, 500-1000 yds. S.W. of Waterloo Hotel and about 900 yds. S. of Blackwell hamlet, 1½ miles N.W. of Taddington.
Carboniferous Limestone ($D_2$ subzone, top).  Good locality for the gastropod *Bellerophon*.
Geol. Surv. O.S. 81 S.E. ;  Ord. New Pop. 111.

**Thorpe.**    Cliffs near Reynard's Cave, Dovedale, 1¾ miles N.W. of village.
Carboniferous Limestone (reef-limestone) with abundance of the brachiopod *Productus humerosus*.
Jackson, J. W. 1919, p. 507 ;  1941a, p. 233.
Geol. Surv. O.S. 72 N.E. ;  Ord. New Pop. 111.

**Thorpe.**    Pike House Quarry, Spend Lane, about ½ mile N.N.W. of Thorpe Cloud station.
Carboniferous Limestone ($D_1$ subzone, shelly limestones, in part chalcedonic, with dolomitic patches and limestone pebbles) with many brachiopods and a few corals.
Jackson, J. W. 1941a, p. 235.
Geol. Surv. O.S. 72 N.E. ;  Ord. New Pop. 111.

**Thorpe.**    Thorpe Cloud, at mouth of Dovedale, about ½ mile N. of Thorpe village.
Carboniferous Limestone ($S_1$ subzone) with brachiopods (*Spirifer bollandensis*) and other brachiopods and some molluscs.  A locality for specimens figured in the classic monographs of Davidson and Hind.
Jackson, J. W. 1941a, p. 233.
Geol. Surv. O.S. 72 N.E. ;  Ord. New Pop. 111.

**Ticknall,** 4½ miles N. of Ashby-de-la-Zouch.  Ticknall Main Quarry, 1025 yds. E. 17° S. of church.
Carboniferous Limestone (D zone) with many corals and brachiopods.
Mitchell, G. H. and Stubblefield, C. J. 1941a, p. 201.
Geol. Surv. N.S. 141 ;  Ord. New Pop. 121.

**Wardlow,** 5½ miles N.N.W. of Bakewell.  Small disused quarry and natural scars on W. side of Wardlow-Bakewell road at the old Crossdale Head Mine, about 1 mile N. of Monsal Head Hotel.
Carboniferous Limestone ($D_2$ subzone) with a band of clisiophyllid corals and many brachiopods.
Cope, F. W. 1936a, p. 140.
Geol. Surv. O.S. 81 S.E. ;  Ord. New Pop. 111.


# DEVONSHIRE

**Axmouth.**  Dowlands Cliff, S.E. of Axmouth.
Cretaceous, Middle Chalk (*Terebratulina* zone) and Upper Chalk (*planus* zone), with many small fossils.
Rowe, A. W. 1903, p. 10.
Geol. Surv. N.S. 326/340 ;  Ord. New Pop. 177.

**Axmouth.**  Incipient landslips near top of hill about halfway between Haven Cliff and Culverhole Point, close to path from Axmouth to Dowlands Landslip, before entering landslip proper.  Much scree-material in and around low scarps separated by ledges with turf and brushwood.
Cretaceous, Lower Chalk (in sandy " Cenomanian Limestone " facies) with plentiful well-preserved ammonites (*Schloenbachia, Mantelliceras, Acanthoceras, Turrilites,* etc.) and other fossils.
Woodward, H. B. and Ussher, W. A. E. 1911, p. 56.
Geol. Surv. N.S. 326/340 ;  Ord. New Pop. 177.

**Barton,** N. Torquay. Old quarries at Lummaton Hill, 220 yds. E. of Lummaton Cross along road to Torquay.

Middle to Upper Devonian, massive slickensided limestones. Stromato-poroids occur in the southern quarries ; corals, brachiopods, trilobites (*e.g. Goldius* [*Bronteus*] *flabellifer*), etc. in the northern, where the brachiopod *Hypothyridina cuboides* indicates the Upper Devonian age of the higher beds. Conditions for collecting are only good when the quarries are in work.

Milne Edwards, H. and Haime, J. 1853. Ussher, W. A. E. 1933, pp. 75-76. Whidborne, G. F. 1888-1892.

Geol. Surv. N.S. 339 ; Ord. New Pop. 188.

**Beer,** 1 mile S.W. of Seaton. Pit ½ mile N.W. of Beer church, on E. side of Court Barn Lane.

Cretaceous, Middle Chalk (*Terebratulina* zone) and Upper Chalk (*planus* zone), richly fossiliferous, with the sea-urchin *Micraster* abundant.

Rowe, A. W. 1903, p. 27.

Geol. Surv. N.S. 326/340 ; Ord. New Pop. 177.

**Beer.** Annis Knob, a bluff in cliff about N. side of harbour.

Cretaceous, Upper Chalk (*planus* and *cortestudinarium* zones), with abundant fossils on weathered surfaces.

Rowe, A. W. 1903, pp. 16-18.

Geol. Surv. N.S. 326/340 ; Ord. New Pop. 177.

**Beer.** Cliff-top exposures, Beer Head, 1 mile S. of village.

Cretaceous, Upper Chalk (*planus* and *cortestudinarium* zones), with many fossils, especially sea-urchins and brachiopods.

Rowe, A. W. 1903, p. 20.

Geol. Surv. N.S. 326/340 ; Ord, New Pop. 177.

**Beer.** W. side of Beer harbour.

Cretaceous, Lower Chalk, and *labiatus* zone of Middle Chalk, well exposed, but not highly fossiliferous.

Rowe, A. W. 1903, p. 18.

Geol. Surv. N. S. 326/340 ; Ord. New Pop. 177.

**Beer.** Hooken beach and eastward to Beer Head.

Cretaceous, Lower and Middle Chalk with abundant fossils, especially the sea-urchin *Conulus* in the Middle Chalk (*labiatus* zone).

Rowe, A. W. 1903, pp. 20-21.

Geol. Surv. N.S. 326/340 ; Ord. New Pop. 177.

**Beer.** The Hooken, W. of Beer ; upper cliff near Beer Stone mine-adit.

Cretaceous, Lower Chalk, arenaceous facies, with abundant sea-urchins.

Geol. Surv. N.S. 326/340 ; Ord. New Pop. 177.

**Beer.** The Hooken ; various bluffs and detached masses of chalk at E. end of Hooken Undercliff.

Cretaceous, Lower and Middle Chalk, with very abundant small fossils (sea-urchins, starfish ossicles, brachiopods, etc.) on air-weathered surfaces.

Rowe, A. W. 1903, p. 21.

Geol. Surv. N.S. 326/340 ; Ord. New Pop. 177.

**Bideford** and district.

Carboniferous, upper Culm Measures. A list of localities for marine fossils is given by Rogers, I. 1910, pp. 559-560. The present condition of these sections is not known.

Geol. Surv. O.S. 26 ; Ord. New Pop. 163, 174.

**Bideford.** Cliffs some 250 yds. S. of Babbacombe Mouth, Bideford Bay.

Carboniferous, upper Culm Measures, finely laminated red, grey and fawn shales with plant-stems.

Rogers, I. 1910, p. 554.

Geol. Surv. O.S. 26 ; Ord. New Pop. 174.

**Bideford.** S. end of Cornborough Cliff, Bideford Bay, near Fanny Bennett rock.
Carboniferous, upper Culm Measures, plant-remains in soft black shales at base of culm bed.
Geol. Surv. O.S. 26 ; Ord. New Pop. 163.

**Bideford.** Pit Quarry, Abbotsham, 2 miles W. of Bideford.
Carboniferous, upper Culm Measures, carbonaceous sandstones with fragments of fossil plants and fruits. This locality was examined by de la Beche and Murchison.
Rogers, I. 1910, pp. 543-544.
Geol. Surv. O.S. 26 ; Ord. New Pop. 163.

**Bideford.** Cliff-sections, Cockington Head, 3½ miles S.W. of Bideford ; N. slope of deep hollow some 300 yds. N. of shore path from Cockington Farm.
Carboniferous, upper Culm Measures, two bands of calcareous shales and nodules with lamellibranchs, goniatites and fish.
Rogers, I. 1909, pp. 311-313, with geol. map.
Geol. Surv. O.S. 26 ; Ord. New Pop. 174.

**Bideford.** Cliff-section, Greenacliff, 3 miles W.N.W. of Bideford.
Carboniferous, upper Culm Measures ; plants and fish-bearing nodules in shales 133 yds. N. of outcrop of culm bed : non-marine shells in shale adjoining thick sandstone 600 yds. N. of same.
Rogers, I. 1909, pp. 315-317, with geol. map ; 1910, p. 542.
Geol. Surv. O.S. 26 ; Ord. New Pop. 163.

**Bishop's Tawton,** 2 miles S.S.E. of Barnstaple. Numerous quarries in Codden Hill, 1 mile S.E. of village, and at Eastacombe, 1¼ miles W.S.W. of village.
Carboniferous, Codden Hill Cherts of Carboniferous Limestone age, with radiolaria, corals, brachiopods, goniatites, etc.
Fox, H. and Hinde, G. J. 1895, p. 609, with geol. map.
Geol. Surv. O.S. 26 ; Ord. New Pop. 163.

**Branscombe.** Bluffs and cliff-top exposures W. of Branscombe Mouth and at Berry Cliffs to the W.
Cretaceous, Middle Chalk, a unique and highly fossiliferous facies with sea-urchins (especially *Cidaris hirudo*) and starfish-ossicles.
Rowe, A. W. 1903, pp. 25-27.
Geol. Surv. N.S. 326/340 ; Ord. New Pop. 176.

**Braunton.** Braunton Down, E. of village.
Upper Devonian, Pilton Beds, with trilobites, molluscs and brachiopods.
Hicks, H. 1896, pp. 367, 372. Whidborne, G. F. 1896-1898.
Geol. Surv. O.S. 27 ; Ord. New Pop. 163.

**Clovelly.** Cliffs and foreshore at W. end of Gallantry Bower, 1¼ miles N.W. of Clovelly.
Carboniferous, Culm Measures of Lower Coal Measures age, with fine, solid goniatites (*Gastrioceras*) in a thin limestone and nodules in accompanying shale.
Rogers, I. 1909, p. 313.
Geol. Surv. O.S. 26 ; Ord. New Pop. 174.

**Combe Martin,** 8½ miles N. of Barnstaple. Limestone quarries W. and S.W. of the village.
Middle to Upper Devonian, Ilfracombe Beds, with corals, crinoids, brachiopods, etc.
Hicks, H. 1896, p. 364. Evans, J. W. 1922, p. 201.
Geol. Surv. O.S. 27 ; Ord. New Pop. 163.

**Croyde,** 8 miles W.N.W. of Barnstaple. Cliffs and foreshore S. of Croyde Bay.
Upper Devonian, Pilton Beds. The rich fauna is fully listed by Hicks, H. 1896, pp. 367, 372 and monographed by Whidborne, G. F., 1896-1898.
Geol. Surv. O.S. 27 ; Ord. New Pop. 163.

**Croyde.** Baggy Point, N.W. of Croyde.
Upper Devonian, Baggy Beds. See Hicks and Whidborne, as above.
Geol. Surv. O.S. 27 ; Ord. New Pop. 163.

**East Ogwell,** S.W. of Newton Abbot. Ransley (Ramsleigh) Quarry, ¼ mile E. of E. Ogwell on N. side of road to Wolborough.
Upper Devonian, limestones, with corals (especially *Acervularia pentagona* in irregular, pinkish, disc-like masses and *Chonophyllum perfoliatum*). Goniatites occur in the rubbly upper beds. Brachiopods are scarce and ill-preserved.
Milne Edwards, H. and Haime, J. 1853. Ussher, W. A. E. 1913, pp. 20-21. Whidborne, G. F. 1888-1892.
Geol. Surv. N.S. 339 ; Ord. New Pop. 188.

**Fremington,** 3 miles W. of Barnstaple. W. bank of R. Taw N. and S. of railway ½ mile N. of the village.
Carboniferous, Culm Measures, shales and decalcified limestones of upper Carboniferous Limestone and Millstone Grit age, with flattened impressions of lamellibranchs and goniatites.
Moore, E. W. J. 1929, p. 356, with topog. map.
Geol. Surv. O.S. 27 ; Ord. New Pop. 163.

**Fremington.** Foreshore, left bank of R. Taw, 190 yds. N. of railway, 1000 yds. N. of the village.
Devonian (? Upper Devonian), thin, green, decalcified limestone, with many well-preserved corals, brachiopods, trilobites, etc.
Paul, H. 1937, p. 433. Whidborne, G. F. 1896-1898.
Geol. Surv. O.S. 27 ; Ord. New Pop. 163.

**Goodrington,** Paignton. N. end of Saltern Cove, due E. of village and reached by Goodrington Sands to N. or Broad Sands to S.
Upper Devonian slaty shales and red mudstones and some limestone. Many goniatites, preserved in haematite, weather out on mudstone surfaces, with lamellibranchs (*Buchiola retrostriata*), but are best collected by digging down from the top. Cleaved shales yield lamellibranchs (*Posidoniella venusta*) and ostracods (*Entomis serrato-striata*). Corals occur in limestone beneath mudstones.
Ussher, W. A. E. 1933, pp. 86-90.
Geol. Surv. N.S. 350 ; Ord. New Pop. 188.

**Ilfracombe.** Hele Bay, 1 mile E. of Lighthouse.
Middle Devonian, Ilfracombe Beds, occasionally with the brachiopod *Stringocephalus burtini.*
Hicks, H. 1896, p. 364.

**Ilfracombe.** Great Shelfin, about 2 miles S. of Ilfracombe.
Upper Devonian, Morte Slates, with many fossils, chiefly brachiopods and lamellibranchs.
Hicks, H. 1896, p. 359.
Geol. Surv. O.S. 27 ; Ord. New Pop. 163.

**Ilfracombe.** Mullacott, S. of Great Shelfin.
Upper Devonian, Morte Slates, with brachiopods and lamellibranchs.
Hicks, H. 1896, p. 359.
Geol. Surv. O.S. 27 ; Ord. New Pop. 163.

**Ilsham,** East Torquay. Quarry in northern part of Hope's Nose promontory.
Middle Devonian limestones, with abundant and well-preserved corals

(especially "*Cyathophyllum*," *Cystiphyllum vesiculosum*, *Heliolites porosa*).
Stromatoporoid, also occur.    Gold has been found in fault-fissures in upper
beds on E. face.
Milne Edwards H. and Haime, J. 1853.   Ussher, W. A. E. 1933, p. 56.
Geol. Surv. N.S. 350 ;  Ord. New Pop. 188.

**Lyme Regis.**  Rhaetic and Lower Lias of Pinhay, see Dorset.

**Lynton.**  Watersmeet, 1½ miles S.E. of Lynton.
Lower Devonian, Lynton Beds, with corals and brachiopods.
Hicks, H. 1896, p. 360.
Geol. Surv. O.S. 27 ;  Ord. New Pop. 163 and 164.

**Lynton.**  Valley of the Rocks, W. side of Lynton.
Lower Devonian, Lynton Beds, with corals and brachiopods.
Hicks, H. 1896, p. 360.
Geol. Surv. O.S. 27 ;  Ord. New Pop. 163 and 164.

**Lynton.**  Barbrook Mill, 1¼ miles S. of Lynton.
Lower Devonian, Lynton Beds, with corals and brachiopods.
Hicks, H. 1896, p. 360.
Geol. Surv. O.S. 27 ;  Ord. New Pop. 163 and 164.

**Marwood,** 3 miles N.W. of Barnstaple.   Quarries at Marwood.
Upper Devonian, Baggy and Marwood Beds.   The rich fauna is listed by
Hicks, H. 1896, pp. 366, 371 and monographed by Whidborne, G. F. 1896-
1898.
Geol. Surv. O.S. 27 ;  Ord. New Pop. 163.

**Meadfoot,** Torquay.   Cliff-slopes N. of shore-drive along Meadfoot Beach
E. of Meadfoot Sands and W. of Kilmorie and Ilsham Valley road.
Lower Devonian, Meadfoot Beds, with badly preserved brachiopods
(*Tropidoleptus rhenanus*).
Ussher, W. A. E. 1933, p. 38, pl. iii.
Geol. Surv. O.S. 350 ;  Ord. New Pop. 188.

**Morthoe.**  Barricane Creek.
Upper Devonian, Morte Slates, with trilobites, crinoids and brachiopods
(including the Upper Devonian form *Spirifer verneuili*).
Evans, J. W. and Pocock, R. W. 1912, p. 112.   Hicks, H. 1896, p. 359.
Geol. Surv. O.S. 27 ;  Ord. New Pop. 163.

**Pilton,** Barnstaple.   Ashford Strand, Pilton.
Upper Devonian, Pilton Beds.   The rich fauna is listed by Hicks, H.
1896, pp. 367, 372 and monographed by Whidborne, G. F. 1896-1898.
Geol. Surv. O.S. 27 ;  Ord. New Pop. 163.

**Rousdon,** 3 miles W. of Lyme Regis (Dorset).   Humble Point, and
Charton Bay.
Cretaceous, Lower and Middle Chalk, boulders on beach, from which alone
several rare ammonite-species are known.
Geol. Surv. N.S. 326/340 ;  Ord. New Pop. 177.

**Saunton,** 6½ miles W.N.W. of Barnstaple.   Cliff and foreshore exposures
at Saunton Downs and Saunton Sands, respectively 2 and 1 miles W. of village.
Hicks, H. 1896, pp. 367, 371.   Whidborne, G. F. 1896-1898.
Geol. Surv. O.S. 27 ;  Ord. New Pop. 163.

**St. Mary Church,** Torquay.   Petit Tor and Petit Tor Combe.
Upper Devonian limestones, synclinally folded about red shales which have
weathered out to form the combe.   Occasional goniatites occur in red shaly
limestone along the walls of the combe.   Derived corals of various Devonian
ages occur as pebbles in Permian conglomerate faulted in to the south.
Ussher, W. A. E. 1933, pp. 82-83, 107.
Geol. Surv. N.S. 350 ;  Ord. New Pop. 188.

**Seaton,** White Cliff.
Cretaceous, Upper Greensand, Lower and Middle Chalk, the two latter magnificently fossiliferous. Sea-urchins are especially abundant in the Middle Chalk.
Rowe, A. W. 1903, p. 11.
Geol. Surv. N.S. 326/340 ; Ord. New Pop. 177.

**Seaton.** Havencliff, E. side of R. Axe ; boulders on undercliff.
Cretaceous, Upper Greensand, Lower and Middle Chalk, with abundant fossils. Note especially a band of ammonites (*Neocardioceras*, etc.) at base of Middle Chalk.
Geol. Surv. N.S. 326/340 ; Ord. New Pop. 177.

**Seaton.** Axecliff Pit.
Cretaceous, Lower Chalk, with abundant ammonites and lamellibranchs.
Geol. Surv. N.S. 326/340 ; Ord. New Pop. 177.

**Sidmouth.** Clifftop exposures and slipped masses, W. of Dunscombe Mouth, 2½ miles E. of Sidmouth.
Cretaceous, Lower Chalk (sandy limestone facies), highly fossiliferous.
Meyer, C. J. A. 1874, p. 369.
Geol. Surv. N.S. 326/340 ; Ord. New Pop. 176.

**Sloley,** about 3 miles N. of Barnstaple. Quarry near Barnstaple-Ilfracombe road.
Upper Devonian, Baggy and Marwood Beds. The fauna is listed by Hicks, H. 1896, pp. 366, 371 and monographed by Whidborne, G. F. 1896-1898.
Geol. Surv. O.S. 27 ; Ord. New Pop. 163.

**Torcross,** 8 miles S.W. of Dartmouth. Cliffs S. of Torcross.
Lower Devonian, Meadfoot Beds, with brachiopods (*Spirifer*) and crinoids in grey slate.
Ussher, W. A. E. 1904, p. 21.
Geol. Surv. N.S. 356 ; Ord. New Pop. 188.

**Torquay.** Dyer's Quarry, E. of harbour, approached by boat or by lane from Parkhill Road at Imperial Hotel to Land's End. Climb over wall on right at end of lane and work carefully down to floor of quarry.
Middle Devonian limestones, the best locality for corals around Torquay. *Mesophyllum dammoniense* and *Cystiphyllum vesiculosum* are very common. *Heliolites porosa* and *Phacelophyllum* (*Disphyllum*) *caespitosum* also occur, the latter in massive colonies on N. slopes of quarry. Brachiopods and a few trilobites can also be found.
Jukes-Browne, A. J. 1913, pp. 26-29. Ussher, W. A. E. 1933, p. 54.
Geol. Surv. N.S. 350 ; Ord. New Pop. 188.

**Torquay.** Triangle Rock and vicinity, a well-known feature on the shore at Meadfoot Sands.
Middle Devonian, massive and bedded limestones. A good dip-surface yields small colonies of the coral *Thamnopora madreporacea* (=*Pachypora cervicornis*) and small brachiopods.
Milne Edwards, H. and Haime, J. 1853. Ussher, W. A. E. 1933, pp. 53, 55, figs. 6, 8.
Geol. Surv. N.S. 350 ; Ord. New Pop. 188.

**Torquay.** See also Barton, Ilsham, Meadfoot, St. Mary Church.

**Westleigh.** Old quarry in S.E. corner of Rocknell Hill, 600 yds. W. of Westleigh.
Carboniferous, limestone of upper Carboniferous Limestone age, with flattened trilobites, goniatites, lamellibranchs and brachiopods in interbedded shales.
Owen, D. E. 1939, p. 339.
Geol. Surv. O.S. 21 ; Ord. New Pop. 164.

**Westleigh,** 5 miles S.W. of Wellington (Somerset). S.W. corner of main quarry of Westleigh Limestone Co., Knowle Hill.

Carboniferous, limestone of upper Carboniferous Limestone age, with impressions of goniatites and lamellibranchs in shale partings.

Geol. Surv. O.S. 21 ; Ord. New Pop. 164.

**Wilmington,** 3 miles S.E. of Honiton. Two pits : 1, on S. side of main road, opposite Inn ; 2, by road leading N. from village to Hayne's Farm.

Cretaceous, Lower Chalk, sandy limestone facies. One of the finest Cretaceous fossil-localities in the country, has yielded some 300 species, including fine ammonites, gastropods, lamellibranchs, bryozoa, sea-urchins and corals.

Jukes-Browne, A. J. 1898, p. 239, with geol. map.
Geol. Surv. N.S. 326/340 ; Ord. New Pop. 177.

**Wolborough,** Newton Abbot. Old quarries about 200 yds. N. of Wolborough Isolation Hospital on both sides of Newton Abbot-Torquay road *via* Ogwell Cross.

Upper Devonian limestones. Whidborne lists an extensive fauna which he compares with that of Barton (Lummaton Cross). Many corals, brachiopods (including *Hypothyridina cuboides*), lamellibranchs, gastropods and goniatites occur, with some crinoids and trilobites.

Ussher, W. A. E. 1913, pp. 21-24. Whidborne, G. F. 1888-1892.
Geol. Surv. N.S. 339 ; Ord. New Pop. 176.


# DORSET

**Abbotsbury.** Fleet shore, Shipmoor Point, Chesters Hill, at S. side of the Swannery.

Jurassic, Cornbrash, complete section ; the Lower Cornbrash is better exposed on the shore ½ mile farther S.E. Many brachiopods, lamellibranchs, sea-urchins, etc., occur.

Douglas, J. A. and Arkell, W. J. 1928, p. 153. Davies, G. M. 1935, p. 50.
Arkell, W. J. 1947b, p. 23.
Geol. Surv. N.S. 341 ; Ord. New Pop. 178.

**Abbotsbury.** Old ironstone workings and lane-cuttings. The best are in Sea Lane, ½ mile W. of the church ; Red Lane, leading up the hill N. of Ilchester Arms Hotel ; and Folly Hollow, N.W. of school towards Ferny Hole Plantation.

Jurassic, Kimmeridge Clay, base (*cymodoce* zone, Abbotsbury Iron Ore), with a unique fauna of brachiopods (*Ornithella* spp.), and small ammonites (*Rasenia*).

Arkell, W. J. 1947b, pp. 86-88. Davies, G. M. 1935, p. 49.
Geol. Surv. N.S. 327-341 ; Ord. New Pop. 178.

**Beaminster.** Whaddon Hill (or Stoke Knap), 2 miles W. of Beaminster, disused quarries and trackside exposures.

Jurassic, Inferior Oolite (*aalensis* to (?) *witchellia* zones). Abundant brachiopods and ammonites in *opalinum* zone.

Richardson, L. 1928-1930, p. 258, with topog. map.
Geol. Surv. N.S. 327 ; Ord. New Pop. 177.

**Bincombe,** on E. side of Weymouth-Dorchester road. Pit on Bincombe Hill, by track 270 yds. E.S.E. of church.

Cretaceous, Lower Chalk, basement bed with many well-preserved ammonites.

Wright, C. W. in Arkell, W. J. 1947b, pp. 212-213.
Geol. Surv. N.S. 342 ; Ord. New Pop. 178.

**Bradford Abbas.** The celebrated East Hill Quarry (No. 16 of Richardson, 1932) is now scarcely to be detected, and later quarries have long been abandoned. This, with Hall's Quarry (No. 15) and Babylon Hill (No. 20) were favourite collecting-grounds of Professor J. Buckman and his son, S. S. Buckman.

Jurassic, Inferior Oolite. The local fossil-bed (*murchisonae* zone) was famous for abundant, fine ammonites, etc.

Buckman, S. S. 1887-1907. Hudleston, W. H. 1887-1896. Richardson, L. 1932, p. 54, with topog. map.

Geol. Surv. N.S. 312 ; Ord. New Pop. 177-8.

**Burton Bradstock.** Cliffs between the village and Burton Freshwater to the W. ; and road-section both sides of Cliff Hill Lane, running S. from village to top of cliffs.

Jurassic, Upper Lias (Bridport Sands) and complete section of Inferior Oolite, best studied in lane-section or in fallen blocks on beach. Fossils of all groups are abundant and well-preserved.

Richardson, L. 1928-1930, pp. 59-68, with topog. map.

Geol. Surv. N.S. 327 ; Ord. New Pop. 177.

**Charmouth.** Cliff-sections of Black Ven and Stonebarrow, and foreshore beneath, from ½ mile N.E. of Lyme Regis to 1 mile E. of mouth of R. Char.

Jurassic, Lower Lias (Black Marls, Belemnite Beds and Green Ammonite Beds) and base of Middle Lias. Fossils (especially ammonites, belemnites, lamellibranchs and brachiopods) may be collected from accessible parts of cliffs and from fallen blocks. *Cliffs dangerous to stand under in places.*

Lang, W. D., Spath, L. F. and Richardson, W. A. 1923, pp. 47-99. Lang, W. D. and Spath, L. F. 1926. Davies, G. M. 1935, p. 21.

Geol. Surv. N.S. 326-327 ; Ord. New Pop. 177.

**Charmouth.** Cliff-section of Westhay and foreshore for 1170 yds. E. of a point 1 mile E. of mouth of R. Char and 1¼ miles E.S.E. of Charmouth Church, to 1½ miles S.W. of St. Gabriel's Church, Morecombelake (*i.e.*, 366 yds. W. of St. Gabriel's Water).

Jurassic, Lower Lias (Belemnite Marls—the lower half in the foreshore—and Green Ammonite Beds) and base of Middle Lias. Abundant ammonites, belemnites, lamellibranchs, brachiopods, etc., can be collected from foreshore-reefs, fallen blocks (*beware of cliff-falls*) and gullies at top of cliff.

Lang, W. D. and others 1928, pp. 179-257 ; 1936, pp. 423-487. Davies, G. M. 1935, p. 21.

Geol. Surv. N.S. 327 ; Ord. New Pop. 177.

**Charmouth.** Cliff-section beneath gap in old coast-road at a point approximately 1 mile N.E. of Lyme Regis and ¾ mile W.S.W. of Charmouth, some 50 yds. E. of Lyme Regis-Charmouth parish boundary.

Cretaceous, Gault and Upper Greensand (loamy and sandy clay, Pebble Bed and Cowstones in ascending order, about 50 ft.). Classic section and source of most of the fossils labelled " Black Ven " in collections. Lamellibranchs are the commonest fossils.

Lang, W. D. 1904, pp. 124-131. Davies, G. M. 1935, p. 25.

Geol. Surv. N.S. 327 ; Ord. New Pop. 177.

**Chesilton,** Portland. West Weare Cliff, ½ mile S. from village along shore.

Jurassic, Portland Sand and Cherty Series of Portland Stone with basal shell-bed. Difficult of access. Rich and well-preserved lamellibranch and gastropod fauna in basal shell-bed. Oysters (*Exogyra*-bed) and casts of ammonites in Portland Sand.

Cox, L. R. 1925. Davies, G. M. 1935, p. 53.

Geol. Surv. N.S. 342 ; Ord. New Pop. 178.

**Chesilton.** Numerous large quarries scattered over N. end of Portland Island, from top of hill above Chesilton along roads to Easton and Weston.

Jurassic, Portland Stone (Freestone Series), with giant ammonites and other mollusca ; casts of lamellibranchs (*Trigonia*, etc.) and gastropods (*Aptyxiella portlandica*, the " Portland Screw ") in the Roach, or top bed : and silicified trees in basal Purbeck Beds with seat-earths (dirt beds).

Arkell, W. J. 1947b, pp. 118-122. Davies, G. M. 1935, p. 53.
Geol. Surv. N.S. 342 ; Ord. New Pop. 178.

**Chickerell.** Claypit of Dorset Brick and Tile Co., Putton Lane, ½ mile S.E. of church.

Jurassic, Kellaways Beds (*koenigi* zone), with ammonites, many oysters and other lamellibranchs (*Oxytoma* in nodules).

Arkell, W. J. 1947b, p. 27. Davies, G. M. 1935, p. 51.
Geol. Surv. N.S. 341 ; Ord. New Pop. 178.

**Chickerell.** Webb, Major and Co.'s brickpit, Crook Hill, ½ miles S. of church.

Jurassic, Oxford Clay (*coronatum* and *athleta* zones) with crushed ammonites (*Kosmoceras*) and lamellibranchs (*Meleagrinella*, etc.) below and mudstone casts of ammonites (*Peltoceras*) above.

Arkell, W. J. 1947b, p. 29. Davies, G. M. 1935, p. 51.
Geol. Surv. N.S. 341 ; Ord. New Pop. 178.

**Chickerell.** Fleet shore, Tidmoor Point, 1¼ miles S. of church and 1 mile S.E. of East Fleet.

Jurassic, Oxford Clay (*lamberti* zone). Pyritized ammonites, with belemnites and crinoid-ossicles, washed out of low cliffs of slipped clay.

Arkell, W. J. 1947b, pp. 30-32. Davies, G. M. 1935, p. 50.
Geol. Surv. N.S. 341 ; Ord. New Pop. 178.

**Chideock.** Cliff-section of Golden Cap and foreshore from just W. of St. Gabriel's Water to mouth of R. Winniford at Seatown, ¾ mile S. of Chideock Church.

Jurassic, Lower Lias (Belemnite Marls and Green Ammonite Beds in cliffs and foreshore) and Middle Lias (in cliffs). Ammonites, lamellibranchs and brachiopods abundant in cliffs, fallen blocks and foreshore reefs.

Lang, W. D. and others 1928, pp. 179-257 ; 1936, pp. 423-487. Davies, G. M. 1935, p. 29.
Geol. Surv. N.S. 327 ; Ord. New Pop. 177.

**Corfe Castle.** Limestone cap of Creechbarrow (637 ft. O.D.), 2¼ miles W. of the castle. Can only be exposed by digging after permission has been obtained.

Oligocene, Bembridge Limestone, with casts of the shell and (?) eggs of the gastropod *Filholia* [*Bulimus*] *elliptica*.

Arkell, W. J. 1947b, pp. 233-241. Davies, G. M. 1935, p. 71. Keeping, H. 1910.
Geol. Surv. N.S. 342 ; Ord. New Pop. 179.

**Corfe Castle.** Marlpit (section now obscured) 200 yds. N. of Blashenwell Farm, ¾ mile S.S.W. of castle.

Mesolithic tufa with many land-snails ; sea-shells carried up for food by Mesolithic man.

Arkell, W. J. 1947b, p. 351. Clark, J. G. D. 1938, p. 332. Davies, G. M. 1935, p. 71.
Geol. Surv. N.S. 343 ; Ord. New Pop. 179.

**Eype,** 1½ miles S.W. of Bridport. Cliff-section between Seatown, ¾ mile S. of Chideock Church, for 2 miles E. to ¼ mile E. of Eype Mouth.

Jurassic, Middle Lias (Eype Clays, with ammonites in nodule-bed), Junction Bed (Middle-Upper Lias) and Bridport Sands (Upper Lias). Many ammonites, brachiopods, etc., can be got from fallen blocks. Blocks of the Starfish Bed (Middle Lias) have delicate brittle-stars on their lower surfaces.

Davies, G. M. 1935, pp. 30-31. Jackson, J. F. 1926, pp. 490-525.
Geol. Surv. N.S. 327 ; Ord. New Pop. 177.

**Goathill,** 1 mile S. of Milborne Port.   Limekiln quarry about ½ mile N.W.
of Goathill Farm.
Jurassic, Fuller's Earth Rock, with abundant brachiopods (*Ornithella*).
White, H. J. O. 1923, p. 22.   Muir-Wood, H. M. 1936.
Geol. Surv. N.S. 313 ; Ord. New Pop. 178.

**Haydon,** 2 miles S. of Milborne Port.   Old quarry in wood about ½ mile
N.E. of village.
Jurassic, Fuller's Earth Rock, with brachiopods (*Ornithella*), etc.
Muir-Wood, H. M. 1936.
Geol. Surv. N. S. 313 ; Ord. New Pop. 178.

**Holwell,** 5 miles S.E. of Sherborne.   Quarries ½ mile W.N.W. of church,
on E. side of road N. of river.
Jurassic, Cornbrash, with ammonites (*Macrocephalites*) in upper part.
(Source of H. H. Wood coll., Sherborne School Museum).
Douglas, J. A. and Arkell, W. J. 1928, p. 148.
Geol. Surv. N.S. 313 ; Ord. New Pop. 178.

**Kimmeridge,** 5 miles S. of Wareham.   Cliffs, accessible at low tide, for
3 miles from pier at Hen Cliff to Chapman's Pool.   Old adits in Kimmeridge
Coal (Blackstone) are at Clavell's Hard, S. of Little Kimmeridge.
Jurassic, Kimmeridge Clay, type-section.   Ammonites (*pseudomutabilis* to
*rotunda* zones), crushed, except for big *Paravirgatites* in nodules in Egmont
Bight and *Pavlovia* at Chapman's Pool.   Fish-scales and oysters (*Exogyra
virgula*, etc.) abound.   Tiny plates of the free-swimming crinoid *Saccocoma*
occur on and near the Blackstone level.
Arkell, W. J. 1947b, pp. 70-80.   Davies, G. M. 1935, pp. 94-98.
Geol. Surv. N.S. 342-343 ; Ord. New Pop. 178-9.

**Langham,** 2 miles W.S.W. of Gillingham.   Quarry on E. side of lane,
½ mile S.E. of village.
Jurassic, Corallian Beds, a bed crowded with well-preserved lamellibranchs,
especially *Lucina rotundata.*
Arkell, W. J. 1934, p. 281.
Geol. Surv. O.S. 18 ; Ord. New Pop. 166.

**Langton Herring.**   Fleet shore ¾ mile S. of village, near ferry and ½-¾ mile
S.W. of manor house.
Jurassic, upper Fuller's Earth clay with a " lumachelle " or oyster-bed
(*Ostrea hebridica* var. *elongata*).   S.W. of the manor house are clays with
flattened ammonites preserved like tile-sherds (*Procerites*) and exquisite lamelli-
branchs (*Trigonia*).
Arkell, W. J. 1940a, p. 42 ; 1947b, pp. 17-18.   Davies, G. M. 1935, p. 50.
Geol. Surv. N.S. 341 ; Ord. New Pop. 178.

**Langton Herring.**   Fleet shore, Herbury, 1 mile S. of church and ½ mile
N.W. of Fleet House.
Jurassic, Forest Marble (*boueti* bed at base) at promontory with masses of
brachiopods (*Goniorhynchia boueti, Digonella ·digona*, etc.) ;   shelly ·Forest
Marble to S.E. of promontory.
Arkell, W. J. 1947b, pp. 18-19 ; Davies, G. M. 1935, p. 50.
Geol. Surv. N.S. 341 ; Ord. New Pop. 178.

**Lillington,** 2½ miles S.S.W. of Sherborne.   Deep gully on W. side of
Lillington Hill, S.E. of Ratcomb Barn.
Jurassic, Forest Marble (*boueti* bed at base) with abundant brachiopods
(*Goniorhynchia boueti*) encrusted with soft tufa from stream.
Kellaway, G. A. and Wilson, V. 1941, p. 162.
Geol. Surv. O.S. 18 ; Ord. New Pop. 178.

**Loders,** Bridport.   Quarries N.E. and S.W. of crossroads (Loders Cross).
Jurassic, Inferior Oolite (*opalinum* to *parkinsoni* zones).   The top beds are
well-exposed in the S.W. quarry ; the *Astarte obliqua* Bed in the N.E. quarry.
Ammonites, lamellibranchs and brachiopods are generally common.
Geol. Surv. N.S. 327 ; Ord. New Pop. 177.

**Long Burton,** 2½ miles S. of Sherborne.   Quarry at Long Burton.
Jurassic, Forest Marble, typical shelly facies, with broken lamellibranchs ;
occasional fish bones and spines.
Geol. Surv. O.S. 18 ; Ord. New Pop. 178.

**Lulworth Cove.**   Fossil Forest, near top of cliff for 1 mile E. of E. end of
cove.
Jurassic, Lower Purbeck Beds, tufa containing prostrate trunks and stumps
of Cycads and Conifers, with seat-earth (dirt-bed).
Arkell, W. J. 1947b, pp. 140-141.
Geol. Surv. N.S. 342 ; Ord. New Pop. 178.

**Lulworth Cove,** cliffs.
Cretaceous, Upper Greensand, Lower and Middle Chalk, all fossiliferous
(ammonites, lamellibranchs, sea-urchins, etc.).
Rowe, A. W. 1901, p. 21. Wright, C. W. in Arkell, W. J. 1947b, pp. 189, 208.
Geol. Surv. N.S. 342 ; Ord. New Pop. 178.

**Lulworth Cove.**   Durdle Cove, between Durdle Door and Swyre Head,
1½-2 miles W. of Lulworth Cove.
Cretaceous, Upper Greensand, Lower, Middle and Upper Chalk (up to
*coranguinum* zone).   Fine ammonites and sea-urchins in Upper Greensand.
Chalk moderately fossiliferous.
Rowe, A. W. 1901, pp. 15-17.   Wright, C. W. in Arkell, W. J. 1947b,
pp. 190, 208.
Geol. Surv. N.S. 342 ; Ord. New Pop. 178.

**Lulworth Cove.**   Arish Mell and Cockpit Head, 2 miles E. of cove.
Cretaceous, Upper Chalk, *planus* to *mucronata* zones.   The *pilula* zone is
the most interesting here.
Rowe, A. W. 1901, p. 28.   Wright, C. W. in Arkell, W. J. 1947b, p. 207.
Geol. Surv. N.S. 342 ; Ord. New Pop. 178.

**Lyme Regis.**   Cliff-section and foreshore from head of Pinhay Bay,
1¾ miles W.S.W. of Lyme, to Seven Rock Point, 1⅜ miles S.W. of Lyme.
*Cliffs dangerous to stand under.*
Jurassic, Lower Lias (White and Blue Lias), resting on Triassic, Rhaetic
Beds.   Ammonites (especially *Psiloceras planorbis* on under side of 13th lime-
stone above base of Lias), lamellibranchs (*Ostrea, Lima*) and scattered sea-
urchin spines abundant.
Lang, W. D. 1924, pp. 169-185, with geol. map.   Davies, G. M. 1935, p. 21.
Geol. Surv. N.S. 326/340 ; Ord. New Pop. 177.

**Lyme Regis.**   Cliff-section and foreshore from Seven Rock Point to
Church Cliffs, ½ mile N.E. of Lyme.   *Cliffs dangerous to stand under.*
Jurassic, Lower Lias (Blue Lias), with abundant ammonites (*Schlotheimia,
Coroniceras*, etc.), lamellibranchs (*Gryphaea, Lima*) and brachiopods.
Lang, W. D. 1924, pp. 169-185, with geol. map.   Davies, G. M. 1935, p. 21.
Geol. Surv. N.S. 326/340 ; Ord. New Pop. 177.

**Oborne,** 1½ miles N.E. of Sherborne.   Frogden Quarry (disused), 1¼ miles
N.E. of Sherborne and ¼ mile W. of N. end of Oborne.
Jurassic, Inferior Oolite, *concavum* to *parkinsoni* zones with many ammonites,
including *Teloceras blagdeni*.   No. 36 of Richardson, 1932.
Richardson, L. 1932, pp. 78-81, with topog. map.
Geol. Surv. O.S. 18 ; Ord. New Pop. 178.

**Osmington,** 4 miles N.E. of Weymouth. Cliffs between Bowleaze Cove and Redcliff Point and from 1 mile W. to 1½ miles E. of Osmington Mills.

Jurassic, complete sections of Corallian Beds. Fossils of the Lower Calcareous Grit are best obtained at Redcliff and Osmington Mills ; of the Osmington Oolite for 1 mile E. of the Mills ; of the Trigonia Beds and higher beds (with some ammonites) at Black Head (½ mile W.) and Bran Point (1-1½ miles E. of the Mills).

Arkell, W. J. 1947b, pp. 44-54. Davies, G. M. 1935, pp. 60-66.
Geol. Surv. N.S. 342 ; Ord. New Pop. 178.

**Osmington.** Cliffs and foreshore, Coggin's Barrow and Black Head, W. of Osmington Mills.

Cretaceous, Gault, Upper Greensand and base of Chalk ; mostly as slipped masses and fallen blocks on the beach. Fine ammonites (*Hoplites*) in purple boulders from Lower Gault ; ammonites and sea-urchins in " Cowstones " and softer beds of Upper Greensand (*inflata* and *dispar* zones) ; ammonites in base of Chalk.

Wright, C. W. in Arkell, W. J. 1947b, p. 192.
Geol. Surv. N.S. 342 ; Ord. New Pop. 178.

**Pinford,** 1½ miles E.N.E. of Sherborne. Deep watercourse at S.W. corner of Highmores Hill, Sherborne Park, approached by Pinford Lane ; also old quarry in the park, S.W. of stone bridge over stream near Pinford Farm and about 2 miles from Sherborne station.

Jurassic, Fuller's Earth Rock (ornithellid brachiopods) and Upper Fuller's Earth (*wattonensis* beds, with different brachiopods, also ammonites and other molluscs in the clays).

Kellaway, G. A. and Wilson, V. 1941, p. 160.
Geol. Surv. O.S. 18 ; Ord. New Pop. 178.

**Portesham,** 1½ miles E.N.E. of Abbotsbury. Road-cutting, Corton, 1¾ miles E. of Portesham Church and 1½ miles W. of Upwey Church.

Jurassic, Portland Sands (sandy cementstones at top) with worm-encrusted oysters (*Exogyra nana*) and other lamellibranchs (*Trigonia*) and giant ammonites.

Arkell, W. J. 1935, pp. 330-331, pl. 25 ; 1947b, p. 116.
Geol. Surv. N.S. 327 ; Ord. New Pop. 178.

**Poxwell,** 1 mile S.S.W. of junction of Weymouth-Wareham and Dorchester-Wareham roads. Road-cutting on N. side of Weymouth road, W. of Poxwell Lodge by turning to Upton.

Jurassic, Middle Purbeck Beds ; many silicified gastropods, lamellibranchs and ostracods in Cherty Freshwater Bed ; oysters in Cinder Bed.

Arkell, W. J. 1947b, pp. 143-144.
Geol. Surv. N.S. 342 ; Ord. New Pop. 178.

**Preston,** 2½ miles N.E. of Weymouth. Cliffs of Jordon Hill (Furzy Cliff) W. of Bowleaze Cove, and between Redcliff Point and Shortlake, E. of Bowleaze Cove.

Jurassic, Oxford Clay, with large oysters (*Gryphaea dilatata*) and many ammonites (pyritized in *lamberti* and *mariae* zones, red casts in nodules in *cordatus* zone).

Arkell, W. J. 1947b, pp. 33-34.
Geol. Surv. N.S. 342 ; Ord. New Pop. 178.

**Ringstead,** 2 miles S.E. of Osmington (q.v.). Cliffs of Ringstead Bay for 1 mile E. of Bran Point.

Jurassic, top of Corallian Beds and base of Kimmeridge Clay, with Ringstead Coral Bed (corals, lamellibranchs and the ammonite *Ringsteadia*) at the junction. The clay next above the Coral Bed yields brachiopods (*Rhactorhynchia inconstans*), oysters (*Exogyra nana*) and the ammonite *Pictonia* ; higher again is a layer of the oyster *Ostrea delta*.

Arkell, W. J. 1947b, pp. 41-47. Davies, G. M. 1935, pp. 64-66.
Geol. Surv. N.S. 342 ; Ord. New Pop. 178.

**Ringstead.** Cliffs and undercliff from Holworth House east to White Nothe.

Cretaceous ; the finest section in the country of the *dispar* zone of the Upper Greensand with some 50 species of ammonites : many ammonites, sea-urchins, etc., in base of Lower Chalk : (Middle Chalk rather barren) : .Upper Chalk (*planus* zone) with many sponges, etc., by " Smugglers' Path " below Coastguard Station. Elsewhere, best collecting is from fallen blocks.
Wright, C. W. in Arkell, W. J. 1947b, pp. 191, 209.
Geol. Surv. N.S. 342 ; Ord. New Pop. 178.

**Sherborne.** Quarry in Marston Road about 1¼ miles N. of Sherborne station. No. 25 of Richardson, 1932.
Jurassic, Inferior Oolite (*opalinum* and *murchisonae* zones) with abundant ammonites (*Graphoceras*), lamellibranchs, brachiopods, etc., on S. side of quarry.
Richardson, L. 1932, p. 70, with topog. map.   Kellaway, G. A. and Wilson, V. 1941, pp. 148-157.
Geol. Surv. O.S. 18 ; Ord. New Pop. 178.

**Sherborne.** Hollow way (" Coombe Lane "), from Marston road to Sandford Road, about 1¾ miles N.W. of Sherborne station.
Jurassic, Upper Lias (Yeovil Sands, *jurense* zone), with ammonites (*Dumortieria*, etc.) in ironshot shelly limestone ; and brachiopods in sandy limestone on both walls of eastern part of section.
Kellaway, G. A. and Wilson, V. 1941, pp. 146-147.
Geol. Surv. O.S. 18 ; Ord. New Pop. 178.

**Sherborne.** Cutting in Marston Road about 1¼ miles N. of Sherborne station.
Jurassic, Upper Lias (Yeovil Sands, *jurense* zone) with ammonites (*Pleydellia*, *Dumortieria*).
Geol. Surv. O.S. 18 ; Ord. New Pop. 178.

**Sherborne.** Cutting in Marston Road, ¼ mile N.W. of above.
Jurassic, Upper Lias (Yeovil Sands, *jurense* zone) with lamellibranchs (*Trigonia, Astarte*).
Kellaway, G. A. and Wilson, V. 1941, p. 147.
Geol. Surv. O.S. 18 ; Ord. New Pop. 178.

**Sherborne.** Limekiln Quarry (disused) on S. side of Yeovil road at Halfway House, 2 miles W. of Sherborne.  No. 18 of Richardson, 1932.
Jurassic, Inferior Oolite (*murchisonae* to *parkinsoni* zones) with trace of Fuller's Earth clay on top.  Only the upper beds are now visible, but they yield large nautili, ammonites, etc.
Richardson, L. 1932, p. 65, with topog. map.
Geol. Surv. O.S. 18 ; Ord. New Pop. 178.

**Sherborne.** Rock Cottage and Chapel Quarries, Halfway House, on N. side of Yeovil road, 2 miles W. of Sherborne.  Nos. 17 and 17a of Richardson, 1932.
Jurassic, Inferior Oolite (*murchisonae* to *parkinsoni* zones) with many fossils throughout.  Note *Astarte obliqua*-bed (lamellibranchs).
Richardson, L. 1932, pp. 62-64, with topog. map.
Geol. Surv. O.S. 18 ; Ord. New Pop. 178.

**Sherborne.** Louse Hill Quarry (disused) at top of steep bank 1¾ miles W. by S. of Sherborne and ½ mile E.S.E. of Halfway House.  No. 21 of Richardson, 1932.
Jurassic, Inferior Oolite (*opalinum* to *parkinsoni* zones) with a local fauna of brachiopods in the Irony Bed ; the lamellibranch *Astarte obliqua* in its own 5-inch bed ; and ammonites below (*Brasilia*).
Richardson, L. 1932, pp. 67-70, with topog. map.
Geol. Surv. O.S. 18 ;. Ord. New Pop. 178.

**Sherborne.** Redhole Lane Quarry (disused) below W. side of Bristol road ¼ mile N. of Sherborne. No. 32 of Richardson, 1932.

Jurassic, Inferior Oolite, top beds, with ammonites (*Parkinsonia*, etc.), lamellibranchs, brachiopods. Foraminifera and ostracods may be washed out of the associated clays.

Richardson, L. 1932, pp. 73-74, with topog. map.
Geol. Surv. O.S. 18 ; Ord. New Pop. 178.

**Sherborne.** Stream-side and bank in Sherborne Park, about 100 yds. W. of Middle Lodge opposite tumbledown barn ; also in watercourse on S. side of private drive about 200 yds. W. of Crackmore Lodge.

Jurassic, Forest Marble (*boueti* bed at base) with brachiopods (*Goniorhynchia boueti*), crinoid-ossicles (*Apiocrinus*) and lamellibranchs.
Geol. Surv. O.S. 18 ; Ord. New Pop. 178.

**Sherborne.** ¼ mile from Sherborne station along hollow lane leading to Town cricket-ground.

Jurassic, Lower Fuller's Earth (brachiopods and the oyster *Ostrea acuminata*) and Fuller's Earth Rock (the ammonite *Tulites*).
Kellaway, G. A. and Wilson, V. 1941, p. 159.
Geol. Surv. O.S. 18 ; Ord. New Pop. 178.

**Sherborne, see** also Lillington, Oborne, Pinford.

**Southwell,** Portland. Cliff just under ¼ mile N.N.W. of Portland Bill lighthouse and old quarries in between.

Pleistocene, raised beach and overlying loams, overlain by head. Marine shells in raised beach indicate a climate cooler than to-day's ; land-snails in the loam are of temperate-climate type.
Arkell, W. J. 1947b, pp. 331-333. Baden-Powell, D. F. W. 1930, p. 67. Davies, G. M. 1935, p. 57.
Geol. Surv. N.S. 342 ; Ord. New Pop. 178.

**Studland,** 2½ miles N. of Swanage. Studland Bay, cliffs from S.W. corner to Handfast Point. Best worked on ebbing tide.

Cretaceous, Upper Chalk (*mucronata* zone), with belemnites (*Belemnitella mucronata*), lamellibranchs, brachiopods, bryozoa, starfish-ossicles and sea-urchins (mostly crushed).
Davies, G. M. 1935, pp. 108-111. Rowe, A. W. 1901, pp. 37-38. Wright, C. W. in Arkell, W. J. 1947b, p. 205.
Geol. Surv. N.S. 343 ; Ord. New Pop. 179.

**Swanage.** Tilly Whim Caves (old quarries) ¼ mile S.W. of Durlston Castle.

Jurassic, Portland Stone (with oyster-bed) and basal Purbeck Beds.
Arkell, W. J. 1947b, p. 99. Davies, G. M. 1935, p. 103.
Geol. Surv. N.S. 343 ; Ord. New Pop. 179.

**Swanage.** Cliffs of Durlston Bay, S. of Swanage.

Jurassic, Purbeck Beds, complete section, largely repeated by a fault near the Zigzag Path. S. of the Zigzag Path the cliffs are much hidden by falls ; the beds can now be best studied in the northern half of the bay, between the path and Peveril Point. Freshwater lamellibranchs and gastropods abound. In the marine beds of the Middle Purbeck, the Cinder Bed (a mass of the oyster *Ostrea distorta*) is conspicuous and has rare sea-urchins (*Hemicidaris*). Ostracods occur in most of the beds. *Unio*, and Purbeck Marble packed with gastropods, lie at the top of the formation, near Peveril Point. Mammals were obtained in a special excavation (Beckles' pit) near the cliff-top 100 yds. S.E. of Belle Vue Restaurant.
Arkell, W. J. 1947b, pp. 126-138. Bristow, H. W. 1857. Davies, G. M. 1935, pp. 103-107.
Geol. Surv. N.S. 343 ; Ord. New Pop. 179.

**Swanage.** Swanage Quarries. Shafts are scattered over the downs S. and S.W. of the town, some still in work.
Jurassic, Middle Purbeck Beds (Building-Stones). The wealth of fish, turtles, crocodiles, etc., has been obtained from the quarrymen, who still have occasional specimens for sale.
Arkell, W. J. 1947b, pp. 126-138. Woodward, A. S. 1916-1919.
Geol. Surv. N.S. 343 ; Ord. New Pop. 179.

**Swanage.** Punfield Cove, northern side of Swanage Bay.
Cretaceous, Lower Greensand. A 1-foot band of limestone (usually concealed by vegetation and slipped material), the "Punfield Marine Band," contains many gastropods and lamellibranchs of Spanish affinities and occasional ammonites (*Deshayesites*).
Arkell, W. J. 1947b, p. 173. Judd, J. W. 1871, p. 207.
Geol. Surv. N.S. 343 ; Ord. New Pop. 179.

**Swanage.** Ballard Cliffs, from Punfield Cove towards Ballard Point.
Cretaceous, Upper Greensand (*inflata* and *dispar* zones), with many ammonites, lamellibranchs, sea-urchins, etc. ; Lower Chalk (with ammonites at the base), Middle Chalk and Upper Chalk (boulders on beach) all fossiliferous.
Rowe, A. W. 1901, p. 33. Wright, C. W. in Arkell, W. J. 1947b, pp. 185, 204.
Geol. Surv. N.S. 343 ; Ord. New Pop. 179.

**Thornford,** 3½ miles S.E. of Yeovil. Troll Quarry, 1270 yds. S.W. of church and just N. of Thornford Halt station.
Jurassic, Fuller's Earth Rock, with brachiopods (*Ornithella*), lamellibranchs, etc., common. A classic locality for the ammonite *Tulites*.
Kellaway, G. A. and Wilson V. 1941, p. 159.
Geol. Surv. O.S. 18 ; Ord. New Pop. 178.

**Thornford.** Deep gully behind Lake Farm on road to Sherborne, between Gaul Hill and Ratcombe Barn, and other gullies between Lake Farm and Watery Lane.
Jurassic, upper Fuller's Earth (*wattonensis* beds) with many brachiopods (*Wattonithyris, Rugitela, Rhynchonelloidella*, etc.).
Kellaway, G. A. and Wilson, V. 1941, p. 160.
Geol. Surv. O.S. 18 ; Ord. New Pop. 178.

**Tyneham,** 5 miles S.S.W. of Wareham. Cliffs of Worbarrow Tout, peninsula at S. end of Worbarrow Bay.
Jurassic, complete section of Purbeck Beds. *Unio*-beds well seen on N. side of Tout. Further round to W. is a thin Cinder Bed (*Ostrea distorta*) and abundant ostracods and silicified spores of the waterweed *Chara*.
Arkell, W. J. 1947b, p. 139.
Geol. Surv. N.S. 342 ; Ord. New Pop. 179.

**Tyneham.** Cliffs of Worbarrow Bay.
Cretaceous, Upper Greensand and base of Lower Chalk, with many ammonites and other fossils.
Rowe, A. W. 1901, p. 30. Wright, C. W. in Arkell, W. J. 1947b, pp. 189, 206.
Geol. Surv. N.S. 342 ; Ord. New Pop. 178.

**West Bay,** Bridport. Watton Cliff (West Cliff) between West Bay and Eypesmouth ; cliff-face, fallen blocks and low-tide reefs.
Jurassic, Forest Marble (shelly limestones near top of cliff) and *boueti* bed, with many brachiopods. In fallen blocks and reefs, Upper Fuller's Earth, with brachiopods (*Wattonithyris*, etc.) and oysters—the *wattonensis* beds.
Buckman, S. S. 1922, pp. 381-384. Muir-Wood, H. M. 1936.
Geol. Surv. N.S. 327 ; Ord. New Pop. 177.

**Weymouth.** Cliffs at Sandsfoot Castle, ¾ mile S.W. of Harbour Bridge. Jurassic, Corallian Beds, Sandsfoot Grit and Clay, the former with large lamellibranchs (*Pecten, Pinna,* etc.) and poorly-preserved ammonites (*Ringsteadia*).
Arkell, W. J. 1947b, pp. 54–57.
Geol. Surv. N.S. 342 ; Ord. New Pop. 178.

**Winterborne Abbas,** 4½ miles W. of Dorchester. Chalkpit, W. side of North Hill, 400 yds. E.S.E. of church.
Cretaceous, Upper Chalk (*planus* zone, Chalk Rock) with sea-urchins, etc., and pebbles of Upper Greensand, sometimes fossiliferous.
Strahan, A. 1898, p. 189.
Geol. Surv. N.S. 327 ; Ord. New Pop. 178.

**Winterborne Abbas.** Small chalkpit 1½ miles N.E. of church and 1¼ miles S.W. of Bradford Peverell Church.
Cretaceous, Upper Chalk (*Marsupites* zone) with many plates of the free-swimming crinoid *Marsupites* in hard chalk.
Geol. Surv. N.S. 327 ; Ord. New Pop. 178.

**Worth Matravers,** 4 miles W.S.W. of Swanage. Cliffs of Chapman's Pool, Hounstout, West Hill and Emmit Hill, 1 mile W.S.W. of church.
Jurassic, upper Kimmeridge Clay and Portland Sand (type-section). Ammonites (*Pavlovia rotunda*) occur in a Nodule Bed 10–15 ft. above the shore at Chapman's Pool. Beds of oysters (*Exogyra nana*) and rhynchonellid brachiopods occur in the Portland Sand, with crushed ammonites (*Zaraiskites albani*) correlating with deposits in Poland and Russia.
Arkell, W. J. 1947b, pp. 78–80, 90–92, 98–105.
Geol. Surv. N.S. 343 ; Ord. New Pop. 179.

**Worth Matravers.** Winspit Quarries and cliff, ¾ mile S.S.E. of village. Similar section at Seacombe cliff and quarries, ½ mile N.E. of Winspit.
Jurassic, Portland Stone, with a serpulite (massed worm-tubes) in the Cherty Series below ; and giant ammonites and many other molluscs here and in the Freestone Series above. Crustacea (*Callianassa*) in Shrimp Bed at top of Portland Stone.
Arkell, W. J. 1947b, pp. 99–102.
Geol. Surv. N.S. 343 ; Ord. New Pop. 179.

**Worth Matravers.** Sheepsleights Quarry (Worth Quarries), just over ½ mile N.W. of church, on S. side of Coombe Bottom.
Jurassic, Portland Beds (Cherty and Freestone Series) with giant ammonites and other molluscs, and crustacea (*Callianassa*) in Shrimp Bed at top ; and basal Purbeck Beds.
Arkell, W. J. 1947b, pp. 99–102.
Geol. Surv. N.S. 343 ; Ord. New Pop. 179.

**Worth Matravers.** Quarry immediately N. of Compact Farm, 750 yds. N.N.E. of church.
Jurassic, Middle Purbeck Beds, with fine, silicified gastropods and lamellibranchs in Cherty Freshwater Bed and oysters (*Ostrea distorta*) in Cinder Bed.
Arkell, W. J. 1941a, p. 82.
Geol. Surv. N.S. 343 ; Ord. New Pop. 179.

**Yetminster,** 4½ miles S.E. of Yeovil. Quarry S.E. of crossroads on W. side of village.
Jurassic, Lower Cornbrash, with abundant brachiopods.
Douglas, J. A. and Arkell, W. J. 1928, p. 149.
Geol. Surv. O.S. 18 ; Ord. New Pop. 178.

## DURHAM

**Blackhall Colliery,** 3 miles E. of Sunderland—W. Hartlepool road at 13½ miles from Sunderland. Blackhall Rocks and coast N. and S.

Permian, shell-limestones with a reef-fauna of brachiopods and molluscs, faulted on the S. against concretionary beds with lamellibranchs.

Geol. Surv. O.S. 103 N.E. ; Ord. New Pop. 85.

**Castle Eden,** ¾ mile E. of Sunderland—W. Hartlepool road at 13¼ miles from Sunderland. Castle Eden Dene. Permission from Mr. Craman near the church.

Permian, bedded dolomite with the lamellibranch *Astarte vallisneriana*, passing eastwards into reef-limestones with dwarfed *Nautilus*, lamellibranchs (*Bakevellia*), etc.

Geol. Surv. O.S. 103 S.E. ; Ord. New Pop. 85.

**Castletown,** N.W. of Sunderland. Section on left bank of R. Wear, ¼ mile W. of Hylton Colliery and opposite Claxheugh.

Carboniferous, Coal Measures (*phillipsi* zone), 90 yards of section 15 ft. high, with lamellibranchs (*Anthraconauta*) in shales and clay-ironstone bands. (Type-locality of "*Carbonicola vinti*").

Trechmann, C. T. and Woolacott, D. 1919, p. 203.

Geol. Surv. O.S. 105 S.E. ; Ord. New Pop. 78.

**Durham.** Cliff on left bank of R. Wear, ⅓ mile E. of Frankland Farm and opposite old rifle-range targets at Kepier, N.E. of Durham.

Carboniferous, Coal Measures (*similis-pulchra* zone, shales above Brass Thill Coal and below a sandstone) with non-marine lamellibranchs (*Anthracosia* cf. *aquilina*).

Geol. Surv. O.S. 103 N.E. ; Ord. New Pop. 85.

**Ford Estate,** Sunderland. Claxheugh Quarry, on right bank of R. Wear, now obscured ; exposure in grounds of Ford Housing Estate school now being filled with refuse.

Permian, Magnesian Limestone, with brachiopods and bryozoa.

Geol. Surv. O.S. 105 S.E. ; Ord. New Pop. 78.

**Ford Estate.** Ford Lime Quarries, S. of Claxheugh Rock.

Permian, Magnesian Limestone. Brachiopods (*Chonetes, Camarophoria*), lamellibranchs (*Pecten*, etc.). Fossils are only common in cuttings in the floor of the quarry.

Trechmann, C. T. 1945, pp. 333-354.

Geol. Surv. O.S. 105 S.E. ; Ord. New Pop. 78.

**Marsden,** 3 miles S.E. of South Shields. Byer's Quarry, on coast S. of Marsden lighthouse : Marsden Quarry, W. of Whitburn Colliery.

Permian, Magnesian Limestone (concretionary beds). Lamellibranchs (*Liebea*) in cannon-ball concretions and on weathered slabs.

King, W. 1850.

Geol. Surv. O.S., 105 S.E. ; Ord. New Pop. 78.

**Offerton,** 3 miles W.S.W. of Sunderland. Section on right bank of R. Wear, ¾ mile below Washington—Cox Green ferry and near Cox Green golf-links, W. of Offerton.

Carboniferous, Coal Measures (*phillipsi* zone), shales with lamellibranchs (*Anthraconauta*) and plants (*Neuropteris, Mariopteris*).

Dix, E. 1934, p. 27 ; Hopkins, W. 1929, p. 126.

Geol. Surv. O.S. 105 S.E. ; Ord. New Pop. 78.

**Shildon,** 3 miles S.E. of Bishop Auckland. Thickley Quarry, by Shildon station. Perhaps the Midderidge Quarry of literature.

Permian, lower Magnesian Limestone, with brachiopods (*Productus, Spirifer*) in calcareous lenses in corner nearest station ; resting on Marl Slate (not easily

accessible), with fish, and a basal pebble-bed with the horny brachiopod *Lingula*.
Trechmann, C. T. 1945, p. 339.
Geol. Surv. O.S. 103 S.W. ; Ord. New Pop. 85.

**Sunderland.** Exposures at N. and S. ends of Tunstall Hill, an elongated knoll 2 miles S. of Sunderland.
Permian, Magnesian Limestone, with brachiopods (*Productus, Camarophoria*) and molluscs (*Bakevellia, Turbo*) less plentiful now than formerly.
Trechmann, C. T. 1945, p. 344.
Geol. Surv. O.S. 105 S.E. ; Ord. New Pop. 78.

**Sunderland.** Humbleton Hill, 2 miles S.W. of Sunderland. A classic locality now in bad condition.
Permian, Magnesian Limestone. Brachiopods in quarry and exposures up eastern flank of hill ; *Nautilus* in cuttings at top of hill, facing W
King, W. 1850. Trechmann, C. T. 1945, p. 341.
Geol. Surv. O.S. 105 S.E. ; Ord. New Pop. 78.

**Sunderland,** see also Castletown, Ford Estate.


# ESSEX

**Ballingdon,** Sudbury. Large chalkpit ¾ mile S.W. of St. Peter's Church, Sudbury, and about 100 yds. E. of Ballingdon Hall.
Cretaceous, Upper Chalk (*Uintacrinus* zone) with plates of the crinoid *Uintacrinus*, belemnites (*Actinocamax verus*), etc. : capped by Tertiary Beds and Pleistocene glacial deposits.
Boswell, P. G. H. 1929, pp. 16-17.
Geol. Surv. N.S. 206 ; Ord. New Pop. 148.

**Beaumont,** 5½ miles W.N.W. of Walton-on-the-Naze. Section (now obscured) along edge of pond in farmyard near Beaumont Church.
Pliocene, Red Crag (? Newbournian), with 90 species of molluscs.
Reid, C. 1890, pp. 80, 85.
Geol. Surv. O.S. 48 S.E. ; Ord. New Pop. 150.

**Great Chesterford,** 3½ miles N.W. of Saffron Walden. Pit by roadside, ½ mile E. of Great Chesterford Church.
Cretaceous, Middle Chalk (*Terebratulina* zone), with the sea-urchins *Echinocorys scutata* (an interesting shape-variation) and *Micraster corbovis* and other fossils.
Brighton, A. G. 1928, p. 369.
Geol. Surv. N.S. 205 ; Ord. New Pop. 148.

**Harwich.** Cliff-top.
Pliocene, Red Crag (now entirely disappeared), resting on Eocene, London Clay. Section described by Dale in 1704.
Reid, C. 1890, pp. 71, 85.
Geol. Surv. O.S. 48 N.E. ; Ord. New Pop. 150.

**Walton-on-the-Naze.** Coast and cliff-section, accessible along foreshore or from bus-route to the Naze. Marked by Tower on cliff about 1½ miles N.E. of Walton station.
Pliocene, Red Crag (Waltonian) and basal Nodule Bed (exposed after cliff-falls), resting on Eocene, London Clay. *Neptunea contraria* and other gastropods very numerous, entire but waterworn. Lamellibranchs (including *Glycymeris glycymeris* in prominent bands) common. Derived fossils, sharks' teeth, worn bones, etc. in Nodule Bed.
Reid, C. 1890. Harmer, F. W. 1913-1922.
Geol. Surv. O.S. 48 S.E. ; Ord. New Pop. 150.

D

## GLOUCESTERSHIRE

**Almondsbury,** 8 miles N. of Bristol. Old quarries on the Ridgeway, near Almondsbury and Ridgeway villages.
Carboniferous Limestone (S and D zones) with corals (*Lithostrotion*) and brachiopods (*Productus*).
Reynolds, S. H. and Innes, D. E. 1914, p. 100, with geol. map.
Geol. Surv. O.S. 35 ; Ord. New Pop. 156.

**Aston Blank,** 4 miles N.E. of Northleach. Large disused quarry with chicken-coops, on W. side of Fosse Way in angle of side-road to Aston.
Jurassic, Inferior Oolite (*Clypeus* Grit, 18 ft.), with the sea-urchin *Clypeus sinuatus* and brachiopods (" *Terebratula globata* "). Note also quarry on opposite side of Fosse Way with fossiliferous Oolite Marl.
Richardson, L. 1933, p. 29.
Geol. Surv. N.S. 235 ; Ord. New Pop. 144.

**Aust,** 4 miles S.W. of Thornbury. Aust Cliff, left bank of R. Severn.
Jurassic, Lower Lias, overlying Triassic, Rhaetic (Cotham Beds, Black Shales) and Keuper Marl. Abundant fish- (including *Ceratodus*) and reptile-bones in conglomeratic bone-bed at base of Rhaetic.
Geol. Surv. O.S. 35 ; Ord. New Pop. 156.

**Avening,** 5 miles S.S.E. of Stroud. Disused quarry on W. side of road to Hampton Fields along wall of Gatcomb Park, nearly opposite Hill House.
Jurassic, Great Oolite (White Limestone). A rubbly bed above massive limestone is packed with rhynchonellid brachiopods, mostly encrusted with worm-tubes and oysters.
Geol. Surv. O.S. 34 ; Ord. New Pop. 156.

**Bibstone,** 2 miles N.W. of Wickwar. Slickstone Quarry, ⅓ mile N.E. of Bibstone by side of road to Charfield.
Carboniferous Limestone ($Z_2$ subzone) with zaphrentid corals and brachiopods. Triassic material in fissures has yielded the reptile *Glevosaurus hudsoni*.
Swinton, W. E. 1939. Wallis, F. S. 1924, p. 61, with geol. map.
Geol. Surv. O.S. 35 ; Ord. New Pop. 156.

**Birdlip,** 7 miles S.E. of Gloucester. Small disused quarry near Fostons Ash Inn, opposite 8th milestone from Cheltenham on Stroud (Slad Valley) road, through belt of trees on W. side of road.
Jurassic, Inferior Oolite (Upper Freestone, one of the few fossiliferous exposures). Brachiopods (*Plectothyris fimbria*), gastropods and lamellibranchs are best obtained by breaking slabs up carefully at home.
Geol. Surv. O.S. 44 ; Ord. New Pop. 143.

**Bishops Cleeve,** 3 miles N. of Cheltenham. Cleeve Hill, S.E. side of Cheltenham-Winchcombe road. Natural scars and disused quarries.
Jurassic, Inferior Oolite (*scissum* beds to *Clypeus* Grit). Many well-preserved fossils (in the Pea Grit, Oolite Marl, Lower *Trigonia* Grit, *Witchellia* Grit and *Clypeus* Grit : for *phillipsiana*- and *Bourguetia*-beds see next item).
Richardson, L. 1929, pp. 45-52.
Geol. Surv. N.S. 217 ; Ord. New Pop. 143 and 144.

**Bishops Cleeve.** Rolling Bank Quarry, 560 yds. E. of Rising Sun Inn, Cleeve Hill.
Jurassic, Inferior Oolite (*phillipsiana*- and *Bourguetia*-beds, only section now visible ; Upper *Trigonia* Grit and *Clypeus* Grit). Brachiopods (*Heimia phillipsiana*, etc.), gastropods (*Bourguetia*), sea-urchins and other fossils.
Richardson, L. 1904, pp. 122-124, 126, 132, with geol. map ; 1929, p. 52.
Geol. Surv. N.S. 217 ; Ord. New Pop. 143 and 144.

**Blockley,** 2½ miles S.S.E. of Chipping Campden. Large brickworks adjoining station.
Jurassic, Lower Lias (*ibex* zone), with abundant lamellibranchs (*Astarte*,

etc.) on dumps of weathered nodules and many large ammonites including *Liparoceras cheltiense.*
Richardson, L. 1929, p. 15 (Pit enlarged since).
Geol. Surv. N.S. 217 ; Ord. New Pop. 144.

**Blockley.** Disused quarry opposite The Holt, now being filled with refuse.
Jurassic, Inferior Oolite (Tilestones, 18 ft., the best section available) with a few lamellibranchs.
Richardson, L. 1929, pp. 67, 68.
Geol. Surv. N.S. 217 ; Ord. New Pop. 144.

**Breadstone,** 20 miles N.E. of Bristol. Old shaft in grounds of Breadstone House, not now accessible.
Cambrian, Tremadoc (Breadstone Shales), with graptolites, brachiopods and trilobites, the first Cambrian fauna discovered in Gloucestershire.
Smith, S. 1933, p. 361, with geol. map.
Geol. Surv. O.S. 35 ; Ord. New Pop. 156.

**Bristol,** see Clifton, Croft's End.

**Brockhampton,** 5½ miles E. of Cheltenham. Small quarry on E. side of track over West Down, 1¼ miles N.W. of village and ¼ mile W. of White Hall Farm.
Jurassic, Great Oolite Series (Sevenhampton Marl and *Rhynchonella*-bed, lying on Stonesfield Slate), with rhynchonellid brachiopods, lamellibranchs and gastropods. Some ammonites in Stonesfield Slate.
Richardson, L. 1929, p. 108.
Geol. Surv. N.S. 217 ; Ord. New Pop. 144.

**Brockworth,** 4 miles S.E. of Gloucester. Fiddlers Elbow Quarries, on E. side of Cheltenham-Stroud road 1¾ miles S.W. of Cross Hands Hotel.
Jurassic, Great Oolite (50 ft., generally obscured), Inferior Oolite (130 ft.), Lias (450 ft., generally obscured). In the Inferior Oolite, the Pea Grit and its overlying Coral Bed, and the Lower *Trigonia* Grit are very fossiliferous ; but the whole series of sections is rapidly being quarried away.
Richardson, L. 1904.
Geol. Surv. O.S. 44 ; Ord. New Pop. 143 and 144.

**Burleigh,** 2½ miles S.S.E. of Stroud. Simmonds Quarry, near Burleigh Post Office, on N. edge of Minchinhampton Common.
Jurassic, Great Oolite (Minchinhampton Shelly Beds and Weatherstones, 44 ft.). By watching the quarrying operations closely, most of the molluscs described by Morris and Lycett (except those peculiar to the Planking) can be found.
Morris, J. and Lycett, J. 1851-1854. Arkell, W. J. and Cox, L.R. 1948.
Geol. Surv. O.S. 34 ; Ord. New Pop. 156.

**Burleigh.** Old quarry on golf-links, Minchinhampton Common, on E. side of Rodborough-Minchinhampton road, ½ mile S.W. of Simmonds Quarry.
Jurassic, Great Oolite Series (Minchinhampton Shelly Beds, Planking, etc.). This classic quarry was the chief source of the material described by Morris and Lycett. It is now being filled with rubbish and fossils can no longer be collected.
Morris, J. and Lycett, J. 1854. Arkell, W. J. and Cox, L. R. 1948.
Geol. Surv. O.S. 34 ; Ord. New Pop. 156.

**Bury Hill,** 2 miles N. of Chipping Sodbury. Quarries N. and S. of the hamlet.
Carboniferous Limestone (S and D zones) with brachiopods, corals and bands of calcareous algae.
Tuck, M. C. 1926, pp. 241-242, with geol. map.
Geol. Surv. O.S. 35 ; Ord. New Pop. 156.

**Cassey Compton,** 3 miles N.W. of Fosse Way at Fossbridge. Seventh railway-cutting (G.W.R.) on line from Andoversford to Chedworth Tunnel, ⅜ mile S. of Cassey Compton on track through Chedworth Woods.
Jurassic, Inferior Oolite (*Clypeus* Grit, 20 ft.) with many sea-urchins (*Clypeus sinuatus*), lamellibranchs and brachiopods.
Richardson, L. 1933, p. 27.
Geol. Surv. N.S. 235 ; Ord. New Pop. 144.

**Cassey Compton.** Chedworth Woods cutting (eighth on G.W.R. from Andoversford to Chedworth Tunnel), ¾ mile S. of Cassey Compton and just N. of Roman Villa.
Jurassic, Inferior Oolite (Upper Freestone to *Clypeus* Grit ; the latter bed, the *Trigonia* Grits and the *buckmani* Grit are fossiliferous) ; Great Oolite Series (Chipping Norton Limestone and Fuller's Earth).
Richardson, L. 1904, p. 134, with geol. map ; 1933, pp. 27, 28.
Geol. Surv. N.S. 235 ; Ord. New Pop. 144.

**Charfield,** 2 miles W.S.W. of Wotton-under-Edge. Cullimore's Quarry, now largely overgrown.
Silurian, Upper Llandovery, abundant corals and brachiopods, rare trilobites.
Weaver, T. 1824, p. 317, with geol. map. Reed, F. R. C. and Reynolds, S. H. 1908, p. 515. Reynolds, S. H. 1921, p. 202.
Geol. Surv. O.S. 35 ; Ord. New Pop. 156.

**Charlton Kings,** Cheltenham. Charlton Kings Common, eastward continuation of Leckhampton Hill, on W. side of Cirencester road, and N.W. of Seven Springs.
Jurassic, Inferior Oolite (Oolite Marl, with the rare brachiopod *Pseudoglossothyris galeiformis*), Lower *Trigonia* Grit (with the brachiopod *Aulacothyris meriani* in a bed which requires excavating) and Gryphite Grit, all well seen in various pits.
Richardson, L. 1933, pp. 22-23.
Geol. Surv. O.S. 44 ; Ord. New Pop. 143 and 144.

**Chedworth,** 6¾ miles N.E. of Cirencester. Long (or Stony) Furlong railway cutting, N. of Fosse Cross station ; also Aldgrove cutting, S. of the station, with a large quarry opened in 1939.
Jurassic, Great Oolite (White Limestone and lower beds down to Stonesfield Slate), with definite bands of brachiopods (*Epithyris*) and gastropods, especially in marly beds.
Richardson, L. 1904, p. 169, with geol. map ; 1933, pp. 41, 61.
Geol. Surv. N.S. 235 ; Ord. New Pop. 144.

**Cheltenham.** Webbs' Brickworks, Battledown, E. suburb of Cheltenham. Turn left off London Road along Haywards Road.
Jurassic, Lower Lias (*ibex* zone), with plentiful ammonites and lamellibranchs. Minute gastropods occur on weathered surfaces. Brachiopods and reptile-bones are scarce. The lamellibranch *Hippopodium ponderosum* was formerly abundant but is now rare. This is the only Lias section still available of those mentioned by Richardson, 1904.
Richardson, L. 1904, p. 45, with geol. map ; 1929, pp. 12-13.
Geol. Surv. N.S. 217 ; Ord. New Pop. 143 and 144.

**Cheltenham.** Extensive old quarries and new workings on top of Leckhampton Hill. Turn left off Birdlip road just before Salterley Grange and double bend in road.
Jurassic, Inferior Oolite (Upper *Trigonia* Grit, 6 ft., with abundant brachiopods, and Notgrove Freestone).
Richardson, L. 1904, p. 126, with geol. map ; 1933, p. 22.
Geol. Surv. N.S. 235 ; Ord. New Pop. 143 and 144.

**Cheltenham.** Crickley Hill, about 3 miles S.S.W. of Cheltenham. Classic section just N. of Gloucester-Oxford road 2 miles E. of Brockworth crossroads ; also on N.W. face of hill along lane to Cold Slad and new quarry above derelict iron lime-kilns at Cold Slad.

Jurassic, Inferior Oolite. Abundant corals, bryozoa, sea-urchins, brachiopods, etc., in Pea Grit and overlying coral bed (at E. end of face). The brachiopod *Pseudoglossothyris simplex* occurs in the top of the Lower Limestone on N.W. side.

Richardson, L. 1904, p. 78, with geol. map.
Geol. Surv. O.S. 44 ; Ord. New Pop. 143 and 144.

**Cheltenham.** Leckhampton Hill, old quarries on E. side of Birdlip road with ruined lime-kilns and mineral line embankment.

Jurassic, Inferior Oolite, complete and classic sections. Though less interesting since the quarries have been abandoned, many good fossils may be collected, especially from the Pea Grit near the old lime-kilns and from the succeeding Lower Freestone near the top of the " Devil's Chimney."

Richardson, L. 1904, pp. 79-80, 102-104, with geol. map ; 1933, p. 20.
Geol. Surv. O.S. 44 ; Ord. New Pop. 143 and 144.

**Cheltenham.** Tuffley's Quarry (disused), below W. side of Birdlip road just S. of Air Balloon Inn and 1 mile N.E. of Birdlip.

Jurassic, Inferior Oolite (Upper Freestone to Upper *Trigonia* Grit), with many brachiopods (especially fine *Lobothyris buckmani* and *L. crickleyensis* in the *buckmani* grit) and lamellibranchs.

Richardson, L. 1904, p. 110, with geol. map.
Geol. Surv. O.S. 44 ; Ord. New Pop. 143 and 144.

**Cheltenham,** see also Charlton Kings.

**Chipping Campden.** Westington Hill Quarry (disused), on W. side of road 1¼ miles S.S.W. of town.

Jurassic, Inferior Oolite (Lower Freestone, formerly mined, to Harford Sands), with many fossils, especially brachiopods, in the Oolite Marl.

Richardson, L. 1929, pp. 64-65.
Geol. Surv. N.S. 217 ; Ord. New Pop. 144.

**Chipping Sodbury.** Quarries extending northward for 1½ miles on W. side of road to Wickwar.

Carboniferous Limestone (S and $D_1$ zones), with corals (*Lithostrotion*), brachiopods, algal bands, etc.

Tuck, M. C. 1926, p. 241, with geol. map.
Geol. Surv. O.S. 35 ; Ord. New Pop. 156.

**Cirencester.** Jarvis' New Quarry, on N.W. side of Tetbury road, about 2 miles S.W. of town. Not to be confused with Jarvis' Old Quarry, now built in, nearby on opposite side of road.

Jurassic, Great Oolite Series (Kemble Beds, best Cotswold section), with brachiopods (*Epithyris*) and lamellibranchs (*Lima cardiiformis*) abundant and some corals.

Woodward, H. B. 1894, p. 232.
Geol. Surv. O.S. 34 ; Ord. New Pop. 157.

**Clifton,** Bristol. Avon Gorge, right bank of R. Avon below railway bridge. See left bank under Somerset.

Upper Old Red Sandstone with fish-fragments.

Wallis, F. S. 1927a, p. 781 ; 1927b, p. 400.
Geol. Surv. O.S. 35 ; Ord. New Pop. 156.

**Clifton.** Avon Gorge, right bank of R. Avon and quarries and road-cutting. See left bank under Somerset.

Carboniferous Limestone, complete section (K to D zones). The zonal

divisions of the Carboniferous Limestone were first worked out here.
Vaughan, A. 1905.
Geol. Surv. O.S. 35 ; Ord. New Pop. 156.

**Coalpit Heath,** 7½ miles N.E. of Bristol. Tip heaps of Coalpit Heath Colliery.
Carboniferous, Coal Measures (Farrington Group). Non-marine lamellibranchs and the small crustacean *Leaia* in roof of High Vein ; plants in roofs of Hollybush and Hard Veins.
Moore, L. R. and Trueman, A. E. 1937, p. 232.
Geol. Surv. O.S. 35 ; Ord. New Pop. 156.

**Coleford.** Quarries 1 mile, 350 yards to 1½ miles S. 25° E. of Coleford Church.
Carboniferous Limestone (S₂ subzone, Drybrook Sandstone) with brachiopods, including *Composita* [*Seminula*] *ficoidea* and *Davidsonina* [*Cyrtina*] *carbonaria*.
Sibly, T. F. 1912, p. 417 ; 1918, p. 23. Trotter, F. M. 1942, p. 20.
Geol. Surv. O.S. 43 S.W. ; Ord. New Pop. 156.

**Coln St. Dennis,** ½ mile S.E. of Fosse Way at Fossbridge. Quarry, worked intermittently, just over ½ mile E.N.E. of road-junctions at Crickley Barrow, N. of road to Eastington.
Jurassic, Great Oolite Series (White Limestone and *Terebratula*-Marl, some 10 ft.) with many brachiopods and some lamellibranchs, especially *Lima cardiiformis*.
Richardson, L. 1933, p. 55.
Geol. Surv. N.S. 235 ; Ord. New Pop. 144.

**Crawley,** near Dursley. Overgrown section in S. side of track leaving road at N. tip of Uley Bury camp and leading to Hodgcombe Farm ; halfway down hill in wood.
Jurassic, Upper Lias, best available section of Cotswold Cephalopod-Bed (many ammonites, lamellibranchs, etc.), now that the classic Frocester Hill section is obscured.
Geol. Surv. O.S. 35 ; Ord. New Pop. 156.

**Crofts End,** Bristol. Crofts End Brickwords, S. face of pit.
Carboniferous, Coal Measures (Crofts End Marine Band, *similis-pulchra* zone), with goniatites, brachiopods and lamellibranchs.
Moore, L. R. and Trueman, A. E. 1937, p. 212.
Geol. Surv. O.S. 35 ; Ord. New Pop. 156.

**Dowdeswell,** 4 miles S.E. of Cheltenham. Cold Comfort Quarry (disused), on N. side of Gloucester-Oxford road ¾ mile S.S.W. of Dowdeswell.
Jurassic, Inferior Oolite. The only available section of the *Witchellia* Grit (1 ft. 3 ins.), with its characteristic brachiopod *Tubithyris wrighti*, but no ammonites.
Richardson, L. 1904, p. 121, with geol. map.
Geol. Surv. N.S. 235 ; Ord. New Pop. 144.

**Dyrham,** 8 miles N. of Bath. Small natural exposure at head of combe 1 mile S.S.E. of Dyrham Church and 1 mile N.W. of Cold Aston.
Jurassic, Fuller's Earth Rock, with many brachiopods (*Ornithella, Rhynchonelloidella*).
Richardson, L. 1910b, p. 78. Muir-Wood, H. M. 1936.
Geol. Surv. O.S. 35 ; Ord. New Pop. 156.

**Fairford.** Ploughed-over site of old excavation ⅛ mile E. of Honeycombe Leaze Farm and N. of by-road from Fairford N.W. to Sunhill.
Jurassic, Great Oolite Series (Fairford Coral Bed). Many fine corals are still turned up by the plough.
Richardson, L. 1933, pp. 59-60. Tomes, R. F. 1883.
Geol. Surv. N.S. 235 ; Ord. New Pop. 157.

**Fairford.** Milton End Quarry, on N. side of Cirencester road, ½ mile W.S.W. of Fairford Church.

Jurassic, Upper Cornbrash, with many brachiopods (those of the *lagenalis* zone better preserved than anywhere else in England).

Douglas, J. A. and Arkell, W. J. 1928, p. 134.

Geol. Surv. N.S. 235 ; Ord. New Pop. 157.

**Falfield,** 14½ miles N.E. of Bristol. Quarry behind old windmill ¼ mile S. of village.

Silurian, Wenlock Limestone. Formerly a famous locality, but fossils are now difficult to obtain.

Murchison, R. I. 1839, p. 455. Reed, F. R. C. and Reynolds, S. H. 1908, p. 526. Reynolds, S. H. 1921, p. 208.

Geol. Surv. O.S. 35 ; Ord. New Pop. 156.

**Falfield.** Quarries in Skeay's Grove, N. of Heneage Court.

Silurian, Wenlock Limestone, with good specimens of *Solenopora gothlandica.*

Reynolds, S. H. 1921, p. 208. Whittard, W. F. and Smith, S. 1944, p. 69.

Geol. Surv. O.S. 35 ; Ord. New Pop. 156.

**Fretherne,** near Frampton-on-Severn. The Hock Cliff, left bank of R. Severn ¼ mile W. of Fretherne, approached by footpath branching off road to Arlingham.

Jurassic, Lower Lias, with many lamellibranchs (*Pecten, Lima, Gryphaea,* etc.), ammonites and brachiopods.

Henderson, I. J. 1935.

Geol. Surv. O.S. 43 S.E. ; Ord. New Pop. 156.

**Frocester,** 4 miles S.W. of Stroud. Frocester Hill, about 1 mile S.E. of village. Classic section of Cotswold Cephalopod-bed (Upper Lias) now obscured. See Crawley.

Richardson, L. 1910b, pp. 118-119.

Geol. Surv. O.S. 35 ; Ord. New Pop. 156.

**Gloucester.** Robin's Wood Hill Brickworks, on E. side of Stroud road 2 miles S. of city.

Jurassic, Lower Lias (with capricorn ammonites and interesting lamellibranchs) and Middle Lias.

Gardiner, C. I. and others 1934, p. 135.

Geol. Surv. O.S. 43 S.E. ; Ord. New Pop. 143.

**Guiting Power,** 6 miles W. of Stow-on-the-Wold. Lane- and track-banks N. of watersplash in Crediford Brook on lane from Kineton to Roel Gate, and in sides of lane W. of brook and banks of track (The White Way) 50 yds. S. of crossing with lane.

Jurassic, Inferior Oolite (*scissum* Beds). Belemnites, lamellibranchs and brachiopods are easily dug out with a trowel.

Richardson, L. 1929, p. 56.

Geol. Surv. N.S. 217 ; Ord. New Pop. 144.

**Halmore,** 2 miles N.N.E. of Berkeley. Side of pond E. of Halmore-Purton road, about 1,200 yds. S. of Purton Church.

Cambrian, Tremadoc (Breadstone Shales) with minute brachiopods (*Acrotreta*).

Smith, S. 1933, p. 361, with geol. map.

Geol. Surv. O.S. 35 ; Ord. New Pop. 156.

**Hampen,** 2 miles E. of Andoversford. Hampen railway-cutting, about ½ mile S. along lane to Compton Abdale ¼ mile N.E. of Hampen.

Jurassic, Great Oolite Series (White Limestone, Hampen Marly Beds, Taynton Stone, Stonesfield Slate, Fuller's Earth, in descending order). Abundant gastropods and lamellibranchs in Hampen Marly Beds. White Limestone and Stonesfield Slate also fossiliferous.

Richardson, L. 1929, pp. 103–106.
Geol. Surv. N.S. 217 ; Ord. New Pop. 144.

**Haresfield,** 6 miles S.W. of Gloucester. Haresfield Beacon, S.E. of village.
Jurassic, Upper Lias (Cephalopod Bed) and Inferior Oolite (up to Pea
Grit). Cephalopod Bed formerly well-exposed and very fossiliferous.
Richardson, L. 1904, pp. 58–59, with geol. map.
Geol. Surv. O.S. 43 S.E. ; Ord. New Pop. 156.

**Henbury,** N.N.W. of Bristol. Two quarries on Brentry Hill, one on the
main road to the Passages, the other on the branch road to Charlton.
Carboniferous Limestone, $S_2$ and $D_1$ subzones, with corals (*Lithostrotion*,
*Syringopora*) and brachiopods (*Composita* [*Seminula*] *ficoidea*, *Productus*, etc.).
Vaughan, A. 1905, p. 235.
Geol. Surv. O.S. 35 ; Ord. New Pop. 156.

**Longborough,** 2½ miles N.N.W. of Stow-on-the-Wold. Newpark Quarry,
worked intermittently, on S.W. side of Broadway road, 1¾ miles N. of Stow in
angle of lane running S. to join lane running to Condicote.
Jurassic, Great Oolite (Chipping Norton Limestone, 25 ft.). When in
work, large reptile bones, teeth, etc., may be collected with the help of the
quarrymen, also a few shells.
Richardson, L. 1929, p. 89. Reynolds, S. H. 1936, p. 62.
Geol. Surv. N.S. 217 ; Ord. New Pop. 144.

**Minchinhampton,** see Burleigh.

**Mitcheldean.** Wilderness Portland Cement Works Quarry (disused),
600 yds. S.W. of Mitcheldean Church.
Carboniferous Limestone (Lower Limestone Shales, K zone and horizon β).
The fauna includes the brachiopod *Camarotoechia mitcheldeanensis*.
Sibly, T. F. and Reynolds, S. H. 1937, pp. 28, 34. Trotter, F. M. 1942,
p. 17.
Geol. Surv. O.S. 43 S.E. ; Ord. New Pop. 143.

**Mitcheldean.** Wilderness Portland Cement Works Quarry (disused), in
Scully Grove, 750 yds. W. by N. of Mitcheldean Church.
Carboniferous Limestone (Whitehead Limestone, $C_2$–$S_1$ subzones). Type-
locality of the calcareous alga *Mitcheldeania gregaria* (now *Garwoodia*).
Sibly, T. F. and Reynolds, S. H. 1937, p. 46. Wood, A. 1941.
Geol. Surv. O.S. 43 S.E. ; Ord. New Pop. 143.

**Mitcheldean.** Old quarries on the Drybrook road 100 yds. W. of Cement
Works Quarry.
Carboniferous Limestone (Crease Limestone, $C_1$ subzone), with corals
(*Caninia*, *Michelinia*), many brachiopods, some molluscs and bryozoa.
Sibly, T. F. and Reynolds, S. H. 1937, p. 41.
Geol. Surv. O.S. 43 S.E. ; Ord. New Pop. 143.

**Mobley,** ½ mile E. of Berkeley. Ditch on S. side of road E. of Plough Inn,
660 yds. E.N.E. of Berkeley Castle.
Cambrian, Tremadoc (Breadstone Shales) with trilobites (*Beltella*) and
brachiopod-fragments.
Smith, S. 1933, p. 361.
Geol. Surv. O.S. 35 ; Ord. New Pop. 156.

**Naunton,** 5 miles W.S.W. of Stow-on-the-Wold. Huntsman's Quarry,
1½ miles N.N.E. of Naunton on E. side of lane from Cheltenham—Stow road
to Stow—Ford road. Large pits in work.
Jurassic, Great Oolite Series (Stonesfield Slate), with ammonites, belemnites,
lamellibranchs, brachiopods and some fish- and reptile-bones, can be obtained
with the help of the quarrymen. These beds are no longer worked for " slates."
Richardson, L. 1929, p. 114.
Geol. Surv. N.S. 217 ; Ord. New Pop. 144.

**North Cerney,** 4 miles N. of Cirencester. Old Gore Barn Quarry (disused), near W. side of railway ½ mile E. of Calmsden and ¾ mile S.W. of Fosse Cross station.

Jurassic, Great Oolite Series (White Limestone). Brachiopods, gastropods and sea-urchins in *Terebratula*-Marl.

Richardson, L. 1933, p. 63.
Geol. Surv. N.S. 235 ; Ord. New Pop. 157.

**Northleach.** Disused quarry about 1 mile S.W. of Northleach on E. side of road to Crickley Barrow and nearly opposite track to Winterwell Farm, 1¼ miles N.N.E. of Crickley Barrow crossroads.

Jurassic, Great Oolite Series (Kemble Beds of unusual facies). Kemble Beds' gastropods, and those of the Minchinhampton Shelly Beds, may be worked out by taking slabs home.

Richardson, L. 1933, p. 55.
Geol. Surv. N.S. 235 ; Ord. New Pop. 157.

**Painswick.** Small disused quarry on E. side of Sheepscombe—Bulls Cross road, ¾ mile E. of Painswick. ("Loveday's Mill," referred to by Richardson, is now a private house.)

Jurassic, Inferior Oolite (Oolite Marl and coral-bed) with lamellibranchs, brachiopods and corals, when well-weathered.

Richardson, L. 1904, p. 96, with geol. map.
Geol. Surv. O.S. 44 ; Ord. New Pop. 156.

**Purton,** 3½ miles N. of Berkeley. Tite's Point, shore of left bank of R. Severn, near the Inn, S. of the point.

Silurian, Ludlow, with worms (*Serpulites*) and brachiopods ; *Dayia navicula* and *Wilsonia davidsoni* in lower beds, *Chonetes striatellus* and *Camarotoechia nucula* in higher beds.

Phillips, J. 1848, p. 199.
Geol. Surv. O.S. 35 ; Ord. New Pop. 156.

**Purton.** Quarry S. of the village.

Silurian, Ludlow (argillaceous limestone) with brachiopods, including *Atrypa, Chonetes, Leptaena, Leptostrophia,* Orthids, *Wilsonia,* occasional corals such as *Favosites* and the ostracod *Beyrichia.*

Geol. Surv. O.S. 35 ; Ord. New Pop. 156.

**Rodborough,** S.W. of Stroud. Disused quarry N. of Rodborough Castle on N. side of upper road from Rodborough to Minchinhampton, in angle of road to Mount Vernon.

Jurassic, Inferior Oolite (*Clypeus* Grit, 2 ft., Upper Coral Bed, 6 ft., Upper *Trigonia* Grit, 8 ft.). The best available section of the Upper Coral Bed, with good slabs of coral. The brachiopod *Acanthothyris spinosa* occurs, but is commoner in quarry on opposite side of road, a little higher up.

Richardson, L. 1904, pp. 129-130.
Geol. Surv. O.S. 34 ; Ord. New Pop. 156.

**Ruspidge,** 1½ miles S. of Cinderford. Shakemantle Quarry, 500 yds. S.E. of Staple Edge Halt.

Carboniferous Limestone (Lower Dolomite, C zone), with zaphrentid corals and brachiopods such as *Schuchertella, Tylothyris* and ? *Daviesiella.*

Trotter, F. M. 1942, p. 16.
Geol. Surv. O.S. 43 S.E. ; Ord. New Pop. 143.

**Sharpness,** 2¼ miles N.N.W. of Berkeley. Cliffs near Severn railway bridge, on left bank of river.

Silurian, Downton Series, marls with fragments of ostracoderms (*Cephalaspis, Phialaspis*) and spines of "*Onchus.*"

White, E. I. 1946, pp. 213, 238.
Geol. Surv. O.S. 35 ; Ord. New Pop. 156.

**Shirehampton,** $4\frac{1}{2}$ miles N.W. of Bristol. Quarry and exposures at Penpole Point, about $\frac{1}{4}$ mile N. of village.
Carboniferous Limestone (Z zone) with zaphrentid corals and brachiopods (*Spirifer clathratus, Schizophoria resupinata*).
Reynolds, S. H. 1920, p. 95.
Geol. Surv. O.S. 35 ; Ord. New Pop. 156.

**Snowshill,** $4\frac{1}{2}$ miles S.W. of Chipping Campden. Quarry or Sandhole on N. side of Snowshill to Springhill Lodges road about $1\frac{1}{2}$ miles N.E. of Snowshill and opposite Seven Wells. Worked periodically.
Jurassic, Inferior Oolite, best available section of Harford Sands, with brachiopods, lamellibranchs and gastropods, difficult to extract from hard sandstone.
Richardson, L. 1929, p. 62.
Geol. Surv. N.S. 217 ; Ord. New Pop. 144.

**South Cerney.** Two adjacent quarries E. of crossroads $\frac{1}{2}$ mile N.N.W. of Shorncote, $1\frac{1}{2}$ miles W. of South Cerney Church.
Jurassic, Cornbrash, highly fossiliferous with large ammonites (*Macro-cephalites*) in Upper Cornbrash.
Douglas, J. A. and Arkell, W. J. 1928, p. 135.
Geol. Surv. O.S. 34 ; Ord. New Pop. 157.

**Southmead,** N. Bristol. Large quarries near Southmead, $\frac{3}{4}$ mile E. of Westbury-upon-Trym.
Carboniferous Limestone ($C_1$ subzone) with corals (*Caninia*) and brachiopods (*Orthotetes, Chonetes, Syringothyris*).
Vaughan, A. 1905, p. 234.
Geol. Surv. O.S. 35 ; Ord. New Pop. 156.

**Southrop,** 3 miles N.N.W. of Lechlade. Quarry $\frac{3}{10}$ mile S. 18° W. of Southrop Church.
Jurassic, Lower Cornbrash (12 ft.) with many fossils, especially brachiopods, overlying Forest Marble ($7\frac{1}{2}$ ft.).
Douglas, J. A. and Arkell, W. J. 1928, p. 133. Richardson, L 1933, p. 78.
Geol. Surv. N.S. 235 ; Ord. New Pop. 157.

**Stoke Bishop,** $2\frac{1}{2}$ miles N.W. of Bristol. Old quarry near Howe Croft.
Upper Old Red Sandstone with fish-fragments.
Wallis, F. S. 1927a, p. 781.
Geol. Surv. O.S. 35 ; Ord. New Pop. 156.

**Stonehouse,** 3 miles W. of Stroud. Large Brickworks S.E. of village.
Jurassic, Lower Lias (*davoei* zone), with capricorn ammonites and many other fossils.
Geol. Surv. O.S. 35 ; Ord. New Pop. 156.

**Stroud.** Selsley Hill, S.W. of Rodborough, numerous disused quarries.
Jurassic, Inferior Oolite (*scissum* beds to White Limestone), with numerous fossils especially in the Pea Grit, Oolite Marl and *Clypeus* Grit.
Richardson, L. 1910b, pp. 123-127 and map, fig 4.
Geol. Surv. O.S. 35 ; Ord. New Pop. 156.

**Stroud,** see also Burleigh, Rodborough.

**Tortworth,** $3\frac{1}{4}$ miles W. of Wotton-under-Edge. Old quarry by the Little Avon, N. of Avening Green Farm, $\frac{1}{4}$ mile N.E. of Tortworth.
Silurian, Upper Llandovery (decalcified sandy limestone) with trilobites (*Encrinurus, Phacops*) and many brachiopods.
Reed, F. R. C. and Reynolds, S. H. 1908, p. 517.
Geol. Surv. O.S. 35 ; Ord. New Pop. 156.

**Tortworth.** Damery Quarry and roadside S. of Damery Bridge over Little Avon N. of Tortworth.

Silurian, Upper Llandovery, with trilobites (*Encrinurus*, *Phacops*) and many brachiopods.
Reed, F. R. C. and Reynolds, S. H. 1908, p. 517.
Geol. Surv. O.S. 35 ; Ord. New Pop. 156.

**Tortworth.** W. edge of Little Daniel's Wood, ⅓ mile N.N.E. of Brook Farm, 700 yds. N. of Tortworth Court.
Silurian, Wenlock Limestone, with trilobites, brachiopods, etc.
Reed, F. R. C. and Reynolds, S. H. 1908, p. 528.
Geol. Surv. O.S. 35 ; Ord. New Pop. 156.

**Tytherington.** Hardwick Quarry, ¼ mile N.W. of village.
Carboniferous Limestone (Z and C zones), with zaphrentid and other corals and many brachiopods (*Schizophoria*, *Orthotetes*, *Chonetes*, *Tylothyris*, etc.).
Wallis, F. S. 1924, p. 66, with geol. map.
Geol. Surv. O.S. 35 ; Ord. New Pop. 156.

**Tytherington.** Church and Camp Quarries.
Carboniferous Limestone (S zone), with corals (*Lithostrotion*, etc.) and brachiopods (*Composita* [*Seminula*], *Productus*, etc.).
Wallis, F. S. 1924, p. 67, with geol. map.
Geol. Surv. O.S. 35 ; Ord. New Pop. 156.

**Tytherington.** Grovesend Quarry, ¾ mile W.N.W. of Tytherington.
Carboniferous Limestone (Z and $C_1$ zones), with zaphrentid and other corals and many brachiopods.
Wallis, F. S. 1924, p. 65, with geol. map.
Geol. Surv. O.S. 35 ; Ord. New Pop. 156.

**Upper Coberley.** Disused quarry about ½ mile S.E. of Seven Springs on S. side of lane from Cheltenham-Cirencester road to Upper Coberley in former larch plantation. Section still in good condition.
Jurassic, Inferior Oolite. The Lower *Trigonia* Grit (with the *buckmani* grit above and the Upper Freestone below) yields the little brachiopod *Aulacothyris meriani* in a 2-inch band above a bed with corals and lamellibranchs.
Richardson, L. 1933, p. 26.
Geol. Surv. N.S. 235 ; Ord. New Pop. 144.

**Upper Slaughter,** 3 miles S.W. of Stow-on-the-Wold. Cotswold Slate Pits, Eyford Hill, 3¼ miles N.W. by N. of Bourton-on-the-Water station, on both sides of track from Chalk Hill to Eyford Park and Cheltenham road.
Jurassic, Great Oolite (Stonesfield Slate, locally called " Pendle "). The interesting fauna includes reptiles, fish, ammonites, belemnites, gastropods, lamellibranchs, insects, cirripedes, etc. The starfish *"Asterias cotteswoldiae"* was adopted as the seal of the Cotteswold Naturalists' Field Club.
Richardson, L. 1929, pp. 113-116.
Geol. Surv. N.S. 217 ; Ord. New Pop. 144.

**Wanswell Green,** 1½ miles N. of Berkeley. Stream-section 300 yds. S. of Haynes Farm for 100 yds. S.E. from Holywell Spring (reservoir).
Cambrian, Tremadoc (Breadstone Shales), with trilobites (*Niobella*) and minute brachiopods (*Acrotreta*).
Smith, S. 1933, p. 361.
Geol. Surv. O.S. 35 ; Ord. New Pop. 156.

**Warmley,** 5 miles E. of Bristol. Warmley Brick and Tile Works, N. of Warmley station.
Carboniferous, Coal Measures (base of *similis-pulchra* zone), with plants (*Alethopteris*, *Neuropteris*) in roof of thin coal on N. side of pit.
Moore, L. R. and Trueman, A. E. 1937, p. 214.
Geol. Surv. O.S. 35 ; Ord. New Pop. 156.

**Westbury-on-Severn,** 8½ miles S.W. of Gloucester. Garden Cliff, ½ mile
S. of Westbury on right bank of R. Severn.
Jurassic, Lower Lias (White Lias), with oysters and other lamellibranchs ;
overlying Triassic, Rhaetic, with lamellibranchs and ostracods in shales above
Bone Bed (well-exposed at low tide).
Richardson, L. 1903, pp. 154-165, Table III ; 1904, p. 23, with geol. map.
Geol. Surv. O.S. 43 S.E. ; Ord. New Pop. 156.

**Westbury-upon-Trym,** 3 miles N.N.W. of Bristol. Blaize Castle grounds,
between Westbury and Henbury.
Carboniferous Limestone (C, S and D zones). The Rhododendron Walk
is a well-known locality for corals (*Lithostrotion*, etc.).
Vaughan, A. 1905, p. 235. Reynolds, S. H. 1920, p. 96.
Geol. Surv. O.S. 35 ; Ord. New Pop. 156.

**Whitfield,** 3 miles E. of Thornbury. Brinkmarsh Quarry, W. of Brinkmarsh
Lane about 300 yds. S. of village, and smaller quarry E. of lane.
Silurian, Wenlock Limestone, with abundant corals and brachiopods.
Reed, F. R. C. and Reynolds, S. H. 1908, pp. 525, 541.
Geol. Surv. O.S. 35 ; Ord. New Pop. 156.

**Wick,** 7 miles E. of Bristol. Quarries and natural exposures in vicinity of
Ochre works.
Carboniferous Limestone (D zone), with corals, brachiopods and many
lamellibranchs and gastropods.
Smith, S. 1930b, pp. 344, 348, with geol. map.
Geol. Surv. O.S. 35 ; Ord. New Pop. 156.

**Wick.** Quarry on E. side of village, between reservoir and Doynton road.
Other quarries on N. side of gorge.
Carboniferous Limestone (S zone), with corals (*Lithostrotion*), brachiopods
(*Composita* [*Seminula*] *ficoidea*) and algal bands.
Smith, S. 1930b, p. 337, with geol. map.
Geol. Surv. O.S. 35 ; Ord. New Pop. 156.

**Wickwar.** Quarries on N. side of town.
Carboniferous Limestone (Z, C and S zones), with many corals and
brachiopods.
Tuck, M. C. 1926, pp. 239-241, with geol. map.
Geol. Surv. O.S. 35 ; Ord. New Pop. 156.

**Woodford,** 5½ miles N.E. of Thornbury. Old " Trap " Quarries, Middle-
mill, ½ mile S.E. of Woodford.
Silurian, Upper Llandovery, with many corals and brachiopods.
Reed, F. R. C. and Reynolds, S. H. 1908, p. 519, with geol. map.
Geol. Surv. O.S. 35 ; Ord. New Pop. 156.

**Yate,** 1 mile W. of Chipping Sodbury. Quarry by Tanhouse Lane, on
opposite side to Tanhouse Farm, 1½ miles N. 5° E. of Yate Church. Pit now
flooded.
Carboniferous, " Millstone Grit," $P_2$ (=$D_3$) subzone, limestones and shales,
with small simple corals and brachiopods and many fossils of other groups.
Smith, S. 1942, p. 335.
Geol. Surv. O.S. 35 ; Ord. New Pop. 156.

**Yate Rocks,** 1½ miles N. of Chipping Sodbury. Quarries N. and S. of
hamlet.
Carboniferous Limestone (C and S zones), with many corals and brachiopods.
Tuck, M. C. 1926, pp. 241-242, with geol. map.
Geol. Surv. O.S. 35 ; Ord. New Pop. 156.

## HAMPSHIRE

**Barton-on-Sea,** 9 miles E. of Bournemouth. Cliff-section at Christchurch Bay, for 4 miles from a point 1 mile E.N.E. of Mudeford to Long Mead End at Hordle.

Eocene, Barton Beds (clays and sands, 200 ft.), with many gastropods (*Volutospina luctatrix* is characteristic) and lamellibranchs, also rarer sea-urchins, bryozoa, ostracods, foraminifera, etc.

Gardner, J. S., Keeping, H., and Monckton, H. W. 1888, pp. 578-635.
Burton, E. St. J. 1933, pp. 131-167.
Geol. Surv. N.S. 329-330 ; Ord. New Pop. 179.

**Barton-on-Sea,** see also Highcliffe.

**Basingstoke.** Newnham (Nuneham), Cuffell, Clewers Green, Old Basing (obsolete localities in railway-cuttings). Musselwhite's brickyard, 2 miles W. of Hook railway station.

Eocene, London Clay, with a rich fauna of lamellibranchs and gastropods.
Edwards, F. E. 1849-1861. Wrigley, A. 1928, pp. 360-368.
Geol. Surv. N.S. 284 ; Ord. New Pop. 168 and 169.

**Blackmoor,** 2¼ miles E..of Selborne.
Selborne Brickworks, Honey Lane, reopened 1946.

Cretaceous, Gault (*dentatus* zone at base of pit) with the ammonite *Hoplites dentatus* and lamellibranchs (*Grammatodon, Nucula, Ostrea*).
White, H. J. O. 1910b, p. 20.
Geol. Surv. N.S. 300 ; Ord. New Pop. 169.

**Bournemouth,** Cliffs W. of Bournemouth Pier to Poole Head (E. horn of Poole Harbour).

Eocene, Bagshot Beds. Lenses of pipe-clay among the sandy beds contain many leaves and plant-fragments.
Gardner, J. S. 1882.
Geol. Surv. N.S. 329 ; Ord. New Pop. 179.

**Brockenhurst.** The classic locality below railway-line at Whitley Ridge, 5 furlongs N.E. of Brockenhurst station is inaccessible. The Victoria Tilery, a little to the N., is still open.

Oligocene, Middle Headon Beds, with many molluscs and corals.
Edwards, F. E. 1849-1861. Duncan, P. M. 1866.
Geol. Surv. N.S. 330 ; Ord. New Pop. 180.

**Brook,** 1¼ miles W. of Cadnam. Brook, Bramshaw and Huntingbridge, in the banks of New Forest streams (marked by the word " Fossils " on a map in Wise's *The New Forest* 1863, p. 276). Bramshaw is still accessible.

Eocene, Upper Bracklesham Beds; with beautiful gastropods and lamellibranchs.
Edwards, F. E. 1840-1861. Fisher, O. 1862.
Geol. Surv. N.S. 315 ; Ord. New Pop. 179.

**Burghclere,** 6 miles S. of Newbury (Berks). Chalkpit 200 yds. N. of Hockley's Hole, near Duncroft Farm, 1 mile N. of Burghclere.

Cretaceous, Upper Chalk (*planus* zone, including Chalk Rock), with the sea-urchins *Echinocorys, Holaster* and *Micraster*, as well as brachiopods, lamellibranchs, etc.
Geol. Surv. N.S. 283 ; Ord. New Pop. 168.

**Chawton,** 1 mile S. of Alton. Pit 1 mile S.W. of Chawton beside Winchester road, near branch-road on left adjoining Imbook Copse.

Cretaceous, Middle Chalk (25 ft.) capped by base of Upper Chalk (Chalk Rock), with ammonites, gastropods, lamellibranchs, brachiopods, etc.
Geol. Surv. N.S. 300 ; Ord. New Pop. 169.

**Crondall.** Brickyard S.W. of the village.

Eocene, London Clay (Basement-Bed) with fine molluscs, best obtained by brushing weathered sandy concretions. Small shells may be found inside the larger specimens.

Geol. Surv. N.S. 284 ; Ord. New Pop. 169.

**Fareham.** Brickyard at Lower Swanwick, on left bank of Hamble River, 6 miles N.W. of Fareham.

Eocene, upper London Clay, with lamellibranchs (including large *Pinna*), gastropods (large *Ficus smithi*) and brachiopods. The Elwes collection, made from lower beds in railway-cuttings N.W. of Fareham station (now grassed over) is in the Yorkshire Museum, York.

White, H. J. O. 1913, pp. 47-50.

Geol. Surv. N.S. 315-316 ; Ord. New Pop. 180.

**Faringdon,** 2½ miles S. of Alton. Old flooded pit 220 yds. to right of lane to W. Worldham, 2 miles N.E. of Faringdon. Access by culvert under road.

Cretaceous, Lower Chalk (Chalk Marl) with ammonites (*Schloenbachia*), lamellibranchs, etc. Can only be visited in dry weather.

White, H. J. O. 1910b, p. 30.

Geol. Surv. N.S. 300 ; Ord. New Pop. 169.

**Hartley Mauditt,** 2¼ miles S.E. of Alton. Small quarry on right of road from church eastwards to Oakhanger, ½ mile from church.

Cretaceous, Upper Greensand. Ammonites (*Mortoniceras rostratum*) and gastropods (*Semisolarium*) may still be found, though the section is much obscured.

White, H. J. O. 1910b, p. 22.

Geol. Surv. N.S. 300 ; Ord. New Pop. 169.

**Highcliffe,** 7½ miles E. of Bournemouth. Cliff-section ¼ mile E.N.E. of Cliff End and 1 mile E.N.E. of Mudeford.

Eocene, base of Barton Beds (dark greenish sandy clay) with foraminifera (*Nummulites prestwichianus*).

Burton, E. St. J. 1933. Curry, D. 1937, pp. 229-246.

Geol. Surv. N.S. 329 ; Ord. New Pop. 179.

**Hordle,** 4 miles W. of Lymington. Cliff-section E. of Beckton Bunny, 1 mile from Barton.

Eocene, top of Barton Beds (Long Mead End Bed), 20 ft. of whitish sand with fragile small molluscs, especially the gastropod *Batillaria pleurotomoides*, in the top 5 ft.

Tawney, E. B. 1881, pp. 140-155. White, H. J. O. 1915, p. 36.

Geol. Surv. N.S. 330 ; Ord. New Pop. 179.

**Hordle.** Cliff-section at Beckton Bunny, ¾ mile from Barton Court and S.E. of New Milton station.

Eocene, Barton Beds (Beckton Bunny Beds), with gastropods, chiefly *Ancilla, Olivella* and *Pollia*. Above is the Long Mead End Bed, as before.

Burton, E. St. J. 1929, pp. 223-239.

Geol. Surv. N.S. 330 ; Ord. New Pop. 179.

**Kingsclere,** 6½ miles S.S.E. of Newbury (Berks). Chalkpit just S.W. of village, at fork in roads to Sydmonton and Ecchinswell.

Cretaceous, Upper Chalk (*planus* zone, with Chalk Rock, *cortestudinarium* and lower *coranguinum* zones, dipping 30° N.), with many fossils, especially the sea-urchin *Micraster*.

Geol. Surv. N.S. 283 ; Ord. New Pop. 168.

**Lasham,** 3¼ miles N.W. of Alton. Small pit near where Alton-Basingstoke road crosses old railway-line ¾ mile S. of Lasham. No. 118 of Brydone, 1912.

Cretaceous, Upper Chalk (*planus* zone 10 ft., with 3 ft. of Chalk Rock at base), with molluscs, brachiopods, sea-urchins (*Micraster*), etc.
Brydone, R. M. 1912, p. 47, with geol. map.
Geol. Surv. N.S. 284 ; Ord. New Pop. 169.

**Lee-on-Solent.** Low sea-cliff and foreshore exposures E. of seaplane station.
Eocene, upper Bracklesham Beds with abundant molluscs and foraminifera (*Nummulites variolarius*). A lenticle with the large gastropod *Campanile* was formerly exposed at Hill Head, W. of Lee, but is now eroded away. These two localities are the " Stubbington " of old literature and collections.
Geol. Surv. N.S. 331 ; Ord. New Pop. 180.

**Lower Froyle,** 3½ miles N.E. of Alton. Old pit 300 yds. from St. Joseph's Church, on E. side of lane to Well. No. 3 of Brydone, 1912.
Cretaceous, Lower Chalk (*subglobosus* zone 50 ft. on *varians* zone) with ammonites, lamellibranchs, etc.
Brydone, R. M. 1912, p. 40, with geol. map.
Geol. Surv. N.S. 284 ; Ord. New Pop. 169.

**Milford-on-Sea,** 3½ miles S.W. of Lymington. Sections in Hordle Cliff, between Beckton Bunny and Milford.
Oligocene, Headon Beds (greenish clays and sands with limestones, up to 80 ft.), with seeds of aquatic plants, numerous fluvio-marine shells and vertebrate remains (alligator, tortoise, birds and mammals).
White, H. J. O. 1915, pp. 37-41.
Geol. Surv. N.S. 330 ; Ord. New Pop. 179.

**Odiham.** Chalkpit in S.W. outskirts of town on Alton road. No. 173 of Brydone, 1912.
Cretaceous, Upper Chalk (*coranguinum* and *Uintacrinus* zones), with abundant fossils, especially a band of the sea-urchin *Conulus* at the junction of the zones.
White, H. J. O. 1909, p. 28. Brydone, R. M. 1912, p. 51.
Geol. Surv. N.S. 284 ; Ord. New Pop. 169.

**Pitt,** 2 miles S.W. of Winchester. Chalkpit just off the Hursley-Winchester road by Pitt Farm. No. 523 of Brydone, 1912.
Cretaceous, Upper Chalk (*coranguinum* zone) with the zonal sea-urchin *Micraster coranguinum.*
Brydone, R. M. 1912, p. 68, with geol. map.
Geol. Surv. N.S. 299 ; Ord. New Pop. 168.

**Portsmouth.** Dockyard Excavations of 1870 yielded many mollusca, crustacea and fish from the Eocene, London Clay, to Meyer, whose collection is at the Sedgwick Museum, Cambridge.
Meyer, C. J. A. 1871, pp. 74-89.
Geol. Surv. N.S. 331 ; Ord. New Pop. 180.

**Shawford,** 2½ miles S. of Winchester. Road-section on Winchester by-pass from junction of Shawford road for 350 yds. to N.
Cretaceous, Upper Chalk (*Uintacrinus* and *Marsupites* zones) with the crinoids of the two zones.
Geol. Surv. N.S. 299 ; Ord. New Pop. 168.

**Shawford.** Road-section on Winchester by-pass from junction of Shawford road for 300 yds. to S.
Cretaceous, Upper Chalk (*pilula* zone, lower part) with the sea-urchin *Echinocorys scutata* var. *depressula* and typical forms.
Geol. Surv. N.S. 299 ; Ord. New Pop. 168.

**Shawford.** Road-cutting and pit at top of hill on road to Otterbourne, ¼ mile S. of road from Shawford station. No. 1041 of Brydone, 1912.
Cretaceous, Upper Chalk (lower part of *pilula* zone) with the sea-urchin *Echinocorys scutata*.
Brydone, R. M. 1912, p. 98, with geol. map.
Geol. Surv. N.S. 299 ; Ord. New Pop. 168.

**Shawford.** Two old pits in Sparrowgrove Copse on up side of railway ⅞ mile S. of Shawford station. No. 1085 of Brydone, 1912.
Cretaceous, Upper Chalk (*quadratus* zone) with the belemnite *Actinocamax quadratus*, generally rare in Hampshire.
Brydone, R. M. 1912, p. 100, with geol. map.
Geol. Surv. N.S. 299 ; Ord. New Pop. 168.

**Shawford.** Pit 1 mile S. of Shawford station on up side of line at Southampton Waterworks. Permission must first be obtained from Waterworks Engineer and Manager, Waterworks Department, Civic Centre, Southampton. No. 1086 of Brydone, 1912.
Cretaceous, Upper Chalk (*quadratus* zone) with belemnites.
Brydone, R. M. 1912, p. 100, with geol. map.
Geol. Surv. N.S. 299 ; Ord. New Pop. 168.

**Southampton.** Well on Southampton Common (Eocene, London Clay) ; and Graving Dock excavatiohs of 1932 near Millbrook station (Eocene, Bracklesham Beds, with a notable abundance of molluscs and such foraminifera as *Nummulites laevigatus*). Neither accessible.
Reid, C. 1902, pp. 6-7. Wrigley, A. 1934, pp. 1-16.
Geol. Surv. N.S. 315 ; Ord. New Pop. 180.

**Southbourne,** 3¼ m. E. of Bournemouth. Cliff-sections, S. flank of Hengistbury Head
Eocene, upper Bracklesham Beds (of Barton Beds facies), with plant remains in green sandy clay (12 ft.) and casts of molluscs in pale chocolate silty clays (49 ft.).
Reed, F. R. C. 1913, pp. 101-103.
Geol. Surv. N.S. 329 ; Ord. New Pop. 179.

**Whitway,** 5 miles S. of Newbury (Berks). Chalkpit ¼ mile S. of Carnarvon Arms Inn on E. side of Newbury-Winchester road. No. 282 of Brydone, 1912.
Cretaceous, Upper Chalk (*coranguinum* zone with trace of *Uintacrinus* zone) with the sea-urchins *Conulus* and *Echinocorys*.
Brydone, R. M. 1912, p. 57, with geol. map. Hawkins, H. L. 1937, p. 145, with geol. map.
Geol. Surv. N.S. 283 ; Ord. New Pop. 168.

**Winchester.** Bar End lime-pit on E. of by-pass road on road to Morestead, S.E. of Winchester. No. 57 of Brydone, 1912.
Cretaceous, Lower Chalk (*subglobosus* zone) with the sea-urchin *Holaster subglobosus*.
Brydone, R. M. 1912, p. 43, with geol. map.
Geol. Surv. N.S. 299 ; Ord. New Pop. 168.

**Winchester.** Section on by-pass road N. of St. Catherine's Hill.
Cretaceous, Middle Chalk (*labiatus* zone) with the lamellibranch *Inoceramus labiatus*.
Geol. Surv. N.S. 299 ; Ord. New Pop. 168.

**Winchester.** Section on by-pass road on W. side of St. Catherine's Hill.
Cretaceous, Middle Chalk (*Terebratulina* zone) with the small brachiopod *Terebratulina lata*.
Geol. Surv. N.S. 299 ; Ord. New Pop. 168.

**Winchester.** Section on by-pass road on W. side of Twyford Down, S. of the town.

Cretaceous, Upper Chalk (*planus* and *cortestudinarium* zones), with sea-urchins (*Holaster*, *Micraster*) and the lamellibranch *Spondylus spinosus*.

Geol. Surv. N.S. 299´; Ord. New Pop. 168.

**Winchester,** see also Pitt, Shawford.

# HEREFORDSHIRE

**Clodock,** 3½ miles N.N.W. of Abergavenny-Hereford road at Pandy, 6 miles N.N.E. of Abergavenny. Castle Mattock roadstone quarry, on E. side of lane ¾ mile S.E. of Clodock Church and 400 yds. S.E. of Lower Hunthouse Farm.

Old Red Sandstone, Ditton Series (cornstone, *c.* 30 ft.) with rare ostracoderms (*Pteraspis*).

White, E. I. 1935, p. 391.

Geol. Surv. O.S. 42 N.E. ; Ord. New Pop. 142.

**Cusop,** 1 mile S.E. of Hay (Brecon). Cusop Dingle, waterfall in tributary of Dulas Brook, 2,450 yds. S.E. of Cusop Church and 730 yds. E.N.E. of New Forest Farm.

Silurian, Downton Series (I. 8) with ostracoderms, especially *Traquairaspis* [*Phialaspis*] *symondsi*.

White, E. I. 1946, p. 212.

Geol. Surv. O.S. 42 N.E. ; Ord. New Pop. 141.

**Dorstone,** 12 miles W. of Hereford. Pen-y-Bwr Quarry, rarely worked, on N. side of road ¾ mile E.N.E. of Dorstone Church and ¾ mile E.S.E. of Llan Farm.

Silurian, Downton Series (I. 9) with rare ostracoderms, plant-fragments, and *Pachytheca*.

Geol. Surv. O.S. 42 N.E. ; Ord. New Pop. 142.

**Downton-on-the-Rock,** 5¼ miles W.S.W. of Ludlow (Salop.). River Teme, section between Bow Bridge and Downton Castle Bridge, in castle grounds.

Silurian, Ludlow and Downton Series (Aymestry Limestone to Temeside Shales) with brachiopods, especially *Conchidium knightii* in the limestone and *Chonetes, Crania, Lingula* and *Spirifer*, etc., in the succeeding shales.

Elles, G. L. and Slater, I. L. 1906, p. 207, with geol. map. Al exander F. E. S. 1936, p. 103, with geol. map.

Geol. Surv. O.S. 55 N.W. ; Ord. New Pop. 129.

**Ewyas Harold,** 10½ miles S.W. of Hereford. King Street Quarry, 1,200 yds. W. of Ewyas Church on N. side of lane to Waterstone, and 1,900 yds. N.N.E. of Rowlstone Church.

Silurian, Downton Series (I. 9), with very rare ostracoderm, eurypterid and plant fragments.

Geol. Surv. O.S. 43 N.W. ; Ord. New Pop. 142.

**Fownhope,** 5 miles S.E. of Hereford. Many disused quarries on Common Hill.

Silurian, Wenlock Limestone, with brachiopods (*Atrypa reticularis*, etc.) corals and other fossils.

Gardiner, C. I. 1927, p. 508, with geol. map. Reed, F. R. C. 1927.

Geol. Surv. O.S. 43 S.W. ; Ord. New Pop. 142.

E

**Kentchurch,** 2 miles S.E. of Abergavenny-Hereford road at Pontrilas, 11½ miles S.W. of Hereford. Great Corras Quarry, rarely worked, on E. side of road to Garway, 600 yds. E.S.E. of Kentchurch Church and 1¼ miles N.E. of Grosmont Church.
Old Red Sandstone, Ditton Series, with rare ostracoderms.
Stensiö, E. A. 1932, p. 200.
Geol. Surv. O.S. 43 S.W. ; Ord. New Pop. 142.

**Kington.** Bradnor Hill Quarry (disused) ⅝ mile N. of Kington Church and ¾ mile S.E. of summit of hill.
Silurian, Downton Sandstone, with rare eurypterids and ostracoderms, especially *Cyathaspis banksi*.
Banks, R. W. 1856, pp. 93-101.
Geol. Surv. O.S. 56 N.E. ; Ord. New Pop. 129.

**Leintwardine,** 9 miles W. of Ludlow (Salop.). Martin's Shell, near Todding, ¾ mile N.N.E. of Leintwardine.
Silurian, Ludlow Series. Type-locality for the " worm " *Protoscolex latus.* Large starfishes (*Lapworthura*) also occur.
Bather, F. A. 1920, p. 124. Hawkins, H. L. and Hampton, S. M. 1927, p. 576, with map.
Geol. Surv. O.S. 55 N.W. ; Ord. New Pop. 129.

**Leintwardine.** Church Hill Quarry, ¼ mile E. of Leintwardine bridge (R. Teme). Now turfed over.
Silurian, Lower Ludlow Series (Leintwardine Flags). Starfishes and seaurchins occurred in two bands. Type-locality of the graptolite *Monograptus leintwardinensis*.
Hawkins, H. L. and Hampton, S. M. 1927, p. 576, with map. Alexander, F. E. S. 1936, p. 111.
Geol. Surv. O.S. 55 N.W. ; Ord. New Pop. 129.

**Mocktree,** 6½ miles W. of Ludlow (Salop.). A series of quarries on Leintwardine-Ludlow road in Wassell Wood, near Todding.
Silurian, Ludlow Series (Aymestry Limestone and Mocktree Shales), with corals and brachiopods (*Conchidium knightii*), etc., in the limestone, and brachiopods (*Dayia navicula*) in the shales.
Elles, G. L. and Slater, I. L. 1906, p. 214, with geol. map. Geol. map in Alexander, F. E. S. 1936.
Geol. Surv. O.S. 55 N.W. ; Ord. New Pop. 129.

**Mordiford,** 4 miles E.S.E. of Hereford. Old lane-section at Haughwood Cottages on W. side of Haugh Wood.
Silurian, top beds of Llandovery Series, with brachiopods (*Stricklandia lirata*) and rare graptolites.
Gardiner, C. I. 1927, with geol. map. Pocock, R. I. 1930, with geol. map.
Geol. Surv. O.S. 43 N.W. ; Ord. New Pop. 142.

**Mordiford.** Field-bank 350 yds. E.S.E. of Upper Littlehope Farm (Loc. 1 of Pocock, 1930), and ditch-, bank- and stream-sections W. of Woolhope and around Haugh Wood.
Silurian, top of Llandovery and base of Wenlock (Woolhope Limestone). A 1-inch limestone with fragments of the crinoid *Petalocrinus* rests on limestone with many tabulate corals and is followed by shales and thin limestones with brachiopods (*Stricklandia lirata*).
Pocock, R. W. 1930, with geol. map.
Geol. Surv. O.S. 43 N.W. ; Ord. New Pop. 142.

**Mordiford.** Sufton Cockshoot, 1 mile N.N.E. of the village, old quarry and section on road to Backbury Hill.
Silurian, shales of Lower Ludlow with graptolites (*Monograptus*).

Gardiner, C. I. 1927, p. 511, with geol. map. Reed, F. R. C. 1927.
Geol. Surv. O.S. 43 N.W. ; Ord. New Pop. 142.

**Mordiford.** Scutterdine Quarries, ½ mile S.E. of the village. Lower part now flooded.
Silurian, Wenlock (Woolhope Limestone) with trilobites (*Bumastus, Dalmanites,* etc.).
Phillips, J. 1848. Gardiner, C. I. 1927, p. 505, with geol. map. Reed, F. R. C. 1927.
Geol. Surv. O.S. 43 N.W. ; Ord. New Pop. 142.

**Nash,** 1 mile S. of Presteign. Nash Scar Limestone Quarries, 1½ miles S.S.W. of Presteign.
Silurian, Wenlock (Woolhope Limestone, reef facies), with algae (*Solenopora*), corals, bryozoa and brachiopods.
Garwood, E. J. and Goodyear, E. 1919, p. 20.
Geol. Surv. O.S. 56 N.E. ; Ord. New Pop. 129.

**Newton,** 11 miles W.S.W. of Hereford, Wayne Herbert Quarry (disused), 1 mile S.E. of Newton Church and 250 yds. S.W. of Wayne Herbert farm.
Old Red Sandstone (Ditton Series), with rare ostracoderms (*Pteraspis*) and eurypterids.
White, E. I. 1935, p. 383.
Geol. Surv. O.S. 42 N.E. ; Ord. New Pop. 142.

**Perton,** 6 miles E. of Hereford. Disused quarry 850 yds. W.S.W. of Stoke Edith Church.
Silurian, Downton Series (Eurypterid Shales) on Upper Ludlow. Eurypterids, *Pachytheca* and very rare corals (*Actinophyllum*) occur.
Stamp, L. D. 1923.
Geol. Surv. O.S. 43 N.W. ; Ord. New Pop. 142.

**Prior's Frome,** 4 miles E. of Hereford. Exposure opposite the Inn.
Silurian, Downton Series, Ludlow Bone Bed (with fish-remains and *Pachytheca*) and Upper Ludlow with brachiopods (*Camarotoechia, Chonetes*).
Gardiner, C. I. 1927, with geol. map. Stamp, L. D. 1923.
Geol. Surv. O.S. 43 N.W. ; Ord. New Pop. 142.

**Rushall,** 4½ miles W.S.W. of Ledbury. Road-cutting 200 yds. S. of the smithy.
Silurian, Upper Ludlow Series and Ludlow Bone Bed, with many fish-fragments (*Thelodus,* etc.) and *Pachytheca*.
Gardiner, C. I. 1927, p. 517, with geol. map. Stamp, L. D. 1923.
Geol. Surv. O.S. 43 N.E. ; Ord. New Pop. 143.

**Suckley** (Worcs.), 3 miles S. of Bromyard-Worcester road at 9 miles W. of Worcester. Ammons Hill railway-cutting, 1½ miles N.W. of Suckley Church and ⅝ mile E.S.E. of Linley Green. Permission must first be obtained from railway authorities.
Silurian, Downton Series and Old Red Sandstone, Ditton Series, with rare molluscs, ostracods and ostracoderms.
King, W. W. 1934, p. 533.
Geol. Surv. O.S. 55 S.E. ; Ord. New Pop. 143.

**Woolhope.** Dormington Woods, 2 miles N.N.W. of village, long range of old quarries in woods of Stoke Edith Park.
Silurian, Wenlock Limestone. Famous in the past for fine corals, brachiopods, etc.
Phillips, J. 1848, p. 170.
Geol. Surv. O.S. 43 N.W. ; Ord. New Pop. 142.

## HUNTINGDONSHIRE

**Warboys,** $3\frac{1}{2}$ miles S. of Ramsey. London Brick Co.'s claypit, $\frac{1}{4}$ mile W.N.W. of Warboys station.

Jurassic, Oxford Clay (*lamberti, mariae* and lower *cordatum* zones) with abundant pyritized ammonites (chiefly *Cardioceras*), gastropods, lamellibranchs, brachiopods, etc.

Spath, L. F. 1939.

Geol. Surv. O.S. 51 N.W. ; Ord. New Pop. 134.


## ISLE OF MAN

**Balladoole,** $1\frac{1}{2}$ miles W. of Castletown. Limestone outcrop (dip 20° S.E.) at S.E. end of Burial Ground $\frac{1}{2}$ mile S.W. of Balladoole School, S. of Port Erin road.

Carboniferous Limestone ($P_{1a}$ subzone, knoll-reef facies), with abundant goniatites.

Smith, J. 1911, pp. 149-164. Lewis, H. P. 1930, pp. 258-260, with geol. map.

Geol. Surv. I.O.M. Special ; Ord. New Pop. 87.

**Balladoole.** Shore exposures, Poyll Richie knolls, 470 yds. S. of school and 50 yds. E. of small jetty.

Carboniferous Limestone (B zone, yellow, powdery knoll-reef limestone), with many bryozoa, brachiopods, goniatites (*Beyrichoceras*) and other mollusca.

Lewis, H. P. 1930, pp. 255-257, with geol. map.

Geol. Surv. I.O.M. Special ; Ord. New Pop. 87.

**Ballasalla,** at fork of Douglas-Port Erin and Douglas-Castletown roads. Rushen Abbey limestone quarry, 200 yds. S.W. of Abbey and 150 yds. N. of Ballasalla House.

Carboniferous Limestone (Mollusca Beds of $S_1$ subzone), with corals, brachiopods, lamellibranchs, gastropods and cephalopods.

Lewis, H.P. 1930, pp. 242, 245, with geol. map.

Geol. Surv. I.O.M. Special ; Ord. New Pop. 87.

**Ballasalla.** Billown Limestone Quarries, 600 yds. W.S.W. of Rushen Abbey and 20 yds. N. of Cross-four-ways.

Carboniferous Limestone ($S_1$-$S_2$ subzones) with corals (*Syringopora spp.*), bryozoa and brachiopods.

Lewis, H. P. 1930, pp. 242-243, with geol. map.

Geol. Surv. I.O.M. Special ; Ord. New Pop. 87.

**Ballasalla.** W. end of disused quarry 100 yds. W. of Cross-four-ways and $\frac{1}{2}$ mile W.S.W. of Rushen Abbey.

Carboniferous Limestone ($S_2$ subzone) with corals (*Nematophyllum minus,* etc.), brachiopods (*Productus corrugato-hemisphericus,* etc.) and molluscs.

Lewis, H. P. 1930, pp. 243-244, with geol. map.

Geol. Surv. I.O.M. Special ; Ord. New Pop. 87.

**Castletown.** Scarlett Quarry and foreshore nearby, $\frac{3}{4}$ mile S.W. of Rushen Castle and $\frac{1}{4}$ mile S. of Sea Mount.

Carboniferous Limestone ($D_1$ subzone), with many corals (*Auloclisia mutata,* large *Caninia*) and other fossils. Type-locality of "*Ammonites henslowi.*"

Lewis, H. P. 1930, pp. 249-254, fig 2, with geol. map.

Geol. Surv. I.O.M. Special ; Ord. New Pop. 87.

**Castletown.** Cliff and foreshore 500 yds. W.S.W. of Balladoole House and 400 yds. N.W. of Poyll Vaaish farm.

Carboniferous Limestone ($D_2$ or $P_{1a}$ subzones) with corals in bedded limestone and shale.

Lewis, H. P. 1930, pp. 257-258, with geol. map. Lamplugh, G. W. 1903, p. 213, with fig. 54.

Geol. Surv. I.O.M. Special ; Ord. New Pop. 87.

**Castletown.** Foreshore 120 yds. W. of Poyll Vaaish farm and 650 yds. S.W. of Balladoole House.
Carboniferous Limestone (P$_{1b}$ subzone) with plants, corals and molluscs, including goniatites. A dendroid graptolite occurs.
Lewis, H. P. 1930, pp. 260-262, with geol. map.
Geol. Surv. I.O.M. Special ; Ord. New Pop. 87.

**Derbyhaven,** 1½ miles E. of Castletown. Outcrops on foreshore 200 yds. E. of Ronaldsway House and mile N.E. of Watch House.
Carboniferous Limestone (C$_2$ subzone) with corals (*Michelinia*), brachiopods and some gastropods.
Lewis, H. P. 1930, pp. 239-240, 244, with geol. map.
Geol. Surv. I.O.M. Special ; Ord. New Pop. 87.

**Derbyhaven.** Outcrops on foreshore 170 yds. N.E. of Ronaldsway House, about ⅝ mile N.E. of the Watch House.
Carboniferous Limestone (C$_2$-S$_1$ subzones), with many corals, brachiopods (including the *Chonetes carinata*-band) and some bryozoa, crinoids, molluscs and trilobites.
Lewis, H. P. 1930, pp. 240-241, with geol. map.
Geol. Surv. I.O.M. Special ; Ord. New Pop. 87.

**Peel.** Cliff-section below old limekiln about 1,600 yds. N.E. of Peel Castle and 200 yds. E. of the Stack.
(?) Carboniferous, Peel Sandstone Group (Stack Series). Sandstones with pebble-beds containing derived fossils of Silurian (Wenlock) age.
Lamplugh, G. W. 1903, pp. 274-276, fig. 77. Lewis, H. P. 1934, p. 93.
Geol. Surv. I.O.M. Special ; Ord. New Pop. 87.

## ISLE OF WIGHT

**Bembridge.** The Foreland, cliff and clay foreshore.
Oligocene, Bembridge Marls, with freshwater and estuarine molluscs.
Reid, C. and Strahan, A. 1889, p. 170.
Geol. Surv. I.O.W. Special ; Ord. New Pop. 180.

**Bembridge,** Brading or Sandown. Whitecliff Bay, cliffs from S.W. corner of bay round headland to " nostrils " of The Culver.
Cretaceous, Upper Chalk (*mucronata* down to *coranguinum* zones with bands of phosphatic nodules in *pilula* zone). Fossils occur throughout, but especially sea-urchins, starfish ossicles and bryozoa in *mucronata* zone.
Rowe, A. W. 1908, p. 243, with geol. map. White, H. J. O. 1921, p. 77.
Geol. Surv. I.O.W. Special ; Ord. New Pop. 180.

**Bembridge,** Brading or Sandown. Whitecliff Bay, cliffs and ledges northwards towards The Foreland.
Eocene, Reading Beds (unfossiliferous) ; London Clay (lamellibranchs in some beds) ; Bagshot Sands (unfossiliferous) ; Bracklesham Beds (foraminifera—*Nummulites*—and many molluscs) ; Barton Beds (*Nummulites* and mollusca). Succeeded by Oligocene, Headon Beds (corals, bryozoa and molluscs at base, molluscs in higher beds, freshwater shells near the top) ; Osborne Beds (freshwater and estuarine shells) ; Bembridge Beds (land and freshwater molluscs). One of the finest coast-sections of Tertiary beds in England.
Reid, C. and Strahan, A. 1889, pp. 110, 143, 168. White, H. J. O. 1921, pp. 91-95, 101, etc. ; Wrigley, A. and Davis, A. G. 1937, p. 203. Curry, D. 1937, p. 232.
Geol. Surv. I.O.W. Special ; Ord. New Pop. 180.

**Bonchurch,** N.E. of Ventnor. Dunnose Point, coast-section.
Cretaceous, Lower Greensand (Carstone) ; and base of Gault (*mammillatum* and *dentatus* zones) with fine ammonites, e.g. *Anahoplites mimeticus, Hoplites benettianus, Lyelliceras,* etc.
White, H. J. O. 1921, p. 51.
Geol. Surv. I.O.W. Special ; Ord. New Pop. 180.

**Brading,** see Bembridge.

**Brighstone,** 6½ miles W. of Ventnor. Cliffs and foreshore from Cowleaze Chine to Atherfield Point.
Cretaceous, Wealden ; non-marine lamellibranchs (*Unio*) in sandstone E. of Cowleaze Chine and lamellibranchs (*Neomiodon*) and gastropods (*Paraglauconia*) in top beds at Atherfield Point. Lower Greensand (Atherfield Clay and Perna Bed) with marine lamellibranchs (*Exogyra sinuata,* etc.), corals and many other fossils at and W. of Atherfield Point.
Reid, C. and Strahan, A. 1889, p. 24.
Geol. Surv. I.O.W. Special ; Ord. New Pop. 180.

**Brook,** 3 miles S.E. of Freshwater. Brook Point, cliffs and low-tide reefs.
Cretaceous, Wealden, fossil tree-trunks (" pine-raft ") in sandstone visible at low tide. Freshwater molluscs and ostracods in cliff, especially W. of Brook Chine. A former locality for reptilian bones (*Iguanodon*).
Mantell, G. A. 1846. Reid, C. and Strahan, A. 1889, p. 5. White, H. J. O. 1921, p. 8.
Geol. Surv. I.O.W. Special ; Ord. New Pop. 180.

**Chale,** 6½ miles W. of Ventnor. Cliffs from Blackgang Chine W. to Atherfield Point, accessible here or from Walpen Undercliff.
Cretaceous, Lower Greensand (Ferruginous Sands). Classic for ammonites (*Tropaeum*) in " *Crioceras* "-Beds. Fossils are generally rare in the Crackers and Lobster Beds below, though abundant and fine in particular dogger-bands.
Reid, C. and Strahan, A. 1889, p. 26. White, H. J. O. 1921, p. 24. Wright, C. W. and E. V. 1942c, p. 283.
Geol. Surv. I.O.W. Special ; Ord. New Pop. 180.

**Cowes,** Gurnard Bay, 1 mile W. of Cowes.
Oligocene, Bembridge Marls. At Gurnard Ledge is a discontinuous 3-inch limestone band (about 3 ft. above the Bembridge Limestone) with a rich flora and many insects.
Reid, E. M. and Chandler, M. E. J. 1926.
Geol. Surv. I.O.W. Special ; Ord. New Pop. 180.

**Freshwater.** Compton Bay, 1 mile E. of Freshwater, cliffs. Beware of tide at projecting point near W. end.
Cretaceous, complete sequence from Wealden to Upper Chalk *cortestudinarium* zone). Freshwater lamellibranchs (*Neomiodon*) in limestone band at top of Wealden. Lower Greensand poor in fossils, but a nodule-bed yields ammonites (*Cleoniceras*). Ammonites and other molluscs in Lower Gault (*dentatus* zone) and Upper Greensand (*dispar* zone). Abundant fossils at base of Lower Chalk and in Middle Chalk (*Terebratulina* zone).
Reid, C. and Strahan, A. 1889, pp. 9, 21, 63, 68. Rowe, A. W. 1908, p. 216 with geol. map. White, H. J. O. 1921, p. 31. Wright, C. W. and E. V. 1942c, p. 236.
Geol. Surv. I.O.W. Special ; Ord. New Pop. 180.

**Freshwater.** Clifftop exposures on Tennyson (High) Down, W. of Freshwater Bay and E. of Tennyson Monument. These bluffs above the main cliff-face should be approached with caution.
Cretaceous, Upper Chalk (*coranguinum* zone), with many sea-urchins, starfish, brachiopods, etc., well weathered-out.
Rowe, A. W. 1908, p. 253, with geol. map.
Geol. Surv. I.O.W. Special ; Ord. New Pop. 180.

**Freshwater.** Brickyard at Afton, 1 mile E. of Freshwater on main Newport road near 9th milestone from Newport on S. side of road. Exposure rapidly deteriorating.

Eocene, Bracklesham and Lower Barton Beds, with foraminifera (*Nummulites*) and molluscs.

Curry, D. 1942.

Geol. Surv. I.O.W. Special ; Ord. New Pop. 180.

**Gunville,** 1½ miles W. of Newport. Brickyard S. of crossing of Newport-Yarmouth railway and Gunville-Carisbrooke road.

Eocene, Bracklesham Beds with foraminifera (*Nummulites variolarius*) and molluscs.

Curry, D. 1942, p. 98.

Geol. Surv. I.O.W. Special ; Ord. New Pop. 180.

**Niton,** 4 miles W. of Ventnor. Reeth Bay, cliffs.

Cretaceous, Lower Greensand (Carstone), doggers in cliffs and on beach, with ammonites, gastropods, lamellibranchs, sea-urchins, crustacea, etc.

Jackson, J. F. 1939.

Geol. Surv. I.O.W. Special ; Ord. New Pop. 180.

**Niton.** Rocken End, Watershoot Bay and St. Catherine's Point, W.S.W. to S.S.W. of Niton, boulders on beach and slipped masses.

Cretaceous, Lower Gault, Upper Greensand and Lower Chalk (Chloritic Marl)—the last with many fine ammonites, sea-urchins, etc.

White, H. J. O. 1921, p. 61.

Geol. Surv. I.O.W. Special ; Ord. New Pop. 180.

**Sandown.** Yaverland Cliffs, N.E. of Sandown.

Cretaceous, Wealden, with non-marine molluscs and reptilian remains (*Iguanodon*, etc.).

Reid, C. and Strahan, A. 1889, p. 16. White, H. J. O. 1921, p. 17.

Geol. Surv. I.O.W. Special ; Ord. New Pop. 180.

**Sandown.** Red Cliff, northern part of Sandown Bay.

Cretaceous, Lower Greensand (Atherfield Clay, Perna Bed, on beach at W. end of Red Cliff) with fine, large lamellibranchs, etc.

Reid, C. and Strahan, A. 1889, p. 35. White, H. J. O. 1921, p. 32.

Geol. Surv. I.O.W. Special ; Ord. New Pop. 180.

**Sandown.** Culver Cliffs, between Sandown and Whitecliff Bay.

Cretaceous, Upper Greensand, Lower and Middle Chalk in cliffs ; boulders of Upper Chalk on beach. Fossils fairly abundant throughout.

Rowe, A. W. 1908, p. 237, with geol. map. White, H. J. O. 1921, p. 59, etc.

Geol. Surv. I.O.W. Special ; Ord. New Pop. 180.

**Sandown,** see also Bembridge.

**Shanklin.** Shanklin Point, Horse Ledge and Yellow Ledge, cliffs and boulders on beach.

Cretaceous, Lower Greensand (Ferruginous Sands), with nests of brachiopods in cliff-face. Green, grey and reddish " Urchin Bed " has many sea-urchins, lamellibranchs and gastropods, and a few ammonites.

White, H. J. O. 1921, p. 36.

Geol. Surv. I.O.W. Special ; Ord. New Pop. 180.

**Shanklin.** Undercliff S. of Luccombe Chine, 1½ miles S. of Shanklin, cliffs and talus.

Cretaceous, Lower Gault (*dentatus* zone) with many ammonites (*Hoplites*, etc.)

Geol. Surv. I.O.W. Special ; Ord. New Pop. 180.

**Totland.** Cliffs of Alum Bay.

Cretaceous, Upper Chalk (*mucronata* zone), with starfish ossicles, bryozoa, etc. Eocene, Reading Beds (unfossiliferous) ; London Clay with mollusca in basement-bed, lamellibranchs (*Pinna*) in septaria near base and at 35 ft. up (*Panope, Pholadomya*). Bagshot Beds with leaf-bed in lower part. Barton Beds (near the pier) yield molluscs throughout and foraminifera (*Nummulites*) near the base.

Reid, C. and Strahan, A. 1889, p. 95, etc. Rowe, A. W. 1908, p. 232, with geol. map (Chalk only).

Geol. Surv. I.O.W. Special ; Ord. New Pop. 180.

**Totland.** Cliffs and foreshore in Colwell Bay, best examined at low tide.

Oligocene, Lower Headon Beds (Freshwater and brackish), Middle (estuarine and marine) and Upper Headon Beds (freshwater and brackish). The " *Venus*-Bed " of the Middle Headon Beds has many well-preserved molluscs, especially the lamellibranch *Cordiopsis incrassata*, and a deep channel filled with the oyster *Ostrea velata*.

Reid, C. and Strahan, A. 1889, pp. 131, 138. White, H. J. O. 1921, p. 116.

Geol. Surv. I.O.W. Special ; Ord. New Pop. 180.

**Totland.** Cliffs at Headon Hill, approached from Totland Bay or Alum Bay.

Oligocene, Headon Beds, with well-preserved freshwater gastropods (*Lymnaea* and *Planorbis*) at several horizons. The Middle Headon Beds abound in the gastropods *Batillaria concava* and *Cerithidea ventricosa*, elsewhere rare or absent, and include the " *Venus*-Bed " with its marine fauna, as above. Higher up, the Bembridge Limestone is rich in land and freshwater gastropods.

Reid, C. and Strahan, A. 1889, p. 129. White, H. J. O. 1921, p. 113.

Geol. Surv. I.O.W. Special ; Ord. New Pop. 180.

**Yarmouth.** Cliff-slopes at Sconce Point, 1 mile W. of Yarmouth.

Oligocene, Bembridge Limestone, fallen blocks. A classic locality for large terrestrial gastropods, including *Filholia* [*Bulimus*] *elliptica* and Helicidae. The actual section is obscured and few fossils can now be collected.

Forbes, E. 1856, p. 55.

Geol. Surv. I.O.W. Special ; Ord. New Pop. 180.

**Yarmouth.** Cliffs and foreshore at Bouldnor and Hamstead, 2 miles E. of Yarmouth.

Oligocene, Bembridge Limestone (low-tide reefs), with mammalian bones, many small brackish-water gastropods and the lamellibranch *Corbicula*. Bembridge Marl (foreshore), unfossiliferous. Hamstead Beds (cliffs) are usually hidden by a great mud-slide from the top of the cliff, but the *Corbula-* clays yield vast numbers of the gastropods *Pirenella monilifera* and *Potamides submargaritaceus*, with a few other species of which some that are important in correlation (indicating a Middle Oligocene age) need careful search.

Reid, C. and Strahan, A. 1889, pp. 179, 186. White, H. J. O. 1921, pp. 133, 140.

Geol. Surv. I.O.W. Special ; Ord. New Pop. 180.


# KENT

**Abbey Wood,** 1¾ miles E. of Woolwich. Rabbit-burrows in wood above site of Lessness Abbey, enlarged into a pit by collectors.

Eocene, Blackheath Beds, with many gastropods (especially *Melanopsis buccinoidea*) and lamellibranchs, with some mammal, reptile and fish fragments.

White, E. I. 1931, pp. 15, 110.

Geol. Surv. London District 4 ; Ord. New Pop. 171.

**Charlton.** Old sandpit in Charlton Football Ground and classic pit in Maryon Park, overgrown, but a typical section is preserved by the co-operation of the L.C.C.

Cretaceous, Upper Chalk (*coranguinum* zone), with sea-urchins (*Conulus, Echinocorys, Micraster*), etc. Eocene, Thanet Sands, with scarce lamellibranchs (*Pholadomya*) and Woolwich and Blackheath Beds, with many molluscs.

Whitaker, W. 1889, pp. 147-150, 211-213, 235-237.
Geol. Surv. London District 4 ; Ord. New Pop. 171.

**Cliffe,** 4½ miles N. of Strood. Francis' Cement Works pit (disused) ¾ mile W.S.W. of Cliffe Church on edge of marshes.

Cretaceous, Upper Chalk (*coranguinum* zone), with sea-urchins (*Micraster, Echinocorys*), crinoid and starfish ossicles, small brachiopods, sponges, etc.

Geol. Surv. O.S. 1 S.E. ; Ord. New Pop. 171.

**Cliffe.** Alpha Cement Works pit, 1 mile S.W. of church on S. side of road to Cliffe Fort. Permission from Cement Works Office.

Cretaceous, Upper Chalk (*coranguinum* zone) with sea-urchins (*Micraster, Conulus, Echinocorys*), crinoid and starfish ossicles, lamellibranchs (*Inoceramus, Ostrea*), etc.

Geol. Surv. O.S. 1 S.E. ; Ord. New Pop. 171.

**Crayford.** Section beside sloping path on W. side of recreation and football ground (formerly Rutter's New Pit), 1 mile W. of Slades Green station. No longer available.

Upper Pleistocene, 50-feet terrace of the Thames, a seam of fine shelly sand in the Crayford Brickearth. Freshwater lamellibranchs include *Corbicula fluminalis* and *Psilunio littoralis*, with teeth of small mammals such as the snow-vole, *Microtus nivalis*.

Kennard, A. S. 1944.
Geol. Surv. N.S. 271 ; Ord. New Pop. 171.

**Ditton,** 3¼ miles W. of Maidstone. Quarry ½ mile S. of Ditton Church on left of road to Ditton Research Station and ⅛ mile S.W. of Holt Hill.

Cretaceous, Lower Greensand (Hythe Beds, rag and hassock), with abundant lamellibranchs (*Exogyra sinuata* and small species) and belemnites, with some large Nautili.

Topley, W. 1875, pp. 117-119.
Geol. Surv. O.S. 6 ; Ord. New Pop. 172.

**Dryhill,** 1½ miles W. of Sevenoaks. Dryhill Quarry in ridge running W.S.W. from Bessels Green to Dryhill.

Cretaceous, Lower Greensand (Hythe Beds, rag and hassock), with many *Exogyra* and small lamellibranchs, also belemnites, ammonites and brachiopods.

Wright, C. W. and Thomas, H. D. 1947, p. 318.
Geol. Surv. N.S. 287 ; Ord. New Pop. 171.

**Dunton Green,** 2 miles N.W. of Sevenoaks. Brickworks just E. of railway line, S. of Dunton Green station.

Cretaceous, Lower and Upper Gault (*dentatus* to *varicosum* zones), with a nodule-bed at the junction. Abundant ammonites (over 65 species), lamellibranchs, crustacea, etc.

Wright, C. W. and Thomas, H. D. 1947, p. 315.
Geol. Surv. N.S. 287 ; Ord. New Pop. 171.

**Folkestone.** Cliff-top near Copt Point, just below site of Roman Villa.
Pleistocene deposits with many land shells, especially *Arianta arbustorum*.
Geol. Surv. O.S. 3 ; Ord. New Pop. 173.

**Folkestone.** Broadmead Pit (flooded), about 150 ft. O.D., below Caesar's Camp at junction of Castle Hill and Cherry Garden Lane.
Pleistocene deposits with many non-marine shells.
Geol. Surv. O.S. 3 ; Ord. New Pop. 173.

**Folkestone.** Killick's Corner, Dover Hill.
Pleistocene, re-deposited Chalk filling a hollow in solid Chalk in the road
bank and containing many land-shells, including *Trochulus hispidus*, *Arianta
arbustorum*, etc.
Geol. Surv. O.S. 3 ; Ord. New Pop. 173.

**Folkestone.** Disused chalkpit just above Killick's Corner, Dover Hill.
Cretaceous, Middle Chalk (*labiatus* zone), with brachiopods (*Rhynchonella
cuvieri*) and sea-urchins (*Conulus*). Chalk piped with Pliocene sands (Lenham
Beds).
Geol. Surv. O.S. 3 ; Ord. New Pop. 173.

**Folkestone.** Folkestone Brick and Tile Co.'s pit, Cherry Garden Lane.
Cretaceous, junction of Lower and Upper Gault, with many ammonites,
lamellibranchs, etc.
Geol. Surv. O.S. 3 ; Ord. New Pop. 173.

**Folkestone.** East Wear Bay and Warren foreshore, E. of town.
Cretaceous, from base of Gault to Middle Chalk. The type-section of the
Gault, with abundant fossils of all groups, especially ammonites in famous
pearly preservation. Ammonites and other fossils in Lower Chalk. Lamelli-
branchs and sea-urchins in fallen blocks of gritty Middle Chalk just beyond
" Horse's Head."
Price, F. G. H. 1870. Jukes-Browne, A. J. 1900, pp. 69-83 ; 1903, pp. 37-44,
371-379. Spath, L. F. 1923-1944.
Geol. Surv. O.S. 3 ; Ord. New Pop. 173.

**Folkestone.** Mill Point, at low tide.
Cretaceous, Lower Greensand (Hythe Beds, rag), with lamellibranchs
(*Exogyra*, *Trigonia*, etc.). A heavy hammer is needed to break up seaweed-
covered boulders.
Geol. Surv. O.S. 4 ; Ord. New Pop. 173.

**Folkestone.** Shore E. of harbour at low water, not now visible. Cretaceous,
Lower Greensand. This was the section that gave Price the material for his
faunal list from the Sandgate Beds.
Price, F. G. H. 1874, pp. 137-138.
Geol. Surv. O.S. 4 ; Ord. New Pop. 173.

**Herne Bay.** Cliff and foreshore E. from Herne Bay for 2 miles to Bishop-
stone (=Oldhaven) Gap and 1 mile further E. to Reculvers.
Eocene ; lowest London Clay at Herne Bay, with pyritized crinoid stems
and a few shells : Oldhaven Beds at Bishopstone, with many molluscs in
sandy pockets : and Thanet Sands at Reculvers, with many molluscs in the
*Corbula regulbiensis*-bed.
Gardner, J. S. 1883, p. 197.
Geol. Surv. O.S. 3 ; Ord. New Pop. 173.

**Higham Upshire**, 2 miles N.W. of Strood. Old pit 200 yds. E. of Stone-
horse Inn and about 1¼ miles E. of Higham Church.
Cretaceous, Upper Chalk (*coranguinum* zone), with sea-urchins (*Micraster,
Conulus, Echinocorys*) with adherent shells (*Spondylus, Thecidea, Crania*),
bryozoa, etc. Crinoid and starfish ossicles common.
Geol. Surv. N.S. 272 ; Ord. New Pop. 171 and 172.

**High Halstow,** 6 miles N.N.E. of Rochester. Rabbit-burrows on N. side
of cutting E. of High Halstow Halt.
Eocene, Oldhaven Beds, with a varied fauna of gastropods (*Natica* is common), lamellibranchs (*Glycymeris, Protocardia, Pitaria* and *Corbula*) and fish-
remains.
White, E. I. 1931, pp. 17, 111.
Geol. Surv. N.S. 272 ; Ord. New Pop. 171 and 172.

**Hythe.** Small quarry, Seabrook, between Sandgate and Hythe, on S. side of lane leading from Horn Street to cemetery, at S.E. corner of wood. Pit now completely overgrown.

Cretaceous, Lower Greensand (Hythe Beds), the source of many ammonites (*Deshayesites*), belemnites and other fossils in museums.

Geol. Surv. O.S. 4 ; Ord. New Pop. 173.

**Hythe.** Sandpit by Sandling Junction station, N. of Hythe.

Cretaceous, Lower Greensand (Folkestone Beds) with bryozoa, sea-urchins (*Holaster*), lamellibranchs and ammonites in calcareous bands ; *mammillatum* bed at base of Gault yields many phosphatic casts of ammonites (*Douvilleiceras, Protohoplites*, etc.).

Casey, R. 1939, p. 368.
Geol. Surv. O.S. 3 ; Ord. New Pop. 173.

**Ightham,** 4½ miles E.N.E. of Sevenoaks. Sandpit $\frac{11}{16}$ mile S.S.E. of Oldbury Farm and ⅞ mile S.S.W. of St. Peter's Church, Ightham.

Cretaceous, Lower Greensand (Folkestone Beds) with irregular seams of large lamellibranchs in fragile condition.

Geol. Surv. N.S. 287 ; Ord. New Pop. 171.

**Little Chart,** 4½ miles N.W. of Ashford. Quarry ⅓ mile S.W. of village on N. side of lane to Pluckley.

Cretaceous, Lower Greensand (Hythe Beds, rag and hassock), with brachiopods, lamellibranchs (large *Exogyra sinuata* common) and some ammonites.

Geol. Surv. O.S. 3 ; Ord. New Pop. 172.

**Lympne.** Shipway Cross Quarry, on N. side of road to Pedlinge Court.

Cretaceous, Lower Greensand (Hythe Beds) with well-preserved brachiopods. The source of many specimens labelled " Lympne " in museums.

Geol. Surv. O.S. 4 ; Ord. New Pop. 173.

**Maidstone.** Small rifle-range pit in Vinter's Park, on S. side of E.-W. path just across stream.

Cretaceous, Lower Greensand (Hythe Beds, rag and hassock), with abundant belemnites, *Exogyra* and other lamellibranchs.

Topley, W. 1875, pp. 117-119.
Geol. Surv. O.S. 6 ; Ord. New Pop. 172.

**Margate.** Cliff-section from W. end of Gore Bay, Birchington, E. to Kingsgate. Tide dangerous at a few places near Westgate.

Cretaceous, Upper Chalk (*Uintacrinus* and *Marsupites* zones), with abundant plates of the zonal crinoids ; the sea-urchins *Conulus, Echinocorys, Micraster* and *Zeuglopleurus* ; the small brachiopod *Terebratulina rowei*, and many other fossils.

Rowe, A. W. 1900, pp. 294-301.
Geol. Surv. N.S. 274 ; Ord. New Pop. 173.

**Minster in Sheppey.** Cliff and foreshore.

Eocene, London Clay (top), with many molluscs, corals, vertebrates and a rich flora of fruits and seeds. Fossils are only found washed out on the beach.

Davis, A. G. 1936, p. 328 ; 1937, p. 77. Reid, E. M. and Chandler, M. E. J. 1933.

Geol. Surv. N.S. 272 and 273 ; Ord. New Pop. 172.

**Newington,** Ramsgate. N.E. corner of brickpit ½ mile N. of village.

Eocene, Woolwich and Reading Beds, clayey sands crowded with fragile shells, including the lamellibranch *Mya*.

Geol. Surv. N.S. 274 ; Ord. New Pop. 173.

**Postling,** 5½ miles W.N.W. of Folkestone. Scattered exposures in N. bank of road from Horton Park, for the first few hundred yards towards Postling.
Cretaceous, Lower Chalk (*varians* zone) with many ammonites (*Schloen-bachia, Mantelliceras*), lamellibranchs, etc.
Geol. Surv. O.S. 3 ; Ord. New Pop. 173.

**Rainham,** 4 miles E.S.E. of Chatham. Vineyard Chalkpit (disused), on W. side of Moor Street Lane and 500-700 yds. N. of London-Dover road.
Cretaceous, Upper Chalk (*coranguinum* zone), with sea-urchins (*Echinocorys, Gauthieria, Micraster*), starfish and crinoid ossicles, small brachiopods, etc.
Geol. Surv. N.S. 272 ; Ord. New Pop. 172.

**Ramsgate.** Cliff-section from Kingsgate S. to Pegwell Bay. Tide dangerous at E. end of Kingsgate and, with quicksands, W. of Ramsgate.
Cretaceous, Upper Chalk (*coranguinum* zone) with abundant sea-urchins, lamellibranchs and other fossils.
Rowe, A. W. 1900, pp. 301-305.
Geol. Surv. N.S. 274 ; Ord. New Pop. 173.

**Ramsgate.** Cliffs in Pegwell Bay about Cliffsend, 3 miles W.S.W. of Ramsgate.
Eocene, Thanet Sands, with many gastropods and lamellibranchs.
Gardner, J. S. 1883, p. 204, fig. 5. Cooper, J. E. 1934.
Geol. Surv. N.S. 274 ; Ord. New Pop. 173.

**St. Margaret's,** on coast between Dover and Deal. Cliffs on S. side of bay.
Cretaceous, Upper Chalk (*cortestudinarium* zone), rough, greyish chalk with yellow nodule-bands. Fossils are very abundant, including sea-urchins (*Micraster, Echinocorys*) and brachiopods. Enormous shells of the lamellibranch *Inoceramus* can be seen but are rarely possible to collect.
Rowe, A. W. 1900, pp. 305-310.
Geol. Surv. N.S. 290 ; Ord. New Pop. 173.

**Sellindge.** Sandpit in Swan Lane, ½ mile from Ashford-Hythe road and ⅓ mile E. of " The Gables."
Cretaceous, Gault, with numerous ammonites of *mammillatum* and *dentatus* zones.
Geol. Surv. O.S. 3 ; Ord. New Pop. 173.

**Sittingbourne.** Associated Portland Cement Co.'s pit, on both sides of road to Rodmersham Green and 1000 yds. S. of " Chilton," Sittingbourne. Permission should be obtained in writing from the company.
Cretaceous, Upper Chalk (*coranguinum* zone) with many sea-urchins and other fossils.
Geol. Surv. N.S. 272 ; Ord. New Pop. 172.

**Stanford,** 6½ miles W.N.W. of Folkestone. Brickpit on E. side of road about 1 mile N. of New Inn Green crossroads.
Cretaceous, Lower Gault (*intermedius* to *niobe* subzones), with lamellibranchs (*Inoceramus concentricus*), crabs (*Notopocorystes*) and many ammonites (*Hoplites, Anahoplites, Euhoplites,* etc.).
Geol. Surv. O.S. 3 ; Ord. New Pop. 173.

**Swanscombe.** Associated Portland Cement Co.'s Swanscombe Pit, S. of Arterial Road, W. of Swanscombe Halt. Enter through cement-works N. of Arterial Road. Permission must first be obtained in writing from the company. This pit is typical of many in the Dartford-Gravesend area.
Cretaceous, Upper Chalk (*coranguinum* zone). In the days of hand-working these pits yielded many superb fossils to the quarrymen, who readily sold them to collectors. Nowadays, machine-working and the enormous size of the pits makes collecting slow and tedious.
Dewey, H. and others 1924, pp. 18-25, 34.
Geol. Surv. N.S. 271 ; Ord. New Pop. 171.

**Swanscombe.** Barnfield Gravel Pit, N.W. of Milton Street, ½ mile S.W. of Swanscombe Halt. Disused, but collecting is possible from an isolated stack in the pit.

Middle Pleistocene, 100ft. terrace of the Thames. Alternating gravels and loams capped by head. Occasional bones of interglacial mammals (*Dama clactoniana, Rhinoceros, Elephas*) with Clactonian flint implements in Lower Gravel and shelly lenses (*Psilunio, Sphaerium, Lymnaea*, etc.) near the top ; other shells, including land forms, in Lower Loam ; Acheulian hand-axes and very rare bones of man in Middle Gravel.

Dewey, H. and others 1924, p. 90. Hinton, M. A. C. and others 1938. Geol. Surv. N.S. 271 ; Ord. New Pop. 171.

**Tilmanstone,** 6½ miles N. of Dover. Old pit 1 mile E. of Tilmanstone Colliery and ¾ mile S. of Tilmanstone Church. A few yards W. of Dover-Sandwich road on N. side of by-road to colliery.

Cretaceous, Upper Chalk (*coranguinum* zone), with sea-urchins (*Conulus*), starfish and crinoid ossicles, etc.

Geol. Surv. N.S. 290 ; Ord. New Pop. 173.

**Tilmanstone.** Old pit on N. side of lane to Deal, 1000 yds. S.E. of Tilmanstone Church.

Cretaceous, Upper Chalk (*Marsupites* zone), with many plates of the zonal crinoid, the zonal form of the sea-urchin *Echinocorys scutatus* var. *elevatus* and other fossils.

Geol. Surv. N.S. 290 ; Ord. New Pop. 173.

**Upnor,** 2 miles N.E. of Rochester. Large sandpits N. of church.

Eocene, Woolwich Beds and Oldhaven Beds, with many molluscs and fish-remains.

Whitaker, W. 1872, pp. 144-145.
Geol. Surv. N.S. 272 ; Ord. New Pop. 172.

**Walmer.** Cliff-section from Walmer Castle S. to St. Margaret's Bay.

Cretaceous, Upper Chalk (*coranguinum* zone) with abundant sea-urchins and other fossils.

Rowe, A. W. 1900, pp. 301-305.
Geol. Surv. N.S. 290 ; Ord. New Pop. 173.

**Wrotham.** Large sandpit E. of Ford Place, by lane from Wrotham Heath to Trottiscliffe.

Cretaceous, *mammillatum* bed at base of Gault, with rolled lamellibranchs, gastropods, ammonites (*Beudanticeras*), etc. Derived Gault fossils in drift at top of pit.

Brown, E. E. S. 1941, with geol. map.
Geol. Surv. O.S. 6 ; Ord. New Pop. 171.


# LANCASHIRE

**Bispham,** 2 miles N. of Parbold. Left bank of stream known as Skellow (Skillaw) Clough, 1¾ miles N.W. of Parbold station.

Permian, Red Marls underlying Magnesian Limestone, with lamellibranchs (*Schizodus, Bakevellia*, etc.).

Jones, R. C. B. and others 1938, pp. 97-98.
Geol. Surv. N.S. 84 ; Ord. New Pop. 100.

**Chatburn,** 2½ miles N.E. of Clitheroe. Bold Venture Quarry, near Chatburn station and Pendle Hotel, N.W. of railway and road to Clitheroe.

Carboniferous Limestone ($C_1$ subzone), with a sparse fauna of corals, brachiopods and gastropods. An early form of the brachiopod *Productus humerosus* in S.W. corner.

Parkinson, D. 1926, pp. 195-198, with geol. map.
Geol. Surv. O.S. 92 S.W. ; Ord. New Pop. 95.

**Chatburn.** Peach Quarry, nearly $\frac{1}{2}$ mile S.S.W. of railway station and 100 yds. S.E. of Clitheroe road.

Carboniferous Limestone ($C_2$ subzone) with zaphrentid corals and abundant brachiopods (*Productus humerosus*).

Parkinson, D. 1926, p. 206, with geol. map.

Geol. Surv. O.S. 92 S.W. ; Ord. New Pop. 95.

**Clitheroe.** Coplow Quarry, 1 mile N.N.E. of Clitheroe Castle and 100 yds. E.S.E. of Black Horse Inn, Pimlico, on N.W. side of railway. Only higher beds now available.

Carboniferous Limestone ($C_1$ subzone), some 400 feet of reef-limestone with corals (*Amplexus*), brachiopods, gastropods and cephalopods. Shale-partings yield rare echinoids and many crinoids.

Wright, J. 1928-1942, *Geol. Mag.* vols. lxv-lxxix. Parkinson, D. 1926, pp. 198-203, with geol. map.

Geol. Surv. O.S. 92 S.W. ; Ord. New Pop. 95.

**Clitheroe.** Salt Hill and Bellman Park Quarries, entrance $\frac{3}{4}$ mile N.E. of Clitheroe Castle and 300 yds. E. of Chatburn road at N.E. corner of Clitheroe cricket-ground. The quarries extend for nearly a mile W.S.W.-E.N.E.

Carboniferous Limestone ($C_2$ subzone), with many brachiopods and molluscs and some corals. The crinoid-bed at the top yields blastoids and numerous crinoids described by Wright, J. as above.

Parkinson, D. 1926, pp. 206-210, with geol. map.

Geol. Surv. O.S. 92 S.W. ; Ord. New Pop. 95.

**Clitheroe.** Stream-section, Little Mearley Clough, Pendle, 1 mile S.S.E. of Worston and immediately S.E. of Little Mearley Hall in Little Mearley Wood.

Lower and Upper Carboniferous (B, P and E zones ; Pendleside Limestone in wood, Bowland Shales and Pendleside Grit above wood, Pendle Top Grit at top of hill). Goniatites (*Beyrichoceras, Goniatites, Cravenoceras*), mostly crushed in shales, uncrushed in rare bullions ; lamellibranchs (*Posidonia*).

Parkinson, D. 1926, pp. 212-222, with geol. map. Moore, E. W. J. 1936, pp. 167-192.

Geol. Surv. O.S. 92 S.W. ; Ord. New Pop. 95.

**Clitheroe,** see also Chatburn, Worston.

**Dalton-in-Furness.** Elliscales Quarry, $\frac{3}{4}$ mile N.W. of Dalton station.

Carboniferous Limestone ($C_2$ subzone) with corals (*Michelinia megastoma, Caninia, Carcinophyllum, Koninckophyllum* and *Zaphrentis*) and spire-bearing brachiopods.

Garwood, E. J. 1912, pp. 532-533, with geol. map.

Geol. Surv. O.S. 98 S.W. ; Ord. New Pop. 88.

**Grange.** Humphry Head, 3 miles S.W. of Grange.

Carboniferous Limestone (D zone). A band with the alga *Girvanella* is exposed for 2 miles and is succeeded by beds with the brachiopod *Davidsonina* [*Cyrtina*] *septosa* and beds with corals (*Lonsdaleia*).

Garwood, E. J. 1916, p. 19, with sketch-map.

Geol. Surv. O.S. 98 S.W. ; Ord. New Pop. 89.

**Higher Twiston,** 3 miles E. of Clitheroe-Gisburn road at Chatburn. Old quarry near Ravensholme Farm, $\frac{1}{2}$ mile S.W. of Twiston by fieldpath and 350 yds. N. of Downham-Barley road through gate 300 yds. N.W. of Pendle Hill End Bridge.

Carboniferous Limestone ($P_{1a}$ subzone), with *Emmonsia parasitica* and other corals in shelly bed at base of section and goniatites (*Goniatites crenistria* and *Beyrichoceratoides*) at top of section.

Parkinson, D. 1926, pp. 216-219, with geol. map.

Geol. Surv. O.S. 92 S.W. ; Ord. New Pop. 95.

**Langho** (bus from Blackburn or Whalley to York Lane). Stream-section, Dinckley Ferry, on farm-land belonging to Mr. Shorrock. Digging into the exposure is forbidden.

Lower and Upper Carboniferous (P and $E_1$ zones), with crushed goniatites in shales, and (rarely) in bullions.

Moore, E. W. J. 1936, pp. 167-192.

Geol. Surv. O.S. 92 S.W. ; Ord. New Pop. 95.

**Liverpool.** St. James' Cemetery, about 100 yds. E. of Cathedral and below Hope Street. Permission must first be obtained.

Triassic, Keuper (Waterstones, near junction with Basement Beds), yellow shales with crustacea (*Euestheria minuta*) and impressions of plants (*Equisetites*).

Wedd, C. B. and others 1923, p. 90.

Geol. Surv. N.S. 96 ; Ord. New Pop. 100.

**Nob End.** Farnworth Cemetery Brickworks, $\frac{1}{2}$ mile W. by S. of Nob End, S.E. of Bolton.

Carboniferous, Coal Measures (*similis-pulchra* zone, with Worsley Four Foot Coal). A rich marine fauna (Dukinfield Marine Band) about 150 ft. below the coal ; ostracods just below and non-marine shells (*Anthraconaia*) in roof of coal.

Tonks, L. H. and others 1931, pp. 108-109, 148-150.

Geol. Surv. N.S. 85 ; Ord. New Pop. 101.

**Parbold.** Delph Tea Gardens, in disused quarry $\frac{1}{2}$ mile N.E. of Parbold station.

Carboniferous, Millstone Grit. At base of N. side of old quarry a replica of a stem of *Calamites* (some 6 ft. long by 10 in. diameter) is shown on enquiry.

Geol. Surv. N.S. 84 ; Ord. New Pop. 100.

**Red Rock,** 3 miles N. of Wigan. Left bank of stream flowing through golf-links N. of Red Rock, about 20 yds. above waterfall.

Carboniferous, Coal Measures (*communis* zone) with non-marine shells (*Carbonicola pseudorobusta*) in cannel-coal.

Geol. Surv. N.S. 84 ; Ord. New Pop. 100.

**Rough Lee,** $1\frac{1}{2}$ miles E. of Settle-Napon road at Barrowford. Stream-section, Pendle Water, E. of Rough Lee.

Carboniferous, Millstone Grit (H and $R_1$ zones), with goniatites in bullions.

Bisat, W. S. and Hudson, R. G. S. 1943, p. 383.

Geol. Surv. O.S. 92 S.W. ; Ord. New Pop. 95.

**Samlesbury,** 3 miles E. of Preston. Section in R. Darwen downstream from bridge $1\frac{1}{2}$ miles S. of Samlesbury Hall.

Carboniferous, Millstone Grit ($E_2$, H and $R_1$ zones), with abundant goniatites crushed in shales and, though difficult to extract, in bullions.

Hull, E. and others 1875, p. 38. Bisat, W. S. and Hudson, R. G. S. 1943, p. 397.

Geol. Surv. N.S. 75 ; Ord. New Pop. 94.

**Stainton,** $1\frac{1}{4}$ miles S.E. of Dalton-in-Furness. Devonshire Quarry, $1\frac{1}{4}$ miles E.S.E. of Stainton station.

Carboniferous Limestone ($D_1$ subzone) with a varied coral fauna and brachiopods including *Davidsonina* [*Cyrtina*] *septosa* and *Gigantoproductus* spp.

Geol. Surv. O.S. 98 S.W. ; Ord. New Pop. 88.

**Stainton.** Crown Quarry, 1 mile S.E. of Dalton station.

Carboniferous Limestone ($S_2$—$D_1$ subzones) with corals (*Lithostrotion*) and productid brachiopods.

Geol. Surv. O.S. 98 S.W. ; Ord. New Pop. 88.

**Torver,** 2 miles S. of Coniston.  Ash Gill Beck, 140 yds. S.W. of Ash Gill Quarry, Torver.
Ordovician, Ashgill Series (type-locality) with trilobites, including *Phacops mucronatus, Calymene planimarginata* and *Phillipsinella parabola.*
Marr, J. E. 1916, p. 189.
Geol. Surv. O.S. 98 N.W. ;  Ord. New Pop. 88.

**Upholland,** 4 miles W. of Wigan.  Ravenhead Brickworks (Upholland Brick and Tile Co.), 1400 yds. N. 14° E. of Upholland station.
Carboniferous, Coal Measures (*lenisulcata* zone) with goniatites (*Gastrioceras*) in bullions and crushed, with various lamellibranchs, in shale. (Tonge's Marine Band, *c.* 120 ft. below Roger Mine coal).
Jones, R. C. B. and others 1938, p. 133. Chalmers, R. M. 1936, pp. 149-151.
Geol. Surv. N.S. 84 ;  Ord. New Pop. 100.

**Whiston,** 1 mile S.E. of Prescot.  Brickpit about ½ mile E. of Huyton Quarry station.
Carboniferous, Coal Measures, shales with a variety of plant- and fish-remains.
Geol. Surv. O.S. 80 N.W. ;  Ord. New Pop. 100.

**Whitewell,** 6 miles N.W. of Clitheroe.  Outcrops 1 mile W. of Whitewell and ¼ mile N.N.W. of Tunstall Ing Farm, N. slope of Long Knotts and S.W. end of Whitemore Knot.
Carboniferous Limestone (C₂ subzone, knoll-reef limestone), with many brachiopods, and gastropods and occasional crinoids and blastoids.
Parkinson, D. 1935, pp. 97-120, with geol. map.
Geol. Surv. O.S. 91 S.E. ;  Ord. New Pop. 94 and 95.

**Wiswell,** 1 mile E. of Whalley.  Section in stream flowing down from Pendle range, just E. of Wiswell.
Carboniferous, Millstone Grit (P₂ and E₁ subzones) with goniatites (type-locality for *Cravenoceras leion*) in shales and a bullion-band near the base.
Bisat, W. S. 1930.  Moore, E. W. J. 1936, fig 1.
Geol. Surv. O.S. 92 S.W. ;  Ord. New Pop. 95.

**Worston,** ¾ mile S. of Clitheroe-Gisburn road at Chatburn.  Stream-section, Burst Clough, 1 mile S.E. of Worston and 100 yds. S. of Angram Green Farm.
Lower Carboniferous (B zone).  Goniatites (*Beyrichoceras hodderense,* etc.) at second waterfall above farm.  Corals (*Lithostrotion arachnoideum*) and other fossils in higher parts of section.
Parkinson, D. 1926, pp. 212-215, with geol. map.  Moore, E. W. J. 1936.
Geol. Surv. O.S. 92 S.W. ;  Ord. New Pop. 95.


# LEICESTERSHIRE

**Barrow-on-Soar,** 3 miles S.E. of Loughborough.  Limestone quarry ¼ mile N. of the village, now flooded.
Jurassic, Lower Lias (pre-*planorbis* beds to *angulatum* zone).  The source of many fine fossil reptiles, fish and insects.
Fox-Strangways, C. 1903, p. 22.
Geol. Surv. N.S. 142 ;  Ord. New Pop. 121.

**Branston,** 8 miles N.E. of Melton Mowbray.  Ironstone quarries ½ mile S. of village.
Jurassic, Upper Lias (*exaratum* and *tenuicostatum* zones), with flattened ammonites, resting on Middle Lias Ironstone (*spinatum* zone) with " nests " of brachiopods.
Geol. Surv. N.S. 142 ;  Ord. New Pop. 122.

**Breedon-on-the-Hill,** 6 miles N.E. of Ashby-de-la-Zouch. Breedon Quarries.

Carboniferous Limestone ($C_2$ subzone), with *Productus humerosus* and other brachiopods in dolomitic limestone.

Mitchell, G. H. and Stubblefield, C. J. 1941a, p. 214.

Geol. Surv. N.S. 141 ; Ord. New Pop. 121.

**Old Dalby,** 6 miles N.W. of Melton Mowbray. Dump of clay over N. end of Grimston tunnel, S. of Old Dalby station, approached from farm on main road over tunnel. Partly overgrown, but still a good collecting-ground.

Jurassic, Lower Lias (*oxynotum* to *ibex* zones), with abundant ammonites and a variety of other fossils. Probably the best Midland locality for the upper zones of the Lower Lias.

Trueman, A. E. 1918, p. 101.

Geol. Surv. N.S. 142 ; Ord. New Pop. 122.

**Scalford,** 4 miles N. of Melton Mowbray. Lion Brickworks, adjoining Six Hills—Eastwell road 1 mile N.N.W. of Scalford.

Jurassic, Middle Lias (*margaritatus* zone) with many fossils (including the ammonite *Amaltheus*) in soft ironstone. The only fossiliferous exposure of this zone in Leicestershire and S. Lincolnshire.

Lamplugh, G. W. and others 1909, pp. 43–45.

Geol. Surv. N.S. 142 ; Ord. New Pop. 122.

**Sproxton,** 7 miles N.E. of Melton Mowbray. Clay Cross Ironstone quarries, immediately E. of village.

Jurassic, Inferior Oolite (Lincolnshire Limestone, Lower Estuarine Series and Northampton Ironstone, in descending order), with lamellibranchs in the limestone.

Richardson, L. 1939b, p. 464.

Geol. Surv. O.S. 70 ; Ord. New Pop. 122.

**Waltham-on-the-Wolds,** 5 miles N.E. of Melton Mowbray. White Lodge Ironstone quarries, 400 yds. N.E. of White Lodge, $2\frac{1}{2}$ miles N.W. of Waltham.

Jurassic, Upper Lias (*tenuicostatum* zone), resting on Middle Lias Ironstone (*spinatum* zone). Ammonites (*Dactylioceras*) in the Upper Lias ; brachiopods locally abundant in " nests " in the ironstone.

Trueman, A. E. 1918, p. 108.

Geol. Surv. N.S. 142 ; Ord. New Pop. 122.

**Waltham-on-the-Wolds.** Roadstone quarry, Bescaby Lane, $\frac{1}{4}$ mile S.E. of the village.

Jurassic, Inferior Oolite (Lincolnshire Limestone, lower beds) with lamellibranchs, etc.

Geol. Surv. N.S. 142 ; Ord. New Pop. 122.

**Worthington,** $4\frac{1}{2}$ miles N.E. of Ashby-de-la-Zouch. Breedon Cloud Quarries, $\frac{1}{2}$ mile N.E. of Worthington.

Carboniferous Limestone ($C_2$ to $B_2$ subzones), with *Productus humerosus* and other brachiopods in dolomitic limestone, and many corals, brachiopods and other fossils in higher beds.

Mitchell, G. H. and Stubblefield, C. J. 1941a, p. 202, with geol. map.

Geol. Surv. N.S. 141 ; Ord. New Pop. 121.

## LINCOLNSHIRE

**Ancaster.** Thompson's and Gregory's Quarries, 1–$1\frac{1}{2}$ miles S.S.E. of the village.

Jurassic, Inferior Oolite (Lincolnshire Limestone), with lamellibranchs at the top ; capped by Great Oolite (Upper Estuarine Beds) with lamellibranchs and brachiopods.

F

Richardson, L. 1939b, p. 472.
Geol. Surv. O.S. 70 ; Ord. New Pop. 113.

**Ancaster.** Castle Lime Co.'s Quarry ¼ mile E. of church.
Jurassic, Inferior Oolite (Lincolnshire Limestone) with abundant small brachiopods and a bed of corals.
Richardson, L. 1939b, p. 473.
Geol. Surv. O.S. 70 ; Ord. New Pop. 113.

**Appleby,** near Scunthorpe. Bank sides of Sir Rowland Winn's Drain, for 400 yds. N. from railway, just over 1 mile E. of Appleby station.
Jurassic, Cornbrash, with lamellibranchs.
Geol. Surv. O.S. 86 ; Ord. New Pop. 104.

**Blankney,** 8 miles N. of Sleaford. Green Man Wood Quarry (disused), 3¼ miles W. 8° S. of Blankney Church and 7½ miles from Lincoln on Sleaford road.
Jurassic, Inferior Oolite (Lincolnshire Limestone), with abundant small brachiopods (*Acanthothyris crossi* and terebratulids).
Richardson, L. 1940, p. 252.
Geol. Surv. O.S. 83 ; Ord. New Pop. 113.

**Bracebridge,** 2½ miles S. of Lincoln. Bracebridge Brick Co.'s pit, immediately S. of village.
Jurassic, top of Lower Lias, Middle Lias and base of Upper Lias (in all, *davoei* to *tenuicsotatum* zones), with well-preserved ammonites.
Trueman, A. E. 1918, p. 103.
Geol. Surv. O.S. 83 ; Ord. New Pop. 113.

**Broughton,** 2½ miles N.W. of Brigg. Ditch leading from spring a few yards S. of Westwood Lodge, 1250 yds. N.N.W. of Broughton Church ; and other ditches on N. side of village and around Castlethorpe.
Holocene, tufa (beneath blown sand) with abundant non-marine mollusca characteristic of a marsh with ponds liable to desiccation, e.g. *Carychium minimum, Lymnaea truncatula, Pisidium obtusale,* etc.
Musham, J. F. 1933 ; Kennard, A. S. and Musham, J. F. 1937.
Geol. Surv. O.S. 86 ; Ord. New Pop. 104.

**Castle Bytham,** 7 miles W. of Bourne. Castle Lime Co's pit, near Castle Bytham station.
Jurassic, Inferior Oolite (Lincolnshire Limestone), with abundant fossils, including the *crossi*-bed (the small brachiopod *Acanthothyris crossi*) in floor of pit.
Richardson, L. 1939a, p. 42.
Geol. Surv. O.S. 64 ; Ord. New Pop. 123.

**Colsterworth,** 7½ miles S. of Grantham. Great North Road Quarry (disused), on E. side of road ¾ mile N. of village.
Jurassic, Inferior Oolite (Lincolnshire Limestone), with many lamellibranchs including *Osteomya dilata,* and corals.
Geol. Surv. O.S. 70 ; Ord. New Pop. 122.

**Denton,** 4 miles S.W. of Grantham. Quarry 1 mile S. of village and ⅜ mile N.W. of Hungerton Hall.
Jurassic, Inferior Oolite (Lincolnshire Limestone, base), with lamellibranchs (*Gervillella, Trigonia,* etc.) and gastropods (*Nerinea*).
Richardson, L. 1939b, p. 472.
Geol. Surv. O.S. 70 ; Ord. New Pop. 122.

**Fulletby,** 3 miles N.E. of Horncastle. Abandoned brickyard 1 mile W. of village.
Jurassic, Kimmeridge Clay (*wheatleyensis* zone), with ammonites, lamellibranchs, brachiopods, fish teeth, etc., in upper part of sloped face.
Geol. Surv. O.S. 84 ; Ord. New Pop. 114.

**Grantham.** Rudd's Brickyard, ¼ mile W. of station ; Gonerby brickpits, 1 mile N.W. of town. Both overgrown and inaccessible.

Jurassic, Middle Lias clays and ironstone, and Upper Lias clays. Ammonites (*Amaltheus, Dactylioceras*, etc.), lamellibranchs, brachiopods and other fossils formerly abundant.

Trueman, A. E. 1918, p. 107.

Geol. Surv. O.S. 70 ; Ord. New Pop. 122.

**Great Ponton,** 3½ miles S. of Grantham. Castle Lime Co.'s Station Quarry, adjoining station.

Jurassic, Inferior Oolite (Lincolnshire Limestone), with abundant gastropods and lamellibranchs and occasional small brachiopods.

Richardson, L. 1939b, p. 471.

Geol. Surv. O.S. 70 ; Ord. New Pop. 122.

**Greetwell,** 2½ miles E. of Lincoln. Greetwell Hollow Quarry (disused), 1¾ miles E. by N. of Lincoln Cathedral and ¾ mile W.N.W. of Greetwell.

Jurassic, Inferior Oolite (Lincolnshire Limestone), with rare ammonites near base and abundant lamellibranchs and small brachiopods (including *Acanthothyris crossi*) in top beds.

Richardson, L. 1940, p. 253.

Geol. Surv. O.S. 83 ; Ord. New Pop. 113.

**Kirton-in-Lindsey,** 6¼ miles S.W. of Brigg. Kirton Cementworks Quarry, on W. side of road about ½ mile N. of village.

Jurassic, Inferior Oolite (Lincolnshire Limestone), with corals, brachiopods and lamellibranchs in concretions (" crog-balls ") and irregular black shales.

Richardson, L. 1940, p. 255.

Geol. Surv. O.S. 86 ; Ord. New Pop. 104.

**Leadenham,** 10 miles S.E. of Newark (Notts). Barnstone Quarry, worked intermittently, ⅓ mile E.S.E. of Leadenham station.

Jurassic, Inferior Oolite (lower Lincolnshire Limestone at top of quarry), with lamellibranchs.

Geol. Surv. O.S. 70 ; Ord. New Pop. 113.

**Lincoln,** see Bracebridge, Greetwell.

**Little Bytham,** S.S.E. of Grantham. Adamantine Clinker and Fireclay Co.'s pit (permission required), on W. side of railway ⅔ mile N. of Little Bytham Church.

Jurassic, Great Oolite Series (Upper Estuarine Beds), with lycopod-spores, pollen, leaf-fragments obtainable by macerating a coaly bed ; and base of White Limestone, with brachiopods and lamellibranchs.

Murray, N. 1939, p. 478 ; Richardson, L. 1939a, p. 44.

Geol. Surv. O.S. 64 ; Ord. New Pop. 123.

**Market Rasen.** Several claypits around the village, all completely overgrown.

Jurassic, base of Kimmeridge Clay. Type-locality of the ammonite genus *Rasenia*, formerly abundant in fine, iridescent preservation.

Geol. Surv. O.S. 83 ; Ord. New Pop. 105.

**Nettleton,** 1 mile S.W. of Caistor. Acre House Mine, 1 mile N. by E. of Claxby Church, now abandoned ; and Nettleton Top Mine, on Normanby road 1½ miles S. of Nettleton.

Lower Cretaceous, Spilsby Sandstone, Claxby Beds, Tealby Clay and sometimes higher beds, in weathered tips from old adits. Claxby beds, especially fossiliferous, exposed in scarp bluffs S. of adits. Ammonites are fairly common, belemnites, lamellibranchs and brachiopods are abundant. At Acre House, a source of many museum specimens, higher beds up to the Red Chalk used to be seen.

Lamplugh, G. W. 1896, p. 179.

Geol. Surv. O.S. 86 ; Ord. New Pop. 104.

**Scunthorpe.** Weathered blocks from overgrown excavation beside Frodingham railway-cutting. Permission from station-master.

Jurassic, Lower Lias (clays and limestones of *angulatum* and *bucklandi* zones), with many ammonites, lamellibranchs, brachiopods, corals, etc.
Cross, J. E. 1875, pp. 115-130. Dudley, H. E. 1942, pp. 152-155.
Geol. Surv. O.S. 88 ; Ord. New Pop. 104.

**Scunthorpe.** Many miles of rock-faces in ironstone quarries. Permission should be obtained from the various offices.

Jurassic, Lower Lias (Frodingham Ironstone, *semicostatum* zone), with ammonites (*Arnioceras, Asteroceras,* etc.), lamellibranchs (a notable locality for *Cardinia*), brachiopods (*Spiriferina*), etc.
Cross, J. E. 1875.
Geol. Surv. O.S. 86 ; Ord. New Pop. 104.

**Scunthorpe.** Santon Hill quarry, disused and partly flooded, 1000 yds. W. of Appleby station (" Winterton *via* Appleby " 'bus from Scunthorpe).

Jurassic, Inferior Oolite (Lincolnshire Limestone), with lamellibranchs (*Lucina, Trigonia*) and the small brachiopod *Acanthothyris crossi.*
Cross, J. E. 1875.
Geol. Surv. O.S. 86 ; Ord. New Pop. 104.

**Scunthorpe.** Brickyard on S. side of railway through Oak Tree Plantation, nearly 2 miles N. of E. of St. John's Church, Scunthorpe (Scunthorpe-Santon 'bus). Permission from Richard Thomas & Baldwin's Ltd., Redbourn Works, Scunthorpe.

Jurassic, Lower Lias (clays and *Pecten* bed, *jamesoni* and *ibex* zones), with ammonites, gastropods, lamellibranchs, brachiopods, crinoids, etc., in the clays and lamellibranchs (especially *Pseudopecten*) and belemnites in the *Pecten* bed.
Cross, J. E. 1875.
Geol. Surv. O.S. 86 ; Ord. New Pop. 104.

**Scunthorpe.** Ironstone Quarries at foot of Lincoln Cliff, on Crosby Warren. Permission from Frodingham Ironstone Mines Ltd., Scunthorpe.

Jurassic, Lower Lias (*oxynotum* zone). Nodules yield many well-preserved fossils, including small ammonites (*Oxynoticeras*).
Geol. Surv. O.S. 86 ; Ord. New Pop. 104.

**Scunthorpe,** see also Appleby.

**Sedgebrook,** 4 miles W.N.W. of Grantham. Old brickyard 400 yds. N. of station, now overgrown.

Jurassic, Lower Lias (*semicostatum* zone), with formerly a varied fauna, including ammonites (*Arnioceras*), gastropods, lamellibranchs and foraminifera.
Trueman, A. E. 1918, p. 7.
Geol. Surv. O.S. 70 ; Ord. New Pop. 113.

**Sleaford.** Quarry at Quarrington, beside Peterborough road, 1 mile S. of town.

Jurassic, Upper Cornbrash, with well-preserved brachiopods, especially the rare *Tegulithyris bentleyi.*
Douglas, J. A. and Arkell, W. J. 1932, p. 135.
Geol. Surv. O.S. 80 ; Ord. New Pop. 113.

**South Ferriby.** S. Ferriby Chalkpit, the second pit along shore of R. Humber, N.E. of village.

Cretaceous, Lower Chalk (*subglobosus* zone), with sea-urchins and brachiopods (*Ornatothyris*), and belemnites abundant in *plenus* Marls at top ; capped by rather unfossiliferous Middle Chalk.
Rowe, A. W. 1904, p. 202, pl. 20.
Geol. Surv. O.S. 86 ; Ord. New Pop. 98.

**South Ferriby.** Foreshore N.E. of village, liable to be obscured by mud.
Cretaceous, Red Chalk (= Gault) with brachiopods and rare ammonites, resting on unfossiliferous Carstone and succeded by Lower Chalk (*varians* zone), with sea-urchins, ammonites, etc.
Geol. Surv. O.S. 86 ; Ord. New Pop. 98.

**South Witham,** 11 miles N.W. of Stamford. Stanton Ironworks Co.'s limestone quarry, on W. side of village.
Jurassic, Inferior Oolite (Lincolnshire Limestone), with brachiopods and gastropods (*Nerinea*), and a bed above with the small brachiopod *Acanthothyris crossi*.
Geol. Surv. O.S. 64 ; Ord. New Pop. 123.

**Stickney,** 9 miles N. of Boston. Brick and tile works ¼ mile W. of village.
Jurassic, Kimmeridge Clay, with many well-preserved ammonites (*Aulacostephanus*). The only permanent section of this formation in the county.
Geol. Surv. O.S. 69 ; Ord. New Pop. 114.

**Sudbrooke.** Shallow quarry in Sudbrooke Park, 4 miles N.E. of Lincoln.
Jurassic, Cornbrash and Kellaways Beds, with abundant well-preserved brachiopods.
Douglas, J. A. and Arkell, W. J. 1932, p. 136.
Geol. Surv. O.S. 83 ; Ord. New Pop. 104.


## LONDON AND MIDDLESEX

**Hampstead.** Well and railway-cutting S. of the Heath, neither now accessible.
Eocene, London Clay (base to middle), with many mollusca.
Wetherell, N. T. 1837.
Geol. Surv. London District 1 ; Ord. New Pop. 160.

**Harefield.** Associated Portland Cement Works Quarry, 300-600 yds. W.N.W. of Harefield Church.
Cretaceous, Upper Chalk (*coranguinum* zone), with few fossils. The top surface is bored by an Eocene worm (*Terebella harefieldensis*), and above are the Eocene, Reading Beds (unfossiliferous) and London Clay (fossiliferous nodules at base).
Wooldridge, S. W. and Wrigley, A. 1929, p. 373. Wrigley, A. 1929. White, E. I. 1923.
Geol. Surv. London District 1 ; Ord. New Pop. 160.

**Highgate.** Deep cutting at Archway Road where it is crossed by a viaduct. No section now visible.
Eocene, upper London Clay. The fossils of this locality stimulated the appearance of Sowerby's " Mineral Conchology " and led to the formation of the London Clay Club, which gave birth to the Palaeontographical Society.
Sowerby, J. and J. de C. 1812-1846. Edwards, F. E. and Wood, S. V. 1849-1877.
Geol. Surv. London District 1 ; Ord. New Pop. 160.

**Hyde Park,** An obsolete excavation, *c.* 1825, probably for deepening the Serpentine.
Eocene, London Clay, mollusca including *Pecten duplicatus*.
Sowerby, J. and J. de C. 1812-1846, pl. 575, figs. 1-3.
Geol. Surv. London District 1-3 ; Ord. New Pop. 170.

**North London.** Cuttings and tunnels on the main railway lines N. from London, constructed *c.* 1830 at Chalk Farm, Haverstock Hill, Highgate Wood, Finchley, Whetstone and Potters Bar. None now visible.
Eocene, London Clay, the sources of much of the material figured by Edwards, F. E. 1849-1861.
Geol. Surv. London District 1-2 ; Ord. New Pop. 170.

## MONMOUTHSHIRE

**Bishopston,** S.E. of Newport. Lane-section ¾ mile N.E. by E. of village, 5 miles E. of Newport.
Triassic, Rhaetic (*contorta* Shales, etc.), with abundant and well-preserved lamellibranchs.
Richardson, L. 1905, p. 377.
Geol. Surv. O.S. 35 ; Ord. New Pop. 155.

## NORFOLK

**Bramerton,** 5 miles S.E. of Norwich. Sandpits below 50 ft. contour on S. bank of R. Yare, 300 yds. W. of S. of Surlingham and 300 yds. N. by E. of Bramerton.
Pliocene, Norwich Crag, with *Astarte borealis, Tellina baltica* and other mollusca.
Harmer, F. W. 1902, p. 443. Boswell, P. G. H. 1923, pp. 212, 232.
Geol. Surv. O.S. 66 N.E. ; Ord. New Pop. 126.

**Caistor St. Edmunds,** 2 miles S. of Norwich. Chalkpit on E. side of road, ½ mile N. of village.
Cretaceous, Upper Chalk (*mucronata* zone), with brachiopods, sea-urchins, belemnites, etc.
Geol. Surv. O.S. 66 S.E. ; Ord. New Pop. 126.

**Eaton,** Norwich. Eaton Limeworks, 2½ miles S.W. of Norwich on Wymondham road. Now overgrown.
Cretaceous, Upper Chalk (*mucronata* zone), with typical bryozoa, brachiopods, belemnites, etc. Sole English locality for the sea-urchin *Galeola.*
Brydone, R. M. 1938.
Geol. Surv. O.S. 66 N.E. ; Ord. New Pop. 126.

**Morston,** 6 miles E. of Wells. West-facing cliff 200 yds. N.E. of white bridge carrying Cromer-Wells road over R. Stiffkey.
Pleistocene, Hunstanton brown boulder-clay ; Holocene, raised beach with Mesolithic flint-implements in top foot.
Solomon, J. D. 1932, p. 257.
Geol. Surv. O.S. 68 N.W. ; Ord. New Pop. 125.

**New Catton,** N. side of Norwich. Attoe's Pit.
Cretaceous, Upper Chalk (middle *mucronata* zone), with abundant bryozoa, brachiopods. starfish ossicles, belemnites, etc., and sponges in a prominent hard band 10 ft. from the top.
Brydone, R. M. 1938.
Geol. Surv. O.S. 66 N.E. ; Ord. New Pop. 126.

**New Catton.** Campling's Pit, Catton Grove.
Cretaceous, Upper Chalk (middle *mucronata* zone) with ammonoids, brachiopods, sea-urchins, etc.
Brydone, R. M. 1938.
Geol. Surv. O.S. 66 N.E. ; Ord. New Pop. 126.

**Norwich.** Two pits at Harford Bridges Limeworks.
Cretaceous, Upper Chalk (middle *mucronata* zone), with ammonoids, lamellibranchs, brachiopods, sea-urchins, etc.
Brydone, R. M. 1938.
Geol. Surv. O.S. 66 N.E. ; Ord. New Pop. 126.

**Norwich,** see also Caistor St. Edmunds, Eaton, New Catton, Thorpe-next-Norwich, Trowse Newton.

**Old Hunstanton.** Hunstanton Cliff and beach-exposures, $\frac{7}{8}$-1$\frac{1}{4}$ miles N.E. of New Hunstanton pier.

Cretaceous, " Lower Greensand " (Carstone) with ammonites in low-tide reefs ; Red Chalk ( = Gault), with brachiopods, belemnites and rare ammonites ; Lower Chalk (*varians* zone), with sea-urchins, lamellibranchs, etc.

Geol. Surv. O.S. 69 ; Ord. New Pop. 124.

**Sheringham.** Beach-exposures W. of the town, depending on state of weather and sea.

Cretaceous, Upper Chalk (middle *mucronata* zone), highly fossiliferous, as in Norwich and district pits.

Brydone, R. M. 1938.

Geol. Surv. O.S. 68 N.W. ; Ord. New Pop. 124.

**Sheringham.** Beach-exposures E. of the town, extending to E. Runton.

Cretaceous, Upper Chalk, middle *mucronata* zone (Beeston Chalk of Brydone, 1938), highly fossiliferous as in Norwich and district pits.

Brydone, R. M. 1938.

Geol. Surv. O.S. 68 E. ; Ord. New Pop. 124.

**Swaffham.** Railway-cutting, Swaffham Heath, 2$\frac{1}{2}$ miles W. of the town, in fork of King's Lynn and Downham Market roads. Permission from railway authorities.

Cretaceous, Upper Chalk (*planus* and ? higher zones), no longer well exposed. The probable source of most of the fossils labelled " Swaffham " in museums.

Jukes-Browne, A. J. 1904, p. 253.

Geol. Surv. O.S. 65 ; Ord. New Pop. 125.

**Thorpe-next-Norwich.** Pit in grounds of Mental Hospital, immediately N. of railway crossing on Yarmouth road, 1 mile E.N.E. of Thorpe Church. Section preserved by local authority, but Chalk overgrown. Permission from Secretary, Thorpe Mental Hospital.

Cretaceous, Upper Chalk (upper *mucronata* zone), with sea-urchins (including *Micraster*), belemnites, etc. ; formerly *Mastodon* and many other mammals in overlying Pliocene, Red Crag.

Woodward, H. B. 1881, p. 74. Boswell, P. G. H. 1923, p. 210.

Geol. Surv. O.S. 66 N.E. ; Ord. New Pop. 126.

**Trimingham,** 5 miles S.E. of Cromer. Little Marl Point (" South Bluff ") between Trimingham and Mundesley, and variable beach-exposures to E. and S.E.

Cretaceous, Upper Chalk (*lunata* and upper *mucronata* zones), the highest Chalk in Britain. Abundant sponges, bryozoa, brachiopods, echinoderms, lamellibranchs, belemnites, etc.

Brydone, R. M. 1906, 1908, 1938.

Geol. Surv. O.S. 68 E. ; Ord. New Pop. 126.

**Trowse, Newton,** 1 mile S.E. of Norwich. Disused chalkpit at Crown Point, Whitlingham, 200 yds. W. of church ruins, S.E. of Whitlingham station. Game preserve, permission required from Crown Point Estate Office, Norwich.

Cretaceous, Upper Chalk (*mucronata* zone), with bryozoa, starfish-ossicles, etc. ; capped by Pliocene, Red Crag with rostro-carinate flint-implements and mammalian bones—a *Mastodon* tooth from here is shewn in the frontispiece of Smith, W. 1816.

Geol. Surv. O.S. 66 N.E. ; Ord. New Pop. 126.

**West Runton,** 1$\frac{1}{2}$ miles E. of Sheringham. Cliff E. of W. Runton gap (Woman Hythe).

Pliocene, Cromer Forest Bed with mammals, freshwater mollusca and many plant seeds and fruits ; capped by *Yoldia myalis*-bed with fragile marine shells.

Newton, E. T. 1882, pp. 12, 15. Reid, C. and E. M. 1908.

Geol. Surv. O.S. 68 E. ; Ord. New Pop. 124.

## NORTHAMPTONSHIRE

**Brixworth,** 6½ miles N. of Northampton. Holcot Lane pit, on Holcot road near Brixworth Grange, 1 mile E.S.E. of Brixworth.

Jurassic, Inferior Oolite (Northampton Ironstone), with many lamellibranchs (*Lima, Pecten, Tancredia, Trigonia,* etc.) in top part, the majority of the shells replaced by vivianite.

Geol. Surv. O.S. 52 N.W. ; Ord. New Pop. 133.

**Byfield,** 9½ miles N.E. of Banbury (Oxon). Disused quarries just N. and S. of railway (the former used as a siding), both about 1000 yds. W. of Byfield station.

Jurassic, Upper Lias " Transition Bed," with many ammonites, on Middle Lias (Marlstone) with " nests " of brachiopods.

Thompson, B. 1888, p. 15.

Geol. Surv. O.S. 53 S.E.-S.W. ; Ord. New Pop. 145.

**Collyweston,** 4 miles S.W. of Stamford (Lincs.). Numerous old quarries E. of village and towards Easton.

Jurassic, Inferior Oolite (Lincolnshire Limestone and " Collyweston Slate " at base), with lamellibranchs (*Pinna, Gervillella,* etc.) and gastropods (the " water-spider " *Phyllocheilus bentleyi*).

Richardson, L. 1939a, p. 40.

Geol. Surv. O.S. 64 ; Ord. New Pop. 122.

**Cranford St. John,** 4½ miles S.E. of Kettering. Old ironstone pit ½ mile S.E. of Cranford Church and ½ mile W.N.W. of Woodford House. Permission from Staveley Coal and Iron Co., Cranford.

Jurassic, Great Oolite, with sea-urchins, brachiopods and lamellibranchs in White Limestone and brachiopods in Upper Estuarine Limestone beneath.

Hollingworth, S. E. and Taylor, J. H. 1947, p. 240.

Geol. Surv. O.S. 52 N.W. ; Ord. New Pop. 133.

**Desborough,** 5 miles S.E. of Market Harborough (Leics.). Old ironstone pit ½ mile S.S.E. of West Lodge and ¼ mile S.E. of Desborough Lodge.

Jurassic, Inferior Oolite (Northampton Ironstone), with brachiopods and lamellibranchs.

Geol. Surv. O.S. 64 ; Ord. New Pop. 133.

**Easton Neston,** 1 mile N.E. of Towcester. Old ironstone pit ½ mile S.E. of Tiffield Church and ¼ mile S.W. of Reformatory.

Jurassic, Great Oolite Series (Upper Estuarine Limestone), with sea-urchins, brachiopods and lamellibranchs.

Geol. Surv. O.S. 53 S.E. ; Ord. New Pop. 146.

**Geddington,** 3½ miles N.E. of Kettering. Geddington Grange Quarry, $\frac{3}{16}$ mile S.W. of the Grange and 1½ miles W. by S. of Geddington Church.

Jurassic, Inferior Oolite (Lincolnshire Limestone) with the nerineid gastropod *Ptygmatis cotteswoldiae* abundant.

Richardson, L. 1938, p. 72.

Geol. Surv. O.S. 64 ; Ord. New Pop. 133.

**Great Weldon,** 8 miles N.N.E. of Kettering. Old gullet leading to Cowthick Pit, 1 mile W.S.W. of Great Weldon. Permission from Messrs. Stewarts and Lloyds, Corby.

Jurassic, Inferior Oolite (Upper Lincolnshire Limestone), shelly oolite with brachiopods, lamellibranchs and gastropods.

Hollingworth, S. E. and Taylor, J. H. 1947, p. 243.

Geol. Surv. O.S. 64 ; Ord. New Pop. 133.

**Great Weldon.** Weldon Stone Quarries. Permission from quarry offices.
Jurassic, Inferior Oolite (Upper Lincolnshire Limestone), with abundant
gastropods, and small oysters and brachiopods in soft beds at top.
Judd, J. W. 1875, p. 151.
Geol. Surv. O.S. 64 ; Ord. New Pop. 133.

**Gretton,** 10 miles N. of Kettering. Old ironstone pit 1½ miles S. by E. of
Gretton Church and ¾ mile W.N.W. of Weldon Lodge. Permission from
Messrs. Stewarts and Lloyds, Corby.
Jurassic, Inferior Oolite (Northampton Ironstone), with many lamellibranchs.
Geol. Surv. O.S. 64 ; Ord. New Pop. 133

**Kettering.** Botany Limekiln (disused), near Glebe Farm, on E. side of
Uppingham road about 1½ miles N. of Kettering.
Jurassic, Inferior Oolite (lower Lincolnshire Limestone), with lamellibranchs
(*Ceratomya, Pinna*) and gastropods (*Ptygmatis*).
Judd, J. W. 1875, p. 145. .
Geol. Surv. O.S. 52 N.W. ; Ord. New Pop. 133.

**King's Sutton,** 3½ miles S.E. of Banbury (Oxon). Disused quarry in
Cobblers Pits Spinney, 1400 yds. N.N.E. of church and 1500 yds. E. of Twyford
Mill.
Jurassic, Upper Lias, with many ammonites in Cephalopod Bed and
ammonites and brachiopods in Transition Bed (*exaratum* and *tenuicostatum*
zones). Belemnites in top bed of Middle Lias (Marlstone).
Geol. Surv. O.S. 45 N.W. ; Ord. New Pop. 145.

**Thrapston.** Old quarry adjoining railway station.
Jurassic, Cornbrash, with many brachiopods and other fossils, especially
in Upper Cornbrash. Some Great Oolite below and Kellaways Clay above.
Douglas, J. A. and Arkell, W. J. 1932, p. 130.
Geol. Surv. O.S. 52 N.W. ; Ord. New Pop. 134.

**Wansford,** 8 miles W. of Peterborough. Quarry at E. end of Wansford
tunnel, 1¼ miles S.S.E. of church.
Jurassic, Inferior Oolite (Upper Lincolnshire Limestone), with brachiopods,
lamellibranchs and gastropods.
Sharp, S. 1873, p. 275.
Geol. Surv. O.S. 64 ; Ord. New Pop. 134.

# NORTHUMBERLAND

**Bamburgh,** 5 miles E. of Belford. Budle Bay, N.W. of Bamburgh. Shore-
section ¼ mile W. of Budle and ½ mile to N.E. near Heatherhouse.
Carboniferous, Middle Limestone Group, Budle Limestone and overlying
shales, with brachiopods (*Buxtonia scabricula*, etc.), lamellibranchs (*Posidonia
becheri*) and other fossils. The principal locality for fossil plants in this area.
Smith, S. 1910, pp. 611-612. Carruthers, R. G. and others 1927, p. 103.
Geol. Surv. N.S. 4 ; Ord. New Pop. 71.

**Beadnell,** 5 miles E. of Alnwick-Berwick road at 8¼ miles from Alnwick.
Shore-section from opposite Linkhouse for 1¼ miles S. to Beadnell Point.
Carboniferous, Middle and Upper Limestone Groups. Algal nodules
(*Girvanella*) in Oxford Limestone ; orthotetid brachiopods with lamellibranchs
(*Posidonia*) in shales over Budle Limestone ; corals (*Lonsdaleia*) near base of
Dryburn Limestone.
Smith, S. 1910, pp. 611-623. Carruthers, R. G. and others 1927, pp. 76-82.
Geol. Surv. N.S. 4 ; Ord. New Pop. 71.

**Berwick-on-Tweed.** Shore from Berwick Pier for 1½ miles N. to Sharpers Head.

Carboniferous, Middle Limestone Group. Algal nodules (*Girvanella*) in Oxford Limestone ; large brachiopods (*Productus*) in Eelwell Limestone ; foraminifera (*Saccaminopsis*) in Acre Limestone.

Smith, S. 1910, pp. 611-620. Fowler, A. 1926, pp. 23-26.

Geol. Surv. N.S. 2 ; Ord. New Pop. 64.

**Corbridge,** 3 miles E. of Hexham. Disused quarry 3 miles E. by N. of Corbridge, ¼ mile N.N.W. of Newton Church and 1100 yds. N. of Newton village.

Carboniferous, Upper Limestone Group, Fell Top or Harlow Hill Limestone, with corals (*Aulina, Dibunophyllum, Lithostrotion*), brachiopods, lamellibranchs, gastropods, etc.

Smith, S. 1910, pp. 629-632. Smith, S. and Yu, C. C. 1943, p. 44.

Geol. Surv. O.S. 105 S.W. ; Ord. New Pop. 77.

**Corbridge.** Section in N. bank of R. Tyne, 2¾ miles E.S.E. of Corbridge bridge, 1200 yds. E. of Styford Hall and 550 yds. W. of Hall Moor Farm.

Carboniferous, Upper Limestone Group, Thornborough Limestone, with corals (*Dibunophyllum*), brachiopods, lamellibranchs, etc., abundant, especially in a bed of shale within the limestone.

Smith, S. 1910, pp. 626-628.

Geol. Surv. O.S. 105 S.W. ; Ord. New Pop. 77.

**Fourstones,** 4 miles N.W. of Hexham. Quarry ⅝ mile N. of Fourstones station.

Carboniferous, Upper Limestone Group, Great Limestone and shales above, with a rich fauna of corals (*Dibunophyllum*), brachiopods (*Productus*), etc.

Smith, S. 1910, pp. 621-623.

Geol. Surv. O.S. 106 N.E. ; Ord. New Pop. 77.

**Hartburn,** 8 miles W. of Morpeth. Section in Hart Burn, 8¾ miles W. of Morpeth and ¼ mile N.W. of Hartburn Grange.

Carboniferous, Upper Limestone Group, Todburn Limestone and associated shales with many brachiopods, chiefly productids and spiriferids.

Fowler, A. 1936, p. 41.

Geol. Surv. N.S. 9 ; Ord. New Pop. 78.

**Hartley,** 6 miles N. of Tynemouth. Cliff-section between Crag Point, N. of Hartley and cliff-steps.

Carboniferous, Coal Measures (*similis-pulchra* zone), non-marine shells (*Anthracosphaerium radiatum, Anthracosia atra,* etc.) in measures associated with Five-Quarters and Bensham seams.

Absalom, R. G. and Hopkins, W. 1926, p. 142.

Geol. Surv. O.S. 105 N.E. ; Ord. New Pop. 78.

**Hepple,** 4½ miles W. of Rothbury. Stream-section ¼ mile S. of Hepple Whitefield House and 1¼ miles S. of village.

Carboniferous, limestone near top of Cementstone Series, with a rich band of the alga *Ortonella furcata.*

Garwood, E. J. 1931, pp. 135-136.

Geol. Surv. O.S. 108 S.E. ; Ord. New Pop. 71.

**Howick,** 5 miles N.E. of Alnwick. Coast-section from Cullernose Point, ¼ mile N.N.E. of Howick, for ½ mile to S.

Carboniferous, Middle Limestone Group. Sandbanks Limestone and shales at Cullernose, with brachiopods and mollusca ; zaphrentid corals in shales above Acre Limestone at S. end of section.

Smith, S. 1910, pp. 614-620. Carruthers, R. G. and others 1930, pp. 49-50.

Geol. Surv. N.S. 6 ; Ord. New Pop. 71.

**Howick.** Shore-section from opposite Sea Houses Farm S. to 300 yds. S. of Howick Burn.

Carboniferous, Upper Limestone Group. Lickar Limestone in cliff-foot N.W. of Sea Houses Farm with many small brachiopods, gastropods, etc. ; Iron Scars and Sugar Sands Limestones S.E. of burn mouth.

Carruthers, R. G. and others 1930, pp. 56-57.

Geol. Surv. N.S. 6 ; Ord. New Pop. 71.

**Lewie Halt,** 2½ miles S.E. of Kielder. Lewie Burn, 450-700 yds. S. by E. of The Forks, 1¾ miles S.S.W. of Lewie Halt.

Carboniferous, Scremerston Coal Group, with brachiopods (*Productus, Punctospirifer,* etc.), bryozoa, mollusca and ostracods.

Geol. Surv. O.S. 108 S.W. ; Ord. New Pop. 76.

**Long Houghton,** 5½ miles E.N.E. of Alnwick. Quarry 1¾ miles N.N.W. of Long Houghton Church and ⅛ mile S.W. of Little Mill station.

Carboniferous, Middle Limestone Group, Acre Limestone, with foraminifera (*Saccaminopsis*), zaphrentid corals, brachiopods, etc.

Smith S. 1910, pp. 615-617. Carruthers, R. G. and others 1930, p. 54.

Geol. Surv. N.S. 6 ; Ord. New Pop. 71.

**Netherwitton,** 6¼ miles N.N.W. of Morpeth. Greenleighton Quarry, 4¼ miles W.N.W. of Netherwitton and 1¼ miles N.W. of Longwitton station.

Carboniferous, Upper Limestone Group, Great Limestone, with abundant corals and brachiopods, especially in shales above limestone.

Smith, S. 1910, pp. 621-624. Fowler, A. 1936, p. 37.

Geol. Surv. N.S. 9 ; Ord. New Pop. 78.

**Rochester,** 5 miles N.W. of Otterburn. Coomsden Burn, 1 mile S.S.W. of White Lee Farm, 8¼ miles N.W. of Rochester, on S.W. side of Jedburgh road.

Carboniferous, limestone near top of Cementstone Group, with algae (*Ortonella, Garwoodia [Mitcheldeania]*), cephalopods (*Orthoceras*), fish-fragments, etc.

Garwood, E. J. 1931, pp. 135-136.

Geol. Surv. O.S. 108 S.E. ; Ord. Pop. 86 (Scotland).

**Rothbury.** Section in Forest Burn, 3⅝ miles S. by W. of Rothbury bridge, ½ mile above Morrelhirst Farm.

Carboniferous, Middle Limestone Group, Oxford Limestone, with algae (*Girvanella*), brachiopods and dibunophyllid corals.

Fowler, A. 1936, p. 27.

Geol. Surv. N.S. 9 ; Ord. New Pop. 71.

**Rothbury.** Glebe Quarry, ⅞ mile S.W. of Rothbury bridge.

Carboniferous, limestone near top of Cementstone Series, with algae (*Ortonella furcata*), worm-tubes (*Spirorbis*), etc.

Garwood, E. J. 1931, pp. 135-136. Fowler, A. 1936, p. 9.

Geol. Surv. N.S. 9 ; Ord. New Pop. 71.

**Rothbury.** Section in Forest Burn near East Row, 2¾ miles S.E. of Rothbury bridge.

Carboniferous, Middle Limestone Group ; Eelwell Limestone ¼ mile E. of East Row ; " Red Bed " calcareous sandstone ¼ mile further E. Crinoids, bryozoa, brachiopods, lamellibranchs, etc., occur.

Fowler, A. 1936, pp. 27-29.

Geol. Surv. N.S. 9 ; Ord. New Pop. 71.

**Scremerston,** 2¼ miles S.S.E. of Berwick-on-Tweed. Coast-section from Hud's Head S.S.E. for 2¼ miles to Far Skerr and quarries immediately behind shore.

Carboniferous, Lower and Middle Limestone Groups, Dun to Sandbanks

Limestone. A fine section for the succession of limestone-faunas, chiefly corals and brachiopods. Note algae (*Girvanella*) in Oxford Limestone and lamellibranchs (*Posidonia*) in succeeding beds.

Smith, S. 1910, pp. 609-620. Fowler, A. 1926, pp. 18-27.

Geol. Surv. N.S. 2 ; Ord. New Pop. 64.

**Stamfordham,** 3 miles N. of Newcastle-Carlisle road at Harlow Hill, 10½ miles W. of Newcastle. Disused quarry 1800 yds. E. of Ouston and 300 yds. N.E. of Stobhill Farm, which is 1½ miles S.E. of Stamfordham.

Carboniferous, Upper Limestone Group, Harlow Hill or Fell Top Limestone, with corals (*Dibunophyllum, Lithostrotion*, etc.), productid brachiopods, and other fossils.

Smith, S. 1910, pp. 629-631.

Geol. Surv. O.S. 105 N.W. ; Ord. New Pop. 77 and 78.

**Wark,** 9 miles N.W. of Hexham. Disused quarry 300 yds. N.W. of Birtley village and 1¼ miles N.E. of Wark bridge.

Carboniferous, Lower Limestone Group, Fourlaws Limestone, with the coral *Lithostrotion* and brachiopods.

Geol. Surv. O.S. 106 N.E. ; Ord. New Pop. 77.

**Whitley Bay.** Coast-section at intervals on foreshore opposite Rex Hotel.

Carboniferous, Coal Measures (*modiolaris* zone, shales and thick sandstone above Low Main seam), with non-marine shells, especially *Anthracosia spp.*, abundant in shale.

Hopkins, W. 1930, p. 101.

Geol. Surv. O.S. 105 N.E. ; Ord. New Pop. 78.

**Woodburn,** 4 miles N.E. of Bellingham. Disused quarry ¼ mile N.N.W. of Waterfalls Farm and 3½ miles S.S.E. of Woodburn on E. side of Dere Street.

Carboniferous, Lower Limestone Group, Fourlaws Limestone, with some corals, abundant productid and other brachiopods, mollusca, etc.

Smith, S. 1910, pp. 606-608.

Geol. Surv. O.S. 106 N.E. ; Ord. New Pop. 77.

**Woodburn.** Disused quarry at Redesdale Ironstone Works, 2½ miles S. of West Woodburn bridge and 1200 yds. W. of Fourlaws Farm.

Carboniferous, base of Lower Limestone Group, Redesdale Ironstone and shale, with abundant brachiopods (*Productus undatus*, etc.), lamellibranchs (*Nucula, Schizodus*) and other fossils.

Smith, S. 1910, pp. 603-605.

Geol. Surv. O.S. 106 N.E. ; Ord. New Pop. 77.


# NOTTINGHAMSHIRE

**Barnstone,** 4 miles S.E. of Bingham. Quarries of Barnstone Cement Co., about ⅓ mile S. of the village, W. of the works.

Jurassic, Lower Lias (pre-*planorbis* beds to *angulatum* zone), with ammonites common in upper stone-bands and occasional reptiles and fish.

Kent, P. E. 1937, p. 164.

Geol. Surv. N.S. 142 ; Ord. New Pop. 122.

**Bunny,** 7½ miles S. of Nottingham. Cutting on Loughborough road, ¾ miles S. of village, at Bunny Hill.

Triassic, Rhaetic black shales with abundant lamellibranchs and rare *Euestheria*, with red and green Keuper Marls below and Jurassic, Lower Lias, above.

Geol. Surv. N.S. 142 ; Ord. New Pop. 121.

**Creswell.** Church Hole Cave, 3 miles S.W. of Worksop.
Upper Pleistocene deposits with bones of mammoth, woolly rhinoceros, reindeer, bison, horse, hyaena, etc.
Dawkins, W. B. 1880, pp. 175-187.
Geol. Surv. N.S. 100 ; Ord. New Pop. 112.

**Cropwell Bishop,** 7 miles S.E. of Nottingham. Blue Hill Claypit, ½ mile S.E. of village, W. of canal and N. of bridge on Cotgrave-Colston Basset road.
Triassic, upper Rhaetic, with rare *Euestheria* in soft limestone-nodules ; Jurassic, Lower Lias (pre-*planorbis* beds), with the characteristic lamellibranch *Pleuromya tatei*
Kent, P. E. 1937, p. 166.
Geol. Surv. N.S. 142 ; Ord. New Pop. 122.

# OXFORDSHIRE

**Ardley,** 14½ miles N.N.E. of Oxford. Quarry beside Great Western railway for ⅔ mile N.W. from Ardley Station.
Jurassic, Great Oolite Series (White Limestone), with many gastropods, lamellibranchs, brachiopods and sea-urchins, and occasionally the reptile *Teleosaurus*.
Arkell, W. J. and others 1933, p. 347, pl. 35. Arkell, W. J. 1947a, pp. 61-62.
Geol. Surv. O.S. 45 N.E. ; Ord. New Pop. 145.

**Asthall,** 2½ miles E.S.E. of Burford. Eton College Quarry, on N. side of Cheltenham road just under 1 mile E. of Asthall.
Jurassic, Great Oolite Series (White Limestone and Kemble Beds), with abundant lamellibranchs and gastropods and rare ammonites.
Arkell, W. J. 1931, p. 607 ; 1947a, pp. 48-49. Richardson, L. 1946, pp. 48-49.
Geol. Surv. N.S. 236 ; Ord. New Pop. 145.

**Beckley,** 5 miles N.E. of Oxford. Large quarry ½ mile S.E. of church.
Jurassic, Corallian Beds (Coral Rag unconformable on Beckley Sands), with usual reef-fauna in Coral Rag and ammonites of *plicatilis* zone in the sands.
Arkell, W. J. 1936, p. 171 ; 1943, p. 189, with geol. map ; 1947a, pp. 95-97.
Geol. Surv. Oxford Special ; Ord. New Pop. 145.

**Bladon,** 1 mile S. of Woodstock. Quarries at back of Old White House Inn, N.W. of church ; on S.E. side of road in middle of village ; and in spinney on S.E. side of road at N.E. end of village.
Jurassic, Great Oolite Series, Forest Marble (with Bradford Fossil Bed) and Lower Cornbrash. Corals, brachiopods and gastropods are abundant. Reptile bones ( ? *Ceteosaurus*) occur.
Arkell, W. J. 1931, p. 582 ; 1933b, p. 177 ; 1947a, p. 55. Richardson, L. 1946, pp. 63-65.
Geol. Surv. N.S. 236 ; Ord. New Pop. 145.

**Bletchingdon,** 7 miles N. of Oxford. Quarries between Greenhill Farm and railway-cutting S.W. of village. (Phillips' *Ceteosaurus* quarry, now overgrown, is on N. side of Lince Lane, immediately E. of station.
Jurassic, Great Oolite, with reptile-bones (*Ceteosaurus*) in green clay at top ; Forest Marble ; and Cornbrash, with interesting brachiopods and mollusca in upper part.
Arkell, W. J. 1931, p. 581 ; 1947a, pp. 58-59. Douglas, J. A. and Arkell, W. J. 1935, pp. 318-321. Richardson, L. 1946, pp. 67-68.
Geol. Surv. N.S. 236 ; Ord. New Pop. 145.

**Broughton Poggs,** 4 miles N. of Lechlade. Extensive, shallow, disused quarries ½ mile W. of Broughton on N. side of road to Southrop.
Jurassic, Lower Cornbrash, with abundant brachiopods and lamellibranchs.
Richardson, L. 1933, p. 79. Arkell, W. J. 1947a, p. 47.
Geol. Surv. N.S. 235 ; Ord. New Pop. 157.

**Carterton,** 4 miles S.S.E. of Burford. Old quarry ⅞ mile S.W. of Carterton crossroads on S. side of road to Kencott, now being filled.
Jurassic, Forest Marble (Bradford Clay) with many brachiopods and some lamellibranchs, on unfossiliferous Great Oolite.
Richardson, L. 1933, p. 50 ; 1946, p. 42. Arkell, W. J. 1947a, p. 50.
Geol. Surv. N.S. 236 ; Ord. New Pop. 157.

**Chipping Norton.** Padley's Quarry (disused) in the part of Chipping Norton known as " The Quarry " (formerly " Tite's End ").
Jurassic, Great Oolite Series (Chipping Norton Limestone, Sharp's Hill Beds with *Ceteosaurus* bones, and White Limestone). A classic section.
Richardson, L. 1911b, p. 225.
Geol. Surv. O.S. 45 N.W. ; Ord. New Pop. 145.

**Culham,** 2 miles S.E. of Abingdon (Berks). Abandoned brickpit on left bank of R. Thames just E. of Culham bridge.
Cretaceous, Lower Gault, with abundant hoplitid ammonites, on Kimmeridge Clay.
Pringle, J. and others 1926, p. 101. Arkell, W. J. 1947a, pp. 169-170.
Geol. Surv. Oxford Special ; Ord. New Pop. 158.

**Fawler,** 4½ miles N.E. of Witney. Old ironstone quarry on E. side of road in the hamlet.
Jurassic, Inferior Oolite (*Clypeus* grit), with many sea-urchins and other fossils ; condensed Upper Lias on Middle Lias ironstone. The fossil-bed at the base of the Upper Lias is hidden under scree.
Richardson, L. 1910a, p. 31 ; 1946, pp. 16, 17, 20. Arkell, W. J. 1933a, p. 244 ; 1947a, pp. 29-30.
Geol. Surv. N.S. 236 ; Ord. New Pop. 145.

**Headington,** Oxford. In the vast area of the old Headington Quarries, the best existing exposures are : Magdalen or Workhouse Quarry, S.W. of hospital on London road ; Vicarage Quarry, opposite the vicarage ; and Crossroads Quarry, near Wingfield Hospital.
Jurassic, Corallian Beds. Abundant corals, sea-urchins, etc. in Coral Rag ; shell bed beneath with many lamellibranchs and ammonites. Lower Calcareous Grit at base.
Arkell, W. J. 1927, pp. 84, 126 ; 1936, p. 164 ; 1947a, p. 94.
Geol. Surv. Oxford Special ; Ord. New. Pop. 158.

**Hook Norton,** 5 miles N.E. of Chipping Norton. Redlands Ironstone Quarry, with variable working-face, 600 yds. N.E. to 800 yds. N. of Hook Norton station. Permission from Brymbo Steel Co., Hook Norton.
Jurassic, Upper Lias, with many ammonites in basal limestone ; Middle Lias (Marlstone rock-bed) with lamellibranchs and " nests " of brachiopods.
Arkell, W. J. 1947a, p. 21.
Geol. Surv. O.S. 45 N.W. ; Ord. New Pop. 145.

**Hook Norton.** Sharp's Hill Quarry, in S.E. angle of crossroads, ½ mile S.S.E. of Traitor's Ford and 2 miles N.W. of Hook Norton station.
Jurassic, Great Oolite Series. Sharp's Hill Beds, with many small gastropods and lamellibranchs, rest on Chipping Norton Limestone with lamellibranchs (*Trigonia signata* bed).
Arkell, W. J. 1933a, p. 300 ; 1947a, p. 63.
Geol. Surv. O.S. 45 N.W. ; Ord. New Pop. 145.

**Islip,** 6 miles N.N.E. of Oxford. Islip Quarry, ¼ mile W.S.W. of church, approached by road to mill.
Jurassic, Forest Marble (Bradford Clay) with abundant corals, sea-urchin spines, bryozoa, brachiopods, etc. ; and Lower Cornbrash.
Arkell, W. J. 1931, p. 576 ; 1944a, p. 63, with geol. map 1947a, p. 60.
Richardson, L. 1946, pp. 71, 79.
Geol. Surv. N.S. 236 ; Ord. New Pop. 145.

**Kirtlington,** 8 miles N. of Oxford. Old cementworks pit, N. of lane, on valley side ½ mile N.W. of church.

Jurassic, Great Oolite Series (White Limestone), with epithyrid brachiopods, nerineid gastropods, corals, etc. ; and *Ceteosaurus* bones in green clay ; capped by Forest Marble and Lower Cornbrash.

Arkell, W. J. 1931, p. 570 ; 1947a, p. 57.
Geol. Surv. O.S. 45 S.W. ; Ord. New Pop. 145.

**Littlemore,** 2½ miles S.E. of Oxford. Quarry adjoining railway-cutting ¼ mile N.W. of Littlemore station.

Jurassic, Corallian Beds. Masses of oysters (*Exogyra nana*) and worm-tubes in clay facies of Coral Rag, overlying shell-bed and Lower Calcareous Grit.

Arkell, W. J. 1927, p. 139 ; 1947a, p. 92.
Geol. Surv. Oxford Special ; Ord. New Pop. 158.

**Long Hanborough,** 3 miles S.W. of Woodstock. Quarry N. of Swan Inn, on S. edge of Evenlode valley.

Jurassic, Forest Marble, capped by highly fossiliferous Cornbrash, and Kellaways Clay.

Douglas, J. A. and Arkell, W. J. 1928, p. 129. Richardson, L. 1946, pp. 57, 76.
Geol. Surv. N.S. 236 ; Ord. New Pop. 145.

**Milton-under-Wychwood,** 3 miles N. of Burford. Milton quarries (disused), 1 mile S. of village.

Jurassic, Great Oolite Series. Taynton Stone overlain by fossiliferous Hampen Marly Beds and White Limestone.

Richardson, L. 1910c, p. 537. Arkell, W. J. 1947a, p. 48.
Geol. Surv. N.S. 236 ; Ord. New Pop. 144.

**Oxford,** northern suburbs. Overgrown brickpits E. of L.M.S. railway N. of Upper Wolvercote tunnel ; and W. of Woodstock Road opposite Morris Radiator Works, Summertown. The principal pits among many formerly worked in and around Oxford.

Jurassic, Oxford Clay, with many ammonites, oysters (*Gryphaea*), brachiopods (*Aulacothyris*) and other fossils formerly obtained. Pleistocene shells and Acheulian flint hand-axes in Wolvercote pit.

Pringle, J. and others 1926, pp. 36, 126. Arkell, W. J. 1947a, pp. 70, 221.
Richardson, L. 1946, pp. 82, 123.
Geol. Surv. N.S. 236 ; Ord. New Pop. 158.

**Oxford.** Shotover brick-pit and sand-pit, on N. side of old coach-road at W. foot of Shotover Hill.

Jurassic, Kimmeridge Clay with fossiliferous nodules ; Glauconitic Beds of Portland Stone very fossiliferous.

Pringle, J. and others 1926, pp. 70, 78. Arkell, W. J. 1947a, p. 107.
Geol. Surv. Oxford Special ; Ord. New Pop. 158.

**Oxford,** see also Headington, Littlemore.

**Reading** (Berks). Caversham Brickworks (disused), at Emmer Green, 2 miles N. of Reading Bridge (R. Thames).

Cretaceous, Upper Chalk (*coranguinum* zone), with sea-urchins, etc. Eocene, Reading Beds, with oysters and fish-teeth ; and London Clay, with abundant mollusca in basement-bed. Section now much obscured.

Hawkins, H. L. 1946, p. 164.
Geol. Surv. N.S. 268 ; Ord. New Pop. 159.

**Sarsden,** 2 miles S.S.W. of Chipping Norton. Castle Barn Quarry, ¾ mile E.S.E. of Sarsden House.

Jurassic, Great Oolite Series, Sharp's Hill Beds, with gastropods, etc., resting on Chipping Norton Limestone.

Arkell, W. J. 1933a, p. 298 ; 1947a, p. 65.
Geol. Surv. O.S. 45 S.W. ; Ord. New Pop. 145.

**Shipton-on-Cherwell,** 2½ miles E. of Woodstock.    Shipton Cement-works pit, on W. side of G.W.R. line, ½ mile N. of Shipton Church.
Jurassic, Great Oolite Series (White Limestone), with many corals, brachio-pods, gastropods, etc., capped by Forest Marble, Cornbrash and Kellaways Clay.
Arkell, W. J. 1931, p. 579 ; 1947a, p. 58.  Richardson, L. 1946, pp. 66, 78.
Geol. Surv. N.S. 236 ;  Ord. New Pop. 145.

**Sibford Ferris,** 6 miles S.W. of Banbury.  Temple Mills Quarry, 1 mile S.W. of the village.
Jurassic, Great Oolite Series and Forest Marble, with corals, and sea-urchins common, and brachiopods and gastropods in bands.
Whitehead, T. H. and Arkell, W. J. 1946, p. 17.  Arkell, W. J. 1947a, p. 64.
Geol. Surv. O.S. 45 N.W. ;  Ord. New Pop. 145.

**Stonesfield,** 3 miles W. of Woodstock.  Waste tip-heaps of old " slate " mines, surrounding village on all sides but the N.
Jurassic, Great Oolite Series (Stonesfield Slate, type-locality).  The famous mammal and reptile remains were obtained from the quarrymen.  Many characteristic lamellibranchs (*Trigonia impressa*, etc). and other fossils may still be found, but the mines are no longer in operation.
Arkell, W. J. 1933a, pp. 294-297 ; 1947a, p. 39 and fig. 27, facing p. 150.
Geol. Surv. N.S. 236 ;  Ord. New Pop. 145.

**Stonesfield.**  Ashford Mill and Whitehill Wood railway-cuttings, 1 mile S.S.E. and 1 mile S. of Stonesfield Church.
Jurassic, Great Oolite Series.  Sharp's Hill Beds, with a bed of the gastropod *Nerinea*, near the bridge ;  Hampen Marly Beds, with abundant brachiopods and oysters ;  and Taynton Stone.
Arkell, W. J. 1931, p. 612 ; 1947a, pp. 51-54.
Geol. Surv. N.S. 236 ;  Ord. New Pop. 145.

**Wheatley,** 5 miles E. of Oxford.  Littleworth brickpit, S. of G.W.R. ½ mile W.S.W. of Wheatley Church.
Jurassic, Kimmeridge Clay and Portland Beds, with many ammonites ; overlain by Cretaceous, Wealden Beds (unfossiliferous).
Arkell, W. J. 1943, p. 194, with geol. map ; 1947a, p. 108.
Geol. Surv. Oxford Special ;  Ord. New Pop. 158.

**Witney.**  Quarry on N.E. side of road to Crawley, ½ mile N.W. of main crossroads in N. end of Witney.
Jurassic, Great Oolite (White Limestone), with corals and brachiopods ; and Forest Marble (Bradford Clay), with many brachiopods.
Arkell, W. J. 1931, p. 590 ; 1947a, pp. 49-50.
Geol. Surv. N.S. 236 ;  Ord. New Pop. 145.

## RUTLAND

**Clipsham,** 8½ miles N.E. of Oakham.  Clipsham Old Quarry and trial pit W. of the main workings.
Jurassic, Great Oolite Series (Upper Estuarine Beds), with brachiopods (*Lingula, Burmirhynchia*), resting on Inferior Oolite (upper Lincolnshire Limestone).  Lamellibranchs (*Lucina*) and brachiopods (*Acanthothyris crossi*) in lower Lincolnshire Limestone in trial pit.
Geol. Surv. O.S. 64 ;  Ord. New Pop. 123.

**Ketton,** 4 miles W. of Stamford.  Ketton Portland Cement Co.'s Quarries.
Permission required from quarry office.
Jurassic, Great Oolite Series (Upper Estuarine Beds), with abundant lamellibranchs (*Cuspidaria, Myopholas, Ostrea*, etc.) and brachiopods (*Lingula*, rhynchonellids) ;  resting on Inferior Oolite (Lincolnshire Limestone) with corals, many lamellibranchs, and gastropods (*Nerinea*).
Richardson, L. 1939a, p. 37.
Geol. Surv. O.S. 64 ;  Ord. New Pop. 123.

## SHROPSHIRE

*(Many of the common fossils of Shropshire are illustrated in La Touche, J. D. 1884.)*

**All Stretton,** 1¼ miles N. of Church Stretton. The Road Quarry in The Cwms, S.E. of All Stretton and 1 mile W. of Comley. Cobbold's Excavation 53.

Lower Cambrian (Wrekin Quartzite and *Obolella groomi* beds), with the oldest known fauna in the district, comprising brachiopods and hyolithids.

Cobbold, E. S. 1921 ; 1927, p. 554, with geol. map ; 1931.

Geol. Surv. O.S. 61 S.W. ; Ord. New Pop. 129.

**Brockton,** 4½ miles S.W. of Much Wenlock. Bankside at entrance to farm immediately N. of Feathers Inn.

Silurian, Downton Series (Ludlow Bone Bed). Lamellibranchs, brachiopods, ostracods, etc., immediately below lower bone-bed and lamellibranchs and gastropods above it. Fish-fragments in main bone-bed.

Robertson, T. 1927, p. 93, with map.

Geol. Surv. O.S. 61 S.W. ; Ord. New Pop. 129.

**Brockton,** 6 miles E.S.E. of Welshpool. Section on S. side of road opposite Leigh Farm, Leigh.

Ordovician, Llanvirn (Stapeley Volcanic Group). Trilobites and brachiopods occur in thin shale-bands interbedded with volcanic tuffs.

Whittard, W. F. 1931, p. 329.

Geol. Surv. O.S. 60 N.E. ; Ord. New Pop. 118.

**Bromlow,** 8½ miles N. of Bishop's Castle. Lyde Cottage, at junction of Betton Dingle with a tributary from the E.N.E.

Ordovician, Llanvirn (Weston Beds, *bifidus* zone), with a rich fauna of brachiopods (*Lingula*), lamellibranchs and trilobites (*Ogygia*).

Whittard, W. F. 1931, p. 330.

Geol. Surv. O.S. 60 N.E. ; Ord. New Pop. 118.

**Bromlow.** Section in Betton Dingle where road to Meadowtown crosses the stream.

Ordovician, Llanvirn (Betton Beds, *murchisoni* zone). A mixed-facies fauna of trilobites and brachiopods and " tuning-fork " graptolites.

Whittard, W. F. 1931, p. 331.

Geol. Surv. O.S. 60 N.E. ; Ord. New Pop. 118.

**Buildwas,** 2 miles W. of Ironbridge. N. bank of R. Severn at low water, 350 yds. S.E. of Buildwas Vicarage and 200-300 yds. W. of road-turning to Little Wenlock.

Silurian, Wenlock (Buildwas Beds) and top beds of Llandovery. Some 60 ft. of shales with thin limestones. G. Maw obtained many brachiopods by washing a quantity of mudstone, see Davidson, T. 1882. Corals, trilobites and gastropods also occur.

Pocock, R. W. and others 1938, pp. 112, 260-273.

Geol. Surv. N.S. 152 ; Ord. New Pop. 118.

**Cheney Longville,** 6 miles S.S.W. of Church Stretton. N. side of lane from Cheney Longville N.W. to Longville Common, 10 yds. N.W. of northern end of earthwork.

Ordovician, Caradoc (Longville Flags, *Kjaerina geniculata* zone), type-locality for zonal brachiopod.

Bancroft, B. B. 1945, p. 249.

Geol. Surv. O.S. 61 S.W. ; Ord. New Pop. 129.

**Cheney Longville.** River Onny, section $\frac{3}{16}$ mile S.S.E. of Glenburrell Cottage and ¾ mile N.W. of crossroads in middle of Cheney Longville.

Ordovician, Caradoc (Acton Scott Beds, *Onniella grandis* zone), with abundant orthid brachiopods.

Bancroft, B. B. 1933, Table 1. Lamont, A. 1945.

Geol. Surv. O.S. 61 S.W. ; Ord. New Pop. 129.

**Cheney Longville.** Longlane Quarry.
Ordovician, Caradoc (Horderley Sandstone, *Wattsella horderleyensis* zone).
The zonal brachiopod came from 46 ft. above base of quarry.
Bancroft, B. B. 1945, p. 193.
Geol. Surv. O.S. 61 S.W. ; Ord. New Pop. 129.

**Cheney Longville.** Longville Plantation, quarry beside track 60 yds. from
N.E. corner of plantation.
Ordovician, Caradoc (Horderley Sandstone, *Wattsella indica* zone), rich
in brachiopods.
Bancroft, B. B. 1945, p. 195.
Geol. Surv. O.S. 61 S.W. ; Ord. New Pop. 129.

**Cheney Longville.** N. side of lane from Cheney Longville N.W. to
Longville Common, 1300 ft. from northern end of earthwork.
Ordovician, Caradoc (Longville Flags, *Kjaerina bipartita* zone), with
brachiopods.
Bancroft, B. B. 1929, p. 52 ; 1945, p. 248.
Geol. Surv. O.S. 61 S.W. ; Ord. New Pop. 129.

**Chirbury,** 3 miles N.E. of Montgomery. Spy Wood Burn, 800 ft. E. of
junction with Aldress Dingle, S. of Chirbury.
Ordovician, Caradoc (Spy Wood Grit), with numerous ostracods (*Tetradella*)
and brachiopods.
Watts, W. W. and others 1925, pp. 342, 400.
Geol. Surv. O.S. 60 S.E. ; Ord. New Pop. 128.

**Chirbury.** Aldress Dingle, 30 yds. N. of its confluence with Spy Wood
Burn, S. of Chirbury.
Ordovician, Caradoc (Aldress Shales), with dendroid graptolites and
orthograptids.
Bulman, O. M. B. 1928, p. 35. Whittard, W. F. 1931, p. 333.
Geol. Surv. O.S. 60 S.E. ; Ord. New Pop. 128.

**Chirbury.** Quarry behind Walcot Farm, 1 mile N. of village.
Silurian, Wenlock (*riccartonensis* zone) with many graptolites (*Monograptus*).
Gupta, T. D. 1932, p. 327.
Geol. Surv. O.S. 60 S.E. ; Ord. New Pop. 128.

**Church Stretton,** see All Stretton, Comley.

**Cleobury Mortimer.** Gardener's Bank, cliff-section in left bank of
R. Rea 600 yds. N.E. of Reaside Farm and 1$\frac{3}{16}$ mile N.W. of Bayton Church,
2 miles S.E. of Cleobury Mortimer.
Silurian, Downton Series (I. 8), with ostracoderms, especially *Traquairaspis*
[*Phialaspis*] *pococki*.
White, E. I. 1946, p. 209.
Geol. Surv. O.S. 55 N.E. ; Ord. New Pop. 130.

**Comley,** 3 miles N.E. of Church Stretton. Comley Quarry on S. side of
road at N. end of Little Caradoc Hill. Cobbold's Excavation No. 1.
Middle Cambrian (*Paradoxides groomi* grits and conglomerates) ; Lower
Cambrian (*Lapworthella, Eodiscus* and *Callavia* limestones and Lower Comley
Sandstone). Type-locality of the trilobite *Callavia callavei*. Other fossils of
various groups were formerly available.
Lapworth, C. 1891. Cobbold, E. S. 1921 ; 1927, with geol. map ; 1931.
Geol. Surv. O.S. 61 S.W. ; Ord. New Pop. 129.

**Comley.** Bed of brook 400 yds. S. of Comley Quarry and 100 yds. W.N.W.
of Gulley Green Farm. Cobbold's Excavation No. 47.
Lower Cambrian (green sandstone at base of Lower Comley Limestone).

Fragments of the trilobite *Callavia* are more easily obtained here than at Comley Quarry.

Cobbold, E. S. 1927, p. 560, with geol. map.
Geol. Surv. O.S. 61 S.W. ; Ord. New Pop. 129.

**Cound,** 6 miles S.E. of Shrewsbury. Coundmoor Brook, 450 yds. N. 10° E. of Fox Inn, Coundmoor.

Ordovician, Caradoc (Harnage Shales), with many ostracods, some machaeridians and trinucleid trilobites.

Pocock, R. W. and others 1938, pp. 250-257.
Geol. Surv. N.S. 152 ; Ord. New Pop. 118.

**Eaton Constantine,** 8 miles S.E. of Shrewsbury. Cherme's Dingle, between localities α 27 and α 23 of Stubblefield and Bulman.

Cambrian, Tremadoc (Transition Beds and *tenellus* zone), with dendroid and true graptolites, brachiopods and rare trilobites.

Stubblefield, C. J. and Bulman, O. M. B. 1927, pp. 106, 110, 118, with geol. map.
Geol. Surv. N.S. 152 ; Ord. New. Pop. 118.

**Eaton Constantine.** Cherme's Dingle, between localities α 59 and α 69 of Stubblefield and Bulman.

Cambrian, Tremadoc (*flabellifome* zone). Good dendroid graptolites (*Dictyonema*).

Stubblefield, C. J. and Bulman, O. M. B. 1927, pp. 106, 109, 118, with geol. map.
Geol. Surv. N.S. 152 ; Ord. New Pop. 118.

**Farlow,** 3½ miles N.W. of Cleobury Mortimer. Oreton Quarries, 950 yds. E. of St. Giles' Church, Farlow.

Carboniferous Limestone ($Z_2$ subzone), with abundant brachiopods (*Syringothyris cuspidata, Camarotoechia mitcheldeanensis*). Noted for fish-teeth and spines, etc. (*Ctenacanthus*).

Vaughan, A. 1905, p. 252.
Geol. Surv. O.S. 55 N.E. ; Ord. New Pop. 129 and 130.

**Farlow.** Old quarry near Farlow Church and road-cutting on Farlow Bank.

Upper Old Red Sandstone (Farlow Sandstone), with fossil fish (*Bothriolepis, Holoptychius, Sauripterus*).

Morris, J. and Roberts, G. E. 1862.
Geol. Surv. O.S. 55 N.E. ; Ord. New Pop. 129 and 130.

**Hope,** 8½ miles N.N.E. of Bishop's Castle. E. bank of Hope Brook immediately S. of the ford, 500 ft. S. of The Fox Inn.

Ordovician, Llanvirn (Hope Shales, *bifidus* zone), a good locality for trilobites (*Illaenus*, etc.).

Whittard, W. F. 1931, p. 328.
Geol. Surv. O.S. 60 N.E. ; Ord. New Pop. 118.

**Hughley,** 4 miles S.W. of Much Wenlock. Hughley Brook, sections in streams N. and S. of the road.

Silurian, Upper Llandovery (Purple or Hughley Shales), with corals, brachiopods and trilobites.

Pocock, R. W. and others 1938, pp. 110, 260-269.
Geol. Surv. N.S. 152 ; Ord. New Pop. 129.

**Hungerford,** Corvedale. Old quarry 200 yds. and quarry on S. side of road 350 yds. N. of Holloway Farm.

Silurian, Ludlow (Aymestry Limestone). Graptolites are associated with a shelly fauna of brachiopods, etc.

Geol. Surv. O.S. 61 S.W. ; Ord. New Pop. 129.

**Hungerford.** Quarry opposite lodge 550 yds. E. of Upper Millichope. Silurian, Ludlow (Aymestry Limestone), with a variety of brachiopods. Geol. Surv. O.S. 61 S.W. ; Ord. New Pop. 129.

**Hungerford.** Stream-section alongside road, 600 yds. N.W. of Upper Millichope. Silurian, Lower Ludlow (*nilssoni* zone), with the graptolite *Monograptus nilssoni* abundant. Geol. Surv. O.S. 61 S.W. ; Ord. New Pop. 129.

**Kenley,** 4 miles W. of Much Wenlock. Evenwood Quarry, at E. end of Black Dick's Coppice, ¾ mile W.N.W. of Kenley Church and 300 yds. S. of Evenwood. Ordovician, Caradoc (Hoar Edge Group), with brachiopods. The occurrence of the graptolite *Nemagraptus gracilis* indicates a correlation with the Caradoc Series of S. Wales. (Beds placed by Bancroft, 1929, in his Costonian Stage, *subplicata* zone). Pocock, R. W. and others 1938, pp. 78, 83, 84, 250-257. Geol. Surv. N.S. 152 ; Ord. New Pop. 118.

**Leighton,** 3½ miles N.N.W. of Much Wenlock. Stream-sections 300 yds. N.N.E. of Morrellswood Farm, 300 yds. below Spout Lane Bridge ; and 100 yds. W. of farm. Silurian, Upper Llandovery (*Pentamerus* Beds), with many corals (type-locality of *Cantrillia*), brachiopods, trilobites, etc. Pocock, R. W. and others 1938, pp. 107-108, 260-270. Whittard, W. F. 1928, p. 742, with geol. maps. Smith, S. 1930a, p. 298. Geol. Surv. N.S. 152 ; Ord. New Pop. 118.

**Little Wenlock,** 2½ miles W. of Dawley. Section at angle where stream from Gibbon's Coppice joins Harper's Dingle, about 1½ miles W. of Little Wenlock. Locality 34 of Whittard, 1928. Silurian, Upper Llandovery (*Pentamerus* Beds), with abundant brachiopods (*Pentamerus oblongus*) associated with graptolites (*Glyptograptus tamariscus*). Whittard, W. F. 1928, p. 742, with geol. maps. Pocock, R. W. and others 1938, pp. 107-108, 260-270. Geol. Surv. N.S. 152 ; Ord. New Pop. 119.

**Ludlow.** Section on right bank of R. Teme, from Dinham Bridge downstream to Ludlow Sewage Works. Silurian, Ludlow and Downton Series (Aymestry Limestone to Temeside Shales). Shelly brachiopods in Aymestry Limestone just S. of bridge and in Mocktree Shales in small quarry nearby. Ostracods, horny brachiopods and lamellibranchs in shales above the bone-bed, which yields its usual fish-fragments. Elles, G. L. and Slater, I. L. 1906, pp. 202-205, with geol. map. Geol. Surv. O.S. 55 N.W. ; Ord. New Pop. 129.

**Meadowtown,** 6 miles N.E. of Montgomery. Tip-heaps of old level N. of road from Meadowtown to Lyde. Ordovician, Llanvirn (Betton Beds, *murchisoni* zone), with the graptolite *Didymograptus murchisoni* abundant. Whittard, W. F. 1931, p. 341. Geol. Surv. O.S. 60 N.E. ; Ord. New Pop. 118.

**Meadowtown.** E. branch of Betton Dingle just N. of where footpath from The Cottage crosses the stream. Ordovician, Llanvirn (Stapeley Shales, *bifidus* zone) with a mixed-facies fauna of trilobites, brachiopods and graptolites. Whittard, W. F. 1931, p. 330. Geol. Surv. O.S. 60 N.E. ; Ord. New Pop. 118.

**Meadowtown.** Old quarry at Meadowtown.
Ordovician, Llandeilo (Meadowtown Beds, *teretiusculus* zone), with abundant trilobites (*Ogygia*) in lowest beds ; volcanic tuff with sponge-spicules in bottom of quarry ; and graptolites (*Diplograptus foliaceus*) in shales at top of quarry.
Whittard, W. F. 1931, p. 331.
Geol. Surv. O.S. 60 N.E. ; Ord. New Pop. 118.

**Meadowtown.** Stream-section 400 yds. N.W. of Meadowtown, towards Desert.
Ordovician, Caradoc (Rorrington Beds, *gracilis* and *peltifer* zones), with abundant graptolites at several places.
Whittard, W. F. 1931, p. 341.
Geol. Surv. O.S. 60 N.E. ; Ord. New Pop. 118.

**Middletown,** 5½ miles N.E. of Welshpool. Trewern Brook, section from S. of Gate Farm to a point due W. of Glyn, ½ mile S. of Middletown.
Silurian, Wenlock *linnarssoni* and *lundgreni* zones) with good specimens of graptolites (*Cyrtograptus*).
Gupta, T. D. 1932, pp. 328-333, with geol. map.
Geol. Surv. O.S. 60 N.E. ; Ord. New Pop. 118.

**Middletown.** Quarry by Rose and Crown Inn.
Silurian, Lower Ludlow, zone of *Monograptus leintwardinensis*, with this graptolite in abundance.
Gupta, T. D. 1932, p. 343, with geol. map.
Geol. Surv. O.S. 60 N.E. ; Ord. New Pop. 118.

**Middletown.** Trewern Brook, section from W. of Glyn along stream leading S. to Trefnant Farm.
Silurian, Lower Ludlow, zones of *Monograptus vulgaris* and *M. nilssoni*, with these and other graptolites in abundance.
Gupta, T. D. 1932, pp. 337-340, with geol. map.
Geol. Surv. O.S. 60 N.E. ; Ord. New Pop. 118.

**Minsterley,** 9 miles S.W. of Shrewsbury. Hope Quarry, 700 yds. N.E. of the Fox Inn, Hope Valley.
Silurian, Upper Llandovery (*Pentamerus* Beds), with abundant brachiopods (*Pentamerus*, etc.) ; unconformable on Ordovician, Llanvirn (*bifidus* zone), with few fossils.
Whittard, W. F. 1932, p. 875, with geol. maps.
Geol. Surv. O.S. 60 N.E. ; Ord. New Pop. 118.

**Minsterley.** Section in lane 500 yds. from Minsterley S.E. towards Habberley.
Silurian, Upper Llandovery (Purple Shales), with trilobites and brachiopods.
Whittard, W. F. 1932, p. 888, with geol. maps.
Geol. Surv. O.S. 60 N.E. ; Ord. New Pop. 118.

**Much Wenlock.** Many quarries on Wenlock Edge, between Much Wenlock and Presthope, 3 miles to S.W. ; chiefly on W. side of road.
Silurian, type-area of Wenlock Limestone. Corals, stromatoporoids, crinoids, brachiopods, mollusca, etc., occur in great profusion.
Pocock, R. W. and others, 1938, pp. 114, 260-272.
Geol. Surv. N.S. 152 ; Ord. New Pop. 129.

**Norbury,** 3½ miles N.E. of Bishop's Castle. Several quarries scattered round the village.
Silurian, Upper Llandovery (*Pentamerus* Beds), with orthid and strophomenid brachiopods.
Whittard, W. F. 1932, p. 871, with geol. maps.
Geol. Surv. O.S. 60 S.E. ; Ord. New Pop. 129.

**Onibury,** 5 miles N.W. of Ludlow. Lane-section midway between Onibury and Upper Onibury, to the N.
Silurian, Downton Series (Temeside Shales).      The horny brachiopod *Lingula cornea* is common.
Elles, G. L. and Slater, I. L. 1906, p. 215 and fig 8.
Geol. Surv. O.S. 55 N.W. ; Ord. New Pop. 129.

**Onibury.**   Large quarry alongside road N. of St. Michael's Church.
Silurian, Downton Series (Downton Castle Sandstone), with horny brachiopods (*Lingula minima*) and some fish-remains.
Elles, G. L. and Slater, I. L. 1906, pp. 215-217 and fig. 8.
Geol. Surv. O.S. 55 N.W. ; Ord. New Pop. 129.

**Onibury.**   Quarries along Weo (View) Edge.
Silurian, Ludlow (Aymestry Limestone), with the brachiopod *Conchidium knightii* abundant.
Geol. Surv. O.S. 55 N.W. ;  Ord. New Pop. 129.

**Onibury.**   Old quarry on N. side of Craven Arms-Ludlow Road, 50 yds. S.E. of 6th milestone from Ludlow.
Silurian, Ludlow (Mocktree Shales), with the brachiopod *Dayia navicula* abundant near top at E. end of Quarry.
Elles, G. L. and Slater, I. L. 1906, p. 215 and fig. 8.
Geol. Surv. O.S. 55 N.W. ; Ord. New Pop. 129.

**Onibury.**    Old quarry in Hale Wood (Craven Arms-Onibury road), immediately W. of Upper Park Farm.
Silurian, Ludlow (Upper Ludlow), with the brachiopod *Camarotoechia nucula,* etc.
Elles, G. L. and Slater, I. L. 1906, p. 215, and fig 8.
Geol. Surv. O.S. 55 N.W. ;· Ord. New Pop. 129.

**Onibury.**   Old quarry in Hale Wood 800 ft. S.W. of Bank House Farm.
Silurian, Ludlow (Upper Ludlow), with the brachiopod *Chonetes striatellus,* etc.
Elles, G. L. and Slater, I. L. 1906, p. 215 and fig. 8.
Geol. Surv. O.S. 55 N.W. ; Ord. New Pop. 129.

**Pennerley** (Penalley), 4 miles S.S.W. of Minsterley.   Roadside quarry 330 yds. N.N.E. of Tankerville Mine.
Ordovician, Arenig (Mytton Flags, *hirundo* zone), with brachiopods, trilobites and graptolites.
Whittard, W. F. 1931, p. 327.
Geol. Surv. O.S. 60 S.E. ; Ord. New Pop. 129.

**Plowden,** 4 miles E.S.E. of Bishop's Castle. Quarry 220 yds. W. of Hillend Bridge on Plowden-Horderley road.
Silurian, Upper Llandovery (*Pentamerus* Beds), with brachiopods, gastropods, ostracods, trilobites, etc.
Whittard, W. F. 1932, p. 868, with geol. maps.
Geol. Surv. O.S. 61 S.W. ; Ord. New Pop. 129.

**Plowden.**   Hillside exposures immediately behind Hillend Cottage.
Silurian, Llandovery (*Pentamerus* Beds).   Type-locality for the ostracods *Leperditia littoralis* and *L. arenacea.* Brachiopods, gastropods, trilobites, etc., also occur.
Whittard, W. F. 1932, p. 866, with geol. maps. Harper, J. C. 1940, p. 389.
Geol. Surv. O.S. 61 S.W. ; Ord. New Pop. 129.

**Rorrington,** 5¼ miles S.W. of Minsterley.   Section in Grey Grass Dingle, S.W. of village.
Ordovician, Caradoc (Rorrington Beds, *gracilis* and *peltifer* zones) Graptolites are exceedingly abundant at many places along brook.
Geol. Surv. O.S. 60 N.E.-S.E. ; Ord. New Pop. 118.

**Rorrington.** Escarpment 1000-1600 yds. E.N.E. of Rorrington Post Office.

Ordovician, Caradoc (Spy Wood Grit), with abundant ostracods (*Tetradella*) and brachiopods.

Whittard, W. F. 1931, p. 332.

Geol. Surv. O.S. 60 N.E. ; Ord. New Pop. 118.

**Shelve,** 4½ miles S.S.W. of Minsterley. Roadside exposure below Shelve Church.

Ordovician, Arenig (Mytton Flags, Shelve Church Beds, *extensus* zone), with abundant dendroid and true graptolites, cystid plates and occasional trilobites.

Whittard, W. F. 1931, p. 326.

Geol. Surv. O.S. 60 S.E. ; Ord. New Pop. 129.

**Shelve.** Exposure 500 ft. S.E. of saw-pit, Ritton Brook.

Silurian, Upper Llandovery (Purple Shales). Many fossils can be obtained from rocks *in situ* and from innumerable blocks scattered over the ground on both sides of Ritton Brook.

Whittard, W. F. 1932, p. 878 and fig. 2.

Geol. Surv. O.S. 60 S.E. ; Ord. New Pop. 129.

**Shineton,** 3 miles N.N.W. of Much Wenlock. Shineton Brook, S.W. of village. Locality RR2 of Stubblefield and Bulman.

Cambrian, Tremadoc (zone of *Shumardia pusilla*). The classic Shineton Farm section is permanently submerged since the building of a weir. Trilobites (*Shumardia, Asaphellus,* etc.) are abundant further upstream.

Stubblefield, C. J. and Bulman, O. M. B. 1927, p. 119 and Pl. v. Pocock, R. W. and others 1938, p. 69.

Geol. Surv. N.S. 152 ; Ord. New Pop. 118.

**Snailbeach,** 2 miles S. of Minsterley. Tip-heaps from Perkin's Level and sides of adit at head of Perkin's Beach.

Ordovician, Arenig (Mytton Flags), with trilobites and brachiopods.

Whittard, W. F. 1931, p. 326.

Geol. Surv. O.S. 60 N.E. ; Ord. New Pop. 118.

**Wistanstow,** 2 miles N. of Craven Arms. River Onny, 1000 ft. N.W. of ford in lane from Cross Way to Cheney Longville.

Ordovician, Caradoc (Onny Shales), a classic locality for trinucleid trilobites ; Silurian, Llandovery (Purple Shales), with many graptolites, and a conglomeratic basement-bed with trilobites, etc.

Murchison, R. I. 1839, p. 217. Whittard, W. F. 1928, pp. 747-751, with geol. maps. Lamont, A. 1945, p. 118, with geol. map.

Geol. Surv. O.S. 61 S.W. ; Ord. New Pop. 129.

**Wotherton,** 2 miles N.E. of Chirbury. Bank on W. side of Ox Wood Dingle and N. of where Rorrington-Wotherton road crosses stream.

Ordovician, Caradoc (Aldress Shales), with ostracods, brachiopods and some graptolites in shales interbedded in volcanic tuffs.

Whittard, W. F. 1931, p. 333.

Geol. Surv. O.S. 60 N.E. ; Ord. New Pop. 118.

# SOMERSET

**Axbridge,** 9 miles S.E. of Weston-super-Mare. Cross Quarry, N. of Bridgewater road, 1 mile E. of Axbridge.

Carboniferous Limestone ($S_1$ subzone), with abundant gastropods.

Bamber, A. E. 1924, pp. 85-86, with geol. map.

Geol. Surv. O.S. 19 ; Ord. New Pop. 165.

**Backwell,** 7 miles S.W. of Bristol.   Quarries in Cheston Coombe, near Backwell.
Carboniferous Limestone (S zone), with corals (*Lithostrotion*) and brachiopods (*Composita* [*Seminula*] *ficoidea, Productus,* etc.).
Wallis, F. S. 1922, pp. 210, 215, with geol. map.
Geol. Surv. O.S. 19 ; Ord. New Pop. 165.

**Banwell,** 3½ miles N.W. of Axbridge.   Quarries on Banwell Hill, N.W. of Banwell Castle.
Carboniferous Limestone ($C_2$ subzone), with many corals and brachiopods.
Bamber, A. E. 1924, p. 87, with geol. map.
Geol. Surv. O.S. 19 ; Ord. New Pop. 165.

**Barrow Gurney,** 5 miles S.W. of Bristol.   Dial Quarry, on S.E. side of Bristol-Bridgewater road, 1 mile S.W. of reservoirs.
Carboniferous Limestone ($S_2$ subzone), with corals (*Lithostrotion*) and brachiopods (*Composita* [*Seminula*] *ficoidea, Productus,* etc.).
Wallis, F. S. 1922, pp. 210, 213, with geol. map.
Geol. Surv. O.S. 19 ; Ord. New Pop. 165.

**Binegar,** 3½ miles N. of Shepton Mallet.   Numerous quarries E. of the village.
Carboniferous Limestone (S and D zones) with corals (*Lithostrotion, Palaeosmilia*) and brachiopods.
Welch, F. B. A. 1929, pp. 48, 68, with geol. map.
Geol. Surv. O.S. 19 ; Ord. New Pop. 166.

**Bleadon,** 3½ miles S. of Weston-super-Mare.   Small gravel-pit opposite Anchor Inn on main Bridgewater-Weston road, just S. of Bleadon.
Upper Pleistocene (talus-breccia on 50-ft. raised beach platform). A sandy basement-bed, 20 ft. below the surface, yields bones, mainly reindeer antlers (*Rangifer tarandus*) and vole-bones (*Microtus ratticeps*).
Palmer, L. S. 1930, p. 51.
Geol. Surv. O.S. 20 ; Ord. New Pop. 165.

**Blue Anchor,** 5 miles S.E. of Minehead.   Reefs in foreshore at low tide.
Triassic, Rhaetic, with fish-remains (*Ceratodus*, etc.) in bone-bed and many lamellibranchs in hard bands, including forms rare elsewhere, such as *Pteromya crowcombeia*.
Richardson, L. 1911a, pp. 15-18, pl. II.
Geol. Surv. O.S. 20 ; Ord. New Pop. 164.

**Burrington,** 4½ miles N.E. of Axbridge.   Natural exposures, screes and quarries in Burrington Combe, S.S.E. of the village.
Carboniferous Limestone (complete succession from K to $D_1$ zones). The full sequence of characteristic corals, brachiopods, etc., can be found.
Reynolds, S. H. and Vaughan, A. 1911, p. 342, with geol. map.
Geol. Surv. O.S. 110 ; Ord. New Pop. 165.

**Camerton,** 2 miles N.N.W. of Radstock.   Tip-heap of Camerton Colliery.
Carboniferous, Coal Measures (Radstock Group), with abundant fossil plants, especially *Pecopteris* and rare non-marine shells (*Anthraconaia prolifera*).
Moore, L. R. and Trueman, A. E. 1937, p. 231.  Moore, L. R. 1938, p. 294.
Geol. Surv. O.S. 19 ; Ord. New Pop. 166.

**Chesterblade,** 3 miles S.E. of Shepton Mallet.   Alham Lane Quarry, on N. side of lane ¼ mile E. of Chesterblade, 2½ miles S.E. of Shepton Mallet station.
Jurassic, Fuller's Earth Rock, with many lamellibranchs, gastropods, etc.
Richardson, L. 1909, p. 212.  Arkell, W. J. 1939c.           .
Geol. Surv. O.S. 19 ; Ord. New Pop. 166.

**Cleeve,** 9½ miles S.W. of Bristol. Goblin Coombe, natural exposures.
Carboniferous Limestone (C and S zones), with corals (*Caninia, Syringopora*
in C zone, *Lithostrotion* in S zone) and brachiopods.
Wallis, F. S. 1922, pp. 209, 215, with geol. map.
Geol. Surv. O.S. 19 ; Ord. New Pop. 165.

**Clevedon.** Cliff and foreshore sections from Clevedon for 1 mile S. to
Pill Bay.
Carboniferous Limestone ; K zone in Clevedon, Littleharp and Salthouse
Bays ; $Z_1$ subzone in cliffs of Green Beach ; $Z_2$ subzone from Salthouse Point
southwards. Many corals and brachiopods occur.
Reynolds, S. H. and Greenly, E. 1924, p. 461, with geol. map. Bush, G. E.
1928.
Geol. Surv. O.S. 35 ; Ord. New Pop. 165.

**Compton Bishop,** 2 miles W.N.W. of Axbridge. Hillside exposures and
quarries on road S. of Crooks Peak, ½ mile W. of Compton Bishop.
Carboniferous Limestone (S zone), with many corals and brachiopods.
Bamber, A. E. 1924, p. 88, with geol. map.
Geol. Surv. O.S. 19 ; Ord. New Pop. 165.

**Corton Denham,** 4 miles N. of Sherborne (Dorset). Limekiln Quarry
(disused), northern slope of Corton Downs, about ¼ mile E. of Corton Denham
and 1⅜ miles W. by S. of Charlton Horethorne Church. No. 59 of Richardson,
1916.
Jurassic, Inferior Oolite (*murchisonae* and *sowerbii* zones), with many
ammonites, belemnites, brachiopods, etc.
Richardson, L. 1916, p. 512, with topog. map.
Geol. Surv. O.S. 18 ; Ord. New Pop. 166.

**Doulting,** 1¾ miles E. of Shepton Mallet. Doulting Bridge Quarry, beside
S. side of railway, S. of Doulting.
Jurassic, Inferior Oolite (upper beds) with lamellibranchs, brachiopods,
sea-urchins and corals ; and Fuller's Earth with oysters, brachiopods and
belemnites.
Richardson, L. 1907, p. 393. Muir-Wood, H. M. 1936.
Geol. Surv. O.S. 19 ; Ord. New Pop. 166.

**Dulcote,** 1 mile S.E. of Wells. Quarries on Dulcote Hill, E. of Dulcote, on
S. side of road to Shepton Mallet.
Carboniferous Limestone (S zone), with corals (*Lithostrotion*) and brachio-
pods (*Composita* [*Seminula*] *ficoidea,* etc.).
Welch, F. B. A. 1929, pp. 48, 72, with geol. map.
Geol. Surv. O.S. 19 ; Ord. New Pop. 165 and 166.

**Dundry,** 4½ miles S.W. of Bristol. Main Road South Quarry, 2 miles
S.S.W. of Dundry Church, and Main Road North Quarry, about 1 mile E. of
the church.
Jurassic, Middle and Upper Inferior Oolite. Formerly famous for the
rich fauna of the " Dundry Ironshot." The South Quarry, source of many
fossils described by Buckman, Hudleston, Tawney, Whidborne, etc., is now
obliterated.
Buckman, S. S. and Wilson, E. 1896, p. 691.
Geol. Surv. O.S. 19 ; Ord. New Pop. 165.

**Dundry.** Rattledown Quarry, about 2½ miles S.E. of Dundry Church.
Jurassic, Inferior Oolite (including the " Dundry Ironshot "). Beds much
disturbed by superficial movement. Ammonites and other mollusca, brachio-
pods, sea-urchins, corals, sponges, etc., abundant.
Buckman, S. S. and Wilson, E. 1896, p. 692.
Geol. Surv. O.S. 19 ; Ord. New Pop. 165.

**Dunkerton,** 4½ miles S.W. of Bath. Road-section at fork in Bath-Radstock and Bath-Timsbury roads, near Cross Ways Inn and 1½ miles N.E. of Dunkerton Church.

Jurassic, Fuller's Earth Rock and Lower Fuller's Earth, with abundant oysters (*Ostrea acuminata*) in shales and many brachiopods and lamellibranchs in rubbly rock-bands.

Cox, L. R. 1941, p. 20.

Geol. Surv. O.S. 19 ; Ord. New Pop. 165.

**Edford,** 5 miles N.E. of Shepton Mallet. Canal cutting 150 yds. S.E. of Bennett's Hill Farm.

Carboniferous, Coal Measures (*communis* zone), with non-marine shells, including *Naiadites flexuosus*.

Moore, L. R. and Trueman, A. E. 1937, p. 204.

Geol. Surv. O.S. 19 ; Ord. New Pop. 166.

**Evercreech,** 4 miles S.S.E. of Shepton Mallet. Somerset Brick and Tile Works near Evercreech Junction, 1½ miles S. of Evercreech.

Jurassic, Lower Lias (*davoei* zone), with ammonites including *Androgynoceras*.

Kellaway, G. A. and Wilson, V. 1941, p. 142.

Geol. Surv. O.S. 19 ; Ord. New Pop. 166.

**Evercreech.** Evercreech Limeworks, by Evercreech station.

Jurassic, Lower Lias (*bucklandi* zone) with large ammonites.

Kellaway, G. A. and Wilson, V. 1941, p. 141.

Geol. Surv. O.S. 19 ; Ord. New Pop. 166.

**Failand,** 5 miles W. of Bristol. Several quarries in vicinity of Failand Inn, on both sides of Bristol-Clevedon road.

Carboniferous Limestone (C zone), with corals (*Caninia, Zaphrentoides*), brachiopods (*Orthotetes, Chonetes*) and gastropods (*Bellerophon*).

Vaughan, A. 1905, pp. 211, 216.

Geol. Surv. O.S. 35 ; Ord. New Pop. 155.

**Frome.** Vallis Vale, W. of Frome. Quarries extending from Egford Bridge to Hapsford Bridge and to Bedlam.

Carboniferous Limestone (Z to S zones) with corals and brachiopods abundant, especially in S zone ; capped by Jurassic, Inferior Oolite (top beds) with brachiopods and sea-urchins, etc.

Bush, G. E. 1925, with geol. map and Welch, F. B. A. 1933, pp. 28-29, with geol. map (for Carboniferous). Richardson, L. 1907, p. 400 (for Jurassic).

Geol. Surv. O.S. 19 ; Ord. New Pop. 166.

**Haselbury Plucknett,** 2 miles N.E. of Crewkerne. Haselbury Mill Quarry (disused).

Jurassic, Inferior Oolite, with abundant sponges and small brachiopods in top beds ; capped by Fuller's Earth.

Richardson, L. 1918, p. 166.

Geol. Surv. O.S. 18 ; Ord. New Pop. 177.

**Hinton Charterhouse,** 4 miles S.S.E. of Bath. Quarry on E. side of main road, ½ mile S. of church and N.E. of Hintonfield Farm.

Jurassic, Great Oolite Series (type-locality of Hinton Sands). Fossils, except for microfossils, are scarce.

Woodward, H. B. 1894, p. 350.

Geol. Surv. O.S. 19 ; Ord. New Pop. 166.

**Holford,** 9½ miles W.N.W. of Bridgewater. Lane-section S. of Holford, W. of Nether Stowey road. Station 4 of Hallam, 1934.

Middle Devonian, Ilfracombe Beds, with casts of brachiopods, lamellibranchs and gastropods.

Evans, J. W. and others 1914, p. 102. Hallam, A. D. 1934, p. 437, with sketch-maps.

Geol. Surv. N.S. 295 ; Ord. New Pop. 164.

**Holford.** Quarry in angle between streams from Holford Combe and Hodders Combe. Station 5 of Hallam, 1934.
Middle Devonian, Hangman Grits, with numerous casts of gastropods.
Evans, J. W. and others 1914, p. 102. Hallam, A. D. 1934, p. 437, with sketch-maps.
Geol. Surv. N.S. 295 ; Ord. New Pop. 164.

**Holwell,** 3½ miles S.W. of Frome. Quarry on S. side of Shepton Mallet road immediately W. of Holwell.
Carboniferous Limestone ($C_2$-$S_1$ subzones), with fissures filled with Rhaetic deposits. The source of the earliest British fossil mammal (*Hypsiprymnopsis rhaeticus*), the mammal-like reptile *Tritylodon* and abundant fish-scales and teeth ; all obtained by washing the fissure-filling material.
Moore, C. 1867. Richardson, L. 1911a, p. 63. Geol. map in Welch, F. B. A. 1933.
Geol. Surv. O.S. 19 ; Ord. New Pop. 166.

**Keynsham.** Keelings Quarry, Wellsway, Keynsham.
Jurassic, Lower Lias (*angulata* to *semicostatum* zones), with ammonites, other mollusca and brachiopods.
Tutcher, J. W. 1923, p. 271.
Geol. Surv. O.S. 19 ; Ord. New Pop. 155.

**Kilve,** 5 miles E.N.E. of Williton. Cliffs and foreshore, W. and E. of Kilve.
Jurassic, Lower Lias (*planorbis* to *semicostatum* zones), with abundant ammonites and many other fossils.
Woodward, H. B. 1893, pp. 92-95.
Geol. Surv. O.S. 20 ; Ord. New Pop. 164.

**Leigh-upon-Mendip,** 5 miles W. of Frome. Quarries of the Leigh-upon-Mendip Quarry Co.
Carboniferous Limestone ($C_2$-$S_1$ subzones), with abundant corals and brachiopods.
Welch, F. B. A. 1933, p. 21, with geol. map.
Geol. Surv. O.S. 19 ; Ord. New Pop. 166.

**Leigh-upon-Mendip.** Tadhill, field near E. corner of Walltyning Plantation, 300 yds. S.S.W. of Tadhill Farm. Surface material.
Silurian, Upper Llandovery, fine volcanic tuff with corals, brachiopods, molluscs, trilobites, etc.
Reynolds, S. H. 1907, pp. 220, 226.
Geol. Surv. O.S. 19 ; Ord. New Pop. 166.

**Long Ashton,** 3 miles S.W. of Bristol. Exposures in Oxhouse Bottom and in lane S. of and parallel to this ravine.
Carboniferous Limestone (K zone), with brachiopods (*Camarotoechia*, *Avonia bassa*, spire-bearing forms, etc.).
Geol. Surv. O.S. 35 ; Ord. New Pop. 155 and 165.

**Long Ashton.** Quarry on N. side of Bristol-Cleveland road, E. of Ashton Park and N. of Providence.
Carboniferous Limestone (S zone), with corals (*Lithostrotion*) and brachiopods (*Composita* [*Seminula*] *ficoidea*, etc.).
Geol. Surv. O.S. 35 ; Ord. New Pop. 155 and 165.

**Maperton,** 3 miles S.W. of Wincanton. Road-cutting between Charlton Horethorne and Maperton, about ½ mile S.S.W. of the latter.
Jurassic, Fuller's Earth Rock, with abundant brachiopods (*Ornithella*) and bryozoa (*Diastopora*) in top beds.
Richardson, L. 1909, p. 212.
Geol. Surv. O.S. 18 ; Ord. New Pop. 166.

**Maperton.** Dancing Cross Quarry, ¾ mile N.N.W. of Maperton Church. Jurassic, Fuller's Earth Rock, with abundant corals, brachiopods, lamellibranchs and ammonites.
Richardson, L. 1909, p. 213. Kellaway, G. A. and Wilson, V. 1941, p. 178.
Geol. Surv. O.S. 18 ; Ord. New Pop. 166.

**Marston Magna,** 5 miles N.N.E. of Yeovil. Bed of mill-stream about 700 yds. W. of the church.
Jurassic, Lower Lias (*obtusum* zone, " Marston Marble "), packed with small ammonites (*Promicroceras* and *Asteroceras*).
Kellaway, G. A. and Wilson, V. 1941, p. 142.
Geol. Surv. O.S. 18 ; Ord. New Pop. 166.

**Midford,** 3½ miles S. of Bath. Road-section ¼ mile S. of Midford station.
Jurassic, Upper Lias (Midford Sands), Inferior Oolite and Fuller's Earth. All beds replete with fossils, especially corals and small brachiopods in top beds of Inferior Oolite.
Richardson, L. 1907, pp. 406-408.
Geol. Surv. O.S. 19 ; Ord. New Pop. 166.

**Midsomer Norton,** 1½ miles W. of Radstock. Tip-heap of Norton Hill Colliery.
Carboniferous, Coal Measures (Farrington Group), with fossil plants : *Sphenopteris*, etc., from roof of Big Seam ; *Mariopteris*, etc., from roof of New Vein ; *Neuropteris*, etc., from roof of Styving Vein.
Moore, L. R. and Trueman, A. E. 1937, pp. 229-230.
Geol. Surv. O.S. 19 ; Ord. New Pop. 166.

**Misterton,** 1½ miles S.E. of Crewkerne. Misterton Limeworks Quarry (disused).
Jurassic, Inferior Oolite (*opalinum* to *parkinsoni* zones), with abundant ammonites and lamellibranchs and a marl-bed near the top rich in microfossils.
Richardson, L. 1918, p. 154.
Geol. Surv. O.S. 18 ; Ord. New Pop. 177.

**North Coker,** 2 miles S.W. of Yeovil. Road-section near lodge about 350 yds. S.W. of N. Coker Mill, and small quarry in field 340 yds. W. of this road-section.
Jurassic, Cornbrash, with many brachiopods, resting on Forest Marble clay, with oysters.
Kellaway, G. A. and Wilson, V. 1941, p. 179.
Geol. Surv. O.S. 18 ; Ord. New Pop. 177.

**Nunney,** 3 miles S.W. of Frome. Large quarry near the village.
Carboniferous Limestone ($C_2$-$S_1$ subzones), with corals and brachiopods.
Welch, F. B. A. 1933, p. 35, with geol. map.
Geol. Surv. O.S. 19 ; Ord. New Pop. 166.

**Portishead.** Cliffs and foreshore, Battery Point and Eastwood Ridge.
Carboniferous Limestone (K and Z zones). Good preparations can be made by dissolving silicified fossils out of the limestone with acid.
Reynolds, S. H. and Greenly, E. 1924, pp. 452-453, with geol. map.
Geol. Surv. O.S. 35 ; Ord. New Pop. 155.

**Seavington St. Mary,** 3 miles E. of Ilminster. Large quarry on hillside about 650 yds. S.S.W. of St. Mary's Church.
Jurassic, Inferior Oolite, with ammonites, lamellibranchs and brachiopods, and a thin algal band.
Geol. Surv. O.S. 18 ; Ord. New Pop. 177.

**Shepton Beauchamp,** 3 miles N.E. of Ilminster. Quarry 550 yds. W. of Hurcot Farm, ¾ mile S.S.W. of Shepton Beauchamp.
Jurassic, Upper Lias clays, Junction Bed and Middle Lias, with abundant ammonites and other fossils.
Geol. Surv. O.S. 18 ; Ord. New Pop. 177.

**Shipham,** 2 miles N.E. of Axbridge. Natural exposures and quarries (Callow Rocks and Quarries) 1 mile S.S.E. of Shipham Church.
Carboniferous Limestone ($C_1$ subzone), with nautiloid cephalopods.
Wallis, F. S. 1935, p. 538.
Geol. Surv. O.S. 19 ; Ord. New Pop. 165.

**South Brewham,** $2\frac{1}{4}$ miles E.N.E. of Bruton. Roadside quarry and road-cutting N. of Cards Farm, $\frac{3}{4}$ mile S. of S. Brewham Church.
Jurassic, Cornbrash, with abundant well-preserved lamellibranchs at top of Lower Cornbrash (*Astarte-Trigonia* bed).
Douglas, J. A. and Arkell, W. J. 1928, p. 144.
Geol. Surv. O.S. 19 ; Ord. New Pop. 166.

**South Cheriton,** $3\frac{1}{2}$ miles S.W. of Wincanton. Quarry on W. side of road to N. Cheriton, $\frac{1}{4}$ mile N.W. of S. Cheriton Church.
Jurassic, Cornbrash, with brachiopods at base, ammonites (*Clydoniceras*) and lamellibranchs (*Astarte-Trigonia* bed) at top of Lower Cornbrash.
Douglas, J. A. and Arkell, W. J. 1928, p. 146.
Geol. Surv. O.S. 18 ; Ord. New Pop. 166.

**Stoford,** 2 miles S.S.W. of Yeovil. Small quarry in field, 150 yds. S.S.E. of Yeovil Junction.
Jurassic, Inferior Oolite (condensed and imperfect sequence), with ammonites, brachiopods, etc.
Kellaway, G. A. and Wilson, V. 1941, p. 150.
Geol. Surv. O.S. 18 ; Ord. New Pop. 177.

**Timberscombe,** S. of Minehead. Timberscombe.
Middle Devonian, Hangman Grits, with plant-remains.
Hicks, H. 1896, p. 361.
Geol. Surv. O.S. 20 ; Ord. New Pop. 164.

**Twerton,** S.W. suburb of Bath. Victoria Brick and Tile Works.
Pleistocene, about 10 ft. of gravel and loam of 100-ft. terrace of R. Avon, resting on Lower Lias clay, and yielding bones of elephant, mammoth, woolly rhinoceros, etc.
Palmer, L. S. 1930, p. 49.
Geol. Surv. O.S. 19 ; Ord. New Pop. 166.

**Uphill,** 2 miles S. of Weston-super-Mare. Brean Down, quarries W. of Uphill Church and cliff-exposures.
Carboniferous Limestone ($Z$-$C_2$ zones), with large corals (*Caninia*) and brachiopods.
Bamber, A. E. 1925, p. 85, with geol. map.
Geol. Surv. O.S. 20 ; Ord. New Pop. 165.

**Waterlip,** 2 miles N.E. of Shepton Mallet. Northern part of Willcox's Quarry, W. side of road.
Carboniferous Limestone ($Z$ zone). Silicified fossils can be dissolved out with acid.
Welch, F. B. A. 1933, p. 18, with geol. map.
Geol. Surv. O.S. 19 ; Ord. New Pop. 166.

**Welton,** $1\frac{1}{2}$ miles W. of Radstock. Bowldish Quarry, about 550 yds. N. of Welton station.
Jurassic, Lower Lias (condensed and broken sequence between *planorbis* and *raricostatum* zones), with ammonites, belemnites and brachiopods (*Spiriferina walcotti*) abundant.
Tutcher, J. W. and Trueman, A. E. 1925, p. 608.
Geol. Surv. O.S. 19 ; Ord. New Pop. 166.

**West Chinnock,** 3 miles N.N.E. of Crewkerne. Quarry on S. side of road on Chiselborough Hill, 2050 yds. N.E. of St. Margaret's Church ; also another quarry on N. side of road.

Jurassic, Inferior Oolite (resting on Upper Lias, Ham Hill Stone). Brachiopods (*Homoeorhynchia cynocephala*, etc.) are common and an occasional ammonite occurs.
Kellaway, G. A. and Wilson, V. 1941, p. 180.
Geol. Surv. O.S. 18 ; Ord. New Pop. 155.

**Weston-in-Gordano,** 3 miles N.E. of Clevedon.   Nightingale and Black Rock Quarries, N.E. and E. of the village.
Carboniferous Limestone (Z and C zones), with corals and brachiopods.
Reynolds, S. H. and Greenly, E. 1924, pp. 448, 450, with geol. map.
Geol. Surv. O.S. 35 ; Ord. New Pop. 155.

**Weston-super-Mare.**   Spring Cove, 200 yds. N. of the pier.
Carboniferous Limestone ($C_1$ subzone). A bed composed almost entirely of the coral *Caninia subibicina* crops out in the cliff by path to shore.
Vaughan, A. 1905, p. 552.
Geol. Surv. O.S. 20 ; Ord. New Pop. 165.

**Wheddon Cross,** $5\frac{1}{2}$ miles S.W. of Dunster.  Middle Devonian, Ilfracombe Beds, with a varied coral fauna and some crinoids, brachiopods, etc.
Hicks, H. 1896, p. 364.
Geol. Surv. O.S. 20 ; Ord. New Pop. 164.

**Winford,** 6 miles S.W. of Bristol.   Small quarry $\frac{1}{2}$ mile S. of Winford, on Crown Hill, on W. side of lane about 300 yds. N. of Crown Inn.
Carboniferous, " Millstone Grit " with plentiful, but badly-preserved, goniatites.
Geol. Surv. O.S. 19 ; Ord. New Pop. 165.

**Withycombe,** 4 miles W. of Williton.   Old quarries near Sandhill Farm, $\frac{1}{2}$ mile S.E. of Withycombe.
Middle Devonian, Ilfracombe Beds, with a rich coral fauna.
Perceval, S. G. 1866.
Geol. Surv. O.S. 20 ; Ord. New Pop. 164.

**Wiveliscombe,** $9\frac{1}{2}$ miles W.N.W. of Taunton.  Quarries near Oakhampton House, $1\frac{3}{4}$ miles N. of Wiveliscombe.
Upper Devonian, Morte Slates, with brachiopods, lamellibranchs and trilobites.
Ussher, W. A. E. 1908, p. 27.
Geol. Surv. N.S. 295 ; Ord. New Pop. 164.

**Wrington,** 10 miles S.W. of Bristol.  Quarries 300 yds. N.E. of Wrington at S. end of Prestow Wood opposite Branches Cross.
Carboniferous Limestone ($D_2$ subzone). A rich fauna of clisiophyllid and other corals and rare echinoderms (blastoids).
Geol. Surv. O.S. 19 ; Ord. New Pop. 165.


# STAFFORDSHIRE

**Biddulph,** 3 miles S.S.E. of Congleton (Cheshire).   Spoil-heap from disused colliery at Woodhouse Lane, about 300 yds. S.E. of Woodhouse Farm and 700 yds. N.E. of the Oxhay, on lane to Biddulph Moor.
Carboniferous, Coal Measures (*lenisulcata* zone, marine band in roof of Crabtree Coal), with solid goniatites (*Gastrioceras listeri*).
Geol. Surv. N.S. 110 ; Ord. New Pop. 110.

**Brindley Ford,** 3 miles N.N.E. of Tunstall.   Right bank of R. Trent in Lion's Paw Wood, 170 yds. W.N.W. of Lion's Paw Farm and 760 yds. N.N.E. of Judgefields.
Carboniferous, Millstone Grit (G zone), with abundant goniatites (*Gastrioceras cancellatum*) and lamellibranchs.
Geol. Surv. N.S. 110 and 123 ; Ord. New Pop. 110.

**Cauldon,** 8 miles W.N.W. of Ashbourne (Derbyshire). Cauldon Low Quarries (Derbyshire Stone Ltd.), 200 yds. S. of church by railway bridge over road.

Carboniferous Limestone ($C_2$ subzone), sparingly fossiliferous, but the brachiopod *Productus humerosus* occurs in massive limestone.

Hind, W. 1910, p. 571. Jackson, J. W. and Charlesworth, J. K. 1920, p. 487. Geol. Surv. O.S. 72 N.E. ; Ord. New Pop. 111.

**Daw End,** 2 miles N.E. of Walsall. Railway-cutting ¼ mile E. of Rushall Aqueduct. Permission in writing from railway authorities.

Silurian, lower Wenlock Limestone, with corals (*Streptelasma,* the rare *Goniophyllum,* etc.) and brachiopods (*Eospirifer radiatus* and *Wilsonia davidsoni*) ; resting on Wenlock Shale, with the corals *Tryplasma* and *Helminthidium* and such brachiopods as *Dinobolus davidsoni, Meristina obtusa* and *Sieberella galeata.* In the limestone, large ballstones are built of reef-corals and stromatoporoids and the surrounding stratified beds yield a rich shelly fauna.

Butler, A. J. and Oakley, K. P. 1936, pp. 135-136. Butler, A. J. 1939, pp. 54-55, with geol. map.

Geol. Surv. N.S. 154 ; Ord. New Pop. 120.

**Dudley.** Old quarries and underground workings on Wren's Nest Hill and Dudley Castle Hill yielded most of the fossils labelled " Dudley " in museums.

Silurian, Wenlock Shale, Wenlock Limestone and Lower Ludlow.

Butler, A. J. 1939.

Geol. Surv. N.S. 167 ; Ord. New Pop. 130 and 131.

**Dudley.** Quarries, cuttings and caverns near old limekilns on S.W. slope of Wren's Nest Hill, 1 mile N.W. of Dudley Castle.

Silurian, complete section through Wenlock Limestone, with Wenlock Shale below and Lower Ludlow above. At locality D of fig. 3 in Butler, 1939 (the best collecting-place) is a rich fauna of corals, stromatoporoids, bryozoa and brachiopods in the Nodular Beds, while two stromatoporoid beds occur at B. Noteworthy Dudley fossils include the tabulate corals *Favosites, Halysites* and *Heliolites* ; the rugose corals *Coenites, Kodonophyllum, Phaulactis* and *Xylodes*; the brachiopods *Atrypa reticularis, Leptaena rhomboidalis* and *Orthis* (*Parmorthis*) *elegantula* ; the trilobites *Calymene blumenbachi, Dalmanites vulgaris* and *Encrinurus,* and many others.

Butler, A. J. 1939, pp. 41-46, fig. 3 and geol. map.

Geol. Surv. N.S. 167 ; Ord. New Pop. 130 and 131.

**Dudley.** Exposures in walls of canal-basin 900 yds. N. of Dudley Castle. No. 12 of fig. 10 in Butler, 1939.

Silurian, Wenlock Limestone, with a rich coral-stromatoporoid-brachiopod fauna in the Nodular Beds and Basement Beds, and ballstones built chiefly of crinoid debris and bryozoa in the Lower Quarried Limestone.

Butler, A. J. 1939, pp. 63-64, text figs. and geol. map.

Geol. Surv. N.S. 167 ; Ord. New Pop. 130 and 131.

**Flash,** S.W. of Leek Road at 4½ miles from Buxton (Derbyshire). Cliff-section by stream on S. side of Flash-Allgreave road about 170 yds. N.E. of Wash Farm, Quarnford and 900 yds. downstream from Flash Bottom.

Carboniferous, Coal Measures (marine band above Six-Inch Mine) with goniatites (*Gastrioceras subcrenatum*) and lamellibranchs.

Cope, F. W. 1946a, p. 145.

Geol. Surv. O.S. 81 S.W. ; Ord. New Pop. 45.

**Gillow Heath,** ½ mile W. of Biddulph. Left bank of stream N. of The Falls about 500 yds. W. by N. of Biddulph station and just below the garden of The Falls.

Carboniferous, Coal Measures (*communis* zone, measures below Cockshead Coal) with abundant solid shells of the non-marine lamellibranch *Carbonicola* in fragile condition.
Cope, F. W. 1946b, p. 75.
Geol. Surv. N.S. 110 ; Ord. New Pop. 110.

**Gillow Heath.** Tip-heap of Gillow Heath Mining and Pottery Co., on S. side of Mow Lane. Permission from Mr. Peake, Director, at the works.
Carboniferous, Coal Measures (*communis* zone, measures below King Coal) with non-marine shells (*Carbonicola*) with well-preserved hinge-structures.
Cope, F. W. 1946b, p. 75.
Geol. Surv. N.S. 110 ; Ord. New Pop. 110.

**Hurst Hill,** near Coseley. Cutting on Hurst Hill-Sedgeley road, 130 yds. S.W. of St. Mary's Church, Hurst Hill, and 1200 yds. E.N.E. of Sedgeley church.
Silurian, Wenlock Limestone (Nodular Beds). Ballstones in bedded limestone and shale yield many corals and brachiopods.
Butler, A. J. 1939, pp. 70-72, with geol. map.
Geol. Surv. N.S. 167 ; Ord. New Pop. 130 and 131.

**Kingsley,** 3 miles N. of Cheadle. N. bank of stream $\frac{3}{4}$ mile N.N.W. of Hazlewall Farm and 300 yds. S.E. of Broadoak Farm, about $1\frac{1}{2}$ miles W. of Kingsley.
Carboniferous, Coal Measures (*communis* zone, measures below Woodhead Coal) with the non-marine lamellibranch *Carbonicola*.
Cope, F. W. 1946b.
Geol. Surv. O.S. 72 N.W. ; Ord. New Pop. 111.

**Meerbrook,** W. of Leek road at $9\frac{1}{2}$ miles from Buxton (Derbyshire). S. bank of R. Churnet on W. side of road bridge, 100 yds. S. of Middle Hulme and 750 yds. E.N.E. of New Grange Farm. Section difficult of access when river is high.
Carboniferous, Millstone Grit ($R_2$ subzone), with goniatites and lamellibranchs.
Geol. Surv. O.S. 81 S.W. ; Ord. New Pop. 111.

**Netherton,** S.W. of Dudley. Exposure below fence 30 yds. from small bridge on side of Doulton's Claypit, Saltwells ; and in E. side of cutting from claypit to canal at Brewin's Bridge, just N. of the small bridge.
Silurian, Ludlow, with fish-remains (*Thelodus*, *Sclerodus*, Acanthodians) in Bone Bed, and brachiopods (*Lingula*, *Camarotoechia*, *Chonetes*) in Upper Ludlow shales in deeper part of cutting.
King, W. W. and Lewis, W. J. 1912, p. 442.
Geol. Surv. N.S. 167 ; Ord. New Pop. 130.

**Waterfall,** 9 miles N.W. of Ashbourne (Derbyshire). Disused quarry W. of road from Waterfall to Saucefield House, 1000 yds. N.N.E. of Waterfall Church and opposite Redwayclose Barn.
Carboniferous Limestone ($D_1$ subzone), crinoidal limestones and shales with abundant bryozoa, brachiopods and lamellibranchs.
Geol. Surv. O.S. 72 N.E. ; Ord. New Pop. 111.

**Waterhouses,** 7 miles W.N.W. of Ashbourne. Two quarries 50 yds. N.E. of bridge over R. Hemps and 200 yds. N.W. of station, the easterly one disused, the westerly one worked. Owner, Mr. Barker of Waterhouses.
Carboniferous Limestone ($D_1$-$D_2$ subzones), crinoidal limestone with numerous corals and brachiopods and a rolled-shell bed at the top.
Sibly, T. F. 1908, pp. 56, 61. Hind, W. 1910, pp. 570, 571.
Geol. Surv. O.S. 72 N.E. ; Ord. New Pop. 111.

**Waterhouses.** Disused quarry 100 yds. E. of Field House and 50 yds. S. of Lamber Low.

Carboniferous Limestone ($D_1$-$D_2$ subzones), with many corals and brachiopods and a rolled-shell bed.
Sibly, T. F. 1908, pp. 56, 61. Hind, W. 1910, pp. 570, 571.
Geol. Surv. O.S. 72 N.E. ; Ord. New Pop. 111.

**Waterhouses.** Limestone outcrops on S. side of small hollow 600 yds. S.S.E. of Caltonmoor House and 400 yds. S.W. of Forest Farm (Mr. Cotton).
Carboniferous Limestone ($B_1$ subzone) with corals and the goniatite *Beyrichoceras hodderense*.
Alexander, G. B. 1940, p. 173.
Geol. Surv. O.S. 72 N.E. ; Ord. New Pop. 111.

**Waterhouses.** Disused quarry immediately S. of station, approached by bridge under railway.
Carboniferous Limestone ($D_1$ subzone). Corals are fairly common.
Geol. Surv. O.S. 72 N.E. ; Ord. New Pop. 111.

**Waterhouses.** Exposure 50 yds. W. of crossroads at Dale Tor, 400 yds. N.W. of Dale Abbey Farm and 800 yds. S. of Miles Knoll.
Carboniferous Limestone ($C_2$ subzone), knoll-reef limestones with *Spirifer bollandensis* and other brachiopods.
Geol. Surv. O.S. 72 N.E. ; Ord. New Pop. 111.

**Waterhouses.** Disused quarry 100 yds. E. of Dale Tor crossroads and 400 yds. N.N.W. of Dale Abbey Farm.
Carboniferous Limestone ($C_2$ subzone), massive limestone with *Michelinia grandis* and other corals.
Alexander, G. B. 1940, p. 173.
Geol. Surv. O.S. 72 N.E. ; Ord. New Pop. 111.

**Wootton,** 5 miles W.S.W. of Ashbourne (Derbyshire). Exposure in Softlow Wood, 1200 yds. E. of △ 1217, Weaver Hills and 1000 yds. S.W. of Thorswood House. Owner, Mr. Archer of Weaver Farm.
Carboniferous Limestone ($C_2$ subzone), knoll-reef limestones, with abundant brachiopods.
Geol. Surv. O.S. 72 N.E. ; Ord. New Pop. 111.

**Wootton.** Disused quarry 300 yds. E. of Weaver Farm, 1200 yds. E.N.E. of △ 1217, Weaver Hills and 900 yds. E.S.E. of Walk Farm. Owner, Mr. Archer of Weaver Farm.
Carboniferous Limestone ($S_1$ subzone), cherty limestones with some corals.
Geol. Surv. O.S. 72 N.E. ; Ord. New Pop. 111.

**Wootton.** Limestone quarry (Kevin Limepits Ltd.), 700 yds. S.W. of △ 1217, Weaver Hills and 900 yds. N.W. of Ramshorn Church.
Carboniferous Limestone ($D_1$-$D_2$ subzones), bedded limestones with large brachiopods (*Productus*) faulted against knoll-reef limestones with numerous brachiopods and some corals.
Hind, W. 1910, p. 571.
Geol. Surv. O.S. 72 N.E. ; Ord. New Pop. 111.

# SUFFOLK

**Aldeburgh.** Disused pit at Crag Pit Farm, 1 mile N. of Aldeburgh station on road to Leiston.
Pliocene, Coralline Crag, with abundant lamellibranchs (*Pecten maximus*, etc.) and bryozoa, and occasional sea-urchins and crabs.
Harmer, F. W. 1902, p. 416. Bell, S. A. and Notcutt, S. A. 1925, p. 41.
Geol. Surv. O.S. 49 S.W. ; Ord. New Pop. 150.

**Bawdsey,** 12 miles E.S.E. of Ipswich. Cliff-section approximately 1 mile N.E. of mouth of R. Deben. The best existing locality for Red Crag fossils ; mined during the war.

**H**

Pliocene, Red Crag (Butleyan), 30 ft., with many lamellibranchs ; derived mammalian bones and stone implements in Boxstones at base.
Boswell, P. G. H. 1928, p. 36.
Geol. Surv. N.S. 208 ; Ord. New Pop. 150.

**Bramford,** 2½ miles N.W. of Ipswich. Coe's Chalkpit and Brickyard, 1¼ miles N. of Bramford Church immediately E. of R. Gipping and opposite Fison and Packard's Chemical Manure Works. Permission from Messrs. Fison Ltd., Harvest Home, Ipswich.
Cretaceous, Upper Chalk (*quadratus* and *mucronata* zones) with belemnites (*Actinocamax* below, - *Belemnitella* above) and a band of large sea-urchins (*Echinocorys*) 50 ft. below top ; capped by Eocene deposits, with Pliocene, Red Crag, above (stone implements at base).
Boswell, P. G. H. 1927, p. 10, pl. 1.
Geol. Surv. N.S. 207 ; Ord. New Pop. 150.

**Butley,** 3 miles W. of Orford. Pit ¼ mile E.N.E. of Oyster Inn (Neutral Farm Pit), E. of Butley.
Pliocene, Red Crag (Butleyan, type-locality). Nearly 200 species of mollusca with derived bryozoa and fish-teeth. Exposure almost entirely overgrown, 1938.
Monckton, H. W. and Skeats, E. W. 1902, p. 482. Boswell, P. G. H. 1928, p. 34.
Geol. Surv. N.S. 208 ; Ord. New Pop. 150.

**Chillesford,** 2½ miles N.W. of Orford. Sandpit behind church, now overgrown.
Pliocene, Chillesford Beds, type-locality. Many lamellibranchs (*Acila cobboldiae,Yoldia lanceolata, Mya truncata,* etc.) may still be obtained by digging.
Boswell, P. G. H. 1928, pp. 41-44.
Geol. Surv. N.S. 208 ; Ord. New Pop. 150.

**Claydon,** 5 miles N.W. of Ipswich. Large chalkpit on E. side of road, ½ mile S.W. of Claydon Church, now largely overgrown.
Cretaceous, Upper Chalk, with corals, brachiopods, *Offaster* and other sea-urchins in *quadratus* zone, and brachiopods, sea-urchins and belemnites (*Belemnitella*) in *mucronata* zone ; covered by contorted glacial deposits.
Boswell, P. G. H. 1927, pp. 11, 53.
Geol. Surv. N.S. 207 ; Ord. New Pop. 150.

**Claydon.** Mason's Portland Cement Co.'s pit, ½ mile W. of Claydon station.
Cretaceous, Upper Chalk (*quadratus* zone), with sea-urchins, belemnites, etc. ; capped by Pleistocene Chalky-Kimmeridgian boulder-clay with derived fossils.
Boswell, P. G. H. 1938, pp. 410-411.
Geol. Surv. N.S. 207 ; Ord. New Pop. 150.

**Gedgrave,** 1½ miles S.W. of Orford. Pit in front of cottages on S.E. side of road from Orford to Gedgrave Hall, now overgrown.
Pliocene, Coralline Crag (Gedgravian), with an exceptionally rich fauna of gastropods and lamellibranchs.
Harmer, F. W. 1914-1925. Boswell, P. G. H. 1928, p. 24.
Geol. Surv. N.S. 208 ; Ord. New Pop. 150.

**Hollesley,** 8 miles S.E. of Woodbridge. Pit ⅜ mile S.W. of church, in good condition, 1946.
Pliocene, Red Crag (Butleyan). A good locality for gastropods and for such lamellibranchs as *Mya trunca:a, Serripes, Spisula, Macoma,* etc.
Boswell, P. G. H. 1928, p. 36.
Geol. Surv. N. S. 208 ; Ord. New Pop. 150.

**Ipswich.** Bolton and Co.'s Dales Road brickfield, near Norwich Road railway bridge, N. of the town.

Pleistocene loams, with Palaeolithic working-floor no longer exposed ; resting on glacially disturbed Pliocene, sub-Crag detritus bed and Eocene, London Clay. A historic locality for rostro-carinate flint implements.

Moir, J. Reid in Bell, A. and Notcutt, S. A. 1925, p. 46.

**Ipswich.** Old pits, now overgrown, immediately S. of Foxhall Hall, about 4 miles E. of Ipswich.

Pliocene, Red Crag (Newbournian), capped by Pleistocene glacial deposits. The rich molluscan fauna of the Crag can be obtained by digging. Flint and bone implements have been found in the Crag and Acheulian and Mousterian flint implements in the glacial gravels.

Boswell, P. G. H. and Moir, J. Reid 1923, p. 229.

Geol. Surv. N.S. 207 ; Ord. New Pop. 150.

**Newbourne,** 7 miles E.S.E. of Ipswich. Newbourne Pit, about 300 yds. N.E. of the church. Permission from Felixstowe Waterworks Co.

Pliocene, Red Crag (Newbournian, type-locality), with lamellibranchs (*Cyprina islandica*, *Spisula*, etc.) and gastropods, including *Neptunea contraria*.

Bell, A. and Notcutt, S. A. 1925, p. 39. Boswell, P. G. H. 1928, p. 39.

Geol. Surv. N.S. 208 ; Ord. New Pop. 150.

**Ramsholt,** 7 miles S.S.E. of Woodbridge. Pit ¼ mile N.W. of church, on left of track to Ramsholt bridge. In good condition, 1946.

Pliocene, Red Crag, with gastropods, including *Neptunea contraria* and lamellibranchs.

Boswell, P. G. H. 1928, p. 36.

Geol. Surv. N.S. 208 ; Ord. New Pop. 150.

**Stutton,** 6 miles S. of Ipswich. River cliff W. of Stutton Ness, 1¼ miles S. of Stutton Street. Exposure and conditions variable.

Pleistocene, Brickearth and Gravel, with estuarine lamellibranchs (*Corbicula fluminalis*, etc.) and bones of elephant, deer, horse and ox.

Whitaker, W. 1885, pp. 95-96.

Geol. Surv. O.S. 48 N.W. ; Ord. New Pop. 150.

**Sudbourne,** 4 miles W. of Aldeburgh. Pit in Sudbourne Park, ¼ mile N.W. of Sudbourne Hall and S.W. of village. Best existing Coralline Crag locality.

Pliocene, Coralline Crag, with numerous foraminifera, bryozoa, lamellibranchs and gastropods.

Boswell, P. G. H. 1928, p. 24.

Geol. Surv. N.S. 208 ; Ord. New Pop. 150.

**Sudbury.** Whorlow's Chalkpit, on N. side of Colchester road adjoining cemetery, nearly ½ mile E. of Market Square.

Cretaceous, Upper Chalk (*Marsupites* zone) with crinoid plates (*Marsupites*) and belemnites (*Actinocamax*).

Boswell, P. G. H. 1929, pp. 10, 13, 30.

Geol. Surv. N.S. 206 ; Ord. New Pop. 149.

**Sudbury.** Brundon Pit, 1¼ miles W.N.W. of Sudbury station.

Pleistocene gravels, etc., with bones of elephant, rhinoceros, bear, bison, red deer, etc., and land molluscs.

Boswell, P. G. H. 1929, pp. 10, 48, 53, 55. Moir, J. Reid and Hopwood, A. T. 1939.

Geol. Surv. N.S. 206 ; Ord. New Pop. 149.

**Sutton,** 3 miles S.E. of Woodbridge. Old pits in knoll ½ mile S. of Pettistree Hall, 1¼ miles S. of Sutton Church and about ½ mile E. of left bank of R. Deben. Section much overgrown.

Pliocene, Coralline Crag, with many bryozoa and poorly preserved lamellibranchs in Bryozoan Rock Bed at junction with Red Crag (Newbournian) above. This latter is exposed in chicken-run pit on W. side of knoll and contains abundant mollusca.

Boswell, P. G. H. 1928, pp. 26-27, 37.
Geol. Surv. N.S. 208 ; Ord. New Pop. 150.

# SURREY

**Albury,** 4 miles S.E. of Guildford. Brickworks on S. side of Guildford-Dorking road, ¼ mile W. of Silent Pool. Pit becoming degraded.

Cretaceous, Gault (*mammillatum* and *dentatus* zones), with ammonites (*Douvilleiceras, Hoplites* and the rare *Lyelliceras*) ; and base of Upper Gault with *Hysteroceras* and lamellibranchs.

Dines, H. G. and Edmunds, F. H. 1929, pp. 41, 72.
Geol. Surv. N.S. 285 ; Ord. New Pop. 170.

**Albury.** Sherbourne Farm pit, ⅓ mile N. of Silent Pool. No. 277 of Young, 1908.

Cretaceous, Upper Chalk (*planus* zone), with moderately abundant sponges, sea-urchins, brachiopods and lamellibranchs.

Young, G. W. 1908, p. 445. Dines, H. G. and Edmunds, F. H. 1929, p. 61.
Geol. Surv. N.S. 285 ; Ord. New Pop. 170.

**Betchworth,** 3 miles E. of Dorking. Betchworth Limeworks, ½ mile N. of Betchworth crossroads on Dorking-Reigate road. Typical of many quarries in neighbourhood, e.g. Dorking Greystone Works, Merstham Greystone Works, Buckland Limeworks, etc.

Cretaceous, Lower Chalk, with ammonites, lamellibranchs, etc., and belemnites (*Actinocamax plenus*) in *plenus* marl at top ; and Middle Chalk (*labiatus* zone) with lamellibranchs, etc.

Dines, H. G. and Edmunds, F. H. 1933, pp. 99, 103.
Geol. Surv. N.S. 286 ; Ord. New Pop. 170.

**Compton,** 3 miles S.W. of Guildford. Cuttings on the Guildford-Godalming Bypass from crest of Hog's Back to foot of hill.

Cretaceous, from Upper Chalk (*coranguinum* zone) to base of Middle Chalk. Abundant sea-urchins (*Micraster* and others) in Upper Chalk, with outstandingly rich Chalk Rock fauna at base, including ammonites, gastropods, etc. Brachiopods, sea-urchins (*Conulus*) and lamellibranchs (*Inoceramus*) in Middle Chalk.

Wright, C. W. and E. V. 1939.
Geol. Surv. N.S. 285 ; Ord. New Pop. 169 and 170.

**Dulwich.** Effra Branch sewer (about 1860) in a tunnel at Dulwich and a trench at Peckham.

Eocene, Woolwich Beds, type-locality of the gastropod *Pitharella rickmani.*
Edwards, F. E. 1860, p. 210. Rickman, C. 1860, p. 151 and 1861, p. 265.
Geol. Surv. London District 3 ; Ord. New Pop. 170.

**Farnham.** Coxbridge sandpits, on Alton road, 350 yds. W. of Alton-Bordon fork, 1 mile S.W. of Farnham.

Cretaceous, Lower Greensand (Folkestone Beds). Irregular ferruginous lenticles yield ammonites (especially *Acanthohoplites*), gastropods, lamellibranchs, sea-urchins, sponges, etc., chiefly in clayey inclusions.

Shepherd, W. B. 1934, p. 436. Wright, C. W. and E. V. 1942a, p. 86.
Geol. Surv. N.S. 285 ; Ord. New Pop. 169.

**Godstone.** Fairall's Pit (permission from H. Fairall, Godstone), and Taylor's Hill Pit, S. of Godstone.

Cretaceous, Lower Greensand (Hythe Beds), with ammonites (*Tropaeum, Cheloniceras*), lamellibranchs, sea-urchins, crinoid ossicles, corals (*Oculina*),

etc., in occasional ragged lumps darker in colour than the majority. Large sponges occur in lumps of indurated sand.
Gossling, F. 1929, p. 197 ; 1936, p. 322.
Geol. Surv. N.S. 286 ; Ord. New Pop. 171.

**Guildford.** The Chimney Pit, The Warren. No. 291 of Young, 1908.
Cretaceous, Upper Chalk (*planus* and *cortestudinarium* zones), with abundant sea-urchins (*Micraster*) and other fossils.
Young, G. W. 1908, p. 447. Dines, H. G. and Edmunds, F. H. 1929, p. 61.
Geol. Surv. N.S. 285 ; Ord. New Pop. 169 and 170.

**Guildford,** see also Onslow.

**Hurtmore,** 2 miles S. of Hog's Back at Puttenham. Squirrel Inn pit, due N. of Inn.
Cretaceous, Lower Greensand (Bargate Beds facies of Sandgate Beds), with sparse ammonites (*Parahoplites*) and a few lamellibranchs and sponges (*Doryderma* and *Plocoscyphia*).
Dines, H. G. and Edmunds, F. H. 1929, p. 27.
Geol. Surv. N.S. 285 ; Ord. New Pop. 169.

**Kenley.** Riddlesdown Limeworks pit, on E. side of London-Eastbourne road opposite Rose and Crown Inn. Permission from quarry office. No. 113 of Young, 1905.
Cretaceous, Upper Chalk (*planus* and *cortestudinarium* zones), with abundant sea-urchins and other fossils ; and top of Middle Chalk.
Young, G. W. 1905, p. 207, with topog. map. Dines, H. G. and Edmunds, F. H. 1933, p. 104.
Geol. Surv. N.S. 286 ; Ord. New Pop. 170.

**Merrow,** 1½ miles E. of Guildford. Large pit worked by disc-harrow, on Merrow-Clandon road. Enlarged from No. 281A and adjoining No. 281 of Young, 1908.
Cretaceous, Upper Chalk (*coranguinum, Uintacrinus* and *Marsupites* zones). Note a band of the sea-urchin *Conulus* at junction of *coranguinum* and *Uintacrinus* zones.
Young, G. W. 1908, p. 446. Dines, H. G. and Edmunds, F. H. 1929, p. 62.
Geol. Surv. N.S. 285 ; Ord. New Pop. 170.

**Mickleham,** 2 miles S. of Leatherhead. Old Forge pit, on E. side of old Leatherhead-Dorking road just N. of Mickleham.
Cretaceous, Upper Chalk (*planus* and base of *cortestudinarium* zones), with the sea-urchin *Micraster* and other fossils abundant.
Geol. Surv. N.S. 286 ; Ord. New Pop. 170.

**Mickleham.** Mickleham Bypass cuttings, both sides of new Leatherhead-Dorking road W. of village.
Cretaceous, top of Middle and base of Upper Chalk, with ammonites, gastropods and other fossils of Chalk Rock fauna.
Geol. Surv. N.S. 286 ; Ord. New Pop. 170.

**Nutfield.** Copyhold Pit, 600 yds. E.N.E. of Redhill Junction, just E. of N. mouth of tunnel on Brighton railway. Permission must be obtained in writing from Fuller's Earth Union Ltd.
Cretaceous, Lower Greensand (Sandgate Beds), with ammonites (*Parahoplites, Tropaeum*) and lamellibranchs.
Dines, H. G. and Edmunds, F. H. 1933, p. 68.
Geol. Surv. N.S. 286 ; Ord. New Pop. 170.

**Onslow,** W. suburb of Guildford. Pit in Onslow Garden Village, about 150 yds. S. of E. end of road called Curling Vale and adjoining footpath running S.W. up the hill.

Cretaceous, Upper Chalk (*pilula* zone, the only permanent exposure in Surrey), with sea-urchins (*Echinocorys, Offaster*), bryozoa, lamellibranchs, etc.
Geol. Surv. N.S. 285 ; Ord. New Pop. 169 and 170.

**Oxted.** Barrow Green sandpit, opposite The Priory, $\frac{9}{10}$ mile W.N.W. of Oxted.

Cretaceous, Lower Greensand and Gault (*mammillatum* zone) with ammonites, notably *Cleoniceras, Prohelicoceras* and *Protanisoceras*, and *Hoplites* above.
Geol. Surv. N.S. 286 ; Ord. New Pop. 171.

**Puttenham,** 4 miles W. of Guildford. Wancote pit, just W. and in grounds of Wancote (now Greyfriars) House, on Hog's Back 1300 yds. E. of Puttenham crossroads.

Cretaceous, Upper Chalk (*planus* and *cortestudinarium* zones) with abundant sea-urchins and casts of ammonites and gastropods (of Chalk Rock fauna) in "Top Rock" at junction of zones.
Dines, H. G. and Edmunds, F. H. 1929, p. 76.
Geol. Surv. N.S. 285 ; Ord. New Pop. 169.

**Runfold,** 2 miles E. of Farnham. Pit immediately S. and W. of Jolly Farmer Inn.

Cretaceous, Lower Greensand (Folkestone Beds). Indurated masses yield well-preserved siliceous sponges (*Doryderma, Plocoscyphia, Renieria* and *Stelleta*) and silicified gastropods, lamellibranchs, brachiopods and sea-urchins.
Wright, C. W. and E. V. 1942a, p. 86.
Geol. Surv. N.S. 285 ; Ord. New Pop. 169.

**Seale,** 3 miles E. of Farnham. Seale quarry, on lane running E.N.E. from village.

Cretaceous, Lower Chalk, with ammonites and many small fossils ; and lower part of Middle Chalk.
Dines, H. G. and Edmunds, F. H. 1929, p. 52.
Geol. Surv. N.S. 285 ; Ord. New Pop. 169.

**Seale.** Victory Inn pit (the Inn is now a private house), on S. slope of Hog's Back. No. 322 of Young, 1908, adjoining No. 323.

Cretaceous, Middle Chalk and base of Upper Chalk, with abundant fossils, especially in weathered N. face of pit in *planus* zone of Upper Chalk.
Young, G. W. 1908, p. 440. Dines, H. G. and Edmunds, F. H. 1929, pp. 53, 55.
Geol. Surv. N.S. 285 ; Ord. New Pop. 169.

**Wanborough,** 3 miles W. of Guildford. Pit on hill just N. of Puttenham crossroads. No. 308 of Young, 1908.

Cretaceous, Upper Chalk (*coranguinum* zone), with sea-urchins, starfish ossicles, lamellibranchs, etc.
Young, G. W. 1908, p. 448. Dines, H. G. and Edmunds, F. H. 1929, p. 61.
Geol. Surv. N.S. 285 ; Ord. New Pop. 169.

**Warlingham.** Old pit on S. side of Tithe Pit, Shaw Lane, $\frac{1}{2}$ mile E. of London-Eastbourne road and E.N.E. of Upper Warlingham station. No. 118 of Young, 1905.

Cretaceous, Upper Chalk (*cortestudinarium* and *coranguinum* zones) with the sea-urchins *Micraster* and *Echinocorys*, etc.
Young, G. W. 1905, p. 207, with topog. map. Dines, H. G. and Edmunds, F. H. 1933, p. 113.
Geol. Surv. N.S. 286 ; Ord. New Pop. 170.

**Warlingham.** Whyteleafe Chalkpit (disused), on E. side of Croydon-Oxted railway, $\frac{1}{2}$ mile S. of Upper Warlingham station. No. 119 of Young, 1905.

Cretaceous, Middle Chalk (*Terebratulina* zone), unusually rich in the zonal brachiopod, *Inoceramus* and other lamellibranchs, sponges ; also bryozoa and small sea-urchins on flint.

Young, G. W. 1905, p. 208, with topog. map. Dines, H. G. and Edmunds, F. H. 1933, p. 104.
Geol. Surv. N.S. 286 ; Ord. New Pop. 170.

**West Clandon,** 3½ miles N.E. of Guildford. Chalkpit on W. side of road from W. Clandon to Newland's Corner, 750 yds. N. of Newland's Corner road-fork. No. 282a of Young, 1908.
Cretaceous, Upper Chalk (upper *coranguinum* zone), with sea-urchins (*Micraster*, etc.) and many starfish ossicles. Has yielded the rare sea-urchins *Hagenowia rostrata* and *Zeuglopleurus rowei* and a variety of lamellibranchs.
Young, G. W. 1908, p. 446. Dines, H. G. and Edmunds, F. H. 1929, p. 62.
Geol. Surv. N.S. 285 ; Ord. New Pop. 170.

**West Horsley,** 5 miles N.E. of Guildford. Coombs Pit, just S. of main crossroads. No. 264 of Young, 1908.
Cretaceous, Upper Chalk (upper *coranguinum* zone). Fossils are scarce, but well-preserved, especially the sea-urchin *Conulus albogalerus.*
Young, G. W. 1908, p. 444. Dines, H. G. and Edmunds, F. H. 1929, p. 62.
Geol. Surv. N.S. 285 ; Ord. New Pop. 170.

## SUSSEX

**Arundel.** Chalkpit behind Black Rabbit Inn, Offham, ¾ mile N.E. of Arundel Castle. Pit Y of Gaster, 1932.
Cretaceous, Upper Chalk (*pilula* zone), with sea-urchins (*Offaster pilula, Echinocorys scutatus*), belemnites, brachiopods, etc.
Gaster, C. T. A. 1932, pp. 219-220, with topog. map.
Geol. Surv. N.S. 317 ; Ord. New Pop. 182.

**Bognor Regis.** Foreshore at low tide, and Barn Rocks and Bognor Rocks offshore at Aldwick.
Eocene, London Clay. The rich fauna includes lamellibranchs (*Cyprina planata*) and gastropods (*Streptolathyrus cymatodis*), etc., in the lower part ; corals, brittle-stars, crustacea and fish, with mollusca, in the Starfish Bed ; and mollusca (*Pholadomya dixoni, Glycymeris, Panope,* etc.) in the higher beds.
Venables, E. M. 1929, with sketch-map.
Geol. Surv. N.S. 332 ; Ord. New Pop. 181.

**Boxglove,** 3½ miles N.E. of Chichester. Chalkpit ½ mile S. of Halnaker Windmill, 1½ miles N.E. of Boxgrove Church.
Cretaceous, Upper Chalk (*quadratus* zone), with sea-urchins, bryozoa, brachiopods, lamellibranchs, sponges, etc.
Gaster, C. T. A. 1944, p. 186, with geol. map.
Geol. Surv. N.S. 317 ; Ord. New Pop. 181.

**Burpham,** 2¼ miles N.E. of Arundel. Small roadside pit ½ mile S. of Burpham-Arundel road, W.N.W. of Warningcamp Hill. No. 25 of Gaster, 1924, N. of Gaster, 1932.
Cretaceous, Upper Chalk (*pilula* zone), with crinoids (*Bourgueticrinus*), sea-urchins (*Echinocorys,* large *Offaster*), lamellibranchs, etc.
Gaster, C. T. A. 1924, p. 98, with topog. map ; 1932, p. 216, with topog. map.
Geol. Surv. N.S. 317 ; Ord. New Pop. 182.

**Durrington,** 2¼ miles N.W. of Worthing. Chalkpit ¼ mile S.S.E. of Salvington Windmill ; and pit in two sections in Cote Bottom. Nos. 15 and 17 of Gaster, 1924.
Cretaceous, Upper Chalk (*quadratus* zone), with sponges, the minute crinoid *Saccocoma cretacea,* sea-urchins, bryozoa (*Bicavea*), etc.
Bather, F. A. 1924. Gaster, C. T. A. 1924, p. 97, with topog. map.
Geol. Surv. N.S. 318 ; Ord. New Pop. 182.

**East Lavington.** Pit E. of △ 684 on Barlavington Down, S. of Duncton Hanger ; and a pit on Woolavington Down, S. of Lavington Park.

Cretaceous, Middle Chalk (*Terebratulina* zone) and Upper Chalk (*planus* zone), with sponges, sea-urchins, brachiopods, lamellibranchs, et:.

Gaster, C. T. A. 1944, p. 179 with geol. map.

Geol. Surv. N.S. 317 ; Ord. New Pop. 181 and 182.

**Eastbourne.** Cliff and foreshore between Eastbourne and Beachy Head. Best approached from Eastbourne or from Cow Gap.

Cretaceous, Upper Greensand, and Lower Chalk, with fallen blocks of Middle and Upper Chalk.   Ammonites, lamellibranchs, brachiopods and bryozoa are common.   Note abundance of the sponge *Stauronema carteri* at base of Lower Chalk.

Milner, H. B. and Bull, A. J. 1925, with geol. map.

Geol. Surv. N.S. 334 ; Ord. New Pop. 183.

**Friston,** 4 miles W. of Eastbourne.  Pit 50 yds. S. of Exceat New Barn, 1 mile W. of Friston Church at 300 ft. O.D.

Cretaceous, Upper Chalk (*Uintacrinus* zone), with plates of the crinoid *Uintacrinus* and brachiopods (*Terebratulina rowei* and rhynchonellids).

Gaster, C. T. A. 1939, p. 523, with geol. map.

Geol. Surv. N.S. 334 ; Ord. New Pop. 183.

**Houghton,** 3 miles N. of Arundel.  Large pit S.W. of Houghton and N. of Houghton Lodge ; and a pit 150 yds. S. of Houghton Lodge, at N.E. end of Arundel Park.  Pit S of Gaster, 1932.

Cretaceous, Middle Chalk (*Terebratulina* zone) and Upper Chalk (*planus* and *cortestudinarium* zones), with sponges, sea-urchins, brachiopods, lamellibranchs, etc.

Gaster, C. T. A. 1932, pp. 217-219, with topog. map.

Geol. Surv. N.S. 317 ; Ord. New Pop. 182.

**Lavant,** 2½ miles N. of Chichester.  Pit on E. side of Chalkpit Lane, adjoining Chalkpit Plantation, E. Lavant.

Cretaceous, Upper Chalk (*pilula* zone), with sea-urchins (*Offaster pilula,* a band of *Echinocorys scutatus*) and other fossils.

Gaster, C. T. A. 1944, p. 185, with geol. map.

Geol. Surv. N.S. 317 ; Ord. New Pop. 181.

**Lavant.**  Pit and workings ¼ mile N. of Stoke Clump and ¾ mile W. of Langford Farm, Lavant.

Cretaceous, Upper Chalk (*pilula* zone, phosphatic chalk), with fish-teeth, oysters, brachiopods (*Terebratulina rowei*), sea-urchins, worm-tubes, etc.

Gaster, C. T. A. 1944, p. 185, with geol. map.

Geol. Surv. N.S. 317 ; Ord. New Pop. 181.

**Lewes.**  Southerham Grey Pit, 1 mile from Lewes on Eastbourne road ; and quarry ¼ mile to the west, S. of Fox Inn.

Cretaceous, Lower Chalk, with ammonites (*Schloenbachia, Acanthoceras, Turrilites,* etc.), lamellibranchs, brachiopods, sea-urchins, etc.

White, H. J. O. 1926, pp. 46-47.

Geol. Surv. N.S. 319 ; Ord. New Pop. 183.

**Lewes,** Bridgwick Pit, old and new pits, Malling Hill, Lewes, 1 mile N. of railway station.

Cretaceous, Middle Chalk (*Terebratulina* zone) and Upper Chalk (*planus* zone), with sponges, sea-urchins, brachiopods (note *Terebratulina lata* in both zones), etc.

White, H. J. O. 1926, pp. 50, 55.

Geol. Surv. N.S. 319 ; Ord. New Pop. 183.

**Lewes,** see also Offham.

**Newhaven.** Meeching Quarry, Newhaven, 700 yds. S. of church. No. 141 of Gaster, 1929.

Cretaceous, Upper Chalk (*Marsupites* and *pilula* zones), with crinoid-plates, sea-urchins, etc.

Gaster, C. T. A. 1929, p. 335, with geol. map.

Geol. Surv. N.S. 334 ; Ord. New Pop. 183.

**Newhaven.** Coast-section enclosed in the fortified area of Castle Hill. Eocene, Woolwich Beds, with many mollusca.

Whitaker, W. 1871, p. 265.

Geol. Surv. N.S. 334 ; Ord. New Pop. 183.

**North Lancing.** Pit by reservoir near Hill Barn, N. of N. Lancing, ¼ mile S.E. of Lancing Ring. No. 2 of Gaster, 1924.

Cretaceous, Upper Chalk (*pilula* and base of *quadratus* zones), with crinoids (*Saccocoma, Bourgueticrinus*), sea-urchins (*Echinocorys, Hagenowia*) and other fossils.

Gaster, C. T. A. 1924, p. 97, with topog. map.

Geol. Surv. N.S. 318 ; Ord. New Pop. 182.

**Offham,** 1½ miles N.W. of Lewes. Quarry at Chalk Pit Inn, ¼ mile S. of Offham Church and North and South Pits on Offham Hill.

Cretaceous, Middle Chalk (*Terebratulina* zone) to Upper Chalk (*cortestudinarium* zone). Sponges, sea-urchins, brachiopods and lamellibranchs occur. Flint-meal from cavernous flints in the North Pit may be washed for microfossils.

White, H. J. O. 1926, pp. 54-55.

Geol. Surv. N.S. 319 ; Ord. New Pop. 183.

**Rottingdean,** Brighton. Pit by cart-track to Newlands Barn, at N. end of East Hill, 700 yds. E.N.E. of Rottingdean Church.

Cretaceous, Upper Chalk (*pilula* zone), with sponges, sea-urchins, bryozoa, brachiopods, etc.

White, H. J. O. 1926, pp. 58-59. Gaster, C. T. A. 1929, p. 337, with topog. map.

Geol. Surv. N.S. 333 ; Ord. New Pop. 183.

**Singleton,** 6 miles N. of Chichester. Pit on E. side of main road, 150 yds. S.S.E. of Littlewood Farm ; and pit on Yorkhurst Hill, ¼ mile S.E. of Broadham Cottages.

Cretaceous, Upper Chalk (*coranguinum* zone), with sea-urchins, bryozoa, lamellibranchs, etc.

Gaster, C. T. A. 1944, p. 182, with geol. map.

Geol. Surv. N.S. 317 ; Ord. New Pop. 181.

**Selsey.** Foreshores at low water at Bracklesham, E. and W. of Selsey Bill. Eocene, Bracklesham Beds, type-locality. A very rich fauna of lamellibranchs and gastropods occurs, with foraminifera (*Nummulites*), corals and vertebrates.

Dixon, F. 1850. Fisher, O. 1862.

Geol. Surv. N.S. 332 ; Ord. New Pop. 181.

**Sompting,** 2 miles N.E. of Worthing. Pit in Dankton Lane, just over ¼ mile N.E. of Sompting Church. No. 5 of Gaster, 1924.

Cretaceous, Upper Chalk (*pilula* zone) with crinoids, sea-urchins and other fossils.

Gaster, C. T. A. 1924, p. 98, with topog. map.

**Sompting.** Pit in Lambley's Lane, N.W. of Sompting Church.

Cretaceous, Upper Chalk, *quadratus* zone, with crinoids (*Saccocoma*), sea-urchins, bryozoa (*Bicavea*) and other fossils.

Gaster, C. T. A. 1924, p. 97, with topog. map. Bather, F. A. 1924.

Geol. Surv. N.S. 318 ; Ord. New Pop. 182.

**Steyning.** Pit on W. side of Newham Lane, ½ mile S.W. of Steyning ; and Steyning Limeworks, E. of Round Hill, 1 mile W. of Steyning.

Cretaceous, *plenus* Marls at junction of Lower and Middle Chalk, with the belemnite *Actinocamax plenus*.

Gaster, C. T. A. 1937, p. 365, with geol. map.

Geol. Surv. N.S. 318 ; Ord. New Pop. 182.·

**Stoughton,** 6 miles N.W. of Chichester. Pit on S. side of road at S.W. end of Lambdown Hill, Stoughton.

Cretaceous, Upper Chalk (*pilula* zone) with sea-urchins, oysters, etc.

Gaster, C. T. A. 1944, p. 185, with geol. map.

Geol. Surv. N.S. 317 ; Ord. New Pop. 181.

**Warningcamp,** 1¼ miles E. of Arundel. Pit in South Woodleighs Plantation, N.E. of Woodleighs Lodge. No. 26 of Gaster, 1924, N of 1932.

Cretaceous, Upper Chalk (*quadratus* zone), with the crinoid *Saccocoma*, the bryozoan *Bicavea* and other fossils.

Gaster, C. T. A. 1924, p. 97; with topog. map ; 1932.

Geol. Surv. N.S. 317 ; Ord. New Pop. 182.

**Warningcamp.** Large pit on Warningcamp Hill, N.E. of Arundel. No. 24 of Gaster, 1924, P of 1932.

Cretaceous, Upper Chalk (*quadratus* zone), with the crinoid *Saccocoma*, bryozoa, sea-urchins, etc.

Gaster, C. T. A. 1924, p. 97, with topog. map ; 1932, p. 216, with topog. map.

Geol. Surv. N.S. 317 ; Ord. New Pop. 182.

**Westdean,** 6 miles W. of Eastbourne. Section at Cliff End on E. side of Cuckmere Haven, S. of coastguard path.

Cretaceous, Upper Chalk (*coranguinum* zone), with *Trochiliopora gasteri* and other bryozoa, starfish-ossicles, etc.

Gaster, C. T. A. 1939, p. 522, with geol. map. Thomas, H. D. 1939.

Geol. Surv. N.S. 334 ; Ord. New Pop. 183.

**West Dean,** 5 miles N. of Chichester. Pits on S. side of road, S. of White Horse Inn, Chilgrove, 2¼ miles N.W. of West Dean.

Cretaceous, Upper Chalk (*Uintacrinus* and *Marsupites* zones), with plates of the zonal crinoids, the belemnite *Actinocamax granulatus*, etc.

Gaster, C. T. A. 1944, pp. 183-184, with geol. map.

Geol. Surv. N.S. 317 ; Ord. New Pop. 181.


# WARWICKSHIRE

**Dosthill,** 3 miles S. of Tamworth. Stoneware Co.'s pits, 700 yds. S.S.E. of Dosthill Church.

Carboniferous, Coal Measures, with non-marine shells (*Carbonicola*, etc.) in roof of Thin Rider seam and the brachiopod *Lingula*, with the worm *Spirorbis* above the Seven Feet coal.

Mitchell, G. H. and Stubblefield, C. J. 1942, pp. 22, 23.

Geol. Surv. N.S. 154 ; Ord. New Pop. 131.

**Hartshill,** 3 miles N.W. of Nuneaton. Woodlands Quarry, disused and partly flooded, about 200 yds. N.W. of the Inn.

Lower Cambrian, Hartshill Quartzite (*Hyolithus* limestone and associated sandstones), with various hyolithids, tubes of *Coleoloides*, and rare brachiopods and lamellibranchs.

Cobbold, E. S. 1919. Eastwood, T. and others 1923, p. 33.

Geol. Surv. N.S. 169 ; Ord. New Pop. 132.

**Longford,** 3¼ miles N.N.E. of Coventry. Brickpit E. of Longford and Exhall station (Foleshill Brick and Tile Co.).

Carboniferous, Coal Measures (Keele Beds, Whitacre-Longford limestone), with the worm *Spirorbis* and the non-marine gastropod *Anthracopupa*.

Eastwood, T. and others 1923, p. 81.

Geol. Surv. N.S. 169 ; Ord. New Pop. 132.

**Napton-on-the-Hill,** 3 miles E. of Southam. Brickyard 800 yds. W. of the church, on E. side of Oxford Canal.

Jurassic, Lower Lias (*ibex* and *davoei* zones) and Middle Lias, with abundant ammonites and other fossils.

Woodward, H. B. 1893, p. 160.

Geol. Surv. O.S. 53 S.W. ; Ord. New Pop. 132.

**Spernal,** 3 miles N. of Alcester. Road-cutting, Burford Lane, 1½ miles E. of Spernal Church.

Triassic, Keuper (Arden Sandstone), with plant-remains, small crustacea (*Euestheria minuta*) and teeth and bones of fishes and Labyrinthodont amphibia.

Wills, L. J. and Campbell Smith, W. 1914, p. 475.

Geol. Surv. O.S. 54 S.E. ; Ord. New Pop. 131.

# WESTMORELAND

**Ambleside.** Skelgill, 1½ miles S.E. of Ambleside, on E. side of Windermere road.

Silurian, Lower Llandovery (Skelgill Shales, type-locality), with numerous graptolites (*Monograptus*), etc.

Marr, J. E. and Nicholson, H. A. 1888, p. 658. Marr, J. E. 1925.

Geol. Surv. O.S. 98 N.W. ; Ord. New Pop. 89.

**Birkdale,** 9 miles by footpath E.N.E. of Dufton. Section at junction of Thistlyhill Sike with Grain Beck, 1 mile W. by N. of Birkdale Ford.

Carboniferous Limestone ($D_1$ subzone, top of Smiddy Limestone), with algal nodules (*Girvanella*).

Turner, J. S. 1927, pp. 347-348, with geol. map.

Geol. Surv. O.S. 102 S.E. ; Ord. New Pop. 84.

**Brough-under-Stainmore.** Waterfall in Swindale Beck near track running W. from Brough-Middleton road near Seavy Rigg, 200 yds. W.N.W. of third milestone from Brough.

Carboniferous Limestone ($D_2$ subzone, base of Four Fathoms Limestone), with many rolled corals (*Dibunophyllum*).

Geol. map in Turner, J. S. 1927.

Geol. Surv. O.S. 102 S.E. ; Ord. New Pop. 84.

**Burrells,** 1½ miles S.S.W. of Appleby. Burrells Brockram Quarry, on W. side of main road, 300 yds. S.W. of village.

Permian, Brockram, with derived corals and brachiopods in pebbles of Carboniferous Limestone.

Geol. Surv. O.S. 102 S.W. ; Ord. New Pop. 83.

**Cautley,** near Sedbergh (Yorks.). Bed and banks of Backside Beck, ¼ mile W. of Mountain View.

Ordovician, Ashgill Series (*Remopleurides* limestone). Some of the calcareous nodules in the mudstones are fossiliferous.

Marr, J. E. 1913, pp. 3, 4.

Geol. Surv. O.S. 97 N.W. ; Ord. New Pop. 89.

**Cautley.** Gully below waterfall in Watley Gill, tributary to Backside Beck, ½ mile W. of Mountain View.

Silurian, Lower Llandovery (basal limestone), with trilobites, etc. (in weathered " gingerbread rock "), below shales with the graptolite *Dimorphograptus*.
Marr, J. E. 1913, p. 11.
Geol. Surv. O.S. 97 N.W. ; Ord. New Pop. 89.

**Cautley.** Spen Gill (headwaters of Backside Beck), steep-sided gully below waterfall 1 mile W. of Adamthwaite.
Silurian, Llandovery with graptolites ; *Dimorphograptus* in screes on E. side of stream ; *Monograptus sedgwicki* in black mudstones on W. side, about 10 ft. above stream, just below waterfall.
Marr, J. E. and Nicholson, H. A. 1888.
Geol. Surv. O.S. 97 N.W. ; Ord. New Pop. 89.

**Crosby Ravensworth,** 5 miles S.W. of Appleby. Gathorn Plain, on Shap-Orton road about ¼ mile N.E. of Blasterfield, 2 miles S.E. of Crosby Ravensworth.
Carboniferous Limestone ($D_1$ subzone, top of Knipe Scar Limestone), with the brachiopods *Daviesiella* cf. *comoides, Davidsonina [Cyrtina] septosa*, etc.
Garwood, E. J. 1912, p. 479, with geol. map ; 1916, p. 9, with geol. map.
Geol. Surv. O.S. 102 S.W. ; Ord. New Pop. 83.

**Crosby Ravensworth.** Raise Howe Quarry, by main Shap-Orton road, ⅜ mile N.N.E. of Blasterfield and 2 miles S.S.E. of Crosby Ravensworth.
Carboniferous, Yoredale Series ($D_2$ subzone, Maulds Meaburn = Jew Limestone), with the coral *Lonsdaleia floriformis*.
Miller, A. A. and Turner, J. S. 1931, p. 14, with geol. map.
Geol. Surv. O.S. 102 S.W. ; Ord. New Pop. 83.

**Drybeck,** 3 miles S.S.W. of Appleby. Small quarry W. of Drybeck.
Carboniferous, Yoredale Series (Little Strickland = Tyne Bottom Limestone), with foraminifera (*Saccaminopsis*) and corals (*Orionastraea*).
Miller, A. A. and Turner, J. S. 1931, p. 16, with geol. map.
Geol. Surv. O.S. 102 S.W. ; Ord. New Pop. 83.

**Dufton,** 3 miles N. of Appleby. Great Rundale Beck, nearly 2 miles N.E. of Dufton, just over 1 mile below Great Rundale Tarn.
Carboniferous Limestone ($C_2$ subzone, Bryozoa Band), with abundant bryozoa and brachiopods.
Turner, J. S. 1927, p. 345, with geol. map.
Geol. Surv. O.S. 102 S.E. ; Ord. New Pop. 83.

**Dufton.** Great Millstone Sike, just above junction with left bank of Maize Beck on W. side of Meldon Hill, 4 miles E.N.E. of Dufton.
Carboniferous, Yoredale Series (Tyne Bottom Limestone), with corals, including *Orionastraea*, and brachiopods.
Turner, J. S. 1927, p. 349, with geol. map.
Geol. Surv. O.S. 102 S.E. ; Ord. New Pop. 84.

**Dufton.** Maize Beck, between Dufton Fell and Marton Fell, ¼ mile N.N.E. of E. end of Seamore Tarn.
Carboniferous, Yoredale Series (Single Post Limestone), with corals, including *Orionastraea*, brachiopods and lamellibranchs.
Turner, J. S. 1927, p. 350, with geol. map.
Geol. Surv. O.S. 102 S.E. ; Ord. New Pop. 84.

**Great Strickland,** 4½ miles N. of Shap. Section in left bank of R. Leith just above Waterfalls Bride, Old Scar Wood.
Carboniferous, Yoredale Series (beds above Four Fathom Limestone). " *Posidonomya* "-phase fauna of bryozoa, brachiopods, lamellibranchs (including *Posidonia*), nautiloids, etc.
Miller, A. A. and Turner, J. S. 1931, p. 20, with geol. map.
Geol. Surv. O.S. 102 S.W. ; Ord. New Pop. 83.

**Hackthorpe,** 5 miles S.S.E. of Penrith. Several quarries ¼ mile S.W. of Hackthorpe (Hackenthorpe).

Carboniferous, Yoredale Series (Lowther=Five Yards Limestone), with bryozoa (*Stenopora*) and brachiopods, including *Gigantoproductus* spp.

Miller, A. A. and Turner, J. S. 1931, p. 17, with geol. map.
Geol. Surv. O.S. 102 S.W. ; Ord. New Pop. 83.

**Hilton,** 3½ miles E. of Appleby. Headwaters of Scoredale Beck, Hilton Fell, 2¼ miles N.E. of the village.

Carboniferous, Yoredale Series, a sequence of limestones with corals and brachiopods.

Turner, J. S. 1927, pp. 348-349, with geol. map.
Geol. Surv. O.S. 102 S.E. ; Ord. New Pop. 84.

**Hilton.** Siss Gill, Burton Fell, 3 miles E.N.E. of Hilton.

Carboniferous, Yoredale Series (Cockle Shell Limestone), with corals (*Lithostrotion* and *Zaphrentoides*) and brachiopods, including *Gigantoproductus giganteus*.

Turner, J. S. 1927, p. 350, with geol. map.
Geol. Surv. O.S. 102 S.E. ; Ord. New Pop. 84.

**Kaber,** 3 miles N.E. of Kirkby Stephen. Quarries S. of Redgate Lane.

Carboniferous Limestone ($D_1$ subzone, Smiddy Limestone), with algal nodules (*Girvanella*).

Turner, J. S. 1935, p. 121, with geol. map.
Geol. Surv. O.S. 102 S.E. ; Ord. New Pop. 84.

**Kaber.** Red Gate Gill, 1 mile S. of Redgate Lane, 1 mile E.S.E. of Kaber.

Carboniferous, limestone in lower Yoredale Series, with zaphrentid corals, bryozoa and brachiopods (chonetids and spiny productids).

Turner, J. S. 1935, p. 121, with geol. map.
Geol. Surv. O.S. 97 N.W. ; Ord. New Pop. 84.

**Kentmere.** Stile End, approximately 2300 yds. E.N.E. of St. Cuthbert's Church, Kentmere.

Ordovician, Caradoc (Stile End Beds=" Style-End Grassing Beds " of Harkness and Nicholson), with trilobites, brachiopods, etc.

Harkness, R. and Nicholson, H. A. 1877, p. 461.
Geol. Surv. O.S. 98 N.E. ; Ord. New Pop. 89.

**Kentmere.** Stream-section ¾ mile E. of Stile End Farm and 1¼ miles E.N.E. of Kentmere Church.

Silurian, lower Llandovery (Skelgill Shales), with abundant and well-preserved graptolites (*Monograptus*).

Marr, J. E. and Nicholson, H. A. 1888, p. 683.
Geol. Surv. O.S. 98 N.E. ; Ord. New Pop. 89.

**Kirkby Stephen.** Quarries 100 yds. E. of Kirkby Stephen station.

Carboniferous Limestone ($S_2$-$D_1$ subzone), with the brachiopod *Daviesiella llangollensis*, etc.

Garwood, E. J. 1912, pl. 53 (geol. map).
Geol. Surv. O.S. 97 N.W. ; Ord. New Pop. 84.

**Milburn,** 6 miles N.N.W. of Appleby. Old quarry E.S.E. of Howgill Castle.

Carboniferous Limestone ($D_1$ subzone, dolomitized beds near top of Melmerby Scar Limestone), with foraminifera (*Saccaminopsis*), corals (*Dibunophyllum, Diphyphyllum*) and brachiopods.

Turner, J. S. 1927, p. 366, with geol. map.
Geol. Surv. O.S. 102 N.W.-S.W. ; Ord. New Pop. 83.

**Nateby,** 1¼ miles S. of Kirkby Stephen.   Kitchen Gill, 1-1½ miles S.E. of Nateby and due N. of Great Bell.

Carboniferous Limestone ($S_2$-$D_1$ subzone).   Two limestone and black shale bands, each about 18 ins. thick, are largely made up of the coral *Lithostrotion irregulare.*   Bryozoa and brachiopods are abundant in the intervening dark shale.

Miller, A. A. 1927, with geol. map.  Miller, A. A. and Turner, J. S. 1931, pp. 5-6, with geol. map.

Geol. Surv. O.S. 97 N.W. ;  Ord. New Pop. 84 and 90.

**Nateby.**   Birkett Hill railway-cutting, 2¼ miles S. of Nateby and ½ mile W.N.W. of Pendragon Castle.

Carboniferous, Yoredale Series (shales and limestones above Great Scar Limestone), with many large productid brachiopods and the plant *Aphralysia.*

Miller, A. A. and Turner, J. S. 1931, p. 13, with geol. map.

Geol. Surv. O.S. 97 N.W. ;  Ord. New Pop. 90.

**North Stainmore,** 2½ miles E. of Brough.   Borrowdale Beck (upper waters of Augill Beck), due N. of N. Stainmore.

Carboniferous, Yoredale Series (Four Fathoms Limestone), with rolled corals (*Dibunophyllum*).

Turner, J. S. 1935, p. 123, with geol. map.

Geol. Surv. O.S. 102 S.E. ;  Ord. New Pop. 84.

**Raisbeck,** 1½ miles S.E. of Orton.   Section in Raisbeck, ⅓ mile above Fawcett Mill and ¾ mile S.W. of fork in road.

Carboniferous Limestone ($C_1$ subzone), with the brachiopods *Productus rotundus* and *P. globosus.*

Garwood, E. J. 1916, p. 9, pl. 1 (geol. map).

Geol. Surv. O.S. 98 N.E. ;  Ord. New Pop. 83.

**Ravenstonedale,** 4¼ miles S.W. of Kirkby Stephen.   Pinskey Gill, 1 mile S. of Ravenstonedale station.

Carboniferous Limestone (? $Z_1$ subzone, Pinskey Gill Beds, type-locality), with *Lingula, Spirifer pinskeyensis* and other brachiopods, also bryozoa, etc. These beds may be of Devonian age.

Garwood, E. J. 1912, pp. 496-499, with geol. map ;  1916, p. 6, with geol. map.

Geol. Surv. O.S. 97 N.W. ;  Ord. New Pop. 89.

**Ravenstonedale.**   Piper Hole quarries, just E. of the village.

Carboniferous Limestone (base of $C_1$ subzone), with silicified brachiopods, including *Camarotoechia proava,* which can be dissolved out with acid.   The alga *Solenopora* also occurs.

Garwood, E. J. 1912, p. 461, with geol. map ;  1916, p. 7, with geol. map.

Geol. Surv. O.S. 97 S.W. ;  Ord. New Pop. 90.

**Ravenstonedale.**   Continuous section in Stone Gill, for ½ mile above its junction with Scandale Beck.

Carboniferous Limestone ($C_1$ subzone), with the coral *Vaughania cleistoporoides,* etc.

Garwood, E. J. 1916, p. 6, with geol. map.

Geol. Surv. O.S. 97 N.W. ;  Ord. New Pop. 90.

**Ravenstonedale.**   Section in bank above right bank of Scandale Beck, between Smardale and Coldbeck bridges ;  and in Coupland Sike, tributary to left bank of Scandale Beck :  all N. of Ravenstonedale.

Carboniferous Limestone (base of $C_2$ subzone), with the coral *Thysanophyllum pseudovermiculare,* etc.

Garwood, E. J. 1916, p. 7, with geol. map.

Geol. Surv. O.S. 97 N.W. ;  Ord. New Pop. 83 and 90.

**Ravenstonedale.** Exposure ⅓ mile E.N.E. of Ravenstonedale station, at crossing of road and railway.
Carboniferous Limestone (C₂ subzone, Brownber Pebble Bed), with brachiopods (*Syringothyris cuspidata*) and gastropods.
Garwood, E. J. 1912, pp. 464–465, with geol. map.
Geol. Surv. O.S. 97 N.W. ; Ord. New Pop. 83.

**Ravenstonedale.** Exposure between Keld Sike and Ashfell Farm, about ½ mile E.N.E. of Ravenstonedale.
Carboniferous Limestone (C₂ subzone), with the coral *Michelinia grandis*.
Garwood, E. J. 1916, p. 8, with geol. map.
Geol. Surv. O.S. 97 S.W. ; Ord. New Pop. 90.

**Ravenstonedale.** Tarn Sike, quarries ⅓ mile S.W. of Tarn House, 1¾ miles E.S.E. of Ravenstonedale.
Carboniferous Limestone (C₂ subzone), with *Caninia, Zaphrentoides* and other corals, and chonetid and productid brachiopods.
Garwood, E. J. 1912, p. 468 ; 1916, p. 8, with geol. map.
Geol. Surv. O.S. 97 N.W. ; Ord. New Pop. 90.

**Ravenstonedale.** Slape Crag Quarries, on Ravenstonedale-Kirkby Stephen road, 1½ miles N.E. of Ravenstonedale.
Carboniferous Limestone (S₂-D₁ subzone), with the coral *Nematophyllum minus* and other fossils.
Geol. Surv. O.S. 97 N.W. ; Ord. New Pop. 84 and 90.

**Ravenstonedale.** Quarries at summit of Ashfell Edge, on both sides of Ravenstonedale-Kirkby Stephen road.
Carboniferous Limestone (S₂-D₁ subzone, Ashfell Sandstone), with zaphrentid corals and such brachiopods as *Cyrtina carbonaria, Composita* [*Seminula*] *spp.*, etc.
Garwood, E. J. 1916, p. 8, with geol. map.
Geol. Surv. O.S. 97 N.W. ; Ord. New Pop. 90.

**Sedbergh** (Yorks). Salley Brow, gullies by side of zigzag track on N. side of valley, 5 miles N.E. of Sedbergh, between 7th and 8th milestones on Kirkby Stephen road.
Ordovician, ? Caradoc, with the trilobite *Calymene*.
Marr, J. E. 1913, p. 7.
Geol. Surv. O.S. 97 N.W. ; Ord. New Pop. 90.

**Shap.** Shap Abbey Cliff, right bank of R. Lowther opposite the abbey.
Carboniferous Limestone (C₁ subzone), with the alga *Solenopora* and the brachiopod *Athyris glabristria*.
Garwood, E. J. 1916, p. 10, pl. 4, with geol. map.
Geol. Surv. O.S. 102 S.W. ; Ord. New Pop. 83.

**Shap.** Docker Beck, immediately above Water's Farm, E. of Shap station.
Carboniferous Limestone (S₂ subzone, top of Ashfell Sandstone), with corals and the brachiopod *Pustula*.
Garwood, E. J. 1916, p. 11, with geol. map.
Geol. Surv. O.S. 102 S.W. ; Ord. New Pop. 83.

**Shap.** Crosby Gill, ½-1 mile below source of Lyvenet Beck, N. of Shap Wells and on Hazel Moor about 4 miles S.E. of Shap.
Carboniferous Limestone (S₂-D₁ subzone, Bryozoa Beds), with corals, bryozoa and brachiopods.
Garwood, E. J. 1912, pp. 473–474, with geol. map.
Geol. Surv. O.S. 102 S.W. ; Ord. New Pop. 83.

**Stockdale,** N.E. of Ambleside. Browgill, immediately N.E. of Stockdale.
Silurian, upper Llandovery (Browgill Beds, type-section), with graptolites (*Monograptus*), etc.
Marr, J. E. and Nicholson, H. A. 1888, p. 674.
Geol. Surv. O.S. 98 N.E. ; Ord. New Pop. 83.

**Tirril,** 3 miles S.S.W. of Penrith.  Quarry W. of Tirril, W. of main road.
Carboniferous, Yoredale Series (base of Askham Limestone), with haematite-stained algal nodules (*Girvanella*).
Garwood, E. J. 1912, p. 449, with geol. map ; 1916, p. 1, with geol. map.
Geol. Surv. O.S. 102 S.W. ; Ord. New Pop. 83.

**Troutbeck,** 2½ miles N. of Windermere.  Crags on Applethwaite Common,
1¼ miles N.E. of Troutbeck Church and ¾ miles E. of Long Green Head Farm.
Ordovician, Ashgill Series (Coniston Limestone), with trilobites and
brachiopods.
Stubblefield, C. J. 1928, p. 427.  Geol. map in Mitchell, G. H. 1929.
Geol. Surv. O.S. 98 N.E. ; Ord. New Pop. 89.

**Warcop,** 3 miles W. of Brough.   Stream-section, Dobbyhole Gill, on
Roman Fell, about 2 miles N. by E. of Warcop.
Carboniferous Limestone (base of $C_2$ subzone), with the coral *Thysano-phyllum pseudovermiculare* and brachiopods.
Turner, J. S. 1927, p. 354, with geol. map.
Geol. Surv. O.S. 102 S.E. ; Ord. New Pop. 84.

**Warcop.**  Highclose Sike, S. of Roman Fell and under Long Fell, about
2 miles N.E. of Warcop.
Carboniferous Limestone ($C_2$ subzone, Brownber Pebble Bed), with
brachiopods, including *Syringothyris cuspidata*.
Turner, J. S. 1927, p. 354, with geol. map.
Geol. Surv. O.S. 102 S.E. ; Ord. New Pop. 84.

**Warcop.**  Small tributary of Hayber Beck under Middle Fell, about 2 miles
N.N.E. of Warcop.
Carboniferous Limestone ($C_2$ subzone), with abundant corals, especially
*Caninia subibicina.*
Turner, J. S. 1927, p. 355, with geol. map.
Geol. Surv. O.S. 102 S.E. ; Ord. New Pop. 84.

**Warcop.**  Col between Roman Fell and Long Fell, 3 miles N.N.E. of
Warcop.
Carboniferous Limestone ($S_2$ subzone, Bryozoa Band), with bryozoa and
brachiopods.
Turner, J. S. 1927, p. 344, with geol. map.
Geol. Surv. O.S. 102 S.E. ; Ord. New Pop. 84.

## WILTSHIRE

**Alderbury,** 3 miles S.E. of Salisbury.  Pit on W. side of Witherington
Ring, N. of Witherington Farm, 1½ miles S. of Alderbury.
Cretaceous, Upper Chalk (*Marsupites* zone), with abundant plates of the
zonal crinoid, starfish ossicles, sea-urchins (*Echinocorys*) and sponges
(*Pharetrospongia*).
Geol. Surv. N.S. 298 ; Ord. New Pop. 167.

**Bradford-on-Avon,** 5 miles S.E. of Bath (Somerset).    Avoncliff
("Ancliff") Quarry, on S. side of lane from Upper Westwood down to R. Avon
and railway halt.
Jurassic, Great Oolite Series, limestones with well-preserved dwarfed lamelli-branchs and gastropods.  Specimens from here were figured by the Sowerbys
in the " Mineral Conchology."
Woodward, H. B. 1894, p. 261.  Arkell, W. J. 1933a, p. 272.
Geol. Surv. O.S. 19 ; Ord. New Pop. 166.

**Bradford-on-Avon.**  Quarries on E. and W. sides of bridge where
Bradford-Frome road crosses the canal, about ¼ mile S. of Bradford station.

Jurassic, Great Oolite Series (Bradford Clay, type-locality, resting on upper beds of Great Oolite limestone). The prolific fauna of crinoids (*Apiocrinus*), brachiopods, etc., at the base of the Bradford Clay can hardly now be obtained.
Woodward, H. B. 1894, p. 262. Arkell, W. J. 1933a, p. 269. Cox, L. R. 1941, p. 33.
Geol. Surv. O.S. 19 ; Ord. New Pop. 166.

**Bratton,** 3 miles E.N.E. of Westbury. Sandpit on Imber road and trackway leading S. to Whitecliff Hill.
Cretaceous, Upper Greensand and Lower Chalk (the latter in sides and floor of track), with abundant ammonites, etc.
Geol. Surv. O.S. 14 ; Ord. New Pop. 166.

**Calne.** Workhouse Quarry, in angle between roads to Chippenham and to Christian Malford.
Jurassic, Corallian Beds. A historic locality for perfect tests of the sea-urchin *Hemicidaris intermedia*, some with spines attached. Many other fossils occur.
White, H. J. C. 1925, p. 22, pl. II.
Geol. Surv. N.S. 266 ; Ord. New Pop. 157.

**Charlton and Garsdon,** 2 miles E.N.E. of Malmesbury. Large quarries ⅜ mile S. of Charlton Church and at Garsdon.
Jurassic, Cornbrash, highly fossiliferous, with large ammonites (*Macrocephalites*) in lower part ; capped by Kellaways Clay.
Douglas, J. A. and Arkell, W. J. 1928, pp. 136-138.
Geol. Surv. O.S. 34 ; Ord. New Pop. 157.

**Chilmark,** 12 miles W. of Salisbury. Large quarries on both sides of Chilmark ravine, 1 mile S.S.E. of the church, not now open to the public.
Jurassic, Portland Beds, a classic locality. The " ragstone " fossils from here were said to be the best-preserved Portland fossils in England.
Hudleston, W. H. 1883, p. 161. Arkell, W. J. 1933a, p. 501.
Geol. Surv. N.S. 298 ; Ord. New Pop. 166.

**Corsham,** 9 miles E. of Bath (Somerset). Quarry near Folly Farm, N. of London-Bath road 1 mile N.E. of Corsham Church and 1½ miles E.N.E. of Lower Pickwick.
Jurassic, Forest Marble and lower Cornbrash. The brachiopod *Epithyris marmorea* occurs near the top of the Forest Marble.
Davidson, T. 1851, pl. IX, fig. 4.
Geol. Surv. O.S. 34 ; Ord. New Pop. 156.

**Devizes.** Caen Hill Brickyard.
Cretaceous, Gault (*dentatus* zone and higher beds), a good locality for ammonites (*Hoplites*) of the *benettianus* subzone.
Jukes-Browne, A. J. 1905, p. 5. Spath, L. F. 1923-1944.
Geol. Surv. N.S. 282 ; Ord. New Pop. 167.

**Dilton Marsh,** 2 miles S.W. of Westbury. Old Ironstone workings E. of Bremeridge Farm, ¾ mile N.E. of Dilton Marsh.
Cretaceous, Gault (no fossils), resting on Lower Greensand, with many well-preserved, but fragile fossils ; lying unconformably on Jurassic, Kimmeridge Clay and Corallian Beds (Westbury Ironstone), the latter with ammonites (*Ringsteadia*) and layers of the oyster *Ostrea delta*.
Geol. Surv. O.S. 14 ; Ord. New Pop. 166.

**Dinton.** Pit on N. side of lane from Teffont Magna to Baverstock, ½ mile N.E. of Dinton Church.
Cretaceous, Upper Greensand, with abundant oysters (*Exogyra*), other lamellibranchs and some brachiopods.
Jukes-Browne, A. J. 1900, p. 231.
Geol. Surv. N.S. 298 ; Ord. New Pop. 167.

I

**Downton,** 7 miles S.E. of Salisbury. Roadside quarry at Barford Cliff, ½ mile E.N.E. of Barford Farm, ¾ mile N. of Downton.

Cretaceous, Upper Chalk (*pilula* zone), with zonal varieties of the sea-urchin *Echinocorys scutatus*.

Geol. Surv. N.S. 314 ; Ord. New Pop. 167.

**Downton.** Pit 100 yds. N. of Lower Pensworth Farm, Redlynch.

Cretaceous, Upper Chalk (*mucronata* zone), with the belemnite *Belemnitella mucronata* and sea-urchins abundant.

Geol. Surv. N.S. 314 ; Ord. New Pop. 167.

**East Harnham,** Salisbury. The upper of two pits on Harnham Hill. The lower one is now overgrown.

Cretaceous, Upper Chalk (*pilula* and *quadratus* zones). Fossils; especially the belemnite *Actinocamax quadratus*, are fairly common.

Reid, C. 1903, p. 58.

Geol. Surv. N.S. 298 ; Ord. New Pop. 167.

**Fyfield,** 2 miles W. of Marlborough. Pit on S. side of Bath road at junction with side-road S. to Lockeridge, just W. of Fyfield.

Cretaceous, Upper Chalk (*planus* zone), with the sea-urchins *Micraster corbovis* and *M. praecursor*, and many other fossils.

White, H. J. O. 1925, p. 62. Moore, P. F. 1937, p. 48.

Geol. Surv. N.S. 266 ; Ord. New Pop. 157.

**Heywood,** 1½ miles N. of Westbury. Ironstone quarries close to Westbury station, ¾ mile N.W. of Westbury. These are now all derelict, except at the N.E. end, 1400 yds. N.E. of the station and about ½ mile S.S.W. of Heywood Church.

Jurassic, Corallian Beds (Westbury Ironstone) and basal Kimmeridge Clay, with many well-preserved ammonites (*Ringsteadia*) and lamellibranchs.

Blake, J. F. and Hudleston, W. H. 1877, p. 284. Arkell, W. J. 1933a, p. 389.

Geol. Surv. O.S. 14 ; Ord. New Pop. 166.

**Highworth,** 6½ miles N.N.E. of Swindon. South Quarries, E. of Swindon road ¼ mile S. of the church ; and Hangman's Elm Quarry, N. of Shrivenham road ⅜ mile S.E. of the church. Both now derelict and partly filled in. Nos. 87 and 83 of Arkell, 1941a.

Jurassic, Corallian Beds. Abundant ammonites and other mollusca were obtained in the past. A coral-bed occurred.

Arkell, W. J. 1927, pp. 108-112, with geol. map ; 1941a, pp. 81-85, with geol. map.

Geol. Surv. O.S. 34 ; Ord. New Pop. 157.

**Kellaways.** Banks of R. Avon, ½ mile S. of Kellaways Bridge. Small pits nearby referred to by William Smith and W. Lonsdale are no longer visible.

Jurassic, Kellaways Beds (type-locality), with numerous ammonites, lamellibranchs and brachiopods.

White, H. J. O. 1925, pp. 10-12. Arkell, W. J. 1933a, p. 346.

Geol. Surv. O.S. 34 ; Ord. New Pop. 157.

**Malmesbury.** Quarry on N. side of Foxley road, ½ mile S.W. of the abbey.

Jurassic, Cornbrash, with many brachiopods, lamellibranchs, etc., resting on Forest Marble.

Douglas, J. A. and Arkell, W. J. 1928, p. 139.

Geol. Surv. O.S. 34 ; Ord. New Pop. 157.

**Marlborough.** Pit on Barton Down ¾ mile N.W. of Barton Farm, ½ mile W. of Marlborough, near N. corner of Barton Copse.

Cretaceous, Upper Chalk (*planus* zone), with the sea-urchin *Micraster* and other fossils.

White, H. J. O. 1925, p. 64. Moore, P. F. 1937, p. 50.

Geol. Surv. N.S. 266 ; Ord. New Pop. 157.

**Marlborough.** Pit on track running N.E. along edge of Rabley Wood, just over ½ mile W.N.W. of Mildenhall Church, 1½ miles E.N.E. of Marlborough.
Cretaceous, Upper Chalk (*cortestudinarium* zone), with the sea-urchin *Micraster*.
White, H. J. O. 1925, p. 65 ; Moore, P. F. 1937, p. 50.
Geol. Surv. N.S. 266 ; Ord. New Pop. 157.

**Oare,** 5 miles S.S.W. of Marlborough. The upper of two pits on W. side of Marlborough-Pewsey road at top of Oare Hill, ¾ mile N.E. of Oare Church.
Cretaceous, Upper Chalk (*planus* zone), with the sea-urchin *Micraster* and other fossils.
White, H. J. O. 1925, p. 63. Moore, P. F. 1937, p. 48.
Geol. Surv. N.S. 266 ; Ord. New Pop. 167.

**Ogbourne St. Andrew,** 2 miles N. of Marlborough. Pit near Ogbourne Maizey, just over ½ mile S.W. of Inn, Ogbourne St. Andrew.
Cretaceous, Upper Chalk (*planus* zone, including Chalk Rock), with the sea-urchin *Micraster* abundant.
White, H. J. O. 1925, pp. 61-62. Moore, P. F. 1937, p. 49.
Geol. Surv. N.S. 266 ; Ord. New Pop. 157.

**Ogbourne St. George,** 3½ miles N. of Marlborough. Limeworks on W. side of track from Ogbourne St. George S.E. to Yielding Copse, nearly 1 mile from the church.
Cretaceous, Upper Chalk (*cortestudinarium* zone), with the sea-urchin *Micraster* and other fossils.
Moore, P. F. 1937, p. 49.
Geol. Surv. N.S. 266 ; Ord. New Pop. 157.

**Pitton,** 4 miles E. of Salisbury. Roadside exposure on hill S. of village.
Cretaceous, Upper Chalk (*quadratus* zone), with fairly abundant belemnites, sea-urchins, etc.
Geol. Surv. N.S. 298 ; Ord. New Pop. 167.

**Purton,** 4½ miles N.W. of Swindon. Hills Brickyard, ½ mile N.N.W. of Purton station.
Jurassic, Oxford Clay (*mariae* and lower *cordatum* zones), with abundant ammonites.
Arkell, W. J. 1941b.
Geol. Surv. O.S. 34 ; Ord. New Pop. 157.

**Salisbury.** Clarendon railway-cutting, 4 miles S.E. of Salisbury. There is an exposure only after landslipping. Permission is required in writing from the railway authorities.
Eocene, London Clay, with mollusca, corals and microfossils.
Elliott, G. F. 1945.
Geol. Surv. N.S. 298 ; Ord. New Pop. 167.

**Seend,** 6 miles E. of Trowbridge. Quarries on S. side of lane from Seend W. to Seend Cleeve, at Cleeve Farm, about ¾ mile W. of Seend Church.
Jurassic, Corallian Beds (Lower Calcareous Grit), a source of many fine ammonites in the national collections and in the Devizes Museum.
Arkell, W. J. 1944b, p. 270, figs.
Geol. Surv. O.S. 14 ; Ord. New Pop. 167.

**Stanton St. Quintin,** 4½ miles N.N.W. of Chippenham. Large quarry ¼ mile S.E. of Lower Stanton St. Quintin, and four quarries to S. and S.W. of the village.
Jurassic, Cornbrash, a celebrated locality for fossils, and Forest Marble.
Douglas, J. A. and Arkell, W. J. 1928, p. 141.
Geol. Surv. O.S. 34 ; Ord. New Pop. 157.

**Steeple Ashton,** 3 miles E. of Trowbridge.   Field-surface E. of road to Bratton, ¾ mile S.S.E. of Steeple Ashton church ; also about 500 yds. N. to N.W. of large pond 600 yds. N. of Crosswelldown Farm, which is 1¾ miles S. of Steeple Ashton.

Jurassic, Corallian Beds, a historic locality for corals, which occur in greater variety and better preservation than at any other Corallian locality in England.

Blake, J. F. and Hudleston, W. H. 1877, pp. 286-287. Arkell, W. J. 1933a, p. 390.

Geol. Surv. O.S. 14 ; Ord. New Pop. 166 and 167.

**Swindon.**   Hill's Brickyard, King's Hill, in N.W. extremity of Old Town Hill, S. of Wootton Bassett road.   Quarry now built in and section obscured.

Jurassic, Kimmeridge Clay (with sandy *pectinatus* zone, lydite bed and base of Swindon Clay).   Ammonites and lamellibranchs are abundant in the clays and there is an oyster-bed (*Exogyra*) at the junction of sands and clays.

Chatwin, C. P. and Pringle, J. 1922.   Arkell, W. J. 1933a, pp. 455-457. Geol. Surv. O.S. 34 ; Ord. New Pop. 157.

**Swindon.**   Okus Quarry, Okus Road, 1 mile W.S.W. of Swindon Church. Quarry now built in and section obscured.

Jurassic, Portland Beds, with many giant ammonites and other mollusca in the Cockly Bed.   Glauconitic beds below also fossiliferous.

Chatwin, C. P. and Pringle, J. 1922.   Arkell, W. J. 1933a, pp. 503-507. Geol. Surv. O.S. 34 ; Ord. New Pop. 157.

**Swindon.**   Town Gardens Quarry, Old Town, between Bath Road, Quarry Road and Westlecott Road, about ½ mile S.W. of the church.

Jurassic, Purbeck Beds, with freshwater and marine ostracods and mollusca. Sylvester-Bradley, P. C. 1940.

Geol. Surv. O.S. 34 ; Ord. New Pop. 157.

**Teffont Evias,** 10 miles W. of Salisbury.   Quarries on N. side of Teffont-Chicksgrove road, ¼ mile S. and W. of Teffont Church.

Jurassic, Purbeck Beds, with a highly fossiliferous Cinder Bed (*Ostrea distorta*, etc.), also insect beds and ostracods.

Andrews, W. R. and Jukes-Browne, A. J. 1894, p. 53, with geol. map.

Geol. Surv. N.S. 298 ; Ord. New Pop. 167.

**Tisbury,** 13 miles W. of Salisbury.   Wockley (Oakley) Quarry, on E. side of valley near Shavers Bridge, ¾ mile E.S.E. of Tisbury station.

Jurassic, Portland Beds, with marine lamellibranchs, etc. ; capped (at top of eastern face) by Lower Purbeck Beds, with freshwater ostracods.   The plane of separation is crowded with fish.

Woodward, H. B. 1895, p. 269.   Edmunds, F. H. 1938, p. 188.

Geol. Surv. N.S. 298 ; Ord. New Pop. 167.

**Westbury,** see Dilton Marsh, Heywood.

**West Harnham,** Salisbury.   Limeworks S. of the village.

Cretaceous, Upper Chalk (*pilula* zone), with sea-urchins (*Offaster pilula, Echinocorys*) and other fossils.

Geol. Surv. N.S. 298 ; Ord. New Pop. 167.

**Whiteparish,** 8 miles S.E. of Salisbury.   Chalkpit on W. side of Salisbury-Southampton road, 270 yds. S. of the Pepperbox, by the Traveller's Rest.

Cretaceous, Upper Chalk (*pilula* zone, *Hagenowia* Beds), with abundant lamellibranchs (especially *Chlamys* and *Lima spp.*), small brachiopods and starfish-ossicles.   Sea-urchins (*Offaster, Echinocorys, Hagenowia*) are more scarce.

Geol. Surv. N.S. 298 ; Ord. New Pop. 167.

**Woodford,** 5 miles N.N.W. of Salisbury. Roadside pit S. of the village.

Cretaceous, Upper Chalk (*cortestudinarium* zone), with abundant lithistid sponges in flints and sea-urchins in the chalk.

Reid, C. 1903, p. 54.

Geol. Surv. N.S. 298 ; Ord. New Pop. 167.

# WORCESTERSHIRE

**Bromsgrove.** Old quarries on Rock Hill, 1 mile S.W. of Bromsgrove, on both sides of road to Worcester.

Triassic, Lower Keuper Sandstone. Fossils are rare and hard to find, but include plant-remains and fragments of the scorpion *Mesophonus*.

Wills, L. J. 1910 ; 1946-1947.

Geol. Surv. O.S. 54 N.W. ; Ord. New Pop. 131.

**Dudley,** see under Staffordshire.

**Great Witley,** 5 miles S.W. of Stourport. Walsgrove Quarry, 900 yds. W. 16° S. of Hundred House and just over ¼ mile S. of Abberley Hall.

Silurian, Ludlow (with Aymestry Limestone) and Downton Series (Downton Sandstone). Graptolites (*Monograptus*) occur in the shales below the limestone.

Groom, T. T. 1900, pp. 164, 172.

Geol. Surv. O. S. 55 N.E. ; Ord. New Pop. 130.

**Shatterford,** 3½ miles N.N.E. of Bewdley. Stream-section where Man Brook enters S. side of Coldridge Wood, N. of Shatterford.

Silurian, Downton Series (I. 6). Cephalaspid fragments are common (*Didymaspis, Ischnacanthus*, spines and jaws) in sandstone and cornstone, with some lamellibranchs.

King, W. W. 1934, pp. 532-533.

Geol. Surv. O.S. 55 N.E. ; Ord. New Pop. 130.


# YORKSHIRE (WEST RIDING)

**Airton,** 3 miles N.E. of Hellifield. Airton Green Quarry, 2 miles W. of Airton on the Orms Gill road.

Carboniferous Limestone ($C_2S_1$ subzone), with brachiopods including *Airtonia, Daviesiella, Chonetes.*

Cope, F. W. 1943, p. 213.

Geol. Surv. O.S. 92 N.W. ; Ord. New Pop. 95.

**Austwick.** Stream-section at Wharfe, 100 yds. above Dam House Bridge.

Silurian, base of Llandovery Series (*Phacops elegans* Limestone), thin calcareous band (about 8 inches) formed of trilobite fragments ; best collected from weathered " ginger-bread " rock.

King, W. B. R., and Wilcockson, W. H. 1934, p. 20, with geol. map.

Reynolds, S. H. 1894, p. 108.

Geol. Surv. O.S. 92 N.W. ; Ord. New Pop. 90.

**Austwick.** Old pit in field in Hunterstye, 530 yds. W.S.W. of Austwick Beck Head.

Ordovician, Ashgill Series ; cleaved mudstones in which brachiopods are common and calyces of the cystid *Stephanocrinus* are rare.

King, W. B. R., and Wilcockson, W. H. 1934, p. 17, with geol. map.

Geol. Surv. O.S. 97 S.W. ; Ord. New Pop. 90.

**Austwick.** Norber Brow, exposure at top of hill on roadside.

Ordovician, Ashgill Series ; slightly cleaved shales in which trilobites, including *Phillipsinella parabola*, are common.

King, W. B. R., and Wilcockson, W. H. 1934, p. 12, with geol. map.

Geol. Surv. O.S. 92 N.W. ; Ord. New Pop. 90.

**Baildon.** Old spoil heaps from coal-workings on Baildon Common, 1 mile W. of Baildon, 4 miles N. of Bradford.

Carboniferous, Coal Measures (*lenisulcata* zone) ; marine band above the Hard Bed Coal containing goniatites, including *Gastrioceras listeri*, and lamellibranchs (*Dunbarella*).

Geol. Surv. O.S. 92 S.E. ; Ord. New Pop. 96.

**Barnoldswick.**    Higher Clough (locally Cowdale Clough), $1\frac{3}{4}$ miles W.S.W. of Barnoldswick and $2\frac{1}{2}$ miles S.E. of Gisburn Church.
Carboniferous (Pendleside Limestone and Bowland Shales) ; with good specimens of goniatites.
Moore, E. W. J. 1941, p. 252, with map.
Geol. Surv. O.S. 92 S.W. ; Ord. New Pop. 95.

**Barnoldswick.**    Sections in streams on north slopes of Weets Hill, on Hill Cloughs Farm, 1 mile W. of Barnoldswick.
Carboniferous ($P_2$ and $E_1$ subzones) ; shales and crinoidal limestones ; uncrushed goniatites (especially *Sudeticeras*) in bullions.
Moore, E. W. J. 1941, p. 252, with map.
Geol. Surv. O.S. 92 S.W. ; Ord. New Pop. 95.

**Bell Busk,** 7 miles N.W. of Skipton. Haw Crag Quarries, 1380 yds. E. of Bell Busk Station and north of lane to Gargrave.
Carboniferous Limestone ($C_2$ subzone) ; boulder beds and interbedded shales on reef limestones ; containing corals including *Cravenia, Palaeosmilia,* etc.
Hudson, R. G. S., and Dunnington, H. V., 1944, p. 204, with geol. map.
Geol. Surv. O.S. 92 N.W. ; Ord. New Pop. 95.

**Blubberhouses.**    Stream-section in left bank of Redlish Gill, 880 yds. W. 27° S. of Redlish House, $6\frac{1}{2}$ miles N.N.W. of Blubberhouses, on a by-road to Greenhow Hill.
Carboniferous, Millstone Grit (H zone) ; marine shales above the Lower Follifoot Grit containing goniatites (*Homoceras*).
Hudson, R. G. S. 1937, p. 319, with geol. map.
Geol. Surv. O.S. 92 N.E. ; Ord. New Pop. 96.

**Bolton-upon-Dearne.**    Manvers Main Brick Pit, 1600 yds. S. 7° W. of Bolton-upon-Dearne Church.
Carboniferous, Coal Measures (Mansfield Marine Band including " cank ").
Geol. Surv. N.S. 87 ; Ord. New Pop. 102.

**Bradgate.**    Bradgate Brickyard, $1\frac{1}{4}$ miles W. of Rotherham.
Carboniferous, Coal Measures ; *Lingula* from marine band in roof of Joan Coal and non-marine lamellibranchs from the overlying measures.
Geol. Surv. N.S. 87 ; Ord. New Pop. 103.

**Cautley,** $3\frac{1}{2}$ miles N.E. of Sedbergh. Fairy Gill, tributary of Ecker Secker Beck, $\frac{1}{4}$ mile N. of Taythes House.
Ordovician, Ashgill Series ; Shales which are most fossiliferous at the top of the gill and in exposures on east side. Original locality for the brachiopod " *Strophomena siluriana.*" This fossil is abundant and the trilobite *Phacops mucronatus* is fairly common.
Davidson, T. 1871, pp. 303-304. Marr, J. E. 1913, p. 10, with map.
Geol. Surv. O.S. 97 N.W. ; Ord. Pop. 20.

**Cononley.**    Right bank of Cononley Beck, 380 yds. S.W. of Cononley Church.
Carboniferous, Millstone Grit Series ($E_2$ subzone) ; Edge Marine Band containing the goniatite *Eumorphoceras bisulcatum.*
Stephens, J. V., and others, 1941, p. 344, with geol. map.
Geol. Surv. N.S. 69 ; Ord. Pop. 26.

**Cowling.**    Stream-section in Monkroyd Beck, 100 yds. upstream from Hargreaves Arms, 3 miles S.W. of Cowling and $\frac{1}{2}$ mile W. of Laneshaw Reservoir.
Carboniferous, Millstone Grit Series (Haslingden Flags) ; shales containing goniatites (*Gastrioceras cumbriense*) and lamellibranchs.
Bray, A. 1927, p. 56, with geol. map.
Geol. Surv. O.S. 92 S.W. ; Ord. Pop. 30.

**Cracoe,** 5½ miles N. of Skipton. Disused quarries and a stream-section in Skelterton Beck.

Carboniferous Limestone (knoll-reef of $S_2D_1$ subzones in quarries, followed by limestones and shales of $P_1$ subzone in stream); corals (*Lithostrotion, Caninia*) in reef; corals and goniatites in the $P_1$ shales.

Booker, K. M. and Hudson R. G. S. 1926, with geol. map.

Geol. Surv. O.S. 92 N.E. ; Ord. New Pop. 95.

**Eastby,** 3½ miles N.E. of Skipton. Stream-section in Heugh (Gill Eastby Beck), 900 yds. N.E. of Embsay Church and 250 yds. N. of Eastby Bridge. (Localities 7-11 of Hudson & Mitchell, 1937.)

Carboniferous, Bowland Shales ($P_2$ and $E_1$ subzones); shale containing many goniatites, mostly crushed.

Hudson, R. G. S. and Mitchell, G. H. 1937, with geol. map.

Geol. Surv. O.S. 92 N.E. ; Ord. New Pop. 96.

**Feizor,** 1½ miles E.S.E. of Austwick. Natural scars.

Carboniferous, Lower Yoredale Series ; corals (*Lonsdaleia* and *Orionastraea*) are common.

Geol. Surv. O.S. 92 N.W. ; Ord. New Pop. 90.

**Gargrave,** 4½ miles W.N.W. of Skipton. West side of Butterhaw Quarry (disused), east of railway south of Gargrave.

Carboniferous Limestone ($C_2S_1$ zone) ; bedded limestones and pebble-beds, containing abundant zaphrentid and other corals.

Hudson, R. G. S. 1944, p. 205, with geol. map.

Geol. Surv. O.S. 92 N.W. ; Ord. New Pop. 95.

**Giggleswick.** Blackrigg Quarry at top of Buckhaw Brow on east side of main Settle-Kirby Lonsdale road.

Carboniferous ($D_2$ subzone, upper beds of Great Scar Limestone) ; containing algal nodules (*Girvanella*) and corals (*Lonsdaleia*).

Geol. Surv. O.S. 92 N.W. ; Ord. New Pop. 90.

**Greenhow,** 3 miles W.S.W. of Pateley Bridge. Coldstone Quarries. (Locality 10 of Dunham and Stubblefield 1944.)

Carboniferous Limestone ($D_2$ subzone, Coldstone Limestone) ; containing corals (*Lonsdaleia, Palaeosmilia, Dibunophyllum,* etc.) and productid brachiopods.

Dunham, K. C. and Stubblefield, C. J. 1944, p. 222, with geol. map.

Geol. Surv. O.S. 92 N.E. ; Ord. New Pop. 96.

**Halton East.** Halton East Quarries, the western quarry, N.W. of New Laithe and E.N.E. of Embsay Station. (Locality 91 of Hudson & Mitchell, 1937.)

Carboniferous Limestone (Embsay Limestone, $C_2S_1$ subzone) ; zaphrentid corals.

Hudson, R. G. S. and Mitchell, G. H. 1937, with geol. map.

Geol. Surv. O.S. 92 N.E. ; Ord. New Pop. 96.

**Hampole.** Moorhouse Lane Quarries, 1000 yds. E. of Moorhouse, Hampole.

Permian, Lower Magnesian Limestone ; oolites, containing well-preserved lamellibranchs (*Schizodus*).

Kendall, P. F. and Wroot, H. E. 1924, p. 917.

Geol. Surv. N.S. 87 ; Ord. New Pop. 91.

**Hampole.** Oak Bank Quarry, 150 yds. W.N.W. of Hampole station.

Permian, Lower Magnesian Limestone ; reef limestone containing brachiopods and bryozoa.

Geol. Surv. N.S. 87 ; Ord. New Pop. 91.

**Hebden Bridge.** Outwood, in Crimsworth Dene.
Carboniferous, Millstone Grit ($R_1$ subzone) ; historic locality for the goniatites *Reticuloceras reticulatum* and *Homoceras striolatum*.
Lloyd, W. and Stephens, J. V. 1927. Bisat, W. S. and Hudson, R. G. S. 1943, p. 383.
Geol. Surv. N.S. 77 ; Ord. New Pop. 95.

**Horsforth,** 5 miles N.W. of Leeds. Hawkesworth Wood Quarries, Butcher Hill, S.E. of Horsforth.
Carboniferous, Coal Measures (Marine Band above Pot Clay Coal, which rests on Millstone Grit), with goniatites (*Gastrioceras subcrenatum*) and other fossils.
Geol. Surv. O.S. 92 N.E. ; Ord. New Pop. 96.

**Horton-in-Ribblesdale.** Railway cutting, 700 yds. S. of Horton station.
Ordovician, Ashgill Series (" dyke " of limestone in the Precambrian Ingletonian Series) ; numerous trilobites and brachiopods in grey limestone. It is almost impossible to get material out at the present time without blasting.
King, W. B. R. 1932, p. 103, with geol. map.
Geol. Surv. O.S. 97 S.W. ; Ord. New Pop. 90.

**Horton-in-Ribblesdale.** Working quarries on west side of railway, ¼ mile W. of Horton.
Carboniferous Limestone ($S_2D_1$ subzone, upper part of Great Scar Limestone) ; contains abundant corals (*Lithostrotion minus*) and associated fossils.
Geol. Surv. O.S. 97 S.W. ; Ord. New Pop. 90.

**Horton-in-Ribblesdale.** Disused quarry by Ribblehead, 5 miles N.N.W. of Horton.
Carboniferous Limestone (D zone, Great Scar Limestone) ; contains the brachiopods *Davidsonina [Cyrtina] septosa* and *Daviesiella cf. comoides* which are common.
Hudson, R. G. S. and King W. B. R. 1933, p. 433.
Geol. Surv. O.S. 97 N.W. ; Ord. New Pop. 90.

**Ingleton.** Meal Bank Quarry (disused), immediately N.N.W. of the village.
Carboniferous Limestone ($S_2D_1$ subzones, Great Scar Limestone ; and nodular band in $D_1$ subzone) ; contain abundant corals.
Garwood, E. J. and Goodyear, E. 1924, p. 279, with geol. map.
Geol. Surv. O.S. 97 S.W. ; Ord. New Pop. 89.

**Keighley.** Park Wood Brick Pit, Park Wood, 600 yds. S. by E. of Keighley station. (Locality 93 of Stephens and others 1941).
Carboniferous, Millstone Grit Series (Middle Grit Group, $R_2$ zone) ; shales containing goniatites (*Reticuloceras reticulatum* muts. α and β).
Stephens, J. V. and others 1941, p. 359, with geol. map.
Geol. Surv. N.S. 69 ; Ord. New Pop. 96.

**Leathley,** 3 miles N.E. of Otley. Stream-section in River Washburn, opposite Fishpool, ¼ mile N. of Leathley.
Carboniferous, Millstone Grit Series (Weeton Shales, $E_2$ subzone) ; shales in which the goniatite *Eumorphoceras bisulcatum* is common.
Hudson, R. G. S. and others 1938, p. 371.
Geol. Surv. O.S. 92 S.E. ; Ord. New Pop. 96.

**Lofthouse,** 7½ miles N.W. of Pateley Bridge. Section in River Nidd, 300 yds. N. of Lofthouse station.
Carboniferous, Yoredale Beds (Cockleshell Limestone) ; contains corals (*Palaeosmilia, Chaetetes*) and productid brachiopods.
Tonks, L. H. 1925, p. 235, with geol. map.
Geol. Surv. O.S. 97 S.E. ; Ord. New Pop. 96.

**Lofthouse.** Section in River Nidd, 135 yds. S.W. of Manchester Holes, 2 miles W. of Lofthouse.

Carboniferous, Yoredale Beds (Single Post Limestone) ; containing corals (*Orionastraea garwoodi*).

Hudson, R. G. S. and others 1938, p. 355.

Geol. Surv. O.S. 97 S.E. ; Ord. New Pop. 96.

**Lothersdale,** 6 miles S.W. of Skipton. Stream-sections at junction of Stone Head and Black Scars becks, and three fields along Black Scars Beck.

Carboniferous, Millstone Grit Series ($E_2$ and H zones) ; shales with ironstones, containing goniatites and lamellibranchs.

Bray, A. 1927, p. 53, with geol. map.

Geol. Surv. O.S. 92 S.W. ; Ord. New Pop. 96.

**Lothersdale.** Stream-section just below Warley Wise Bridge, 2 miles S.W. of Lothersdale, in left bank of Stone Head Beck.

Carboniferous, Millstone Grit Series ($E_2$ subzone), shales containing goniatites and lamellibranchs.

Bray, A. 1927, p. 53, with geol. map.

Geol. Surv. O.S. 92 S.W. ; Ord. New Pop. 96.

**Lothersdale.** Stream-section in right bank of Lane House Beck, just N. of Upper Lane House.

Carboniferous, Millstone Grit Series ($E_2$ subzone) ; shales, below a thick grit, containing goniatites *Cravenoceras stellarum* (type-locality) and lamellibranchs.

Bray, A. 1927, p. 54, with geol. map. Bisat, W. S. 1932, p. 33.

Geol. Surv. O.S. 92 S.W. ; Ord. New Pop. 96.

**Lothersdale.** Natural exposure on hillside E. of Lothersdale Limestone Quarry. Carboniferous, Bowland Shales ($P_2$ and $E_1$ subzones) ; containing abundant goniatites. Bray, A., 1927, p. 49, with geol. map.

Geol. Surv. O.S. 92 S.W. ; Ord. New Pop. 96.

**Malham.** Natural exposure at foot of south slope of Cawden Burst, 500 yds. N.E. of Methodist Chapel, Malham.

Carboniferous Limestone ($D_1$ subzone, reef facies) ; containing abundant brachiopods and rare goniatites.

Hudson, R. G. S. and Cotton, G. 1945, pp. 304-305.

Geol. Surv. O.S. 92 N.W. ; Ord. New Pop. 90.

**Malham.** Clattering Sike.

Carboniferous, middle Yoredale Beds ; containing corals (*Orionastraea*) and crinoids.

Garwood, E. J. and Goodyear, E. 1924, p. 229, with geol. map.

Geol. Surv. O.S. 92 N.W. ; Ord. New Pop. 90.

**Malham.** Stream-section in Cow Close Sike (tributary to Gordale Beck), 750 yds. S.E. of Methodist Chapel, Malham.

Carboniferous, Bowland Shales ($E_1$ subzone) ; goniatites (*Eumorphoceras*) abundant in bullions.

Geol. Surv. O.S. 92 N.W. ; Ord. New Pop. 90.

**Marsden,** 7 miles S.W. of Huddersfield. Stream-section, Pule Hill, Marsden.

Carboniferous, Millstone Grit Series (R zone, shales below the Pule Hill Grit) ; goniatites common.

Wray, D. A. and others 1930, pp. 36-39, 147-148.

Geol. Surv. N.S. 77 ; Ord. New Pop. 102.

**Newton-in-Bowland,** 6½ miles N.W. of Clitheroe, Lancs. Small quarry on N. side of Knoll Wood, 1 mile W.S.W. of Newton-in-Bowland and 100 yds. S. of Newton-Dunsop Bridge road.

Carboniferous Limestone ($C_2$ zone) ; knoll-reef limestone containing abundant fauna of brachiopods with fenestellid bryozoa, gastropods and occasional corals, trilobites and blastoids. Crinoids are represented by the genera *Amphoracrinus, Gilbertsocrinus, Platycrinus* and *Pleurocrinus*.

Parkinson, D. 1936, pp. 301-304, with geol. map.

Geol. Surv. O.S. 92 S.W. ; Ord. New Pop. 95.

**Newton-in-Bowland.** Stream-section in Ashnott Wood, 1½ miles S. of Newton-in-Bowland and 250 yds. N.E. of Ashnott Farm.

Carboniferous (*Merocanites* zone [$S_1$ ?], Worston Shales ) ; shales with limestone containing the goniatite *Merocanites* cf. *compressus* at intervals in the lower 150 feet, also *Pterinopecten* and trilobites.

Parkinson, D. 1936, p. 305, with geol. map.

Geol. Surv. O.S. 92 S.W. ; Ord. New Pop. 95.

**Newton-in-Bowland.** Stream-sections at south end of Ing Barn Wood, 1¾ miles S.S.W. of Newton-in-Bowland and ¼ mile W. of Ashnott Farm.

Carboniferous (P zone unconformable on B zone) ; goniatites (*G. crenistria*) in shales resting on cementstone with *Beyrichoceras hodderense* : *Nomismoceras* occurs near mouth of tributary stream : goniatites of $P_2$ subzone occur in wood west of Crag Beck.

Parkinson, D. 1936, p. 307, with geol. map.

Geol. Surv. O.S. 92 S.W. ; Ord. New Pop. 95.

**Rotherham.** Rotherham Sanitary Tube and Brickworks, Primrose Hill, 300 yds. E. of Clough House, on north-west side of Rotherham.

Carboniferous, Coal Measures (mussel-bands associated with Kent's coals) ; non-marine lamellibranchs.

Mitchell and others 1948.

Geol. Surv. N.S. 87 ; Ord. New Pop. 103.

**Rylstone,** 7½ miles N. of Skipton. Clints Quarry (planted and overgrown), 1,600 yds. S.S.W. of Rylstone Church, on E. side of railway.

Carboniferous Limestone ($S_2D_1$ subzone) ; condensed section with fossiliferous shale in middle of exposed sequence, containing many corals (*Rylstonia, Caninia, Rhopalolasma*), goniatites (*Beyrichoceras*), nautiloids and zaphrentid corals in shale ; corals (*Emmonsia, Michelinia*) in top beds.

Wilmore, A. 1910, p. 550. Booker, K. M. and Hudson, R. G. S. 1926, with geol. map. Hudson, R. G. S. and Platt, M. I. 1927, p. 39. Hudson, R. G. S. 1943, p. 81, and 1945, p. 193.

Geol. Surv. O.S. 92 S.W. ; Ord. New Pop. 95.

**Scar Village,** Nidderdale, 9 miles N.W. of Pateley Bridge. Stream-section in Top Gill, tributary to left bank of R. Nidd from Dead Man's Hill, ½ mile E.N.E. of Lodge Farm, Scarhouse, on north side of reservoir.

Carboniferous, Millstone Grit Series (Colsterdale Limestone, $E_2$ subzone) ; containing the goniatite *Cravenoceratoides* and other fossils.

Tonks, L. H. 1925, p. 250, with geol. map.

Geol. Surv. O.S. 97 S.E. ; Ord. New Pop. 102.

**Sedbergh.** Banks of R. Rawthey immediately downstream from Rawthey Bridge, 5 miles N.E. of Sedbergh.

Ordovician, Ashgill Series, (*Phacops robertsi* Beds) ; trilobites (trinucleids and *Phacops*) common in mudstones. The most accessible locality for the *Phacops robertsi* Beds.

Marr, J. E. 1913, p. 8.

Geol. Surv. O.S. 97 N.W. ; Ord. New Pop. 89.

**Settle.** South bank of Stockdale Beck, S. of Stockdale and S. of Settle-Malham road.

Carboniferous, Yoredale Series ($D_2$ subzone) ; the coral *Orionastraea* is common.

Garwood, E. J. and Goodyear, E. 1924, p. 232, with geol. map.

Geol. Surv. O.S. 92 N.W. ; Ord. New Pop. 90.

**Settle.** Scaleber Quarry, 120 yds. N.W. of Scaleber Bridge, 1½ miles S.E. of Settle on the Kirkby-Malham road ; and natural exposures nearby.

Carboniferous Limestone (cherts followed by dolomites and reef-limestones of $S_2$ and $B_2$ subzones) ; corals (*Lithostrotion*) and brachiopods in $S_2$ subzone ; brachiopods, bryozoa, trilobites, etc., in reef-limestones.

Garwood, E. J. and Goodyear, E. 1924, p. 229, with geol. map. Hudson, R. G. S. 1930, p. 95.

Geol. Surv. O.S. 92 N.W. ; Ord. New Pop. 90.

**Settle.** Victoria Cave, Langcliffe or King's Scar, 1 mile N.E. of Settle.

Pleistocene, Middle and Upper ; lower cave earth contained remains of *Hippopotamus, Elephas antiquus* and *Rhinoceros haematicus* (= *leptorhinus*). The cave also yielded Mesolithic and Romano-British relics.

Dawkins, W. B. 1874. Tiddeman, R. H. 1875-1879.

Geol. Surv. O.S. 92 N.W. ; Ord. New Pop. 90.

**Silsden,** 4 miles N.W. of Keighley. Stream-section at Throstle Nest, 580 yds. S. 53° E. of Bracken Hill, ½ mile N.W. of Silsden.

Carboniferous, Millstone Grit Series (Marchup Marine Beds, $E_2$ subzone) ; type-locality of the goniatite *Anthracoceras glabrum.*

Bisat, W. S. 1924, p. 49.

Geol. Surv. N.S. 69 ; Ord. New Pop. 96.

**Skipton.** North side of railway-cutting, Holywell Bridge, 600 yds. E.N.E. of Far Skibeden, 2¼ miles E.N.E. of Skipton. (Locality 105 of Hudson & Mitchell, 1937.)

Carboniferous Limestone (Beds of $Z_2C_1$ subzone) ; contain the alga *Pseudochaetetes* [*Solenopora*].

Hudson, R. G. S. and Mitchell, G. H. 1937, p. 7, with geol. map. Hudson, R. G. S. 1934, p. 195, with geol. map.

Geol. Surv. Q.S. 92 N.E. ; Ord. New Pop. 96.

**Slaidburn,** 7 miles N.N.W. of Clitheroe, Lancs. Stream-section, 1½ miles N. of Slaidburn, Phynis Beck, near Phynis Farm.

Carboniferous ($C_2$ subzone, Phynis Shales, immediately above massive bedded limestone) ; with corals (zaphrentids, *Cyathaxonia, Emmonsia*), bryozoa and brachiopods.

Parkinson, D. 1936, pp. 299-303, with geol. map.

Geol. Surv. O.S. 92 N.W. ; Ord. New Pop. 95.

**Slaidburn.** Stream-section in Tinklers Brook, 1½ miles E.S.E. of Slaidburn, immediately S. of Langcliff Cross Bridge on the Slaidburn-Grindleton road.

Carboniferous, Lower Bowland Shales (upper part of $P_1b$ and $P_1c$, 90 feet) ; *Goniatites falcatus* in two bands separated by a crinoidal limestone bed, top of $P_1b$ ; *Goniatites elegans* near base of $P_1c$.

Parkinson, D. 1936, pp. 314-316, with geol. map.

Geol. Surv. O.S. 92 N.W.-S.W. ; Ord. New Pop. 95.

**Slaidburn.** Stream-section in Croasdale Brook, 2 miles N.N.W. of Slaidburn, extending upstream from a point ¼ mile W. of Croasdale House.

Carboniferous, Bowland Shales (P and $E_1$ subzones) ; shales with bands containing many goniatites.

Parkinson, D. 1936, pp. 315-319, with geol. map.

Geol. Surv. O.S. 92 N.W. ; Ord. New Pop. 95.

**Stanbury,** 4 miles S.W. of Keighley. Scar Hill, Stanbury Moor, 200 yds. E. of Lower Withins and 800 yds. W. of Forks House.

Carboniferous, Millstone Grit Series (G zone, shales with *cumbriense* Marine Band) ; type-locality for the goniatite *Gastrioceras crenulatum.*

Bisat, W. S. 1924, p. 58.

Geol. Surv. N.S. 69 ; Ord. New Pop. 96.

**Stocks-in-Bowland,** 7½ miles S.W. of Settle. Quarry and stream-section in Rig Gill Syke, 1¾ miles N. of Stocks-in-Bowland and 150 yds. S.E. of Dale House Farm.

Carboniferous (40 ft. of reef limestone and breccia, $B_2$ subzone, overlain by shales alternating with conglomeratic limestone ; boulder-bed (limestone blocks in shale matrix) near top of section) ; reef brachiopods in $B_2$, particularly pustulose *Producti*, striatoid goniatites and *Posidonia becheri* in shales. *Goniatites falcatus* band at top of section.

Parkinson, D. 1936, p. 310, with geological map.

Geol. Surv. O.S. 92 N.W. ; Ord. New Pop. 95.

**Todmordon.** Head of small gully on left bank of Heeley Clough.

Carboniferous, Millstone Grit Series (R zone) ; 2 ft. of shale with numerous goniatites (*Reticuloceras* and *Hudsonoceras*).

Bisat, W. S. and Hudson, R. G. S. 1943, p. 395.

Geol. Surv. N.S. 76 ; Ord. New Pop. 95.

**Todmorden.** Section in bank of tributary to right bank of Shewbroad Clough.

Carboniferous, Millstone Grit ($R_2$ zone). 1 ft. of shale with the goniatites *Reticuloceras* and *Hudsonoceras*.

Wright, W. B. and others 1927, pp. 112, 125. Bisat, W. S. and Hudson, R. G. S. 1943, pp. 393-394.

Geol. Surv. N.S. 76 ; Ord. New Pop. 95.

**Tosside,** 6 miles S.W. of Settle. Small quarry 1 mile S.W. of Tosside and 300 yds. W.N.W. of Brock Thorn Farm.

Carboniferous (base of $P_1$a subzone) ; several feet of limestone including a conglomeratic bed crowded with fossils such as *Goniatites crenistria, Beyricho-ceratoides truncatus, Dibunophyllum bourtonense, Emmonsia parasitica* and numerous brachiopods.

Parkinson, D. 1936, p. 314, with geological map.

Geol. Surv. O.S. 92 N.W. ; Ord. New Pop. 95.

**Whitewell,** 7 miles N.W. of Clitheroe (Lancs). Disused quarry, 200 yds. S. of lane, one mile E of Whitewell and about ½ mile from Roman road.

Carboniferous Limestone ; numerous stems and heads of crinoids.

Geol. Surv. O.S. 91 S.E. ; Ord. New Pop. 95.

**Whitewell.** Stream-section in Porter Wood near confluence with R. Hodder at bend N. of Whitewell and immediately E. of Whitewell-Dunsop Bridge road.

Carboniferous ($C_2$ subzone, black shales of zaphrentid phase) ; contain corals (*Zaphrentoides*), brachiopods (*Productus*), bryozoa and lamellibranchs.

Parkinson, D. 1935, p. 103, with geological map.

Geol. Surv. O.S. 91 S.E. ; Ord. New Pop. 95.

# YORKSHIRE (NORTH RIDING)

**Ampleforth,** 4 miles S.S.W. of Helmsley. Quarry, 900 yds. N.E. of Beacon House, one mile E.N.E. of Ampleforth.

Jurassic, Corallian Beds (12 ft. of Osmington Oolite Coral Reef) ; an exposure typical of many between this locality and East Ness. Contains corals such as *Thecosmilia* and *Rhabdophyllia* in position of growth. Other corals also common, together with a profusion of mollusca and echinoderms.

Geol. Surv. N.S. 53 ; Ord. New Pop. 92.

**Appleton-le-Street,** 3½ miles W.N.W. of Malton. Two quarries 400 yds. W. of Appleton-le-Street.

Jurassic, Corallian Beds (Osmington Oolites ; the " Urchin Dirt Beds," on

Lower Calcareous Grit) ; echinoderms abundant in the impure oolites. The brachiopod *Thurmanella* and various lamellibranchs found in the grits below ; also the microscopic spicules of the sponge *Rhaxella*.

Blake, J. F. and Hudleston, W. H. 1877, p. 363 ; Wilson, V. 1933, pp. 490, 498 ; 1936, p. 264, with geol. map.

Geol. Surv. N.S. 53 ; Ord. New Pop. 92.

**Arkengarthdale,** 11 miles S.E. of Brough. Stream-section in Mirk Fell Beck, south of Mirk Fell Bridge, near Tan Hill Colliery.

Upper Carboniferous (Mirk Fell Beds, $E_2$ subzone) ; abundant zaphrentid corals, goniatites (*Cravenoceras*), lamellibranchs (*Nuculopsis*), etc., in ironstone beds.

Hudson, R. G. S. 1941, p. 259. Chubb, L. J. and Hudson, R. G. S. 1923, p. 274.

Geol. Surv. O.S. 97 N.W. ; Ord. New Pop. 84.

**Askrigg,** Wensleydale, 12 miles W. of Leyburn. Stream-section in Arn Gill, 1400 yds. N.N.E. of Askrigg Church.

Carboniferous, Yoredale Beds (Middle Limestone and shales, $D_2$ subzone) ; corals (*Orionastraea, Lithostrotion*) at base of, and brachiopods (*Gigantoproductus*) in, Middle Limestone with sponges in shale-parting (*Erythrospongia lithodes*). Zaphrentid corals in overlying shales.

Hudson, R. G. S. 1929, p. 181. Hudson, R. G. S. and King, W. B. R. 1933, p. 429. Hudson, R. G. S. and Fox, T. 1943, p. 101.

Geol. Surv. O.S. 97 N.W. ; Ord. New Pop. 90.

**Askrigg.** Stream-section, Grange Gill, from below Bow Bridge upstream to Abbey Force, on both sides of Askrigg-Sedbergh road.

Carboniferous, Yoredale Series (Gayle Limestone and Shale, $D_{1-2}$ subzones); algal nodules (*Girvanella*) below Bow Bridge ; corals (*Lithostrotion*) between Hockett and Bow Bridge ; and corals (*Aulophyllum, Zaphrentis*) with brachiopods at Abbey Force.

Hudson, R. G. S. and King, W. B. R. 1933, pp. 429, 431.

Geol. Surv. O.S. 97 N.W. ; Ord. New Pop. 90.

**Askrigg.** Stream-section, lower part of Mill Gill, about half-a-mile W.N.W. of Askrigg Church.

Carboniferous, Yoredale Series (Gayle Limestone and Hardraw Shale, $D_1$ subzone) ; brachiopods (*Chonetes, Gigantoproductus*) in limestone ; productids, lamellibranchs (*Posidonia*) and goniatites in shale.

Hudson, R. G. S. and others 1933, p. 227. Hudson, R. G. S. and King, W. B. R. 1933, p. 429.

Geol. Surv. O.S. 97 N.W. ; Ord. New Pop. 90.

**Aysgarth,** Wensleydale, $7\frac{1}{2}$ miles W. of Leyburn. Section in left bank of stream by bridge at Aysgarth Falls.

Carboniferous, Yoredale Series (Gayle Shale and Limestone, $D_1$ subzone) ; corals (*Aulophyllum* and zaphrentids) and brachiopods common in the Gayle Shale.

Hudson, R. G. S. and King, W. B. R. 1933, p. 432.

Geol. Surv. O.S. 97 S.E. ; Ord. New Pop. 90.

**Boltby,** 5 miles N.E. of Thirsk. Natural exposure below Boltby Scar, about 1 mile S.E. of Boltby village.

Jurassic, Oxford Clay (15-20 ft.) on Kellaways Rock ; ammonites very common in the Oxford Clay.

Geol. Surv. N.S. 52 ; Ord. New Pop. 91.

**Burniston,** 5 miles N. of Scarborough. Coast section in Burniston Wyke and at Cromer Point.

Jurassic, Inferior Oolite, sandstones of Middle Estuarine Series and the Scalby Plant Bed just S. of Cromer Point ; footprints of small dinosaurs in

the Burniston Footprint Bed ; drifted plant remains in the Scalby Plant Bed.
Hargreaves, J. A. 1913, p. 92. Wilson, V. and others 1934, p. 298.
Geol. Surv. N.S. 35 ; Ord. New Pop. 93.

**Cawton,** 5 miles S.S.E. of Helmsley. Quarry on Cawton Heights, 400 yds.
N.E. of Syke Gate Farm and about ⅔ mile S.W. of Cawton.
Jurassic, Corallian Beds (about 8 ft. of Osmington Oolite) ; echinoderms
very common in upper part of section ; ammonites common in lowest bed
(now largely obscured by debris) ; lamellibranchs and other fossils common
throughout.
Blake, J. F. and Hudleston, W. H. 1877, p. 369.
Geol. Surv. N.S. 53 ; Ord. New Pop. 92.

**Cayton,** 3 miles S. of Scarborough. Coast sections about 1¾ miles E.N.E.
of Cayton and N.W. of Red Cliff Point (Yons Nab), at half and low tide.
Jurassic, Inferior Oolite, Middle Estuarine Series (Gristhorpe Plant Bed) ;
the plant bed is visible in the cliff, adjacent rocks being black with sulphur-
yellow stains ; plants of the groups *Bennettitales* and *Ginkgoales*, with conifers
and ferns. The Caytoniales were first discovered in this plant bed. The classic
Yorkshire plant locality.
Thomas, H. H. 1925, pp. 299-363.
Geol. Surv. N.S. 54 ; Ord. New Pop. 93.

**Cayton.** Coastal sections in southern half of Cayton Bay (Red Cliff),
from Yons Nab northwards.
Jurassic, Corallian Beds, Lower Calcareous Grit (inaccessible except as
boulders), Oxford Clay, Hackness Rock, Kellaways Beds, Cornbrash. Fine
and abundant ammonites and lamellibranchs in Hackness Rock ; abundant
lamellibranchs, gastropods, echinoids, etc., in Cornbrash.
Geol. Surv. N.S. 54 ; Ord. New Pop. 93.

**Cloughton,** 6 miles N. of Scarborough. Coast section at Hundale Point,
between Salt Pans and Petrifying Springs ; at low spring tide.
Jurassic, Inferior Oolite, sandstones of the Middle Estuarine Series and the
Grey Limestone ; plants (*Ptilophyllum, Williamsonia*) and reptilian footprints
in the Middle Estuarine Series ; lamellibranchs (*Gervillia, Perna, Pinna,
Pleuromya, Pecten,* etc.), crinoids and belemnites are common in the Grey
Limestone.
Fox-Strangways, C. and Barrow, G. 1915, p. 38.
Geol. Surv. N.S. 35 ; Ord. New Pop. 93.

**Cloughton.** Coast section at Cloughton Wyke both S. and N. to Iron Scar.
Jurassic, Great Oolite (Upper Estuarine Series) ; Inferior Oolite (Scar-
borough Limestone, Middle Estuarine Series, Millepore Oolite, Lower
Estuarine Series, Eller Beck Bed), in descending order ; alternate estuarine,
beds with plants, and marine beds with lamellibranchs, ammonites, belemnites
sea-urchins, bryozoa, etc.
Arkell, W. J. 1933a, pp. 221-222.
Geol. Surv. N.S. 35, 44 ; Ord. New Pop. 93.

**East Ayton,** 4 miles S.W. of Scarborough. Quarry behind Betton Farm,
¾ mile N.E. of East Ayton. Numerous quarries in these beds occur at intervals
between this point and Brompton, farther west.
Jurassic, Corallian Beds (Osmington Oolite Coral Rag), an inter-reef facies
consisting of reef stacks buried in fossiliferous mud and debris from nearby
reefs. Large gastropods, echinoderms and a small brachiopod (terebratulid)
are very common. Thamnastraean coral stacks and other fossils also present.
Blake, J. F. and Hudleston, W. H. 1877, p. 327. Wilson, V. and others
1934, pp. 285, 301.
Geol. Surv. N.S. 54 ; Ord. New Pop. 93.

**Filey.** Coast section, S. and N. sides of Filey Brigg, from N.W. corner of bay northwards to fourth Doodle (cave).

Jurassic, Corallian Beds (Lower Calcareous Grit to Berkshire Oolite Series) ; abundant ammonites, lamellibranchs, sea-urchins, brachiopods, sponges, etc., with a band of crinoid and starfish ossicles between the first and second Doodles.

Arkell, W. J. 1933a, pp. 426-432.

Geol. Surv. N.S. 54 ; Ord. New Pop. 93.

**Glaisdale,** 10 miles W.S.W. of Whitby. Spoil heaps from old workings on Post Gate Hill, one mile S.W. of Glaisdale.

Jurassic, Inferior Oolite (spoil heaps from old workings in 12 ft. of Dogger ironstones and ferruginous sandstones) ; brachiopods (*Homeorhynchia cynocephala*) and lamellibranchs (*Astarte, Trigonia*, etc.) abundant.

Fox-Strangways, C., Reid, C. and Barrow, G. 1885, p. 23.

Geol. Surv. N.S. 43 ; Ord. New Pop. 86.

**Gristhorpe,** 2 miles N.W. of Filey. Cliff sections in Gristhorpe Bay, from north of Filey Brigg north-westwards to Yons Nab.

Jurassic, Corallian Beds (Lower Calcareous Grit, at top of cliff), Oxford Clay, Hackness Rock, Kellaways Beds, Cornbrash, Upper Estuarine Beds, Scarborough Limestone and Middle Estuarine Beds, from south to north. Fossils rare in Oxford Clay ; ammonites and lamellibranchs abundant in Hackness Rock ; molluscs, echinoids, etc., abundant in Cornbrash ; world-famous plant bed in Middle Estuarine Beds.

Geol. Surv. N.S. 54 ; Ord. New Pop. 93.

**Hawes.** Natural exposure at head of Shunner Fell Gill, best reached from Cotterdale, 5½ miles N.W. of Hawes, and 660 yds. from Shunner Fell Currack.

Carboniferous, Millstone Grit Series (thin argillaceous limestone in $R_2$ subzone) ; contains zaphrentid corals, brachiopods, molluscs and trilobites.

King, W. B. R. 1914, p. 390. Chubb, L. J. and Hudson, R. G. S. 1923, p. 260.

Geol. Surv. O.S. 97 N.W. ; Ord. New Pop. 90.

**Hawes.** Stream-section in Shivery Gill, Abbotside Common, W. of Buttertubs road.

Carboniferous, Yoredale Beds ; contain abundant *Dibunophyllum* and other corals.

Hudson, R. G. S. 1925.

Geol. Surv. O.S. 97 N.W. ; Ord. New Pop. 90.

**Hayburn,** 8 miles N. of Scarborough. Cliff-foot, ¼ to ½ mile N. of Hayburn Wyke ; accessible except at full high tide.

Jurassic, Inferior Oolite (Lower Estuarine Series) ; contain stems of the "horsetail" *Equisetites columnaris.*

Geol. Surv. N.S. 35, 44 ; Ord. New Pop. 93.

**Kepwick,** 6 miles N.N.E. of Thirsk. Kepwick Quarry, 1 mile E.N.E. of Kepwick.

Jurassic, Corallian Beds (the best section in the Hambleton Oolite, about 70 ft. of beds exposed) ; contains lamellibranchs, gastropods, echinoderms, etc. ; all common.

Geol. Surv. N.S. 42 ; Ord. New Pop. 91.

**Levisham,** 5 miles N.E. of Pickering. The narrow gorge of Havern Beck, ¾ mile N.W. of Slatersgate Inn, 2¾ miles N.N.E. of Levisham.

Jurassic, Kellaways Rock above fossiliferous Upper Cornbrash and Upper Estuarine Shales ; seen in natural sections ; Cornbrash contains the brachiopod, *Burmirhynchia fusca*, with *Ostrea marshii*, *O. undosa* and other lamellibranchs.

Douglas, J. A. and Arkell, W. J. 1932, p. 140.

Geol. Surv. N.S. 43 ; Ord. New Pop. 92.

**Leyburn,** Wensleydale. Two quarries N.W. of Leyburn.
Carboniferous (Main Limestone and Red Beds, $E_1$ subzone) ; fish teeth in north quarry ; corals (*Lonsdaleia*) in south quarry.
Hudson, R. G. S. and King, W. B. R. 1933, p. 432.
Geol. Surv. O.S. 97 N.E. ; Ord. New Pop. 91.

**Nosterfield,** $3\frac{1}{2}$ miles E. of Masham. Old quarries, Nosterfield Limekilns, 800 yds. W.N.W. of Methodist Chapel, Nosterfield.
Permian, Lower Magnesian Limestone (thin-bedded dark grey limestone) ; brachiopods (*Productus horridus*) fairly common.
Kendall, P. F. and Wroot, H. E. 1924, p. 847.
Geol. Surv. N.S. 52 ; Ord. New Pop. 91.

**Pickering.** Old quarries extending for about 800 yds. northwards from Pickering Castle, on the N. side of the town.
Jurassic, Corallian Beds, Middle Calcareous Grit (*Trigonia hudlestoni* Beds), Osmington Oolites and Upper Calcareous Grit. *Trigonia hudlestoni* and other *Trigoniae* along with other lamellibranchs are very common, in bands, near the top of the Middle Calcareous Grit. Lamellibranchs, gastropods, echinoderms, etc., are common in the Osmington Oolite Series.
Blake, J. F. and Hudleston, W. H. 1877, pp. 333-340.
Geol. Surv. N.S. 53 ; Ord. New Pop. 92.

**Ravenscar,** 8 miles S.E. of Whitby. Coast section between Old Peak and Blea Wyke Point ; best approached by path north of The Peak ; the tide must be watched.
Jurassic, Bituminous Shales of the Upper Lias (*serpentinum* zone) to the top of the Blea Wyke Beds (*jurense* zone) and overlying Dogger (Inferior Oolite, ? *murchisonae* zone). Ammonites (*Harpoceras*, etc.) and other fossils common ; the rich Nerinea bed at the base of the Dogger is full of gastropods (*Nerinea cingenda*), lamellibranchs (*Astarte, Trigonia*, etc.) and corals (*Thecosmilia*, etc.) ; " *Terebratula* " *trilineata* is common in the Blea Wyke Beds.
Rastall, R. H. 1905, pp. 441-457. Wilson, V. and others 1934, pp. 259, 297.
Geol. Surv. N.S. 35, 44 ; Ord. New Pop. 93.

**Robin Hood's Bay,** 7 miles S.E. of Whitby. The Scars and intervening softer beds forming the cliffs and floor of Robin Hood's Bay.
Jurassic, Lower Lias (*semicostatum* to *raricostatum* zones, shales and calcareous mudstone bands) ; characteristic zonal ammonites, *Echioceras, Asteroceras, Arietites, Arnioceras*, etc., and such lamellibranchs as *Gryphaea, Cardinia*, and *Hippopodium*, with many belemnites and other fossils.
Tate, R. and Blake, J. F. 1876. Fox-Strangways, C. and Barrow, G. 1915. Arkell, W. J. 1933a, pp. 139-141.
Geol. Surv. N.S. 35, 44 ; Ord. New Pop. 93.

**Scalby,** N.W. of Scarborough. Section at foot of Scalby Ness and on foreshore ; other outcrops on beach at half-tide level.
Jurassic, Great Oolite (Upper Estuarine Series) ; the best locality for Upper Estuarine plants ; fairly well-preserved *Ginkgo*-like leaves occur.
Black, M. 1929.
Geol. Surv. N.S. 35, 44 ; Ord. New Pop. 93.

**Scarborough.** Peacock's Quarry, in side of hill W. of railway station.
Jurassic, Cornbrash ; a classic locality ; many ammonites and other fossils collected in the past.
Arkell, W. J. 1933a, p. 337.
Geol. Surv. N.S. 54 ; Ord. New Pop. 93.

**Scarborough.** Cliff and beach sections from White Nab to esplanade in South Bay, Scarborough.
Jurassic, Great Oolite (Upper Estuarine Series) ; Inferior Oolite (Scarborough Limestone, Middle Estuarine and Millepore Oolite, in descending

order). Plants occur in the Estuarine Beds ; lamellibranchs, echinoderms and occasional ammonites in the Scarborough Limestone.

Geol. Surv. N.S. 54 ; Ord. New Pop. 93.

**Scarborough.** Cliff section on N. and E. sides of Castle Hill, Scarborough. Jurassic, Oxford Clay and Corallian (Lower Calcareous Grit and overlying Hambleton Oolite). Exposures largely concealed by buildings and the Marine Drive. Abundant lamellibranchs occur in the Hambleton Oolite ; ammonites, belemnites, lamellibranchs and other fossils are less common in the Lower Calcareous Grit ; many ammonites in Hackness Rock along diagonal path behind southern Toll House of Marine Drive.

Blake, J. F. and Hudleston, W. H. 1877, p. 324. Fox-Strangways, C. 1892, p. 318.

Geol. Surv. N.S. 54 ; Ord. New Pop. 93.

**Seamer,** 3½ miles S.W. of Scarborough. Brown's Lime Works Quarry, other pits in the vicinity show similar sections. Jurassic, Corallian Beds (4 ft. of Coral Rag on 29 ft. of Osmington Oolite Series) ; reef fossils (corals, etc.) in the upper 4 ft. ; fossils of most groups are very common in the beds below.

Geol. Surv. N.S. 54 ; Ord. New Pop. 93.

**Staithes,** 10 miles N.W. of Whitby. Coast sections at Old Nab, east of Staithes. Jurassic, Middle Lias (the " Main," " Pecten," " Two-foot " and "Avicula " Ironstone seams, in descending order, with abundant fossils) ; ammonites (*Pleuroceras*), belemnites, lamellibranchs (*Oxytoma, Aequipecten, Modiolus,* etc.) and brachiopods (*Tetrarhynchia tetrahedra, Lobothyris punctata,* etc.) are abundant.

Barrow, G. 1888, p. 17.
Geol. Surv. N.S. 34 ; Ord. New Pop. 86.

**Suffield,** 4 miles N.W. of Scarborough. Quarries in Limestone Lane : (a) two quarries about ⅓ mile N.E. of Suffield Heights Farm ; (b) two quarries about ½ mile N. and ¾ mile N. (nearer Suffield Hill) of Suffield Ings Farm respectively. Jurassic, Corallian Beds : (a) good exposures in about 15 ft. of shelly Hambleton Oolite ; (b) sections in the Hambleton Oolite Sponge-Coral Rag. There are numerous other sections in this Rag all around Hackness. From (a) lamellibranchs and echinoderms are common, and in the lower beds, ammonites ; from (b), a rich fauna of calcareous sponges, terebratulid brachiopods, corals and many other fossils. Most of the Corallian calcareous sponges described by G. J. Hinde in his Pal. Soc. Mon. came from this district.

Blake, J. F. and Hudleston, W. H. 1877, pp. 329-332. Fox-Strangways, C. 1892, p. 326 ; Hinde, G. J. 1893. Wilson, V. and others 1934, p. 301.

Geol. Surv. N.S. 44 ; Ord. New Pop. 93.

**Wath,** 7¼ miles W.N.W. of Malton. Quarry, 250 yds. W. of the bridge at Wath, ¾ mile S.E. of Hovingham. Jurassic, Corallian Beds (14 ft. of Osmington Oolite in Coral Rag facies) ; there are many other similar exposures between Slingsby and Hovingham, and farther west, on Cawton Heights, Cawton. Contain a rich variety of corals, echinoderms, gastropods and lamellibranchs. The rare sea-urchin, *Glypticus hieroglyphicus,* occurs here.

Geol. Surv. N.S. 53 ; Ord. New Pop. 92.

**Whitby.** Coast section along " The Scar," Whitby, towards Saltwick Nab. Jurassic, Lower beds of the Upper Lias ; Alum Shales and Jet Rock Series, *bifrons* and *serpentinum* zones. The zonal and other ammonites occur (*Hildoceras, Dactylioceras, Harpoceras,* etc.) together with lamellibranchs (*Nuculana*

**K**

*ovum, Inoceramus dubius*, etc.).  The Alum Shale was the source of most of the Upper Lias reptiles (*Ichthyosaurus*, etc.) in old collections.
Wilson, V. and others 1934, p. 293.
Geol. Surv. N.S. 35, 44 ;  Ord. New Pop. 86.

**Whitby.** Coast section at foot of cliff ;  " Long Bight " (midway to Saltwick Bay).  Available only at half to low tide ;  cut off at high tide ;  danger of cliff falls.
Jurassic, Inferior ˙Oolite, Lower Estuarine Series (just above Dogger) ; best Lower Estuarine plant locality ;  many *Ptilophyllum* leaves.
Geol. Surv. N.S. 35, 44 ;  Ord. New Pop. 86.

**Whitwell,** 6 miles S.W. of Malton.  Large quarry at Welburn crossroads, 1600 yds. N.E. of Whitwell Church.
Jurassic, Inferior Oolite (Millepore Oolite) ;  the most common fossil is the small polyzoan *Entalophora straminea* with terebratulids, echinoderms and mollusca.
Fox-Strangways, C. 1892, pp. 213-215.
Geol. Surv. N.S. 63 ;  Ord. New Pop. 92.


# YORKSHIRE (EAST RIDING)

**Bessingby,** 2 miles S.W. of Bridlington.  Quarry just S.W. of road-junction, ¼ mile N.E. of Bessingby Hall. (No. 107 of Wright 1942 ;  No. 30 of Rowe 1904.)
Cretaceous, Upper Chalk (*pilula*, locally *lingua*, zone ;  *binodosus* subzone) ; one of the best localities for the ammonites *Discoscaphites binodosus* and *Scaphites inflatus*.
Rowe, A. W. 1904, p. 237, with geol. map ;  Wright, C. W. and E. V. 1942b, pp. 120, 135.
Geol. Surv. N.S. 65 ;  Ord. New Pop. 93.

**Beverley.** Whiting Works (Messrs. Storey, Whitty & Co.), ˙immediately S. of Beverley Barracks.  (No. 29 of Wright 1942.)  Permission to enter pit should be obtained from Enquiry Office.
Cretaceous, Upper Chalk (*Uintacrinus* and *Marsupites* zones) ;  belemnites (*Actinocamax granulatus*), lamellibranchs (*Inoceramus pinniformis*) and sea-urchins (truncated *Echinocorys*) in bands at top of *Uintacrinus* zone.
Wright, C. W. and E. V. 1942b, p. 124.
Geol. Surv. N.S. 72 ;  Ord. New Pop. 99.

**Bridlington.** White Hill Pit, on Scarborough Road, 1¼ miles N. of Old Town, Bridlington.  Now being filled in with refuse.  (No. 109 of Wright 1942 ;  No. 27 of Rowe 1904.)
Cretaceous, Upper Chalk (*pilula*, locally *lingua*, zone ;  *binodosus* subzone) ; contains belemnites (including *Actinocamax quadratus*), ammonoids, sponges, etc.
Rowe, A. W. 1904, p. 236, with geol. map. Wright, C. W. and E. V. 1942b, p. 236.
Geol. Surv. N.S. 65 ;  Ord. New Pop. 93.

**Burdale,** 11 miles W.N.W. of Great Driffield.  Burdale Chalk Pit, just N.W. of Burdale station.  (No. 67 of Wright 1942.)
Cretaceous, from base of Middle Chalk to the *cortestudinarium* zone of Upper Chalk ;  the chalk is extremely hard ;  sea-urchins, *Conulus* from upper part of Middle Chalk ;  *Micraster* and *Infulaster* in *planus* zone of Upper Chalk.
Wright, C. W. and E. V. 1942b, p. 124.
Geol. Surv. N.S. 64 ;  Ord. New Pop. 98.

**Flamborough,** 4 miles N.E. of Bridlington. Cliffs from High Stacks, Flamborough Head, to South Landing.

Cretaceous, Upper Chalk (*coranguinum*, locally *rostrata*, zone ; upper two-thirds of zone exposed) ; abundant sea-urchins (*Hagenowia rostrata*), with belemnites and siliceous sponges.

Rowe, A. W. 1904, p. 217, with geol. map.
Geol. Surv. N.S. 55, 65 ; Ord. New Pop. 93.

**Flamborough.** Cliffs from South Landing to Dane's Dyke.

Cretaceous, Upper Chalk (*coranguinum*, locally *rostrata*, zone, *Uintacrinus* and *Marsupites* zones); abundant sea-urchins (*Hagenowia rostrata*) in *rostrata* zone ; crinoid ossicles (*Uintacrinus*), a band of belemnites and of lamellibranchs (*Inoceramus pinniformis*) with rare sea-urchins (*Zeugolpleurus*) in the *Uintacrinus* zone ; sponges fairly common.

Rowe, A. W. 1904, pp. 217-221, with geol. map.
Geol. Surv. N.S. 65 ; Ord. New Pop. 93.

**Hotham,** 5 miles E. of Market Weighton. "Cliffe," a fairly large pit, on escarpment, in field just S.E. of cross-roads, ½ mile W. of Hotham.

Jurassic, Lower Lias (*planorbis* and *angulata* zones) ; abundant ammonites (*Caloceras* and *Waehneroceras*), lamellibranchs and many other fossils.

Fox-Strangways, C. 1892, pp. 33-34.
Geol. Surv. N.S. 72 ; Ord. New Pop. 98.

**Kiplingcotes,** 3 miles E. of Market Weighton. Quarry by railside at Kiplingcotes station. (No. 38 of Wright 1942.)

Cretaceous, Upper Chalk (*planus* zone, with occasional iron-stained lenses full of aragonite-shelled gastropods and lamellibranchs) ; fauna very rich for Yorkshire ; the sea-urchin, *Infulaster excentricus*, common, with many interesting starfish ossicles, aragonite-shelled molluscs and siliceous sponges in flint.

Wright, C. W. 1935. Wright, C. W. and E. V. 1942b, p. 116.
Geol. Surv. N.S. 72 ; Ord. New Pop. 98.

**Little Weighton,** 5 miles S.W. of Beverley. Little Weighton Cutting and Pit, just E. of tunnel W. of Little Weighton station. (No. 18 of Wright 1942.) Permission from station master.

Cretaceous, Upper Chalk (*cortestudinarium* zone) ; abundant *Micraster*, *Inoceramus*, sponges ; rare *Infulaster* and ammonoids (including *Scaphites geinitzi*).

Wright, C. W. and E. V. 1942b, p. 123.
Geol. Surv. N.S. 72 ; Ord. New Pop. 98.

**Market Weighton.** Rifle Butts Pit (Goodmanham), 1¼ miles E.N.E. of Market Weighton ; Red Chalk exposed in disused Rifle Range W. of small pit, and hillside scars showing Lower Chalk. (No. 35 of Wright 1942.)

Cretaceous, Red Chalk (resting on Lower Lias) and Lower Chalk (*varians* zone) up to Lower Pink Band. Ossicles of the crinoid *Acrochordocrinus* [*Bourgueticrinus*] *rugosus* in the Red Chalk ; fairly large fauna in Lower Chalk including the belemnite *Belemnocamax howeri*.

Wright, C. W. and E. V. 1942b, p. 124.
Geol. Surv. N.S. 72 ; Ord. New Pop. 98.

**Middleton-on-the-Wolds,** 8 miles N.E. of Market Weighton. Limeworks, 500 yds. N. of railway bridge, N. of centre of village. (No. 52 of Wright 1942.) Permission should be obtained beforehand in writing.

Cretaceous, Upper Chalk (*coranguinum*, locally *rostrata*, zone and ? *cortestudinarium* zone) ; *Micraster*, *Inoceramus involutus* and "Flamborough" sponges in ferruginous preservation occur.

Wright, C. W. and E. V. 1942b, p. 124.
Geol. Surv. N.S. 72 ; Ord. New Pop. 98.

**North Grimston,** 5 miles S.E. of Malton. (i) Road section leading up North Grimston Hill and two large quarries on the hill, S.E. of North Grimston. (ii) Extensive old workings along the north side of the railway about ⅜ mile S.E. of North Grimston Church.

Jurassic, Corallian Beds (classic sections in Osmington Oolite Series and Upper Calcareous Grit (North Grimston Cementstones) ; in (i) a rich profusion of corals, echinocerms, lamellibranchs and other fossils ; in (ii) the oyster, *Gryphaea dilatata*, is very common, and also fragments of ammonites and other fossils.

Wilson V., 1933, pp. 500, 503.  Blake, J. F. and Hudleston, W. H. 1877, pp. 374-380.

Geol. Surv. N.S. 63, 64 ; Ord. New Pop. 92.

**Ruston Parva,** 4 miles N.E. of Driffield. Ruston Parva Limeworks, at cross-roads on main Bridlington road, 500 yds. S.E. of village. (No. 97 of Wright, 1942 ; No. 33 of Rowe, 1904.)

Cretaceous, Upper Chalk (*pilula*, locally *lingua*, zone) ; contains belemnites and sponges.

Rowe, A. W. 1904, p. 237, with geol. map. Wright, C. W. and E. V. 1942b, p. 125.

Geol. Surv. N.S. 64 ; Ord. New Pop. 99.

**Sewerby,** Bridlington.  Cliffs and scars from Danes Dyke W.S.W. to Sewerby Cliff End.

Cretaceous, Upper Chalk (*Marsupites* and *pilula*, locally *lingua*, zones) ; the *Marsupites* zone contains abundant crinoids (*Marsupites*) ; the *lingua* zone contains abundant *Inoceramus*, belemnites and a sponge-fauna (" Flamborough Sponge Bed ") of 35 species or more ; best seen in scars on beach.

Rowe, A. W. 1904, pp. 221-227, with geol. map.

Geol. Surv. N.S. 65 ; Ord. New Pop. 93.

**South Cave,** 7 miles S.S.E. of Market Weighton. Quarry near, and just S.W. of South Cave station, 1 mile N. of South Cave.

Jurassic, Inferior Oolite (Millepore Oolite and underlying beds thrust over Kellaways Beds by glacial action) ; contain abundant polyzoa, lamellibranchs, brachiopods, echinoids, etc.

Stather, J. W. 1922, p. 244.

Geol. Surv. N.S. 72 ; Ord. New Pop. 98.

**South Cave.** Railwayside Quarry, just east of South Cave station, 1 mile N. of South Cave.

Jurassic, Kellaways Rock (*calloviense* zone) and Oxford Clay ; extremely abundant and beautifully preserved ammonites and many other fossils in the Kellaways Rock ; occasional poor fossils in the Oxford Clay.  The hard crystalline lumps of rock in the ferruginous top bed of the Kellaways Rock require a heavy sledge hammer.

Geol. Surv. N.S. 72 ; Ord. New Pop. 98.

**Speeton,** 6 miles N.W. of Bridlington. Speeton Cliffs, between a point S.E. of Reighton Gap to about 1000 yds. S.E. of mouth of Speeton Beck. Approach from Reighton Gap, or by path down cliff from Speeton Church.

Cretaceous, Speeton Clay (from D beds at base to A at top) ; abundant belemnites occur almost throughout ; fine ammonites but abundant only from D3 to C4 and even there only in bands ; Crioceratids common in " Cement Beds " in middle B ; numerous other fossils.

Lamplugh, G. W. 1889 and 1896.  Pavlow, A. and Lamplugh, G. W. 1892. Spath, L. F. 1924.

Geol. Surv. N.S. 54, 55 ; Ord. New Pop. 93.

**Speeton.** Speeton Cliffs, S.E. from a point about 1000 yds. S.E. of Speeton Beck ; chalk cliffs and scars on beach.

Cretaceous, Red Chalk (greatest known thickness), Lower Chalk and, 2½ miles S.E. of Speeton Beck, base of Middle Chalk at foot of cliff. Red Chalk contains abundant belemnites and brachiopods and a number of peculiar echinoderms. The " Green Bed " full of large *Concinnithyris*. Base of Lower Chalk up to " Lower Pink Band " with interesting echinoids (" *Offaster* " *sphericus, Hemiaster, Holaster, Salenia,* etc.).

Hill, W. 1888, pp. 337, 343-345.
Geol. Surv. N.S. 55 ; Ord. New Pop. 93.

**Willerby,** 5½ miles S. of Beverley. Kirkella Cutting Pits, beside railway line, north-westwards from Whiting Works, N.W. of Willerby village. (No. 16 of Wright 1942.)

Cretaceous, Upper Chalk *(cortestudinarium* zone) ; *Micraster* is unusually common for Yorkshire ; many starfish ossicles occur.

Wright, C. W. and E. V. 1942b, p. 123.
Geol. Surv. O.S. 86 ; Ord. New Pop. 99.

## LIST OF WORKS REFERRED TO

N.B.—Papers written jointly by more than two authors are referred to in the text as by the first author " and others." An asterisk indicates that the work includes plates of fossils.

ABSALOM, R. G. and HOPKINS, W. 1926. " The Geological Relations of the Coast Sections between Tynemouth and Seaton Sluice." *Proc. Univ. Durham Phil. Soc.*, vol. vii, 17 pp., with geol. map. (Dept. Geol. Publ. 14, Sci. Lab. Univ. Durham.)

ALEXANDER, F. E. S. 1936. " The Aymestry Limestone of the Main Outcrop." *Quart. Journ. Geol. Soc.*, vol. xcii, pp. 103-115, with geol. map.

ALEXANDER, G. B. 1940. In Report of Field Meetings for 1939. *Proc. Yorks. Geol. Soc.*, vol. xxiv, pp. 172-173.

ANDREWS, W. R. and JUKES-BROWNE, A. J. 1894. " The Purbeck Beds of the Vale of Wardour." *Quart. Journ. Geol. Soc.*, vol. 1, pp. 44-71, with geol. map.

ARBER, E. A. N. 1904. " The Fossil Flora of the Culm Measures of North-West Devon and the Palaeobotanical Evidence with regard to the Age of the Beds." *Phil. Trans. Roy. Soc.*, Ser. B, vol. cxcvii, pp. 291-325.*

ARKELL, W. J. 1927. " The Corallian Rocks of Oxford, Berks. and North Wilts." *Phil. Trans. Roy. Soc.*, Ser. B, vol. ccxvi, pp. 67-181, geol. map.*

——. 1931. " The Upper Great Oolite, Bradford Beds and Forest Marble of South Oxfordshire and the Succession of Gastropod Faunas in the Great Oolite." *Quart. Journ. Geol. Soc.*, vol. lxxxvii, pp. 563-629.*

——. 1933a. " The Jurassic System in Great Britain." *Oxford.*

——. 1933b. " New Evidence on the Great Oolite Succession at Bladon, near Woodstock, Oxfordshire." *Proc. Geol. Assoc.*, vol. xliv, pp. 177-183.

——. 1934. "A Monograph of British Corallian Lamellibranchia," Part VII. *Palaeont. Soc.*

——. 1935. " The Portland Beds of the Dorset Mainland." *Proc. Geol. Assoc.*, vol. xlvi, pp. 301-347.

——. 1936. " The Ammonite Zones of the Upper Oxfordian of Oxford and the Horizons of the Sowerbys' and Buckman's Types." *Quart. Journ. Geol. Soc.*, vol. xcii, pp. 146-187.*

——. 1937a. " Report on Ammonites Collected at Long Stanton, Cambs., and on the Age of the Ampthill Clay." *Summ. Prog. Geol. Surv. for 1935,* Pt. II, pp. 64-86.*

——. 1937b. "A Monograph of British Corallian Lamellibranchia," Part X. *Palaeont. Soc.*

——. 1939a. " The Ammonite Succession at the Woodham Brick Company's Pit, Akeman Street Station, Buckinghamshire, and its Bearing on the Classification of the Oxford Clay." *Quart. Journ. Geol. Soc.*, vol. xcv, pp. 135-222.*

——. 1939b. "A Map of the Corallian Beds between Marcham and Faringdon, Berkshire." *Proc. Geol. Assoc.*, vol. l, pp. 487-509, geol. map.

——. 1939c. " The Richardson Collection of Lamellibranchs from the Fuller's Earth Rock." *Proc. Dorset Nat. Hist. and Arch. Soc.*, vol. lx, pp. 165-174.

——. 1940. " Fossils from the Fuller's Earth of the Weymouth Anticline." *Geol. Mag.*, vol. lxxvii, pp. 42-49.*

——. 1941a. " Map of the Corallian Beds around Highworth, Wiltshire." *Proc. Geol. Assoc.*, vol. lii, pp. 79-109, with geol. map.

——. 1941b. " The Upper Oxford Clay at Purton, Wilts. and the Zones of the Lower Oxfordian." *Geol. Mag.*, vol. lxxviii, pp. 161-172.

——. 1941c. " The Gastropods of the Purbeck Beds." *Quart. Journ. Geol. Soc.*, vol. xcvii, pp. 79-128.*

——. 1943. " Stratigraphy and Structures East of Oxford." *Quart. Journ. Geol. Soc.*, vol. xcviii, pp. 187-204, with geol. map.

——. 1944a. " Stratigraphy and Structures East of Oxford. Part II : The Miltons and Haseleys. Part III : Islip." *Quart. Journ. Geol. Soc.*, vol. c, pp. 45-72, with geol. maps.

——. 1944b. "A Monograph on the Ammonites of the English Corallian Beds, Part X." *Palaeont. Soc.**

——. 1947a. " The Geology of Oxford." *Oxford.**

——. 1947b. " The Geology of the Country around Weymouth, Swanage, Corfe and Lulworth." *Mem. Geol. Surv.**

——, RICHARDSON, L. and PRINGLE, J. 1933. " The Lower Oolites Exposed in the Ardley and Fritwell Railway-Cuttings, between Bicester and Banbury, Oxford." *Proc. Geol. Assoc.*, vol. xliv, pp. 340-354.

BADEN-POWELL, B. F. W. 1930. " Notes 'on Raised Beach Mollusca from the Isle of Portland." *Proc. Malac. Soc.*, vol. xix, pp. 67-76.

BAMBER, A. E. 1924. " The Avonian of the Western Mendips from the Cheddar Valley to the Sea." *Proc. Bristol Nat. Soc.*, Ser. 4, vol. vi, pp. 75-91, with geol. map.

BANCROFT, B. B. 1929. " Some new Genera and Species of Strophomenacea from the Upper Ordovician of Shropshire." *Mem. and Proc. Manchester Lit. and Phil. Soc.*, vol. lxxiii, pp. 33-65.*

——. 1933. " Correlation-tables of the Stages Costonian-Onnian in England and Wales." *Blakeney.*

——. 1945. " The Brachiopod Zonal Indices of the Stages Costonian to Onnian in Britain." *Journ. Pal.*, vol. xix, pp. 181-252.*

BANKS, R. W. 1856. " On the Tilestones or Downton Sandstones, in the Neighbourhood of Kington, and their Contents." *Quart. Journ. Geol. Soc.*, vol. xii, pp. 94-101.*

BARRETT, H. H. and RICHEY, J. E. 1945. " The Economic Geology of the Canonbie Coalfield." *Geol. Surv. Wartime Pamphlet*, No. 42.

BARROW, G. 1888. " The Geology of North Cleveland." *Mem. Geol. Surv.*

BATHER, F. A. 1920. " *Protoscolex latus*, a new ' worm ' from Lower Ludlow Beds." *Ann. Mag. Nat. Hist.*, Ser. 9, vol. v, pp. 124-132.*

——. 1924. " *Saccocoma cretacea* n. sp. : a Senonian Crinoid." *Proc. Geol. Assoc.*, vol. xxxv, pp. 111-121.*

BELL, A. and NOTCUTT, S. A. 1925. A Field Guide to the Upper Pliocene of the Ipswich District, pp. 37-48. With a note on the Sub-Crag Detritus Bed and its contained Flint Implements, by J. Reid Moir, pp. 44-48. *Ipswich.*

BISAT, W. S. 1924. " The Carboniferous Goniatites of the North of England and their Zones." *Proc. Yorks. Geol. Soc.*, vol. xx, pp. 40-124.*

——. 1930. " On *Cravenoceras leion*, sp. nov., the basement goniatite of the Namurian, Upper Carboniferous." *Trans. Leeds Geol. Assoc.*, Pt. xx, (vol. iv), pp. 28-32.

——. 1932. " On some Lower Sabdenian Goniatites." *Trans. Leeds Geol. Assoc.*, vol. v, pt. I, pp. 27-36.*

—— and HUDSON, R. G. S. 1943. " The Lower Reticuloceras (R₁) Goniatite Succession in the Namurian of the North of England." *Proc. Yorks. Geol. Soc.*, vol. xxiv, pp. 383-440.*

BLACK, M. 1929. "Drifted Plant Beds of the Upper Estuarine Series of Yorkshire." *Quart. Journ. Geol. Soc.*, vol. lxxxv, pp. 389-439.

BLAKE, J. F. and HUDLESTON, W. H. 1877. "On the Corallian Rocks of England." *Quart. Journ. Geol. Soc.*, vol. xxxiii, pp. 260-405.*

BOOKER, K. M. and HUDSON, R. G. S. 1926. "The Carboniferous Sequence of the Craven Lowlands South of the Reef Limestones of Cracoe." *Proc. Yorks. Geol. Soc.*, vol. xx, pp. 411-438, with geol. map.

BOSWELL, P. G. H. 1923. "The Geology of the Country around Cromer and Norwich." *Proc. Geol. Assoc.*, vol. xxxiv, pp. 207-222.

——. 1927. "The Geology of the Country around Ipswich." *Mem. Geol. Surv.*

——. 1928. "The Geology of the Country around Woodbridge, Felixstowe and Orford." *Mem. Geol. Surv.*

——. 1929. "The Geology of the Country around Sudbury." *Mem. Geol. Surv.*

——. 1938. "Whitsun Field Meeting, 3rd June to 7th June, 1938. Ipswich District." *Proc. Geol. Assoc.*, vol. xlix, pp. 410-414.

—— and MOIR, J. REID. 1923. "The Pleistocene Deposits and their contained Palaeolithic Flint Implements at Foxhall Road, Ipswich." *Journ. Roy. Anthrop. Inst.*, vol. lxiii, pp. 229-262, text-illust.

BRAY, A. 1927. "The Carboniferous Sequence between Lothersdale and Cowling (Colne)." *Journ. Manchester Geol. Assoc.*, vol. i, pp. 44-57, with geol. map.

BRIGHTON, A. G. 1928. "Notes on the Middle and Upper Chalk of the Cambridge District." *Geol. Mag.*, vol. lxv, pp. 368-371.

BRISTOW, H. W. 1857. "Comparative Sections of the Purbeck Strata of Dorset." *Vertical Sections, Geol. Surv.* Sheet 22.

BROWN, E. E. S. 1941. "The Folkestone Sands and Base of the Gault near Wrotham Heath, Kent." *Proc. Geol. Assoc.*, vol. lii, pp. 1-15, with geol. map.

BRYDONE, R. M. 1906. "Further Notes on the Stratigraphy and Fauna of the Trimmingham Chalk." *Geol. Mag.*, Dec. 5, vol. iii, pp. 13-22 ; pp. 72-78 ; pp. 124-130 ; pp. 289-300.

——. 1908. "On the Subdivisions of the Chalk of Trimingham (Norfolk)." *Quart. Journ. Geol. Soc.*, vol. lxiv, pp. 401-412.

——. 1912. "The Stratigraphy of the Chalk of Hants ", with geol. map. *London.*

——. 1938. "On Correlation of some of the Norfolk Exposures of Chalk with *Belemnitella mucronata.*" *London.*

BUCKMAN, S. S. 1887-1907. "A Monograph of the Ammonites of the ' Inferior Oolite Series.' " *Palaeont. Soc.*

——. 1922. "Jurassic Chronology : II—Preliminary Studies. Certain Jurassic Strata near Eypesmouth (Dorset) ; the Junction-Bed of Watton Cliff and Associated Rocks." *Quart. Journ. Geol. Soc.*, vol. lxxviii, pp. 378-457.

—— and WILSON, E. 1896. "Dundry Hill : its Upper Portion, or the Beds Marked as Inferior Oolite (g 5) in the Maps of the Geological Survey." *Quart. Journ. Geol. Soc.*, vol. lii, pp. 669-720.

BULMAN, O. M. B. 1927-1934. "A Monograph of British Dendroid Graptolites." Parts I-III. *Palaeont. Soc.*

BURTON, E. ST. J. 1929. "The Horizons of Bryozoa (Polyzoa) in the Upper Eocene Beds of Hampshire." *Quart. Journ. Geol. Soc.*, vol. lxxxv, pp. 223-241.

——. 1933. "Faunal Horizons of the Barton Beds in Hampshire." *Proc. Geol. Assoc.*, vol. xliv, pp. 131-167.

BUSH, G. E. 1925. " The Avonian Succession of Spring Gardens and Vallis Vale, Frome, Somerset." *Proc. Bristol Nat. Soc.*, Ser. 4, vol. vi, pp 250-259, with geol. map.

——. 1928. " The Avonian Succession at Clevedon—A Description of the Coast Section." *Proc. Bristol Nat. Soc.*, Ser. 4, vol. vi, pp. 392-399.

BUTLER, A. J. 1939. " The Stratigraphy of the Wenlock Limestone of Dudley." *Quart. Journ. Geol. Soc.*, vol. xcv, pp. 37-74, with geol. map.

—— and OAKLEY, K. P. 1936. *See* Hill, D., Butler, A. J., Oakley, K. P. and Arkell, W. J. 1936.

CARRUTHERS, R. G., DINHAM, C. H., BURNETT, G. A. and MADEN, J. 1927. " The Geology of Belford, Holy Island and the Farne Islands. 2nd ed." *Mem. Geol. Surv.*

——, BURNETT, G. A. and ANDERSON, W. 1930. " Geology of the Alnwick District." *Mem. Geol. Surv.*

CASEY, R. 1939. " The Upper Part of the Lower Greensand around Folkestone." *Proc. Geol. Assoc.*, vol. l, pp. 362-378.*

CHALMERS, R. M. 1936. " The Genus Gastrioceras occurring in the Lower Coal Measures of the Lancashire Coalfield." *Journ. Manchester Geol. Assoc.*, vol. i, pp. 147-166.*

CHATWIN, C. P. and PRINGLE, J. 1922. " The Zones of the Kimmeridge and Portland Rocks at Swindon." *Summ. Prog. Geol. Surv. for 1921*, pp. 162-168.

CHUBB, L. J. and HUDSON, R. G. S. 1923. " The Nature of the Junction between the Lower Carboniferous and the Millstone Grit of North-West Yorkshire." *Proc. Yorks. Geol. Soc.*, vol. xx, pp. 257-291.

CLARK, J. G. D. 1938. " Microlithic Industries from Tufa Deposits at Prestatyn, Flintshire and Blashenwell, Dorset." *Proc. Prehist. Soc.*, N. Ser., vol. iv, pp. 330-334.

COBBOLD, E. S. 1919. " Cambrian Hyolithidae, etc., from Hartshill in the Nuneaton District, Warwickshire." *Geol. Mag.*, Dec. 6, vol. vi, pp. 149-158.*

——. 1921. " The Cambrian Horizons of Comley (Shropshire) and their Brachiopoda, Pteropoda, Gastropoda, etc." *Quart. Journ. Geol. Soc.*, vol. lxxvi, pp. 325-386.*

——. 1927. " The Stratigraphy and Geological Structure of the Cambrian Area of Comley (Shropshire)." *Quart. Journ. Geol. Soc.*, vol. lxxxiii, p. 551-573, with geol. map.

——. 1931. "Additional Fossils from the Cambrian Rocks of Comley, Shropshire." *Quart. Journ. Geol. Soc.*, vol. lxxxvii, pp. 459-512.*

COOPER, J. E. 1934. " Oldhaven and Thanet Sand Mollusca of Herne Bay." *Journ. Conch.*, vol. xx, pp. 4-8.

COPE, F. W. 1936a. " The Lower Carboniferous Succession in the Wye Valley Region of North Derbyshire." *Journ. Manchester Geol. Assoc.*, vol. i, pp. 125-145, with sketch-maps.

——. 1936b. " The *Cyrtina septosa* Band in the Lower Carboniferous Succession of North Derbyshire." *Summ. Prog. Geol. Surv. for 1934*, Pt. II (1936), pp. 48-51.

——. 1937. " Some Features in the $D_1$-$D_3$ Limestones of the Miller's Dale Region, Derbyshire." *Proc. Yorks. Geol. Soc.*, vol. xxiii, pp. 178-195.

——. 1943. " Daviesiella llangollensis (Davidson) and Related Forms." *Journ. Manchester Geol. Assoc.*, vol. i, pp. 199-231.*

——. 1946a. " Intraformational Contorted Rocks in the Upper Carboniferous of the Southern Pennines." *Quart. Journ. Geol. Soc.*, vol. ci, pp. 139-176.

——. 1946b. "The Correlation of the Coal Measures of the Cheadle Coalfield, North Staffordshire." *Trans. Inst. Min. Eng.*, vol. cv, pp. 75-102.

Cox, L. R. 1925. "The Fauna of the Basal Shell-Bed of the Portland Stone, Isle of Portland." *Proc. Dorset Nat. Hist. and Ant. F.C.*, vol. xlvi, pp. 113-172.*

——. 1941. "Easter Field Meeting, 1940. Bath." *Proc. Geol. Assoc.*, vol. lii, pp. 16-35.

Crookall, R. and others. 1930. "The Geology of the Bristol District, with some Account of the Physiography." *Brit. Assoc. Adv. Sci.*, Bristol Meeting, 1930.

Cross, J. E. 1875. "The Geology of North-West Lincolnshire." *Quart. Journ. Geol. Soc.*, vol. xxxi, pp. 115-130.*

Curry, D. 1937. "The English Bartonian Nummulites." *Proc. Geol. Assoc.*, vol. xlviii, pp. 229-246.*

——. 1942. "The Eocene Succession at Afton Brickyard, I.O.W." *Proc. Geol. Assoc.*, vol. liii, pp. 88-101.

Davidson, T. 1851. "A Monograph of the British Fossil Brachiopoda. Part III. The Oolitic and Liassic Brachiopoda." *Palaeont. Soc.*

——. 1871. "A Monograph of the British Fossil Brachiopoda, vol. iii, Part. VII, The Silurian Brachiopoda." *Palaeont. Soc.*

——. 1882. "A Monograph of the British Fossil Brachiopoda, vol. v, Silurian and Devonian Supplements." *Palaeont. Soc.*

Davies, A. M. 1907. "The Kimmeridge Clay and Corallian Rocks of the Neighbourhood of Brill (Buckinghamshire)." *Quart. Journ. Geol. Soc.*, vol. lxiii, pp. 29-49.

——. 1934. "Field Meeting at Aylesbury." *Proc. Geol. Assoc.*, vol. xlv, pp. 104-106.

Davies, G. M. 1935. "The Dorset Coast. A Geological Guide." *London.*

Davis, A. G. 1936. "The London Clay of Sheppey and the Location of its Fossils." *Proc. Geol. Assoc.*, vol. xlvii, pp. 328-345.

——. 1937. "Additional Notes on the Geology of Sheppey." *Proc. Geol. Assoc.*, vol. xlviii, pp. 77-80.

Davis, J. W. 1886. "Notes on a Collection of Fossil Fish-Remains from the Mountain Limestone of Derbyshire." *Geol. Mag.* Dec. 3, vol. iii, pp. 148-157.

Dawkins, W. B. 1874. "Report of the Committee appointed for the Purpose of Exploring the Settle Caves." *Rep. Brit. Assoc.*, Bradford (1873), pp. 250-251.

——. 1880. "Early Man in Britain." *London.*

Deans, T. 1932. "A Borehole Section in the Millstone Grits of Rombalds Moor." *Trans. Leeds Geol. Assoc.*, vol. v, pp. 9-22.

Dewey, H. and others. 1924. "The Geology of the Country around Dartford." *Mem. Geol. Surv.*

Dines, H. G. and Edmunds, F. H. 1929. "The Geology of the Country around Aldershot and Guildford." *Mem. Geol. Surv.*

—— and Edmunds, F. H. 1933. "The Geology of Country around Reigate and Dorking." *Mem. Geol. Surv.*

Dix, E., 1934. "The Sequence of Floras in the Upper Carboniferous, with Special Reference to South Wales." *Trans. Roy. Soc. Edin.*, vol. lvii, pp. 789-838.

Dixon, F. 1850. "The Geology and Fossils of the Tertiary and Cretaceous Formations of Sussex." *London.*

DOUGLAS, J. A. and ARKELL, W. J. 1928. " The Stratigraphical Distribution of the Cornbrash : I—The South-Western Area." *Quart. Journ. Geol. Soc.*, vol. lxxxiv, pp. 117-178.*

—— and ARKELL, W. J. 1932. " The Stratigraphical Distribution of the Cornbrash : II—The North-Eastern Area." *Quart. Journ. Geol. Soc.*, vol. lxxxviii, pp. 112-170.*

—— and ARKELL, W. J. 1935. " On a New Section of Fossiliferous Upper Cornbrash of North-Eastern Facies at Enslow Bridge, near Oxford." *Quart. Journ. Geol. Soc.*, vol. xci. pp. 318-322.

DUDLEY, H. E. 1942. " The Lower Lias Beds in the Frodingham Railway Cutting, North-West Lincolnshire." *Proc. Geol. Assoc.*, vol. liii, pp. 152-155.

DUNCAN, P. M. 1866-1872. "A Monograph of the British Fossil Corals. Second Series." *Palaeont. Soc.*

DUNHAM, K. C. and STUBBLEFIELD, C. J. 1944. " The Stratigraphy, Structure and Mineralization of the Greenhow Mining Area, Yorkshire." *Quart. Journ. Geol. Soc.*, vol. c, pp. 209-268, with geol. map.*

EASTWOOD, T. and others, 1923. " The Geology of the Country around Coventry." *Mem. Geol. Surv.*

EASTWOOD, T., DIXON, E. E. L., HOLLINGWORTH, S. E. and SMITH, B. 1931. " The Geology of the Whitehaven and Workington District." *Mem. Geol. Surv.*

EDMUNDS, F. H. 1938. "A Contribution on the Physiography of the Mere District, Wiltshire." *Proc. Geol. Assoc.*, vol. xlix, pp. 174-196, with geol. map.

EDWARDS, F. E. 1849-1861. "A Monograph of the Eocene Mollusca, or Descriptions of Shells from the Older Tertiaries of England." Parts I-III. *Palaeont. Soc.*

——. 1860. " Notice of the Fossil Remains of a new Freshwater Mollusc from the Lower London Tertiaries." *The Geologist*, vol. iii, pp. 208-211.*

——., the late, and WOOD, S. V. 1877. "A Monograph of the Eocene Mollusca, or Descriptions of Shells from the Older Tertiaries of England ". Part IV. *Palaeont. Soc.*

ELLES, G. L. 1898. " The Graptolite-Fauna of the Skiddaw Slates." *Quart. Journ. Geol. Soc.*, vol. liv, pp. 463-539.

——. 1933. " The Lower Ordovician Graptolite Faunas with Special Reference to the Skiddaw Slates." *Summ. Prog. Geol. Surv. for* 1932, Pt. II, pp. 94-111, text-figs.

—— and SLATER, I. L. 1906. " The Highest Silurian Rocks of the Ludlow District." *Quart. Journ. Geol. Soc.*, vol. lxii, pp. 195-222, with geol. map.

ELLIOTT, G. F. 1945. " Faunal Horizons in the London Clay of Clarendon, Wilts." *Proc. Geol. Assoc.*, vol. lvi, pp. 151-152.

EVANS, J. W. 1922. "The Geological Structure of the Country round Combe Martin, North Devon and Excursion to Combe Martin." *Proc. Geol. Assoc.*, vol. xxiii, pp. 201-234.

—— and POCOCK, R. W. 1912. " The Age of the Morte Slates." *Geol. Mag.*, Dec. 5, vol. ix, pp. 113-115.

——, RICHARDSON, L. and MARTIN, E. C. 1914. " Report of an Excursion to West Somerset." *Proc. Geol. Assoc.*, vol. xxv, pp. 97-105.

FISHER, O. 1862. " On the Bracklesham Beds of the Isle of Wight Basin." *Quart. Journ. Geol. Soc.*, vol. xviii, pp. 65-94.

FORBES, E. 1856. " On the Tertiary Fluvio-Marine Formation of the Isle of Wight." *Mem. Geol. Surv.*

FOWLER, A. 1926. " The Geology of Berwick-on-Tweed, Norham and Scremerston." *Mem. Geol. Surv.*

——. 1936. " The Geology of the Country around Rothbury, Amble and Ashington." *Mem. Geol. Surv.*

FOX, H. and HINDE, G. J. 1895. " On a well-marked Horizon of Radiolarian Rocks in the Lower Culm Measures of Devon, Cornwall and West Somerset." *Quart. Journ. Geol. Soc.*, vol. li, pp. 609-668, with geol. map.

FOX-STRANGWAYS, C. 1892. " The Jurassic Rocks of Britain. Vol. I. Yorkshire. Vol. II. Yorkshire, Tables of Fossils." *Mem. Geol. Surv.*

——. 1903. " The Geology of the Country near Leicester." *Mem. Geol. Surv.*

—— and BARROW, G. 1915. " The Geology of the Country between Whitby and Scarborough." *Mem. Geol. Surv.*

——, REID, C. and BARROW, G. 1885. " The Geology of Eskdale, Rosedale etc." *Mem. Geol. Surv.*

GARDINER, C. I. 1927. " The Silurian Inlier of Woolhope (Herefordshire)." *Quart. Journ. Geol. Soc.*, vol. lxxxiii, pp. 501-530, with geol. map.

—— and others. 1934. " The Geology of the Gloucester District." *Proc. Geol. Assoc.*, vol. xlv, pp. 110-144, with maps.

GARDNER, J. S. 1882. " Description and Correlation of the Bournemouth Beds. Part II. Lower or Freshwater Series." *Quart. Journ. Geol. Soc.*, vol. xxxviii, pp. 1-15.

——. 1883. " On the Lower Eocene Section between Reculvers and Herne Bay, and on some Modifications in the Classification of the Lower London Tertiaries." *Quart. Journ. Geol. Soc.*, vol. xxxix, pp. 197-210.

——, KEEPING, H. and MONCKTON, H. W. 1888. " The Upper Eocene, comprising the Barton and Upper Bagshot Formations." *Quart. Journ. Geol. Soc.*, vol. xliv, pp. 578-635.

GARWOOD, E. J. 1912. " The Lower Carboniferous Succession in the North-West of England." *Quart. Journ. Geol. Soc.*, vol. lxviii, pp. 449-586, geol. map.*

——. 1916. " The Faunal Succession in the Lower Carboniferous Rocks of Westmorland and North Lancashire." *Proc. Geol. Assoc.*, vol. xxvii, pp. 1-43, with geol. map.*

——. 1931. " The Tuedian Beds of Northern Cumberland and Roxburgh-shire East of the Liddel Water." *Quart. Journ. Geol. Soc.*, vol. lxxxvii, pp. 97-159, geol. maps.*

—— and GOODYEAR, E. 1919. " On the Geology of the Old Radnor District, with special reference to an Algal Development in the Woolhope Lime-stone." *Quart. Journ. Geol. Soc.*, vol. lxxiv, pp. 1-30, with geol. map.*

—— and GOODYEAR, E. 1924. " The Lower Carboniferous Succession in the Settle District, and along the Line of the Craven Fault." *Quart. Journ. Geol. Soc.*, vol. lxxx, pp. 184-273, with geol. map.*

GASTER, C. T. A. 1924. " The Chalk of the Worthing District, Sussex." *Proc. Geol. Assoc.*, vol. xxxv, pp. 89-110, with topog. map.*

——. 1929. " Chalk Zones in the Neighbourhood of Shoreham, Brighton and Newhaven, Sussex." *Proc. Geol. Assoc.*, vol. xl, pp. 328-340, with topog. map.

——. 1932. " The Zones of the Chalk of the Arun Gap, Sussex." *Proc. Geol. Assoc.*, vol. xliii, pp. 212-223, with topog. map.

——. 1937. " The Stratigraphy of the Chalk of Sussex. Part I. West Central Area—Arun Gap to the Valley of the Adur, with Zonal Map." *Proc. Geol. Assoc.*, vol. xlviii, pp. 356-373, with geol. map.

——. 1939. " The Stratigraphy of the Chalk of Sussex. Part II. Eastern Area—Seaford to Cuckmere Valley and Eastbourne, with Zonal Map." *Proc. Geol. Assoc.*, vol. l. pp. 510-526, with geol. map.

——. 1944. " The Stratigraphy of the Chalk of Sussex. Part III. Western Area—Arun Gap to the Hampshire Boundary, with Zonal Map." *Proc. Geol. Assoc.*, vol. lv, pp. 173-188, with geol. map.

GIBSON, W., BARROW, G., WEDD, C. B., and WARD, J. 1905. " The Geology of the North Staffordshire Coalfields." *Mem. Geol. Surv.**

GOSSLING, F. 1929. " The Geology of the Country around Reigate." *Proc. Geol. Assoc.*, vol. xl, pp. 197-259, with geol. map.

——. 1936. " Field Meeting at Oxted and Godstone." *Proc. Geol. Assoc.*, vol. xlvii, pp. 322-327.

GROOM, T. T. 1900. " On the Geological Structure of Portions of the Malvern and Abberley Hills." *Quart. Journ. Geol. Soc.*, vol. lvi, pp. 138-197, with geol. map.

GUPTA, T. D. 1932. " The Salopian Graptolite Shales of the Long Mountain and Similar Rocks of Wenlock Edge." *Proc. Geol. Assoc.*, vol. xliii, pp. 325-263, with geol. map.

HALLAM, A. D. 1934. " The Geology of the Hangman Grits of the Quantock Hills." *Geol. Mag.*, vol. lxxi, pp. 433-446, with sketch-map.

HARGREAVES, J. A. .1913. " Fossil Footprints near Scarborough." *The Naturalist*, pp. 92-93.

HARKNESS, R. and NICHOLSON, H. A. 1877. " On the Strata and their Fossil Contents between the Borrowdale Series of the North of England and the Coniston Flags." *Quart. Journ. Geol. Soc.*, vol. xxxiii, pp. 461-484.

HARMER, F. W. 1902. "A sketch of the Later Tertiary History of East • Anglia." *Proc. Geol. Assoc.*, vol. xvii, pp. 416-479.

——. 1913-1922. " The Pliocene Mollusca of Great Britain." *Palaeont. Soc.**

HARPER, J. C. 1940. " The Upper Valentian Ostracod Fauna of Shropshire." *Ann. Mag. Nat. Hist.*, Ser. 11, vol. v, pp. 385-400.*

HAWKINS, H. L. 1937. "A Road-Section at Whitway, North Hampshire." *Proc. Geol. Assoc.*, vol. xlviii, pp. 142-159, geol. map.

——. 1946. " Field Meeting at Reading." *Proc. Geol. Assoc.*, vol. lvii, pp. 164-171.

—— and HAMPTON, S. M. 1927. " The Occurrence, Structure and Affinities of *Echinocystis* and *Palaeodiscus*." *Quart. Journ. Geol. Soc.*, vol. lxxxiii, pp. 574-600.*

HENDERSON, I. J. 1935. " The Lower Lias at Hock Cliff, Fretherne." *Proc. Bristol Nat. Soc.*, Ser. 4, Vol. vii, pp. 545-564.

HICKS, H. 1896. " The Palaeozoic Rocks of West Somerset and North Devon." *Proc. Geol. Assoc.*, vol. xiv, pp. 357-370, 387.

HILL, D., BUTLER, A. J., OAKLEY, K. P. and ARKELL, W. J. 1936. " Report of ' Coral Reef ' Meeting at Wenlock Edge, the Dudley District and the Oxford District." *Proc. Geol. Assoc.*, vol. xlvii, pp. 130-139.

HILL, W. 1888. " The Lower Beds of the Upper Cretaceous Series in Lincolnshire and Yorkshire." *Quart. Journ. Geol. Soc.*, vol. xliv, pp. 320-367.

HIND, W. 1910. " Staffordshire." " Geology in the Field " (*Geol. Assoc.*), Pt. III, pp. 564-591.

HINDE, G. J. 1893. "A Monograph of the British Fossil Sponges, vol. i, Pt. III." *Palaeont. Soc.**

HINTON, M. A. C. and others. 1938. " Report on the Swanscombe Skull Prepared by the Swanscombe Committee of the Royal Anthropological Institute." *Journ. Roy. Anthropol. Inst.*, vol. lxviii. pp. 17-98.*

HOLLINGWORTH, S. E. and TAYLOR, J. H. 1947. " Kettering Field Meeting." *Proc. Geol. Assoc.*, vol. lvii, pp. 235-245.

HOPKINS, W. 1929. " The Distribution and Sequence of the Non-Marine Lamellibranchs in the Coal-Measures of Northumberland and Durham." *Trans. Inst. Min. Eng.*, vol. lxxviii, pp. 126-144.

———. 1930. "A Revision of the Upper Carboniferous Non-Marine Lamellibranchs of Northumberland and Durham and a Record of their Sequence." *Trans. Inst. Min. Eng.*, vol. lxxx, pp. 101-110, 254-257.

HUDLESTON, W. H. 1883. " On the Geology of the Vale of Wardour." *Proc. Geol. Assoc.*, vol. vii, pp. 161-185, with geol. map.

———. 1887-1896. "A Monograph of the British Jurassic Gasteropoda." *Palaeont. Soc.**

HUDSON, R. G. S. 1925. " Faunal Horizons in the Lower Carboniferous of North-West Yorkshire." *Geol. Mag.*, vol. lxi, pp. 181-186.

———. 1929. "A Carboniferous Lagoon Deposit with Sponges." *Proc. Yorks. Geol. Soc.*, vol. xxi, pp. 181-196.

———. 1930. " The Age of the ' Lithostrotion arachnoideum ' Fauna of the Craven Lowlands." *Proc. Leeds Phil. Lit. Soc.*, vol. ii, pp. 95-101.

———. 1937. " The Millstone Grit Succession of the Simonseat Anticline, Yorkshire." *Proc. Yorks. Geol. Soc.*, vol. xxiii, pp. 319-349, with geol. map.

———. 1941. " The Mirk Fell Beds (Namurian, $E_2$) of Tan Hill, Yorkshire." *Proc. Yorks. Geol. Soc.*, vol. xxiv, pp. 259-289.*

———. 1943. " On the Lower Carboniferous Corals : *Rhopalolasma bradbournense* (Wilmore) and *Rhopalolasma rylstonense* sp. nov." *Quart. Journ. Geol. Soc.*, vol. xcix, pp. 81-92.*

———. 1944. " The Carboniferous of the Broughton Anticline, Yorkshire." *Proc. Yorks. Geol. Soc.*, vol. xxv, pp. 190-214, with geol. map.

———. 1945. " The Variation in an Assemblage of the *Caninia cornucopiae* plexus, from the Middle Viséan." *Quart. Journ. Geol. Soc.*, vol. c, pp. 193-207.*

———, BISAT, W. S., HAYWOOD, H. W. and RAISTRICK, A. 1933. " The Geology of the Yorkshire Dales." *Proc. Geol. Assoc.*, vol. xliv, pp. 227-269, with geol. maps.

——— and COTTON, G. 1943. " The Namurian of Alport Dale, Derbyshire." *Proc. Yorks. Geol. Soc.*, vol. xxv, pp. 142-173, with topog. map.

——— and COTTON, G. 1945. " The Lower Carboniferous in a Boring at Alport, Derbyshire." *Proc. Yorks Geol. Soc.*, vol. xxv, pp. 254-330.

——— and DUNNINGTON, H. V. 1944. " The Carboniferous Rocks of the Swinden Anticline, Yorkshire." *Proc. Geol. Assoc.*, vol. lv, pp. 195-215, with geol. maps.

——— and FOX, T. 1943. "An Upper Viséan Zaphrentoid Fauna from the Yoredale Beds of North-West Yorkshire." *Proc. Yorks. Geol. Soc.*, vol. xxv, pp. 101-126.*

——— and KING, W. B. R. 1933. " The Yorkshire Dales. The Summer Field Meeting, 1933." *Proc. Geol. Assoc.*, vol. xliv, pp. 428-440.

——— and MITCHELL, G. H. 1937. " The Carboniferous Geology of the Skipton Anticline." *Summ. Prog. Geol. Surv. for* 1935, Pt. II, pp. 1-45, with geol. map.

——— and PLATT, M. I. 1927. " On the Lower Carboniferous Corals : The Development of *Rylstonia benecompacta*, gen. et sp. n." *Ann. Mag. Nat. Hist.*, Ser. 9, vol. xix, pp. 39-48.*

———, VERSEY, H. C., EDWARDS, W. N. and RAISTRICK, A. 1938. " The Geology of the Country around Harrogate." *Proc. Geol. Assoc.*, vol. xlix, pp. 294-372.

HULL, E. and others. 1875. " The Geology of the Burnley Coalfield." *Mem. Geol. Surv.*

JACKSON, J. F. 1926. " The Junction-Bed of the Middle and Upper Lias on the Dorset Coast." *Quart. Journ. Geol. Soc.*, vol. lxxxii, pp. 490-525.

——. 1939. " Notes on the Discovery of Fossiliferous Nodules in the Carstone near Niton." *Proc. I.O.W. Nat. Hist. Soc.*, vol. iii, pp. 73-80.

JACKSON, J. W. 1908. " Carboniferous Fish-Remains in North Derbyshire." *Geol. Mag.*, Dec. 5, vol. v, pp. 309-310.

——. 1919. " On the Occurrence of *Productus humerosus* (= *sublaevis*) in Dove Dale ; and its Value as a Zone-fossil." *Geol. Mag.*, Dec. 6, vol. vi, pp. 507-509.

——. 1922. " On the Occurrence of *Daviesiella llangollensis* (Davidson) in Derbyshire." *Geol. Mag.*, vol. lix, pp. 335, 461-468.

——. 1927. " The Succession below the Kinderscout Grit in North Derbyshire." *Journ. Manchester Geol. Assoc.*, vol. i, pp. 15-32, with geol. map.

——. 1941a. " *Spirifer bollandensis* Muir-Wood at Thorpe Cloud, with Notes on the Sequence in Dove Dale, Derbyshire." *Journ. Manchester Geol. Assoc.*, vol. i, Pt. 4, pp. 233-237.

——. 1941b. " Description of a Carboniferous Limestone Section with *Girvanella* in North Derbyshire." *Journ. Manchester Geol. Assoc.*, vol. i, Pt. 4, pp. 239-246.

—— and CHARLESWORTH, J. K. 1920. " The Quartzose Conglomerate at Caldon Low, Staffordshire." *Geol. Mag.*, vol. lvii, pp. 487-492.

JONES, R. C. B., TONKS, L. H. and WRIGHT, W. B. 1938. " Wigan District." *Mem. Geol. Surv.*

JUDD, J. W. 1871. " On the Punfield Formation." *Quart. Journ. Geol. Soc.*, vol. xxvii, pp. 207-227.

——. 1875. " The Geology of Rutland, etc." *Mem. Geol. Surv.*

JUKES-BROWNE, A. J. 1898. " On an Outlier of Cenomanian and Turonian [equivalent to Lower and Middle Chalk] near Honiton, etc." *Quart. Journ. Geol. Soc.*, vol. liv, pp. 239-250, with geol. map.

——. 1900. " The Cretaceous Rocks of Britain. Vol. I. The Gault and Upper Greensand of England." *Mem. Geol. Surv.*

——. 1903. " The Cretaceous Rocks of Britain. Vol. II. The Lower and Middle Chalk of England." *Mem. Geol. Surv.*

——. 1904. " The Cretaceous Rocks of Britain. Vol. III. The Upper Chalk of England." *Mem. Geol. Surv.*

——. 1905. " The Geology of the Country South and East of Devizes." *Mem. Geol. Surv.*

——. 1913. " The Devonian Limestones at Dartington, and their equivalents at Torquay." *Proc. Geol. Assoc.*, vol. xxiv, pp. 14-32.

KEEPING, H. 1910. " On the Discovery of Bembridge Limestone Fossils on Creechbarrow Hill, Isle of Purbeck." *Geol. Mag.*, Dec. 5, vol. vii, pp. 436-439.*

KEEPING, W. 1883. " The Fossils and Palaeontological Affinities of the Neocomian Deposits of Upware and Brickhill." (Sedgwick Prize Essay.) *Cambridge.**

KELLAWAY, G. A. and WILSON, V. 1941. "An Outline of the Geology of Yeovil, Sherborne and Sparkford Vale." *Proc. Geol. Assoc.*, vol. lii, pp. 131-174.*

KENDALL, P. F. and WROOT, H. E. 1924. " The Geology of Yorkshire." *Vienna.*

KENNARD, A. S. 1944. " The Crayford Brickearths." *Proc. Geol. Assoc.*, vol. lv, pp. 121-169.

—— and MUSHAM, J. F.   1937.   " On the Mollusca from a Holocene Tufaceous Deposit at Broughton-Brigg, Lincolnshire."   *Proc. Malac. Soc.*, vol. xxii, pp. 374-379.

KENT, P. E.   1937.   " The Lower Lias of South Nottinghamshire."   *Proc. Geol. Assoc.*, vol. xlviii, pp. 163-174.

KING, W.   1850.   "A Monograph of the Permian Fossils of England."   *Palaeont. Soc.**

KING, W. B. R.   1914.   "A New Trilobite from the Millstone Grit of North Yorkshire."   *Geol. Mag.*, Dec. 6, vol. i, pp. 390-394.*

——.   1932.   "A Fossiliferous Limestone associated with Ingletonian Beds at Horton-in-Ribblesdale, Yorkshire."   *Quart. Journ. Geol. Soc.*, vol. lxxxviii, pp. 100-111, with geol. map.

—— and WILCOCKSON, W. H.   1934.   " The Lower Palaeozoic Rocks of Austwick and Horton-in-Ribblesdale, Yorkshire."   *Quart. Journ. Geol. Soc.*, vol. xc, pp. 7-31, with geol. map.

KING, W. W.   1934.   " The Downtonian and Dittonian Strata of Great Britain and North-Western Europe."   *Quart. Journ. Geol. Soc.*, vol. xc, pp. 526-570.

—— and LEWIS, W. J.   1912.   " The Uppermost Silurian and Old Red Sandstone of South Staffordshire."   *Geol. Mag.*, Dec. 5, vol. ix, pp. 437-443.

LAMONT, A.   1945.   " Excursion to Onny River, Shropshire."   *Quarry Managers' Journal*, vol. xxix, pp. 118-119, with geol. map.

LAMPLUGH, G. W.   1889.   " On the Subdivisions of the Speeton Clay."   *Quart. Journ. Geol. Soc.*, vol. xlv, pp. 575-618.

——.   1896.   " On the Speeton Series in Yorkshire and Lincolnshire."   *Quart. Journ. Geol. Soc.*, vol. lii, pp. 179-220.

——.   1903.   " The Geology of the Isle of Man."   *Mem. Geol. Surv.*

——.   1922.   " On the Junction of Gault and Lower Greensand near Leighton Buzzard (Bedfordshire)."   *Quart. Journ. Geol. Soc.*, vol. lxxviii, pp. 1-81, topog. map.

—— and WALKER, J. F.   1903.   " On a Fossiliferous Band at the top of the Lower Greensand near Leighton Buzzard (Bedfordshire)."   *Quart. Journ. Geol. Soc.*, vol. lix, pp. 234-235, geol. map.*

—— and others.   1909.   " The Geology of the Melton Mowbray District and South-East Nottinghamshire."   *Mem. Geol. Surv.*

LANG, W. D.   1904.   " The Zone of *Hoplites interruptus* (Bruguière) at Black Ven, Charmouth."   *Geol. Mag.*, Dec. 5, vol. i, pp. 124-131.

——.   1924.   " The Blue Lias of the Devon and Dorset Coasts."   *Proc. Geol. Assoc.*, vol. xxxv, pp. 169-185, with geol. map.

——, SPATH, L. F. and RICHARDSON, W. A.   1923.   " Shales-with-' Beef,' a Sequence in the Lower Lias of the Dorset Coast."   *Quart. Journ. Geol. Soc.*, vol. lxxix, pp. 47-99.

—— and SPATH, L. F.   1926.   " The Black Marl of Black Ven and Stonebarrow, in the Lias of the Dorset Coast."   *Quart. Journ. Geol. Soc.*, vol. lxxxii, pp. 144-187.*

——, SPATH, L. F., COX, L. R. and MUIR-WOOD, H. M.   1928.   " The Belemnite Marls of Charmouth, a Series in the Lower Lias of the Dorset Coast."   *Quart. Journ. Geol. Soc.*, vol. lxxxiv, pp. 179-257.*

——, COX, L. R. and MUIR-WOOD, H. M.   1936.   " The Green Ammonite Beds of the Dorset Lias."   *Quart. Journ. Geol. Soc.*, vol. xcii, pp. 423-487.*

LAPWORTH, C.   1891.   " On *Olenellus Callavei* and its Geological Relationships."   *Geol. Mag.*, Dec. 3, vol. viii, pp. 529-536.*

LA TOUCHE, J. D. 1884. "A Hand-Book of the Geology of Shropshire." *London and Shrewsbury.*

LEA, F. A. 1939. "Chalk Rock Fossils from Latimer." *Records of Bucks.*, vol. xiii, pp. 436-439.

LEWIS, H. P. 1930. "The Avonian Succession in the South of the Isle of Man." *Quart. Journ. Geol. Soc.*, vol. lxxxvi, pp. 234-290, with geol. map.

——. 1934. "The Occurrence of Fossiliferous Pebbles of Salopian Age in the Peel Sandstones (Isle of Man)." *Summ. Prog. Geol. Surv. for* 1933, Pt. 2, pp. 91-108.*

LLOYD, W. 1933. See USSHER, W. A. E. 1933.

—— and STEPHENS, J. V. 1927. "The Stratigraphical Succession below the Kinderscout Grit in the Todmorden District." *Proc. Yorks. Geol. Soc.*, vol. xxi, pp. 47-58.

MANTELL, G. 1846. "Notes on the Wealden Strata of the Isle of Wight, with an Account of the Bones of Iguanodons and other Reptiles discovered at Brook Point and Sandown Bay." *Quart. Journ. Geol. Soc.*, vol. ii, pp. 91-96.

MARR, J. E. 1913. "The Lower Palaeozoic Rocks of the Cautley District (Yorkshire)." *Quart. Journ. Geol. Soc.*, vol. lxix, pp. 1-18.

——. 1916. "The Ashgillian Succession in the Tract to the West of Coniston Lake." *Quart. Journ. Geol. Soc.*, vol. lxxi, pp. 189-204.

——. 1920. "The Pleistocene Deposits around Cambridge." *Quart. Journ. Geol. Soc.*, vol. lxxv, 1919, pp. 204-244, with topog. map.

——. 1925. "Conditions of Deposition of the Stockdale Shales of the Lake District." *Quart. Journ. Geol. Soc.*, vol. lxxxi, pp. 113-136.

—— and NICHOLSON, H. A. 1888. "The Stockdale Shales." *Quart. Journ. Geol. Soc.*, vol. xliv, pp. 654-732.*

MEYER, C. J. A. 1871. "On Lower Tertiary Deposits recently Exposed at Portsmouth." *Quart. Journ. Geol. Soc.*, vol. xxvii, pp. 74-89.

——. 1874. "On the Cretaceous Rocks of Beer Head and the Adjacent Cliff-Sections, etc." *Quart. Journ. Geol. Soc.*, vol. xxx, pp. 369-393.

MILLER, A. A. 1927. "Some Unmapped Faults in the Lower Carboniferous of Westmorland and their Relation to the Dent Fault System." *Geol. Mag.*, vol. lxiv, pp. 80-85, with geol. map.

—— and TURNER, J. S. 1931. "The Lower Carboniferous Succession along the Dent Fault and the Yoredale Beds of the Shap District." *Proc. Geol. Assoc.*, vol. xlii, pp. 1-28, with geol. map.

MILNE EDWARDS, H. and HAIME, J. 1853. "A Monograph of the British Fossil Corals. Part 4. Corals from the Devonian Formation." *Palaeont. Soc.**

MILNER, H. B. and BULL, A. J. 1925. "The Geology of the Eastbourne-Hastings Coastline." *Proc. Geol. Assoc.*, vol. xxxvi, pp. 291-316.

MITCHELL, G. H. 1929. "The Succession and Structure of the Borrowdale Volcanic Series in Troutbeck, Kentmere and the Western Part of Long Sleddale (Westmorland)." *Quart. Journ. Geol. Soc.*, vol. lxxxv, pp. 9-44, with geol. map.

—— and STUBBLEFIELD, C. J. 1941a. "The Carboniferous Limestone of Breedon Cloud, Leicestershire, and the Associated Inliers." *Geol. Mag.*, vol. lxxviii, pp. 201-219, with geol. map.

—— and STUBBLEFIELD, C. J. 1941b. "The Geology of the Leicestershire and South Derbyshire Coalfield." *Geol. Surv. Wartime Pamphlet*, No. 22.

—— and STUBBLEFIELD, C. J. 1942. "The Geology of the Warwickshire Coalfield." *Geol. Surv. Wartime Pamphlet*, No. 25.

L

MOIR, J. REID. 1925. "Sub-Crag Detritus Bed and its contained Flint Implements." (*See* BELL, A. and NOTCUTT, S. A.)

—— and HOPWOOD, A. T. 1939. "Excavations at Brundon, Suffolk (1935-1937)." *Proc. Prehist. Soc.*, N.S., vol. v, pp. 1-32.

MONCKTON, M. W. and SKEATS, E. W. 1902. "Excursion to Suffolk and Norfolk." *Proc. Geol. Assoc.*, vol. xvii, pp. 480-488.

MOORE, C. 1867. "On Abnormal Conditions of Secondary Deposits when connected with the Somersetshire and South Wales Coal-Basin ; and on the age of the Sutton and Southerndown Series." *Quart. Journ. Geol. Soc.*, vol. xxiii, pp. 449-568.*

MOORE, E. W. J. 1929. "The Occurrence of *Reticuloceras reticulatum* in North Devon." *Geol. Mag.*, vol. lxvi, pp. 356-358, with topog. map.

——. 1936. "The Bowland Shales from Pendle to Dinckley." *Journ. Manchester Geol. Assoc.*, vol. i, pp. 167-192.*

——. 1941. "Sections in the Bowland Shales West of Barnoldswick." *Proc. Yorks. Geol. Soc.*, vol. xxiv, pp. 252-258, with map.

MOORE, L. R. 1938. "The Sequence and Structure of the Radstock Basin." *Proc. Bristol Nat. Soc.*, Ser. 4, vol. viii, pp. 267-305.

—— and TRUEMAN, A. E. 1937. "The Coal Measures of Bristol and Somerset." *Quart. Journ. Geol. Soc.*, vol. xciii, pp. 195-240.

MOORE, P. F. 1937. "*Micraster* in the Marlborough District." *Rep. Marlborough Coll. Nat. Hist. Soc.*, No. 85, pp. 48-50.

MORRIS, J. and LYCETT, J. 1851-1855. "A Monograph of the Mollusca of the Great Oolite, chiefly from Minchinhampton." *Palaeont. Soc.**

—— and ROBERTS, G. E. 1862. "On the Carboniferous Limestone of Oreton and Farlow, Clea Hills, Shropshire. With a Description of a New *Pterichthys* by Sir P. de M. G. Egerton." *Quart. Journ. Geol. Soc.*, vol. xviii, pp. 94-106.*

MUIR-WOOD, H. M. 1936. "The Brachiopoda of the British Great Oolite Series. Part I. The Brachiopoda of the Fuller's Earth." *Palaeont. Soc.**

MURCHISON, R. I. 1839. "The Silurian System." *London.**

MURRAY, N. 1939. "The Microflora of the Upper and Lower Estuarine Series of the East Midlands." *Geol. Mag.*, vol. lxxvi, pp. 478-489.

MUSHAM, J. F. 1933. "Important finds of Land and Freshwater Shells in the Lime Deposits around Broughton, near Brigg." *Trans. Lincs. Nat. Union* for 1932 (1933), pp. 93-98.

NEWTON, E. T. 1882. "The Vertebrata of the Forest Bed Series of Norfolk and Suffolk." *Mem. Geol. Surv.**

OAKLEY, K. P. 1936. "Field Meeting at Cheddington, Ivinghoe and Gubblecote." *Proc. Geol. Assoc.*, vol. xlvii, pp. 38-41.

OWEN, D. E. 1934. "The Carboniferous Rocks of the North Cornish Coast and their Structures." *Proc. Geol. Assoc.*, vol. xlv, pp. 451-471, with geol. map.

——. 1939. "The Geological Structure of Mid-Devon and North Cornwall." *Proc. Liverpool Geol. Soc.*, vol. xvii, pp. 141-159.

PALMER, L. S. 1930. *See* CROOKHALL, R. and others. 1930.

PARKINSON, D. 1926. "The Faunal Succession in the Carboniferous Limestone and Bowland Shales of Clitheroe and Pendle Hill (Lancashire)." *Quart. Journ. Geol. Soc.*, vol. lxxxii, pp. 188-249, geol. map.*

——. 1935. "The Geology and Topography of the Limestone Knolls in Bolland (Bowland), Lancs. and Yorks." *Proc. Geol. Assoc.*, vol. xlvi, pp. 97-120, with geol. map.

——. 1936. " The Carboniferous Succession in the Slaidburn District, Yorkshire." *Quart. Journ. Geol. Soc.*, vol. xcii, pp. 294-331, with geol. map.

——. 1943. " The Age of the Reef-Limestones in the Lower Carboniferous of North Derbyshire." *Geol. Mag.*, vol. lxxx, pp. 121-131.

PAUL, H. 1937. " The Relationships of the Pilton Beds of North Devon to their Equivalents on the Continent." *Geol. Mag.*, vol. lxxiv, pp. 433-442.

PAVLOW, A. and LAMPLUGH, G. W. 1892. "Argiles de Speeton et leurs Équivalents." *Moscow.*\*

PERCEVAL, S. G. 1866. " On the Discovery of a Bed of Devonian Corals at Withycombe, West Somerset." *Geol. Mag.*, Dec. 1, vol. iii, p. 184.

PHILLIPS, J. 1848. " The Malvern Hills, compared with the Palaeozoic Districts of Abberley, etc." *Mem. Geol. Surv.*, vol. ii.\*

POCOCK, R. W. 1930. " The *Petalocrinus* Limestone Horizon at Woolhope (Herefordshire)." *Quart. Journ. Geol. Soc.*, vol. lxxxvi, pp. 50-63, with geol. map.

——, WHITEHEAD, T. H., WEDD, C. B. and ROBERTSON, T. 1932. " Shrewsbury District, including the Hanwood Coalfield." *Mem. Geol. Surv.*

PRICE, F. G. H. 1874. " On the Lower Greensand and Gault of Folkestone." *Proc. Geol. Assoc.*, vol. iv, pp. 135-150.

——. 1879. " The Gault." *London.*

PRINGLE, J., SANDFORD, K. S. and BAYZAND, C. J. 1926. " The Geology of the Country around Oxford." 2nd Ed. *Mem. Geol. Surv.*

RASTALL, R. H. 1905. " The Blea Wyke Beds and the Dogger in North-East Yorkshire." *Quart. Journ. Geol. Soc.*, vol. lxi, pp. 441-460.

REED, F. R. C. 1897. "A Handbook to the Geology of Cambridgeshire." *Cambridge.*

——. 1913. " Note on the Eocene Beds of Hengistbury Head." *Geol. Mag.*, Dec. 5, vol. x, pp. 101-103.

——. 1927. " Palaeontological Notes on the Silurian Inlier of Woolhope." *Quart. Journ. Geol. Soc.*, vol. lxxxiii, pp. 531-550.\*

—— and REYNOLDS, S. H. 1908. " On the Fossiliferous Silurian Rocks of the Southern Half of the Tortworth Inlier." *Quart. Journ. Geol. Soc.*, vol. lxiv, pp. 515-545, with geol. map.

REID, C. 1890. " The Pliocene Deposits of Britain." *Mem. Geol. Surv.*

——. 1902. " The Geology of the Country around Southampton." *Mem. Geol. Surv.*

——. 1903. " The Geology of the Country around Salisbury." *Mem. Geol. Surv.*

—— and FLETT, J. S. 1907. " The Geology of the Land's End District." *Mem. Geol. Surv.*

—— and E. M. 1908. " On the Pre-Glacial Flora of Britain." *Journ. Linn. Soc. Bot.*, vol. xxxviii, pp. 206-227.\*

—— and STRAHAN, A. 1889. " The Geology of the Isle of Wight. 2nd Ed." *Mem. Geol. Surv.*

REID, E. M. and CHANDLER, M. E. J. 1926. " Catalogue of Cainozoic Plants in the Department of Geology. Vol. i. The Bembridge Flora." *Brit. Mus. (Nat. Hist.).*\*

—— and CHANDLER, M. E. J. 1933. " The London Clay Flora." *Brit. Mus. (Nat. Hist.).*\*

REYNOLDS, S. H. 1894. " Certain Fossils from the Lower Palaeozoic Rocks of Yorkshire." *Geol. Mag.*, Dec. 4, vol. i, pp. 108-111.

——. 1907. "A Silurian Inlier in the Eastern Mendips." *Quart. Journ. Geol. Soc.*, vol. lxiii, pp. 217-240.

——. 1920. "The Carboniferous Limestone of the Clifton-Westbury-King's Weston Ridge." *Proc. Bristol Nat. Soc.*, Ser. 4, vol. v, pp. 92-100.

——. 1921. "A Geological Excursion Handbook for the Bristol District," 2nd ed., with geol. sketch-maps. *Bristol.*

——. 1936. "Fossil Reptiles of Gloucestershire." *Proc. Cotteswold Nat. F.C.*, vol. xxvi, pp. 51-65.

—— and GREENLY, E. 1924. "The Geological Structure of the Clevedon-Portishead Area (Somerset)." *Quart. Journ. Geol. Soc.*, vol. lxxx, pp. 447-467, with geol. map.

—— and INNES, D. E. 1914. "On the Carboniferous Limestone of the District between Over and Tytherington, Gloucestershire." *Proc. Bristol Nat. Soc.*, Ser. 4, vol. iv, pp. 100-103, with geol. map.

—— and VAUGHAN, A. 1911. "Faunal and Lithological Sequence in the Carboniferous Limestone Series (Avonian) of Burrington Combe (Somerset)." *Quart. Journ. Geol. Soc.*, vol. lxvii, pp. 342-392, sketch-map.*

RICHARDSON, L. 1903. "The Rhaetic Rocks of North-West Gloucestershire." *Proc. Cotteswold Nat. F.C.*, vol. xiv, pp. 127-174.

——. 1904. "A Handbook to the Geology of Cheltenham." *Cheltenham*, with geol. map.*

——. 1905. "The Rhaetic Rocks of Monmouthshire." *Quart. Journ. Geol. Soc.*, vol. lxi, pp. 374-384.

——. 1907. "The Inferior Oolite and Contiguous Deposits of the Bath-Doulting District." *Quart. Journ. Geol. Soc.*, vol. lxiii, pp. 383-436.*

——. 1909. "Excursion to the Frome District, Somerset." *Proc. Geol. Assoc.*, vol. xxi, pp. 209-228.

——. 1910a. "Excursion to Stonesfield and Fawler." *Proc. Cotteswold Nat. F.C.*, vol. xvii, pp. 28-31.

——. 1910b. "The Inferior Oolite and Contiguous Deposits of the South Cotswolds." *Proc. Cotteswold Nat. F.C.*, vol. xvii, pp. 63-136.

——. 1910c. "The Great Oolite Section at Groves' Quarry, Milton-under-Wychwood, Oxfordshire." *Geol. Mag.*, Dec. 5, vol. vii, pp. 537-542.

——. 1911a. "The Rhaetic and Contiguous Deposits of West, Mid, and Part of East Somerset." *Quart. Journ. Geol. Soc.*, vol. lxvii, pp. 1-74.*

——. 1911b. "The Inferior Oolite and Contiguous Deposits of the Chipping-Norton District, Oxfordshire." *Proc. Cotteswold Nat. F.C.*, vol. xvii, pp. 195-231.

——. 1916. "The Inferior Oolite and Contiguous Deposits of the Doulting-Milborne-Port District (Somerset)." *Quart. Journ. Geol. Soc.*, vol. lxxi, pp. 473-520, with topog. maps.*

——. 1918. "The Inferior Oolite and Contiguous Deposits of the Crewkerne District (Somerset)." *Quart. Journ. Geol. Soc.*, vol. lxxiv, pp. 145-173, with topog. map.

——. 1928-1930. "The Inferior Oolite and Contiguous Deposits of the Burton Bradstock-Broadwindsor District, Dorset." *Proc. Cotteswold Nat. Field Club*, vol. xxiii, pp. 35-68, 149-185, 253-264, with topog. map.

——. 1929. "The Country around Moreton-in-Marsh." *Mem. Geol. Surv.*

——. 1932. "The Inferior Oolite and Contiguous Deposits of the Sherborne District, Dorset." *Proc. Cotteswold Nat. Field Club*, vol. xxiv, pp. 35-85, with geol. map.

——. 1933. "The Country around Cirencester." *Mem. Geol. Surv.*

——. 1938. "Week-End Field Meeting in the Kettering District." *Proc. Geol. Assoc.*, vol. xlix, pp. 59-76.

——. 1939a. "Week-End Field Meeting in the Stamford District." *Proc. Geol. Assoc.*, vol. l, pp. 29-45.

——. 1939b. "Week-End Field Meeting in the Grantham District." *Proc. Geol. Assoc.*, vol. l, pp. 463-486.

——. 1940. "Field Meeting at Lincoln." *Proc. Geol. Assoc.*, vol. li, pp. 246-256.

——. 1946. "The Geology of the Country around Witney." *Mem. Geol. Surv.*

RICKMAN, C. 1860. "Notice and Description of *Cyrena dulwichiensis*." *The Geologist*, vol. iii, pp. 211-212.*

ROBERTS, T. 1892. "The Jurassic Rocks of the Neighbourhood of Cambridge." (Sedgwick Prize Essay.) *Cambridge.*

ROBERTSON, T. 1927. "The Highest Silurian Rocks of the Wenlock District." *Summ. Prog. Geol. Surv. for 1926*, Pt. II, pp. 80-97, sketchmaps.

ROGERS, I. 1909. "On a Further Discovery of Fossil Fish and Mollusca in the Upper Culm Measures of North Devon." *Rep. and Trans. Devon Assoc.*, vol. xli, pp. 309-319, with geol. map.

——. 1910. "A Synopsis of the Fossil Flora and Fauna of the Upper Culm Measures of North-West Devon." *Rep. and Trans. Devon Assoc.*, vol. xlii, pp. 538-564.

ROWE, A. W. 1900. "The Zones of the White Chalk of the English Coast, Part I. Kent and Sussex." *Proc. Geol. Assoc.*, vol. xvi, pp. 289-368, sections.*

——. 1901. "The Zones of the White Chalk of the English Coast, Part II. Dorset." *Proc. Geol. Assoc.*, vol. xvii, pp. 1-80, sections.

——. 1903. "The Zones of the White Chalk of the English Coast, Part III. Devon." *Proc. Geol. Assoc.*, vol. xviii, pp. 1-51.

——. 1904. "The Zones of the White Chalk of the English Coast, Part IV. Yorkshire." *Proc. Geol. Assoc.*, vol. xviii, pp. 193-296, with geol. map and sections.

——. 1908. "The Zones of the White Chalk of the English Coast, Part V. The Isle of Wight." *Proc. Geol. Assoc.*, vol. xx, pp. 209-352, with geol. maps.

SHARP, S. 1873. "The Oolites of Northamptonshire." *Quart. Journ. Geol. Soc.*, vol. xxix, pp. 225-302.

SHEPHERD, W. B. 1934. "Some Observations on the Folkestone Beds around Farnham." *Proc. Geol. Assoc.*, vol. xlv, pp. 436-444, with geol. map.

SHERLOCK, R. L., NOBLE, A. H. and PRINGLE, J. 1922a. "The Geology of the Country around Beaconsfield." *Mem. Geol. Surv.*

——, PRINGLE, J., CHATWIN, C. P. and POCOCK, R. W. 1922b. "The Geology of the Country around Aylesbury, and Hemel Hempstead." *Mem. Geol. Surv.*

SHIRLEY, J. and HORSFIELD, E. L. 1940. "The Carboniferous Limestone of the Castleton-Bradwell Area, North Derbyshire." *Quart. Journ. Geol. Soc.*, vol. xcvi, pp. 271-299, with geol. map.

SIBLY, T. F. 1908. "The Faunal Succession in the Carboniferous Limestone (Upper Avonian) of the Midland Area (North Derbyshire and North Staffordshire)." *Quart. Journ. Geol. Soc.*, vol. lxiv, pp. 34-82.*

——. 1912. "The Carboniferous Succession in the Forest of Dean Coalfield." *Geol. Mag.*, Dec. 5, vol. ix, pp. 417-422.

——. 1918. "On the Geological Structure of the Forest of Dean." *Geol. Mag.*, Dec. 6, vol. v, pp. 23-38. (*Colliery Guardian*, vol. cxiv, No. 2966, Nov. 1917, pp. 839-840).

—— and REYNOLDS, S. H. 1937. " The Carboniferous Limestone of the Mitcheldean Area, Gloucestershire." *Quart. Journ. Geol. Soc.*, vol. xciii, pp. 23-51.

SMITH, J. 1911. " Carboniferous Limestone Rocks of the Isle of Man." *Trans. Geol. Soc. Glasgow*, vol. xiv, pp. 119-164.

SMITH, S. 1910. " The Faunal Succession of the Upper Bernician." *Trans. Nat. Hist. Soc. Northumberland, Durham and Newcastle-on-Tyne*, N.S., vol. iii, pp. 591-645.*

——. 1915. " The Genus *Lonsdaleia* and *Dibunophyllum rugosum* (M'Coy)." *Quart. Journ. Geol. Soc.*, vol. lxxi, pp. 218-271.*

——. 1930a. " Valentian Corals from Shropshire and Montgomeryshire, with a note on a new Stromatoporoid." *Quart. Journ. Geol. Soc.*, vol. lxxxvi, pp. 291-330.*

——. 1930b. " The Carboniferous Inliers at Codrington and Wick (Gloucestershire). *Quart. Journ. Geol. Soc.*, vol. lxxxvi, pp. 331-354, with geol. map.

——. 1933. " On the Occurrence of Tremadoc Shales in the Tortworth Inlier (Gloucestershire)." *Quart. Journ. Geol. Soc.*, vol. lxxxix, pp. 357-378, with geol. map.

——. 1942. " A High Viséan Fauna from the Vicinity of Yate, Gloucestershire : with special reference to the Corals and to a Goniatite." *Proc. Bristol Nat. Soc.*, Ser. 4, vol. ix, pp. 335-348.

—— and YÜ, C. C. 1943. " A Revision of the Coral Genus *Aulina* Smith and Descriptions of New Species from Britain and China." *Quart. Journ. Geol. Soc.*, vol. xcix, pp. 37-61.*

SMITH, WM. 1816. " Strata Identified by Organized Fossils." *London.*

SOLOMON, J. D. 1932. " The Glacial Succession on the North Norfolk Coast." *Proc. Geol. Assoc.*, vol. xliii, pp. 241-271.

SOWERBY, J. and J. DE C. 1812-1846. " The Mineral Conchology of Great Britain." *London.*

SPATH, L. F. 1923-1944. " A Monograph of the Ammonoidea of the Gault." *Palaeont. Soc.*

——. 1924. " On the Ammonites of the Speeton Clay and the Subdivisions of the Neocomian." *Geol. Mag.*, vol. lxi, pp. 73-89.

——. 1939. " The Ammonite Zones of the Upper Oxford Clay of Warboys, Huntingdonshire." *Bull. Geol. Surv.*, No. 1, pp. 82-96.*

STAMP, L. D. 1923. " The Base of the Devonian, with Special Reference to the Welsh Borderland." *Geol. Mag.*, vol. lx, pp. 276, 331, 367, 385.

STATHER, J. W. 1922. " A New Section in the Oolites and Glacial Deposits, near South Cave." *Trans. Hull Geol. Soc.*, vol. vi (1901-1925), pp. 244-245.

STENSIÖ, E. A. 1932. " Cephalaspids of Great Britain." *Brit. Mus. (Nat. Hist.)*.*

STEPHENS, J. V., EDWARDS, W. N., STUBBLEFIELD, C. J. and MITCHELL, G. H. 1941. " The Faunal Divisions of the Millstone Grit of Rombald's Moor and Neighbourhood." *Proc. Yorks. Geol. Soc.*, vol. xxiv, pp. 343-372, with geol. map.

STUBBLEFIELD, C. J. 1928. " A New Trilobite, *Acidaspis (Pseudomonaspis) magnospina* from the Coniston Limestone." *Ann. Mag. Nat. Hist.*, Ser. 10, vol. i, pp. 427-433.*

—— and BULMAN, O. M. B. 1927. " The Shineton Shales of the Wrekin District : with Notes on their Development in other parts of Shropshire and Herefordshire." *Quart. Journ. Geol. Soc.*, vol. lxxxiii, pp. 96-146, with geol. map.*

SWINTON, W. E. .1939. "A New Triassic Rhynchocephalian from Gloucestershire." *Ann. Mag. Nat. Hist.*, Ser. 11, vol. iv, pp. 591-594.

SYLVESTER-BRADLEY, P. C. 1940. " The Purbeck Beds of Swindon." *Proc. Geol. Assoc.*, vol. li, pp. 349-372. (Note also Anderson, F. W. on the Ostracods, pp. 373-384, and Arkell, W. J. on the Mollusca, pp. 385-399, figs.)*

TATE, R. and BLAKE, J. F. 1876. " The Yorkshire Lias." *London.**

TAWNEY, E. B. 1881. " On the Upper Bagshot Sands of Hordwell Cliffs, Hampshire." *Proc. Camb. Phil. Soc.*, vol. iv, pp. 140-155.

THOMAS, H. D. 1939. " On *Trochiliopora humei* Gregory and *T. gasteri* sp. nov." *Proc. Geol. Assoc.*, vol. l, pp. 527-529.*

THOMAS, H. HAMSHAW. 1925. " The Caytoniales, a new Group of Angiospermous Plants from the Jurassic Rocks of Yorkshire." *Phil. Trans. Roy. Soc.*, vol. ccxiii B, pp. 299-363.*

THOMPSON, B. 1888. " The Middle Lias of Northamptonshire." (Reprinted from *Midland Naturalist.*) *London.*

TIDDEMAN, R. H. 1875-1879. " Reports of the Committee appointed for the Purpose of Exploring the Settle Caves." *Rep. Brit. Assoc.* Belfast (1874), pp. 133-138. Bristol (1875), pp. 166-175. Glasgow (1876), pp. 115-118. Plymouth (1877), pp. 215-220. Dublin (1878), pp. 377-380.

TOMES, R. F. 1883. " On the Fossil Madreporaria of the Great Oolite of the Counties of Gloucester and Oxford." *Quart. Journ. Geol. Soc.*, vol. xxxix, pp. 168-196.*

TONKS, L. H. 1925. " The Millstone Grit and Yoredale Rocks of Nidderdale." *Proc. Yorks Geol. Soc.*, vol. xx, pp. 226-256, with geol. map.

——, JONES, R. C. B., LLOYD, W. and SHERLOCK, R. L. 1931. " The Geology of Manchester and the South-East Lancashire Coalfield." *Mem. Geol. Surv.*

TOPLEY, W. 1875. " The Geology of the Weald." *Mem. Geol. Surv.*

TRECHMANN, C. T. 1945. " On Some New Permian Fossils from the Magnesian Limestone near Sunderland." *Quart. Journ. Geol. Soc.*, vol. c, 1944, pp. 333-354.*

—— and WOOLACOTT, D. 1919. " On the Highest Coal-Measures or ' Zone ' of *Anthracomya phillipsi* in the Durham Coalfield." *Geol. Mag.*, Dec. 6, vol. vi, pp. 203-211.

TROTTER, F. M. 1942. " Geology of the Forest of Dean Coal and Iron-ore Field." *Mem. Geol. Surv.*

TRUEMAN, A. E. 1918. " The Lias of South Lincolnshire." *Geol. Mag.*, Dec. 6, vol. v, pp. 64-73, 103-111.

TUCK, M. C. 1926. " The Avonian Succession between Wickwar and Chipping Sodbury (Glos.). *Proc. Bristol Nat. Soc.*, Ser. 4, vol. vi, pp. 237-249, with geol. map.

TURNER, J. S. 1927. " The Lower Carboniferous Succession in the Westmorland Pennines and the Relations of the Pennine and Dent Faults." *Proc. Geol. Assoc.*, vol. xxxviii, pp. 339-374, with geol. map.

——. 1935. " Structural Geology of Stainmore, Westmorland, and Notes on the Late-Palaeozoic (Late-Variscian) Tectonics of the North of England." *Proc. Geol. Assoc.*, vol. xlvi, pp. 121-151, with geol. map.

TUTCHER, J. W. 1923. " Some recent Exposures of the Lias (Sinemurian and Hettangian) and Rhaetic about Keynsham." *Proc. Bristol Nat. Soc.*, Ser. 5, vol. v, pp. 268-278.

—— and TRUEMAN, A. E. 1925. " The Liassic Rocks of the Radstock District (Somerset)." *Quart. Journ. Geol. Soc.*, vol. lxxxi, pp. 595-666, sketch-maps.*

USSHER, W. A. E.   1904.   " The Geology of the Country around Kingsbridge and Salcombe."   *Mem. Geol. Surv.*

——.   1908.   " The Geology of the Quantock Hills and of Taunton and Bridgwater."   *Mem. Geol. Surv.*

——.   1913.   " The Geology of the Country around Newton Abbot."   *Mem. Geol. Surv.*

——.   1933.   " The Geology of the Country around Torquay."   2nd ed. (revised) by W. Lloyd.   *Mem. Geol. Surv.**

VAUGHAN, A.   1905.   " The Palaeontological Sequence in the Carboniferous Limestone of the Bristol Area."   *Quart. Journ. Geol. Soc.*, vol. lxi, pp. 181-307.*

VENABLES, E. M.   1929.   " On the London Clay of the Bognor District."   *Proc. Geol. Assoc.*, vol. xl, pp. 41-51, sketch-map.

WALLIS, F. S.   1922.   " The Carboniferous Limestone (Avonian) of Broadfield Down, Somerset."   *Proc. Bristol Nat. Soc.*, Ser. 4, vol. v, pp. 205-221, with geol. map.

——.   1924.   " The Avonian of the Tytherington-Tortworth-Wickwar Ridge, Gloucestershire."   *Proc. Bristol Nat. Soc.*, Ser. 4, vol. vi, pp. 57-74, with geol. map.

——.   1927a.   " The Old Red Sandstone of the Bristol District."   *Quart. Journ. Geol. Soc.*, vol. lxxxiii, pp. 760-789.

——.   1927b.   " Notes on Sections of Old Red Sandstone in the Bristol District."   *Proc. Bristol Nat. Soc.*, Ser. 4, vol. vi, pp. 400-405.

——.   1935.   " Carboniferous Cephalopods from Shipham, Somerset."   *Proc. Bristol Nat. Soc.*, Ser. 4, vol. vii, pp. 538-541.*

WATTS, W. W. and others.   1925.   " The Geology of South Shropshire."   *Proc. Geol. Assoc.*, vol. xxxvi, pp. 321-405.

WEAVER, T.   1824.   " Geological Observations on Part of Gloucestershire and Somersetshire."   *Trans. Geol. Soc.*, Ser. 2, vol. i, pp. 317-368, with geol. map.

WEDD, C. B., SMITH, B., SIMMONS, W. C., and WRAY, D. A.   1923.   " The Geology of Liverpool, with Wirral and part of the Flintshire Coalfield."   *Mem. Geol. Surv.*

WELCH, F. B. A.   1929.   " The Geological Structure of the Central Mendips."   *Quart. Journ. Geol. Soc.*, vol. lxxxv, pp. 45-76, with geol. map.

——.   1933.   " The Geological Structure of the Eastern Mendips."   *Quart. Journ. Geol. Soc.*, vol. lxxxix, pp. 14-52, with geol. map.

WETHERELL, N. T.   1837.   " Observations on a Well dug on the South side of Hampstead Heath."   *Trans. Geol. Soc.*, Ser. 2, vol. v, pp. 131-138.

WHIDBORNE, G. F.   1888-1892.   "A Monograph of the Devonian Fauna of the South of England."   Vols. i, ii.   *Palaeont. Soc.**

——.   1896-1898.   "A Monograph of the Devonian Fauna of the South of England."   Vol. iii.   *Palaeont. Soc.**

WHITAKER, W.   1871.   " On the Cliff-Sections of the Tertiary Beds West of Dieppe in Normandy and at Newhaven in Sussex."   *Quart. Journ. Geol. Soc.*, vol. xxvii, pp. 263-268.

——.   1872.   " The Geology of the London Basin. Part I."   *Mem. Geol. Surv.*, vol. iv.

——.   1885.   " The Geology of the Country around Ipswich, Hadleigh and Felixstowe."   *Mem. Geol. Surv.*, Qr. Sheets 48 N.W. and N.E.

——.   1889.   " The Geology of London and Part of the Thames Valley. Vol. I."   *Mem. Geol. Surv.*

WHITE, E. I. 1923. "Notes on a New Species of 'Terebelloid' and other Phenomena in the Great Pit at Harefield, Middlesex." *Proc. Geol. Assoc.*, vol. xxxiv, pp. 43-46.

——. 1931. "The Vertebrate Faunas of the English Eocene. Vol. i- From the Thanet Sands to the Basement Bed of the London Clay." *Brit. Mus. (Nat. Hist.).**

——. 1935. "The Ostracoderm *Pteraspis* Kner and the Relationships of the Agnathous Vertebrates." *Phil. Trans. Roy. Soc.*, Ser. B, vol. ccxxv, pp. 381-457.*

——. 1946. "The Genus *Phialaspis* and the '*Psammosteus* Limestones.'" *Quart. Journ. Geol. Soc.*, vol. ci (1945), pp. 207-242.*

WHITE, H. J. O. 1909. "The Geology of the Country around Basingstoke." *Mem. Geol. Surv.*

——. 1910a. "Berkshire and Part of the Thames Valley." "*Geology in the Field*," Pt. 2, pp. 216-220, map.

——. 1910b. "Geology of the Country around Alresford." *Mem. Geol. Surv.*

——. 1913. "The Geology of the Country near Fareham and Havant." *Mem. Geol. Surv.*

——. 1915. "The Geology of the Country around Lymington and Portsmouth." *Mem. Geol. Surv.*

——. 1921. "A Short Account of the Geology of the Isle of Wight." *Mem. Geol. Surv.*

——. 1923. "The Geology of the Country South and West of Shaftesbury." *Mem. Geol. Surv.*

——. 1925. "The Geology of the Country around Marlborough." *Mem. Geol. Surv.*

——. 1926. "The Geology of the Country near Lewes." *Mem. Geol. Surv.*

——. 1932. "The Geology of the Country near Saffron Walden." *Mem. Geol. Surv.*

WHITEHEAD, T. H. and ARKELL, W. J. 1946. "Field Meeting at Hook Norton and Sibford, Oxfordshire." *Proc. Geol. Assoc.*, vol. lvii, pp. 16-18.

WHITTARD, W. F. 1928. "The Stratigraphy of the Valentian Rocks of Shropshire. The Main Outcrop." *Quart. Journ. Geol. Soc.*, vol. lxxxiii, pp. 737-759, with geol. map.

——. 1931. "The Geology of the Ordovician and Valentian Rocks of the Shelve Country, Shropshire." "Easter Field Meeting to Minsterley." *Proc. Geol. Assoc.*, vol. xlii, pp. 322-344.

——. 1932. "The Stratigraphy of the Valentian Rocks of Shropshire. The Longmynd-Shelve and Breidden Outcrops." *Quart. Journ. Geol. Soc.*, vol. lxxxviii, pp. 859-902, with geol. maps.

—— and SMITH, S. 1944. "Unrecorded Inliers of Silurian Rocks near Wickwar, Gloucestershire." *Geol. Mag.*, vol. lxxxi, pp. 65-76, with geol. map.

WILLS, L. J. 1910. "On the Fossiliferous Lower Keuper Rocks of Worcestershire." *Proc. Geol. Assoc.*, vol. xxi, pp. 249-331.*

——. 1946-47. "A Monograph of British Triassic Scorpions." *Palaeont. Soc.**

—— and CAMPBELL SMITH, W. 1914. "Notes on the Flora and Fauna of the Upper Keuper Sandstones of Warwickshire and Worcestershire." *Rep. Brit. Assoc.* (Birmingham, 1913), pp. 475-476.

WILMORE, A. 1910. "On the Carboniferous Limestone South of the Craven Fault (Grassington-Hellifield District)." *Quart. Journ. Geol. Soc.*, vol. lxvi, pp. 539-585.

WILSON, V. 1933. " The Corallian Rocks of the Howardian Hills (York-shire)." *Quart. Journ. Geol. Soc.*, vol. lxxxix, pp. 480-509.

——. 1936. " The Upper Jurassic Rocks of the Country between Malton and Castle Howard, East Yorkshire." *Proc. Geol. Assoc.*, vol. xlvii, pp. 254-264, with geol. map.

——, HEMINGWAY, J. E. and BLACK, M. 1934. "A Synopsis of the Jurassic Rocks of Yorkshire. With a Report of the Summer Field Meeting to North-East Yorkshire." *Proc.- Geol. Assoc.*, vol. xlv, pp. 247-306.

WOOD, A. 1937. " The Non-Marine Lamellibranchs of the North Wales Coalfield." *Quart. Journ. Geol. Soc.*, vol. xciii, pp. 1-22.*

——. 1941. " The Lower Carboniferous Calcareous Algae *Mitcheldeania* Wethered and *Garwoodia*, gen. nov." *Proc. Geol. Assoc.*, vol. lii, pp. 216-226.

WOOD, S. V. 1861-1877. "A Monograph of the Eocene Bivalves of England. Vol. I and Supplement." *Palaeont. Soc.**

WOODWARD, H. B. 1881. " The Geology of the Country around Norwich." *Mem. Geol. Surv.*

——. 1893. " The Jurassic Rocks of Britain. Vol. iii, The Lias of England and Wales." *Mem. Geol. Surv.*

——. 1894. " The Jurassic Rocks of Britain. Vol. iv, The Lower Oolitic Rocks of England." *Mem. Geol. Surv.*

——. 1895. " The Jurassic Rocks of Britain. Vol. v, Middle and Upper Oolites of England." *Mem. Geol. Surv.*

—— and USSHER, W. A. E. 1911. " The Geology of the Country around Sidmouth and Lyme Regis." *Mem. Geol. Surv.*, 2nd ed.

WOOLDRIDGE, S. W. and WRIGLEY, A. 1929. " Field Meeting at Northwood and Harefield." *Proc. Geol. Assoc.*, vol. xl, pp. 373-375.

WRAY, D. A., STEPHENS, J. V. and BROMEHEAD, C. E. N. 1930. " The Geology of the Country around Huddersfield and Halifax." *Mem. Geol. Surv.*

WRIGHT, C. W. 1935. " The Chalk Rock Fauna in East Yorkshire." *Geol. Mag.*, vol. lxxii, pp. 441-442.

—— and THOMAS, H. D. 1947. " Notes on the Geology of the Country round Sevenoaks, Kent." *Proc. Geol. Assoc.*, vol. lvii, pp. 315-321.

—— and E. V. 1939. " The Geology of the Guildford-Godalming Bypass Road, Surrey." *Proc. Geol. Assoc.*, vol. l, pp. 1-12.*

—— and E. V. 1942a. " Some New Sections and Fossils from the Folkestone Beds of the Farnham District." *Proc. Geol. Assoc.*, vol. liii, pp. 86-87.

—— and E. V. 1942b. " The Chalk of the Yorkshire Wolds." *Proc. Geol. Assoc.*, vol. liii, pp. 112-127, map.

—— and E. V. 1942c. " New Records of Cretaceous Fossils from the Isle of Wight." *Proc. I.O.W. Nat. Hist. Soc.*, vol. iii, pp. 283-287.

—— and E. V. 1947. " The Stratigraphy of the Albian Beds at Leighton Buzzard." *Geol. Mag.*, vol. lxxxiv, pp. 161-168.

WRIGHT, W. B. and others. 1927. " The Geology of the Rossendale Anti-cline." *Mem. Geol. Surv.**

WRIGLEY, A. 1922. " Excursion to Bracknell." *Proc. Geol. Assoc.*, vol. xxxiii, pp. 79-80.

——. 1925. " Notes on the Section in Fishponds Pit, Wokingham." *Proc. Geol. Assoc.*, vol. xxxvi, pp. 452-455.

——. 1928. " The London Clay of Newnham (Hants)." *Proc. Geol. Assoc.*, vol. xxxix, pp. 360-368.

——. 1929. " Notes on English Eocene Boring Mollusca, with Descriptions of New Species." *Proc. Geol. Assoc.*, vol. xl, pp. 376-383.*

——. 1934. "A Lutetian Fauna at Southampton Docks." *Proc. Geol. Assoc.*, vol. xlv, pp. 1-16.

WRIGLEY, G. and DAVIS, A. G. 1937. " The Occurrence of Nummulites *planulatus* in England, with a Revised Correlation of the Strata containing it." *Proc. Geol. Assoc.*, vol. xlviii, pp. 203-228.

YOUNG, G. W. 1905. " The Chalk Area of North-East Surrey." *Proc. Geol. Assoc.*, vol. xix, pp. 188-219, with topog. map.

——. 1908. " The Chalk Area of Western Surrey." *Proc. Geol. Assoc.*, vol. xx, pp. 422-455.

# WALES

## ANGLESEY

**Amlwch.** Parys Mountain, 1½ miles S. of Amlwch ; spoil bank in East Pit (" Hillside " opencast) in its N.E. corner.

Silurian, Llandovery, shale, not *in situ*. Graptolites from most of the Llandovery zones have been obtained from the spoil heaps of this and the adjoining (west) pit. They are abundant and relatively well preserved, but perish unless protected from oxidation by a varnish film. Numerous species of *Monograptus* with diplograptids and climacograptids.

Greenly, E. 1919, Vol. 2, pp. 480-482.
Geol. Surv. Anglesey Special ; Ord. New Pop. 106.

**Benllech.** W. side of Red Wharfe Bay. Interior of area between E. coast and western escarpment. Often good places in cliffs on flanks of lofty plateaux.

Carboniferous Limestone (D₂ subzone). Corals (*Dibunophyllum, Lithostrotion*) with brachiopods (productids), etc. often plentiful.

Greenly, E. 1919, Vol. 2, pp. 610 and 633-635.
Geol. Surv. Anglesey Special ; Ord. New Pop. 106 and 107.

**Bryngwran,** 8 miles S.E. of Holyhead on Bangor road. At roadside, ⅛ mile N.W. of Ty-hen, ¾ mile N. of Bryngwran.

Ordovician, Arenig (grit at base of *Didymograptus extensus* zone). Brachiopods (*Orthis proava*) with trilobites (*Calymene* [*Synhomalonotus*] *monensis*, " *Ogygia* " *selwyni*).

Greenly, E. 1919, Vol. 2, p. 442. Shirley, J. 1936, p. 402.
Geol. Surv. Anglesey Special ; Ord. New Pop. 106.

**Cemaes.** On N. coast, 5 miles W. of Amlwch. N.E. of Cemaes, Sandy Bay (Porth Padrig of 6 inch map). Foreshore 300 yds. S. of Llanbadrig Church. Accessible at low water.

Ordovician, basal Caradoc (ironstone and black shales of *Nemagraptus gracilis* zone). The zone fossil with *Dicellograptus, Dicranograptus* and some biserial graptolites.

Greenly, E. 1919, Vol. 2, p. 470.
Geol. Surv. Anglesey Special ; Ord. New Pop. 106.

**Cemaes.** N.E. of Cemaes, brow of cliff S. of Ogof Gynfor.

Ordovician, Caradoc (grits at base of *Nemagraptus gracilis* zone). Orthid brachiopods including *Harknessella,* " *Dalmanella,*" etc.

Greenly, E. 1919, Vol. 2, p. 469.
Geol. Surv. Anglesey Special ; Ord. New Pop. 106.

**Cemaes.** Porth Wen Bay, W. side, S. of brick works, N. of road midway between Amlwch and Cemaes, tramway coming down from Graig-wen.

Ordovician, basal Caradoc, grits with brachiopods, particularly *Orthis bailyana*.

Greenly, E. 1919, Vol. 2, p. 470.
Geol. Surv. Anglesey Special ; Ord. New Pop. 106.

**Holland Arms,** 16½ miles S.E. of Holyhead on Bangor road. Spoil banks N. of main road, a little W. of Holland Arms Inn.

Carboniferous, Coal Measures, not *in situ*. Fossil plants (*Sphenopteris*) rare, with fish remains (Coelacanth and palaeoniscid scales and fragments).

Greenly, E. 1919, Vol. 2, p. 665.
Geol. Surv. Anglesey Special ; Ord. New Pop. 106.

**Llanbabo,** 6 miles S.W. of Amlwch. E. side of road 250 yds. W.S.W. of Fferam-uchaf Farm, ¾ miles W. of Llanbabo.

Ordovician, Llanvirn (*Didymograptus murchisoni* zone), gritty shales yielding the zone fossil (well preserved) with brachiopods and trilobites.

Greenly, E. 1919, Vol. 2, p. 452.

Geol. Surv. Anglesey Special ; Ord. New Pop. 106.

**Llanbabo.** 270 yds. E. of Fferam-uchaf Farm, ¾ mile W. of Llanbabo.

Ordovician, basal Caradoc (*Nemagraptus gracilis* zone), gritty ironstones and shales with the zone fossil, diplograptids, dicellograptids, etc.

Greenly, E. 1919, Vol. 2, p. 453.

Geol. Surv. Anglesey Special ; Ord. New Pop. 106.

**Llanbabo.** 400 yds. N.E. of church, and N. of Glan-y-gors.

Ordovician, Caradoc, *Climacograptus wilsoni* zone, shales with grits. A poorly preserved *C.* cf. *wilsoni* has been recorded, but further search is desirable. Stream section 50 yds. S.S.E. has yielded graptolites of the *Dicranograptus clingani* zone.

Greenly, E. 1919, Vol. 2, pp. 455-456.

Geol. Surv. Anglesey Special ; Ord. New Pop. 106.

**Llanddeusant,** 5½ miles N.W. of Llanerchymedd. Farm N.E. of Caergwrli, 1¾ miles S.E. of Llanddeusant Church.

Ordovician, Llanvirn, shale near base of *Didymograptus bifidus* zone. The zone fossil, with other *Didymograptus* species.

Greenly, E. 1919, Vol. 2, p. 444.

Geol. Surv. Anglesey Special ; Ord. New Pop. 106.

**Llanddona,** 3 miles N.W. of Beaumaris. Beach E. of Careg-onen, near limestone quarries.

Ordovician, (? Caradoc), grey shales underlying red stained shales. Graptolites suggestive of *Climacograptus peltifer* or high *Nemagraptus gracilis* zone, while trilobites (*Ampyx*) suggest zone of *Didymograptus bifidus*.

Greenly, E. 1919, Vol. 2, p. 433.

Geol. Surv. Anglesey Special ; Ord. New Pop. 106 and 107.

**Llanddyfnan,** 6½ miles W. of Beaumaris. Cors Bodeilio (an alluvial marsh), S.S.W. of village.

Holocene, fresh-water alluvium, *Chara* marl. Fossils scarce: seeds of *Chara* and other plants ; fragment of beetle.

Greenly, E. 1919, Vol. 2, pp. 770-771.

Geol. Surv. Anglesey Special ; Ord. New Pop. 106 and 107.

**Llanerchymedd,** 6 miles W.S.W. of Amlwch. In escarpment, 1½ miles S.W. of Llanerchymedd, by side of lane between Bryn-clyd and Prys-owen.

Ordovician, Arenig (grits at base of *Didymograptus extensus* zone), with brachiopods (*Orthis proava*) and trilobites ("*Ogygia*" *selwyni*).

Greenly, E. 1919, Vol. 2, p. 442.

Geol. Surv. Anglesey Special ; Ord. New Pop. 106.

**Llanerchymedd.** Old quarry by roadside, 400 yds. N. of Bryn Gwallen, 1 mile W. of Llanerchymedd.

Ordovician, Arenig (*Didymograptus extensus* zone). Type-locality of the trilobite *Synhomalonotus monensis*. Other trilobites, besides brachiopods (*Orthis proava*) recorded.

Greenly, E. 1919, Vol. 2, p. 446. Shirley, J. 1936, p. 401.

Geol. Surv. Anglesey Special ; Ord. New Pop. 106.

**Llangaffo,** 4½ miles S. of Llangefni. Spoil banks of former mines at Morfa-mawr, in the midst of the great alluvium.

Carboniferous, Coal Measures, not *in situ*. Plants (*Lepidodendron*), non-marine shells (*Carbonicola*) and fish scales and spines.

Greenly, E. 1919, Vol. 2, p. 664.

Geol. Surv. Anglesey Special ; Ord. New Pop. 106.

**Llangoed,** 2 miles N. of Beaumaris. Bryn-celyn, old ironstone quarry. Ordovician, Llanvirn (*Didymograptus murchisoni* zone). Large specimens of the zone fossil.

Greenly, E. 1919, Vol. 2, pp. 415, 434.
Geol. Surv. Anglesey Special ; Ord. New Pop. 107.

**Llangoed.** Escarpment from Careg-onen to the Penmon quarries : also coast section from cliff N. of Bwrdd Arthur to lighthouse at Puffin Strait.

Carboniferous Limestone ($D_1$ to $D_3$ subzones). Corals and brachiopods plentiful at intervals : *Dibunophyllum, Lithostrotion, Athyris, Chonetes, Productus,* etc.

Greenly, E. 1919, Vol. 2, pp. 652-658.
Geol. Surv. Anglesey Special ; Ord. New Pop. 107.

**Llangwyllog,** 3 miles N.W. of Llangefni. Glan-y-gors, roadside quarry. Ordovician, basal Caradoc (*Nemagraptus gracilis* zone). Zone fossil not obtained, but other graptolites indicative of the *gracilis* zone : *Climacograptus, Dicellograptus, Diplograptus.*

Greenly, E. 1919, Vol. 2, p. 438.
Geol. Surv. Anglesey Special ; Ord. New Pop. 106.

**Llangwyllog.** 320 yds. W.S.W. of Capel-coch windmill, $2\frac{1}{4}$ miles N.E. of Llangwyllog.

Ordovician, Caradoc (shale, slightly cleaved, of upper part of *Nemagraptus gracilis* or *Climacograptus peltifer* zone). *Nemagraptus* occurs with *Climacograptus, Dicellograptus, Diplograptus,* etc.

Greenly, E. 1919, Vol. 2, p. 437.
Geol. Surv. Anglesey Special ; Ord. New Pop. 106.

**Lligwy to Llangefni.** Principal escarpment in a general S.S.W. direction from Lligwy to Llangefni.

Carboniferous Limestone ($D_1$ to $D_2$ subzones). Fossils abundant at frequent exposures. Mainly corals (*Lithostrotion, Dibunophyllum*) and brachiopods (*Chonetes, Productus*) ; a few trilobites (*Phillipsia*) have been recorded at Cefn-iwrch. Gastropods are exceptionally abundant.

Greenly, E. 1919, Vol. 2, pp. 638-640.
Geol. Surv. Anglesey Special ; Ord. New Pop. 106.

**Menai Bridge.** Ty'n-y-caeau (W. of Menai Bridge), gravel pits alongside main road. Huts have recently been built in the pits, but access could probably be obtained on application.

Ordovician, Arenig and Llanvirn, not *in situ*. Well preserved graptolites are not uncommon in pebbles in glacial gravels and include *Didymograptus extensus, D. hirundo* and *D. bifidus*. Also the trilobite *Cyclopyge* and the crustacean *Caryocaris*.

Greenly, E. 1919, Vol. 2, p. 431.
Geol. Surv. Anglesey Special ; Ord. New Pop. 106 and 107.

**Moelfre,** 6 miles S.E. of Amlwch. Ynys Dulas, the island with a tower in Dulas Bay. Accessible from Moelfre only in calm weather.

Carboniferous Limestone ($D_1$ subzone). Rich in corals, e.g. *Alveolites, Syringopora.*

Greenly, E. 1919, Vol. 2, p. 630.
Geol. Surv. Anglesey Special ; Ord. New Pop. 106.

**Moelfre.** Cliff section from Moelfre to Traeth Bychan and Benllech (about $2\frac{1}{2}$ miles). Examine at low tide.

Carboniferous Limestone ($D_1$ to $D_2$ subzones). Coral beds with *Lithostrotion* and clisiophyllids well seen on the foreshore at Moreyn and Traeth Bychan. Fossils can also be collected from the old spoil banks of the S. quarry at Traeth Bychan.

Greenly, E. 1919, Vol. 2, pp. 631-633.
Geol. Surv. Anglesey Special ; Ord. New Pop. 106 and 107.

**Moelfre.** Along the coast from Moelfre to Benllech.
Pleistocene, boulder clay with molluscs. All the shells are broken, and the fragments are often too small for identification.
Greenly, E. 1919, Vol. 2, pp. 746-748.
Geol. Surv. Anglesey Special ; Ord. New Pop. 106 and 107.

**Penmon,** see Llangoed.

**Pentraeth,** 5 miles W.N.W. of Beaumaris. Roadside quarry at Pentraeth Mill, S.W. of village.
Carboniferous Limestone (D$_2$ subzone), dark limestone and shale rich in brachiopods especially *Gigantoproductus latissimus.*
Greenly, E. 1919, Vol. 2, p. 637.
Geol. Surv. Anglesey Special ; Ord. New Pop. 106 and 107.

**Rhosneigr,** 7 miles S.E. of Holyhead, on coast. Llyn Maelog, W. shore.
Ordovician, Arenig (pebbly grits near base of *Didymograptus extensus* zone), with the brachiopod *Orthis proava.*
Greenly, E. 1919, Vol. 2, p. 439.
Geol. Surv. Anglesey Special ; Ord. New Pop. 106.

**Rhosneigr.** Towards N. end of shore section, $\frac{1}{3}$ mile from mouth of Crigyll river.
Ordovician, Arenig or Llanvirn, dark shale with graptolites (*Didymograptus nicholsoni*) and brachiopods (*Acrotreta*). Fossils rare and poorly preserved. Further search desirable.
Greenly, E. 1919, Vol. 2, p. 440.
Geol. Surv. Anglesey Special ; Ord. New Pop. 106.

**Tre-Arddur.** 3 miles N.N.W. of Rhoscolyn. Tre-Arddur Bay. Similar beds exposed at Borth-wen (Rhoscolyn), Lligwy Bay and Red Wharfe Bay.
Holocene, submerged forest visible only at low water, peat underlain by blue marine clay. Fossil wood, twigs, etc., from peat. The marine clay has yielded the lamellibranch *Scrobicularia,* sometimes in vertical attitude of burrowing.
Greenly, E. 1919, Vol. 2, pp. 766-768.
Geol. Surv. Anglesey Special ; Ord. New Pop. 106.

**Trefdraeth.** 5 miles S.W. of Llangefni. Spoil banks of former mines in the " Glantraeth Coal." The first is a few yds. N. of the main line railway and all are close to the margin of the marsh (Malldraeth).
Carboniferous, Lower Coal Measures and Millstone Grit. Plant remains (*Stigmaria*) with fish spines and fragments, goniatites (*Anthracoceras, Gastrioceras*) and lamellibranchs (*Dunbarella papyracea*).
Greenly, E. 1919, Vol. 2, p. 662.
Geol. Surv. Anglesey Special ; Ord. New Pop. 106.

## BRECKNOCK·

**Abercrave,** 5$\frac{1}{2}$ miles N.E. of Ystalyfera, Glam. Left bank of R. Tawe by small waterfall below mouth of Nant-y-ffon 1$\frac{1}{8}$ miles above Abercrave House.
Carboniferous, Millstone Grit (base of shale group, R$_2$ subzone). Ten feet of shales above and 5 ft. below a thin grit. Abundant goniatites (*Reticuloceras superbilingue*), lamellibranchs and brachiopods.
Robertson, T. 1932, p. 68.
Geol. Surv. N.S. 231 ; Ord. New Pop. 153.

**Abercrave.** Left bank of R. Tawe at bend in river 160 yds. S. of Abercrave House, 200 yds. upstream from bridge.

Carboniferous, Millstone Grit (G zone). Up to 5 ft. of shale with well-preserved goniatites : *Gastrioceras subcrenatum* abundant, and occasional uncrushed *G*. cf. *cumbriense*. Lamellibranchs in higher part of bed.

Robertson, T. 1932, p. 69.
Geol. Surv. N.S. 231 ; Ord. New Pop. 153.

**Abercrave.** Left bank of R. Llech 80 yds. above confluence with R. Tawe, 800 yds. E.S.E. of Abercrave House.

Carboniferous, Millstone Grit (G zone, shale group). Light grey shale dipping steeply into stream : beds much faulted and disturbed. Varied marine fauna with brachiopods (*Dictyoclostus*, *Lingula*), nautiloids (*Metacoceras*), lamellibranchs (*Aviculopecten*, *Nuculana*), goniatite fragments, etc. Generally well preserved.

Geol. Surv. N.S. 231 ; Ord. New Pop. 153.

**Abercrave.** Cliff, left bank of Nant Llech, about ½ mile below Henrhyd Waterfall.

Carboniferous, base of Coal Measures, 5 ft. of shales with plants above thin coal and below 1-inch band of non-marine shells. Among plants are *Lyginopteris*, *Alethopteris*, *Mariopteris*. Shells include *Carbonicola* and *Naiadites*. (Loose material.)

Crookall, R. in Robertson, T. 1932, p. 243. Dix, E. 1933, p. 164.
Geol. Surv. N.S. 231 ; Ord. New Pop. 153.

**Abercrave.** R. Llech, right bank and bed of stream 1500 yds. downstream from Henrhyd Waterfall, and 150 yds. upstream from tributary on left bank.

Carboniferous, Coal Measures (*lenisulcata* zone). Sandy shale 5-6 ft. on underclay. *Neuropteris rectinervis* very abundant, many other plants.

Robertson, T. 1932, pp. 98 and 243. Dix, E. 1933, p. 165.
Geol. Surv. N.S. 231 ; Ord. New Pop. 153.

**Abercrave.** Left bank of Nant Llech opposite old mill, ¾ mile E.N.E. of Abercrave Colliery, and 500 yds. upstream from union of Llech and Tawe.

Carboniferous, Coal Measures (*lenisulcata* zone). Sandy shales up to 30 ft. overlying thin coal seam. Abundant plants, but mainly of interest for tree trunk casts in position of growth. Probably this site was discovered by Logan and described by de la Beche. Some of the trunks are in the grounds of the Royal Institution at Swansea.

Beche, H. T. de la, 1846, p. 184. North, F. J. 1931, p. 121. Robertson, T. 1932, p. 98.
Geol. Surv. N.S. 231 ; Ord. New Pop. 153.

**Abercrave.** Right bank of R. Tawe immediately S. of bridge, 750 yds. E. of Inn (Lamb and Flag), 880 yds. E.S.E. of " Garth."

Carboniferous, Coal Measures (*lenisulcata* zone). Dark grey shale up to 5 ft. resting on thin coal. Marine fossils abundant and varied, brachiopods (*Dictyoclostus*, *Lingula*), *Conularia*, Fish scales, etc.

Robertson, T. 1932, p. 99.
Geol. Surv. N.S. 231 ; Ord. New Pop. 153.

**Abercrave.** Small tributary on left bank of R. Tawe 150 yds. downstream from bridge, 880 yds. S. of Garth. Bed lies some 80 ft. above level of river.

Carboniferous, Coal Measures. Ironstone and shale 1½ ft. Crushed non-marine shells abundant (*Carbonicola* cf. *recta*, etc.).

Robertson, T. 1932, p. 98.
Geol. Surv. N.S. 231 ; Ord. New Pop. 153.

**Colbren,** 11 miles N.E. of Neath, Glam. Left bank of Nant Llech-pellaf, 600 yds. upstream from union with Nant-cwm-byddar, 1½ miles N.E. of Colbren.

Carboniferous, Millstone Grit (G zone, shale group). Shales 2 ft. with non-marine shells (*Carbonicola* spp.).
Ware, W. D. 1939, p. 179.
Geol. Surv. N.S. 231 ; Ord. New Pop. 153.

**Colbren.** Stream section in westerly of two small tributaries to Nant-cwm-byddar, ⅞ mile above junction with Nant Llech-pellaf, and 660 yds. N.E. of Bryn Bugeiliad.
Carboniferous, Millstone Grit (Shale group, G zone). Abundant crushed goniatites (*Anthracoceras*, etc.), lamellibranchs, etc.
Robertson, T. 1932, p. 66.
Geol. Surv. N.S. 231 ; Ord. New Pop. 153.

**Colbren.** In bed of Nant Llech-pellaf and on left bank, 500 yds. upstream from union with Nant-cwm-byddar, 1½ miles N.E. of Colbren Junction.
Carboniferous, Millstone Grit (Shale group, G zone). One-inch black shale with goniatites (*Gastrioceras cancellatum, Reticuloceras superbilingue*), lamellibranchs and brachiopods.
Robertson, T. 1932, pp. 66, 67.
Geol. Surv. N.S. 231 ; Ord. New Pop. 153.

**Crickhowell.** Primrose Hill Quarry E. side of lane, 1½ miles N.W. of Crickhowell Church, and ¾ mile E.N.E.· of Pont-y-bryn-hurt.
Lower Old Red Sandstone, Senni Beds, grey sandstone with rare Ostraco-derms (*Pteraspis dunensis*).
White, E. I. 1938, p. 110.
Geol. Surv. O.S. 42 S.E. ; Ord. New Pop. 141.

**Penwyllt,** 3 miles N.E. of Abercrave (q.v.). Silica stone quarries 800 yds. S. of Penwyllt station and near railway, ½ mile N.E. of vicarage.
Carboniferous, Millstone Grit (Basal Grit group, H zone ?). Impersistent lenticular shales in grits, up to 2 ft. in thickness ; most of them are plant bearing, particularly a bed about 15 ft. from floor of quarry. Plants include *Lyginopteris stangeri*.
Crookall, R. in Robertson, T. 1932, p. 242. Dix, E. 1933, p. 160.
Geol. Surv. N.S. 231 ; Ord. New Pop. 153.

**Ystradgynlais** (Gurnos). 1½ miles N.E. of Ystalyfera, Glam. Old colliery tip ¾ mile W. of Ystradgynlais Church, near bend of road. The most northerly of several tips. A small stream flows E. of tip.
Carboniferous, Coal Measures (*ovalis* zone, measures between Bryn and Lower Veins), with occasional casts of non-marine shells (*Carbonicola* cf. *pseudorobusta, C.* cf. *communis*).
Geol. Surv. N.S. 230 ; Ord. New Pop. 153.

**Ystradgynlais.** Old tips of Diamond Colliery, 1 mile S. of Ystradgynlais Church. The conical tip is the best for collecting.
Carboniferous, Coal Measures (*modiolaris* zone, shales above Brass Vein, with solid specimens of the non-marine lamellibranchs *Carbonicola exigua, C. affinis* and *Anthraconaia* abundant.
Davies, J. H. and Trueman, A. E. 1927, p. 239, etc.
Geol. Surv. N.S. 230 ; Ord. New Pop. 153.

**Ystradgynlais.** Tip from old ironstone workings 150 yds. E.N.E. of Hendreladis Farm, Penrhos.
Carboniferous, Coal Measures (*similis-pulchra* zone, shales above Soap Vein) with abundant " Carbonicolas " (*Anthracosia* and *Anthracosphaerium*).
Trueman, A. E. and Ware, W. D. 1932, p. 83.
Geol. Surv. N.S. 231 ; Ord. New Pop. 153.

M

**Ystradgynlais.** Partly overgrown tip from old ironstone workings 20 yds. N.E. of Hendreladis Farm, and ¼ mile E. of Penrhos.

Carboniferous, Coal Measures (*similis-pulchra* zone, weathered shales from Pennypieces Ironstone) containing solid specimens of *Anthracosia* [*Carbonicola*] *planitumida*, and *Anthraconaia* [*Anthracomya*] *rubida* in moderate abundance.

Robertson, T. 1932, p. 155.

Geol. Surv. N.S. 231 ; Ord. New Pop. 153.


# CARDIGANSHIRE

**Pont-Erwyd,** 12 miles E. of Aberystwyth. Strike-sections in banks of Nant Fuches Gau, ¾ mile S.W. of Dyffryn Castell Hotel (14 miles E. of Aberystwyth) and 50 yds. S.W. of Fuches Gau Farm on road to Devil's Bridge. Locs. F7 and F8 of Jones, 1909.

Silurian, Llandovery Shales (Lower zone of Eisteddfa Group). Blue flags with dark pyritous shale bands dipping 31° W.12°S. Graptolites of the *Glyptograptus persculptus* zone occur, including the zone fossil.

Jones, O. T. 1909, pp. 480–481, fig. 5 and maps.

Geol. Surv. O.S. 57 N.E. ; Ord. New Pop. 127.

**Pont-Erwyd.** East bank of R. Rheidol, 450 yds. N.E. of Bryn-bras, 350 yds. N.W. of Bryn Chwith, and 1½ miles S. of Pont-Erwyd on road to Devil's Bridge.

Silurian, Lower Llandovery (Upper zone of Eisteddfa Group). Shales with graptolites of the *Akidograptus acuminatus* zone (including the zone fossil) in hard sandy flags.

Jones, O. T. 1909, p. 484, with maps.

Geol. Surv. O.S. 57 N.E. ; Ord. New Pop. 127.

**Pont-Erwyd.** W. side of gorge of R. Rheidol from 330 yds. due E. of Bryn-bras Farm to falls 700 yds. S.W. of this point downstream. S. of Pont-Erwyd on road to Devil's Bridge. F15 of Jones, 1909.

Silurian, Middle Llandovery (Rheidol Group, 400 ft.). Classic section. Alternations of flags, shales and mudstones with some calcareous nodules. Graptolites of zones from *Monograptus atavus* to *M. leptotheca,* and some shelly fossils of *M. triangulatus* zone.

Jones, O. T. 1909, pp. 484-90. Challinor, J. 1928, pp. 364-368.

Geol. Surv. O.S. 57 N.E. ; Ord. New Pop. 127.

**Waun-Fawr,** 1 mile E. of Aberystwyth. Cefn Hendre Quarry, disused, ¼ mile N.E. of Llanbadarn Church, 700 yds. W. of Commins Coch School.

Silurian, Upper Llandovery (Ystwyth Group). Dark blue shales, mudstones and thin grits. Bedding surfaces well exposed. Graptolites characteristic of the Aberystwyth Grits fairly common.

Jones, O. T. 1909, p. 520.

Geol. Surv. O.S. 57 N.E. ; Ord. New Pop. 127.


# CARMARTHENSHIRE

**Abergwili,** 2 miles E. of Carmarthen. Road bank opposite corn mill, Felin-wen, 1 1/10 miles E. of Abergwili on Llandilo road.

Ordovician, Llanvirn Series (highest beds of zone of *Didymograptus bifidus*), with abundant " tuning-fork " graptolites.

Strahan, A. and others 1909, p. 36.

Geol. Surv. N.S. 229 ; Ord. New Pop. 139 and 152.

**Brynamman.** W. side of road (near bend), 1 mile 250 yds. N.N.E. of cross-roads, Brynamman, 200 yds. N. of Craigderlwyn.

Carboniferous, Millstone Grit, Farewell Rock. Black and grey shales 20 ft. with numerous goniatites : *Gastrioceras subcrenatum* in dark shale, *Anthracoceras* and *Homoceratoides* in grey shale.

Ware, W. D. 1939, p. 182.
Geol. Surv. N.S. 230 ; Ord. New Pop. 153.

**Carmarthen.** Allt-Pen-y-coed dingle, banks of stream. S.E. of lane leading S. from Carmarthen-Ammanford road to Beaulieu-fawr, 1½ miles E. of Carmarthen on S. side of Towy Valley.

Cambrian, Tremadoc Series, *Peltura punctata* beds. Important locality for the trilobite *Peltura punctata*.

Strahan, A. and others 1909, p. 7.
Geol. Surv. N.S. 229 ; Ord. New Pop. 139 and 152.

**Carmarthen.** Nant-y-glasdwr, a tributary of Nant-cwm-ffrwd, banks of stream E. of Carmarthen-Kidwelly road at Cwm-ffrwd, 2 miles S. of Carmarthen.

Cambrian, Tremadoc Series, *Peltura punctata* beds. Trilobites abundant in dark mudstones.

Crosfield, M. C. and Skeat, E. G. 1896, p. 525 with geol. map. Strahan, A. and others 1909, p. 7.
Geol. Surv. N.S. 229 ; Ord. New Pop. 152.

**Carmarthen.** In lane leading down to R. Pibwr, near Glan Pibwr cottage, E. of main Carmarthen-Kidwelly road just over 1 mile S. of Carmarthen.

Ordovician, Arenig Series (shales low in *Tetragraptus* zone), with graptolites, lamellibranchs, and trilobites. Type-locality for *Ogygia marginata* beds of Crosfield and Skeat.

Crosfield, M. C. and Skeat, E. G. 1896, p. 523 with geol. map. Strahan, A. and others 1909, p. 14.
Geol. Surv. N.S. 229 ; Ord. New Pop. 152.

**Cwmllynfell** (Glam.), 2½ miles S.E. of Brynamman. Right bank of R. Twrch, 660-680 yds. S.S.W. of " Dorwen," 1½ miles above Cwmllynfell.

Carboniferous, Millstone Grit (Shale group, G zone). 7 ft. of finely laminated non-marine shales above *Gastrioceras cancellatum* marine band. Well-preserved non-marine lamellibranchs (*Carbonicola* and *Anthraconaia* [*Anthracomya*]. The marine band with goniatites and many other fossils is exposed a little upstream, but is difficult of access in wet weather.

Ware, W. D. 1939, p. 179.
Geol. Surv. N.S. 230 ; Ord. New Pop. 153.

**Cwmllynfell** (Glam.). R. Twrch, right bank just below sharp loop in river, 400 yds. S.S.W. of " Dorwen," 1⅞ miles N.N.E. of Cwmllynfell.

Carboniferous, Millstone Grit (Shale group, base of G zone). Shales up to 40 ft. succeeding a grit band. Lowest beds reached by narrow path along water's edge. Abundant goniatites : *Anthracoceras arcuatilobum, Homoceratoides* sp., *Gastrioceras* sp.

Ware, W. D. 1939, p. 177.
Geol. Surv. N.S. 230 ; Ord. New Pop. 153.

**Cwmllynfell** (Glam.). Cliff, right bank of R. Twrch 200 yds. above Pen-y-wern, 1⅞ miles N.N.E. of Cwmllynfell.

Carboniferous, Millstone Grit (G zone, shales with nodular limestone). Abundant crushed goniatites high in cliff (*Gastrioceras*, etc.). Lamellibranchs (*Schizodus, Edmondia*, etc.) a few yds. upstream at water level.

Ware, W. D. 1939, p. 180.
Geol. Surv. N.S. 230 ; Ord. New Pop. 153.

**Cwmllynfell** (Glam.). Right bank of R. Twrch ¼ mile W. of Pen-y-wern, and 1¼ miles upstream from Cwmllynfell, alongside footpath. The most northerly of the tip heaps of the Black Mountain Colliery (abandoned).

Carboniferous, Coal Measures (*ovalis* zone). Weathered shale from roof of Lower Vein, with solid non-marine lamellibranchs (*Carbonicola communis* and *C. ovalis*) well preserved and abundant.

Geol. Surv. N.S. 230 ; Ord. New Pop. 153.

**Cwmllynfell** (Glam.). Right bank of R. Twrch, 100 yds. upstream from "Dorwen," 2 miles N.N.E. of Cwmllynfell.

Carboniferous, Millstone Grit (Shale group, $R_2$ subzone, thin limestones interbedded with shales). Goniatites (*Reticuloceras superbilingue, Gastrioceras* sp.) solid but difficult to extract.

Geol. Surv. N.S. 230 ; Ord. New Pop. 153.

**Cwmllynfell** (Glam.). Left bank of R. Twrch 100 yds. upstream from waterfall, Llwyn-cwnstabl, 2 miles 550 yds. N.N.E. of Cwmllynfell.

Carboniferous, Millstone Grit (Basal Grit group, ? H zone, 3 ft. black shale). Goniatites are numerous but poorly preserved : *Homoceras* sp. Also the lamellibranch *Dunbarella* [*Pterinopecten*].

Ware, W. D. 1939, p. 175.

Geol. Surv. N.S. 230 ; Ord. New Pop. 153.

**Cwmllynfell** (Glam.). Right bank of R. Twrch opposite "Dorwen," 200 yds. N. of sharp loop in river : low cliff.

Carboniferous, Millstone Grit (Shale group, $R_2$ subzone). Most of the exposures in this part of the river yield marine fossils such as the goniatites *Reticuloceras superbilingue, Gastrioceras lineatum,* lamellibranchs, etc.

Ware, W. D. 1939, p. 177.

Geol. Surv. N.S. 230 ; Ord. New Pop. 153.

**Cwmllynfell** (Glam.). Right bank of R. Twrch, 50-60 yds. downstream from tributary forming waterfall, 620 yds. N.N.E. of "Dorwen," 2¼ miles N.N.E. of Cwmllynfell.

Carboniferous, Millstone Grit (Basal Grit group, $R_1$ zone, shale up to 6 ft. between grits, also showing in waterfall). Goniatites (*Reticuloceras* aff. *reticulatum, Homoceras striolatum, Anthracoceras*). Lamellibranchs (*Dunbarella* [*Pterinopecten*], *Posidonia*) and crinoid stems.

Ware, W. D. 1939, p. 176.

Geol. Surv. N.S. 230 ; Ord. New Pop. 153.

**Cwmllynfell** (Glam.). Tributary to left bank of R. Twrch, 60 yds. below waterfall, Llwyn-cwnstabl, 670 yds. N.N.E. of "Dorwen," 2¼ miles N.N.E. of Cwmllynfell.

Carboniferous, Millstone Grit ($R_1$ subzone, two thin limestones in left bank of tributary). Small solid goniatites in upper band (*Reticuloceras inconstans, Homoceratoides varicatum,* etc.). Brachiopods in lower band (*Productus* and spire-bearing forms).

Ware, W. D. 1939, pp. 175-176.

Geol. Surv. N.S. 230 ; Ord. New Pop. 153.

**Cwmllynfell** (Glam.). Left bank of R. Twrch ½ mile S. of junction with R. Twrch Fechan, and 4 mile N.N.E. of Cwmllynfell.

Carboniferous, Millstone Grit (Basal Grit group, $E_2$ subzone, shales with limy bands between grit bands). Goniatites (*Cravenoceras stellarum*), lamellibranchs and brachiopods.

Strahan, A. and others 1907, p. 82 ; Ware, W. D. 1939, p. 174.

Geol. Surv. N.S. 230 ; Ord. New Pop. 153, 140.

**Ferryside**, 3½ miles N.W. of Kidwelly on left bank of Towy estuary. Pen-y-gau, 1¼ miles S.S.E. of Ferryside.

Lower Old Red Sandstone (greenish sandstones low in Senni Beds). Shields of Ostracoderms (*Cephalaspis*) numerous and well preserved.

Strahan, A. and others 1909, pp. 67-68.
Geol. Surv. N.S. 229 ; Ord. New Pop. 152.

**Ferryside.** Railway cuttings between St. Ishmael's Church and Ferryside. Lower Old Red Sandstone, red marls, with shields of the ostracoderm *Pteraspis* fairly common.

·Strahan, A. and others 1909, p. 68.
Geol. Surv. N.S. 229 ; Ord. New Pop. 152.

**Garnant,** 4 miles E. of Ammanford. Section (partly obscured by slipping) 24 yds. above small waterfall in Nant Berach (tributary to R. Amman), 1 mile 600 yds. N.N.E. of Glanamman station and 900 yds. S.S.W. of Tair Carn Isaf.
Carboniferous, Millstone Grit (Shale group, G zone). Goniatites (*Gastrioceras cancellatum*), brachiopods, etc. Non-marine lamellibranchs (*Carbonicola*) 50 yds. further upstream.

Ware, W. D. 1939, p. 185.
Geol. Surv. N.S. 230 ; Ord. New Pop. 153.

**Garnant.** Nant Berach (tributary to R. Amman), banks and bed of stream 1¾ miles N.N.E. of Glanamman station, and ⅝ mile S.S.W. of Tair Carn Isaf.
Carboniferous, Millstone Grit (Shale group, G zone). Numerous goniatites (*Anthracoceras, Homoceratoides*) and lamellibranchs.

Evans, D. G. and Jones, R. O. 1929, p. 170 ; Ware, W. D. 1939, p. 185.
Geol. Surv. N.S. 230 ; Ord. New Pop. 153.

**Garnant.** Nant Pedol, 2¼ miles N. of Garnant Church, 1¼ mile E. of Tair Carn Isaf.
Carboniferous, Millstone Grit (Basal Grit group, $R_2$ subzone, black and grey shale exposed up to 8 ft.). Goniatites (*Reticuloceras superbilingue, Gastrioceras lineatum*) with lamellibranchs, abundant and well preserved.

Ware, W. D. 1939, p. 183.
Geol. Surv. N.S. 230 ; Ord. New Pop. 153.

**Garnant.** Nant Pedol (tributary of R. Amman) 1½ miles N.N.E. of Garnant Church, near Foel-deg-ar-Pedol. Left bank of stream.
Carboniferous, Millstone Grit (Basal Grit group, $R_2$ subzone), with well-preserved goniatites (*Reticuloceras bilingue*) and lamellibranchs (*Dunbarella* [*Pterinopecten*] *speciosa*).

Evans, D. G. and Jones, R. O. 1929, p. 164.
Geol. Surv. N.S. 230 ; Ord. New Pop. 153.

**Garnant.** Section at foot of waterfall near junction of northernmost of group of small streams with Nant Pedol (W. side), 1½ miles N. of Garnant Church and 1 mile S.E. of Tair Carn Isaf.
Carboniferous, Millstone Grit (Shale group, G zone). Goniatites (*Gastrioceras* ? *sigma, Reticuloceras superbilingue*) and plants.

Ware, W. D. 1939, p. 183-184.
Geol. Surv. N.S. 230 ; Ord. New Pop. 153.

**Gorslas,** ⅞ mile N.E. of Cross Hands. Stream section (effluent of Llyn Llech Owen) ⅔ mile below lake at Craig-y-geifr, 1 mile W.N.W. of Gorslas on and near footpath.
Carboniferous, Coal Measures (*lenisulcata* zone), faulted against Millstone Grit (Shale group). Plants in roof of coal seam on E. side of footpath, and brachiopods (*Lingula, Orbiculoidea*) in left bank of stream just W. of footpath. Goniatites, etc., in Millstone Grit just E. of fault.

Ware, W. D. 1939, pp. 191-192.
Geol. Surv. N.S. 230 ; Ord. New Pop. 153.

**Johnstown,** 1 mile S.W. of Carmarthen. Near spring 200 yds. W.S.W. of Wernddu, 1¾ mile S.W. of Johnstown.
Ordovician, Llanvirn Series, zone of *Didymograptus bifidus.* Trilobites are numerous.
Strahan, A. and others 1909, p. 32.
Geol. Surv. N.S. 229 ; Ord. New Pop. 139 and 152.

**Kidwelly.** Crags 340 yds. S.E. of Pen-lan-uchaf, ½ mile W. of Carmarthen-Kidwelly road at 8th milestone from Carmarthen.
Upper Old Red Sandstone (Penlan Quartzite). Numerous plants : Lycopod stems and rhizomes, and pith casts of *Calamites.*
Strahan, A. and others 1909, p. 69.
Geol. Surv. N.S. 229 ; Ord. New Pop. 152.

**Kidwelly.** Mynydd-y-gareg, quarries S.E. of Mount Pleasant.
Carboniferous Limestone Series, $D_1$ subzone. Corals and Productid brachiopods abundant. Co-types of *P. hemisphericus* were obtained from the light grey oolitic limestones quarried here.
Strahan, A. and others 1909, p. 79.
Geol. Surv. N.S. 229 ; Ord. New Pop. 152.

**Kidwelly.** Mynydd-y-gareg, quarries E. and S. of Horeb Chapel.
Carboniferous Limestone Series ($D_2$ subzone). Corals, bryozoa and brachiopods abundant.
Strahan, A. and others 1909, p. 79.
Geol. Surv. N.S. 229 ; Ord. New Pop. 152.

**Llanarthney,** 8 miles E. of Carmarthen. Quarry 100 yds. S.E. of Middleton Park Lodge, 1¼ miles S.S.W. of Llanarthney.
Silurian, Wenlock-Ludlow Series. Silty mudstones with abundant brachiopods and trilobites. Murchison, in " Silurian System " figures a number of specimens from this locality.
Strahan, A. and others 1907, pp. 46–47.
Geol. Surv. N.S. 230 ; Ord. New Pop. 140.

**Llandebie** (Llandybie), 2 miles N. of Ammanford. 100 yds. E. of Careg-Dwyfan (Dwfn) cottage, 2⅜ miles N.E. of Llandebie alongside footpath.
Carboniferous, Millstone Grit (E zone, cherts and brown shales exposed to 6 ft., succeeded by grits). Scarce goniatites (*Eumorphoceras*), and many lamellibranchs (*Posidoniella minor*).
Dix, E. 1933, p. 163.
Geol. Surv. N.S. 230 ; Ord. New Pop. 153.

**Llandebie.** Disused quarries, " Garnbica," 1½ miles N.E. of Llandebie on W. side of road near Garnbica Farm.
Carboniferous, Millstone Grit (H zone, two shale bands divided by thin grit). Solid goniatites (*Homoceras* cf. *diadema*) and brachiopods in upper shale ; crushed goniatites in lower shale.
Evans, D. G. and Jones, R. O. 1929, p. 170.
Geol. Surv. N.S. 230 ; Ord. New Pop. 153.

**Llandilo.** Right bank of R. Cennen, 250 yds. N.E. of railway station at Ffairfach, ¾ miles S.W. of Llandilo.
Ordovician, Llanvirn (shales of *Didymograptus bifidus* zone), with numerous graptolites and trilobites.
Strahan, A. and others 1907, p. 16.
Geol. Surv. N.S. 230 ; Ord. New Pop. 140.

**Llandilo.** Dynevor Park, old quarries round castle.
Ordovician, Llandeilo Series (Llandeilo Flags and Limestones). Trilobites are abundant in the flaggy beds. Locality well known to Murchison.
Murchison, R. I. 1839, Vol. 2, p. 662 et seq. (trilobites described).
Geol. Surv. O.S. 41 ; Ord. New Pop. 140.

**Llandilo.** Old quarries 200 yds. N.W. of Birdshill Farm, 1¼ miles N.E. of Llangathen and ₇ₒ mile N.W. of Dynevor Castle, Llandilo.
Ordovician, Ashgill Series, highly fossiliferous limestone beds with abundant brachiopods and trilobites.
Strahan, A. and others 1907, p. 32.
Geol. Surv. O.S. 41 ; Ord. New Pop. 140.

**Llandilo.** Old quarries 200 yds. E. of cross-roads at Storm Hill Lodge, ₇ₒ mile S. of Maerdy, 1¼ mile S. of Ffair-fach, Llandilo.
Silurian, Downton Series (Tilestones). Abundant lamellibranchs. A locality known to John Phillips.
Phillips, J. 1848, p. 326. Strahan, A. and others 1907, p. 52.
Geol. Surv. N.S. 230 ; Ord. New Pop. 140.

**Llandilo Abercowin,** 3½ miles W. of Carmarthen-Llanstephan road at 6½ miles S.S.W. of Carmarthen. In old road ¼ mile S.W. of Pentre-newydd, and ½ mile N.E. of Llandilo Abercowin.
Ordovician, Llanvirn Series (zone of *Didymograptus bifidus*). Trilobites abundant, associated with " tuning-fork " graptolites.
Strahan, A. and others 1909, p. 33.
Geol. Surv. N.S. 229 ; Ord. New Pop. 152.

**Llandowror,** 2 miles S.W. of St. Clears. Large quarry at Craig-y-deilo Farm, N. of Picton House, Llandowror.
Ordovician, Ashgill Series (Shoalshook Limestone). Abundant brachiopods and trilobites.
Phillips, J. and Salter, J. W. 1848, pl. v. Strahan, A. and others 1909, pp. 56-58.
Geol. Surv. N.S. 229 ; Ord. New Pop. 152.

**Llandowror.** On path 200 yds. N.E. of Cwm, 1¼ miles W. of Llandowror.
Ordovician, Ashgill Series (Slade Beds). A representative fauna of corals, orthid brachiopods and trilobites.
Phillips, J. 1848, p. 323. Strahan, A. and others 1909, p. 60.
Geol. Surv. N.S. 229 ; Ord. New Pop. 152.

**Llandowror.** Roadside exposure at Cnyciau, 1½ miles W. of Llandowror.
Ordovician, Ashgill Series (Slade Beds). Mudstones and sandstones with abundant brachiopods and trilobites.
Strahan, A. and others 1909, p. 61.
Geol. Surv. N.S. 229 ; Ord. New Pop. 152.

**Llandowror.** Footpath in Great Pale Wood, 450 yds. E.N.E. of Great Pale, 2¼ miles N.W. of Llandowror.
Silurian, Lower Llandovery Series, abundant brachiopod and trilobite fauna preserved in limonite in grey-green mudstones.
Strahan, A. and others 1909, p. 62.
Geol. Surv. N.S. 229 ; Ord. New Pop. 152.

**Mydrim,** 8 miles W. of Carmarthen. Quarry 50 yds. W. of Cefn-crwth House, 1½ miles E.S.E. of Mydrim.
Ordovician, Llanvirn Series (zone of *Didymograptus murchisoni*). Abundant graptolites (*D. murchisoni*) in shales.
Strahan, A. and others 1909, p. 38.
Geol. Surv. N.S. 229 ; Ord. New Pop. 139 and 152.

**Nantgaredig,** 5½ miles E.N.E. of Carmarthen on Llandilo road. Old quarry 300 yds. N. of Ffynnon-dewi, W. of Capel-Dewi-Uchaf, on left bank of R. Towy, 2 miles S. of Nantgaredig.
Ordovician, Llandeilo Series (flags and limestones) with numerous brachiopods and trilobites. Murchison and Phillips referred to this locality.
Murchison, R. I. 1839, vol. 1, p. 357. Phillips, J. 1848, pp. 236, 239.
Strahan, A. and others 1909, p. 40.
Geol. Surv. N.S. 229 ; Ord. New Pop. 140.

**Nantgaredig.**   Ty-newydd Quarry, 200 yds. S.E. of Nantgaredig Post Office.
Ordovician, Caradoc Series (Mydrim Shales, *Dicranograptus* Shales of Survey).   Abundant graptolites.
Strahan, A. and others 1907, p. 30 ; 1909, pp. 49-50.
Geol. Surv. O.S. 41 ; Ord. New Pop. 140.

**St. Clears,** 9 miles W.S.W. of Carmarthen.   Pont-y-Fenni, old quarry 60 yds. E. of bridge on St. Clears-Whitland road, 2½ miles W. of St. Clears.
Ordovician, Arenig Series (zone of *Didymograptus extensus*).   Numerous graptolites, lamellibranchs and trilobites.
Evans, D. C. 1906, p. 597, with geol. map. Strahan, A. and others 1909, p. 20.
Geol. Surv. N.S. 229 ; Ord. New Pop. 152.

**St. Clears.**   Lane 50 yds. W. of Glan-dwr cottage, 250 yds. S.E. of Pant-y-grig Farm, about 3½ miles N.W. of St. Clears, and 3 miles S. of Llanboidy.
Ordovician, Arenig Series (zone of *Didymograptus hirundo*).   Extensiform graptolites abundant.
Strahan, A. and others 1909, pp. 20-21.
Geol. Surv. N.S. 229 ; Ord. New Pop. 152 and 139.

**St. Clears.**   Quarry in Clog-y-fran Farmyard, 1½ miles W. of St. Clears.
Ordovician, Llanvirn Series (zone of *Didymograptus bifidus*).   Trinucleid trilobites abundant.
Strahan, A. and others 1909, p. 35.
Geol. Surv. N.S. 229 ; Ord. New Pop. 152.

**St. Clears.**   Quarry 250 yds. S.E. of Melin-y-Castell, on right bank of R. Cynin, S. of Castell-gorfod, 3 miles N. of St. Clears.
Ordovician, Llanvirn Series (zone of *Didymograptus bifidus*).   " Tuning-fork " graptolites, and trilobites abundant.
Strahan, A. and others 1909, p. 30.
Geol. Surv. N.S. 230 ; Ord. New Pop. 139 and 152.

**St. Clears.**   Old quarry at Clog-y-fran, 3 miles W. of St. Clears.
Ordovician, Llandeilo Series, limestones with abundant brachiopods and trilobites.   This locality was mentioned as long ago as 1595, by George Owen of Henllys, in his " Description of Pembrokeshire."
Strahan, A. and others 1909, pp. 41-44, figs. 8, 9.
Geol. Surv. N.S. 229 ; Ord. New Pop. 152.

**St. Clears.**   Quarry 500 yds. N.N.E. of Lower Court, 1½ miles S.E. of St. Clears.
Ordovician, Llandeilo Series, flags and limestones with abundant brachiopods and trilobites.
Phillips, J. 1848, p. 323.   Roberts, T. 1893, p. 166, with geol. map.   Strahan, A. and others 1909, p. 41.
Geol. Surv. N.S. 229 ; Ord. New Pop. 152.

**St. Clears.**   Old quarry and brook section E. of Bron-haul, ⅓ mile N. of Cresswell and 1¾ miles S. of St. Clears.
Ordovician, Caradoc Series, Robeston Wathen Limestone.   Abundant corals and brachiopods.
Strahan, A. and others 1909, pp. 57-58.
Geol. Surv. N.S. 229 ; Ord. New Pop. 152.

**St. Clears.**   Left bank of R. Taf, 70 yds. above bridge at Lower St. Clears.
Ordovician, Caradoc Series (Mydrim Shales).   Abundant graptolites (*Dicranograptus*, etc.).
Strahan, A. and others 1909, p. 51.
Geol. Surv. N.S. 229 ; Ord. New Pop. 152.

**St. Clears.** Road cutting ¼ mile S.W. of Mylet, 1¼ miles S.S.W. of St. Clears.
Ordovician, Caradoc Series. Graptolites abundant both here and in large quarry nearby (*Dicranograptus, Diplograptus,* etc.).
Strahan, A. and others 1909, pp. 51-52.
Geol. Surv. N.S. 229 ; Ord. New Pop. 152.

**St. Clears.** Lower Cresswell Farmyard, 2¼ miles S. of St. Clears.
Ordovician, Ashgill Series (Redhill and Slade Beds). Richly fossiliferous, with many brachiopods and trilobites. A Phillips locality.
Phillips, J. 1848, p. 323. Strahan, A. and others 1909, p. 59.
Geol. Surv. N.S. 229 ; Ord. New Pop. 152.

**St. Clears.** Old quarries E. of Old Foxhole and W. of Trefanty, 2 miles S. of St. Clears-Carmarthen road at Llanfihangel Abercowin.
Ordovician, Caradoc Series (Robeston Wathen Limestone). Corals (*Heliolites,* etc.) and orthid brachiopods abundant.
Strahan, A. and others 1909, pp. 56-58.
Geol. Surv. N.S. 229 ; Ord. New Pop. 152.

**Whitland,** 6 miles E.N.E. of Narberth (Pembs.): Small quarry 300 yds. N.W. of Blaen-cediw, 2 miles E. of Henllan Amgoed (2½ miles N.N.W. of Whitland).
Ordovician, Arenig (shales and grit bands low in the zone of *Didymograptus extensus*). Abundant and well-preserved dendroid graptolites.
Strahan, A. and others 1914, p. 17.
Geol. Surv. N.S. 228 ; Ord. New Pop. 139 and 152.

**Whitland.** In river bank at Allt-y-beili, a few yards S.W. of Whitland railway station.
Ordovician, Llanvirn, zone of *Didymograptus bifidus*. "Tuning-fork" graptolites abundant in shales.
Evans, D. C. 1906, p. 597 and map. Strahan, A. and others 1909, p. 25.
Geol. Surv. N.S. 228. Ord. New Pop. 152.

# CARNARVONSHIRE

**Bangor.** S. shore of Menai Strait between Tubular Bridge at Menai and wall of Vaynol Park, past Treborth hamlet.
Carboniferous (local base). Shale and sandstone with plants (*Rhodea, Telangium, Lepidodendron*) abundant for a few yards.
Greenly, E. 1928, pp. 420-421.
Geol. Surv. O.S. 78 S.E. ; Ord. New Pop. 106 and 107.

**Bangor.** Various places between Bangor and Port Dinorwic.
Carboniferous Limestone (D zone), with corals and brachiopods. Near the middle are mudstones with the brachiopod *Pleurodon.*
Greenly, E. 1928, pp. 421-424.
Geol. Surv. O.S. 78 S.E.-S.W. ; Ord. New Pop. 106 and 107.

**Bangor.** Penrhyn Park, E. of Bangor ; about a mile of shore section and low reefs.
Ordovician, Arenig (*Didymograptus hirundo* zone). Slightly cleaved shales with well preserved graptolites.
Geol. Surv. O.S. 78 S.E. ; Ord. New Pop. 107.

**Bangor.** Cliff at E. end of Bangor.
Ordovician, Arenig, shales and basal grit of *Didymograptus extensus* zone. Graptolites (*Didymograptus, Azygograptus*).
Geol. Surv. O.S. 78 S.E. ; Ord. New Pop. 106 and 107.

**Bethesda,** 5 miles S.S.E. of Bangor. Penrhyn Slate Quarries, 1 mile S. of Bethesda.
Lower Cambrian, green slates at top of quarry. Trilobites fairly well pre-served in spite of much cleavage.
Geol. Surv. O.S. 78 S.E. ; Ord. New Pop. 107.

**Borth-y-gest,** 2 miles S. of Portmadoc. Exposures in streets W. of village.
Upper Cambrian (Ffestiniog Beds), many slabs covered with the horny brachiopod *Lingulella davisi.*
Fearnsides, W. G. 1910a, p. 152 with geol. map.
Geol. Surv. O.S. 75 N.E. ; Ord. New Pop. 116.

**Carnarvon.** Along River between Castle and Sciont Bridge, mainly on W. side of river.
Ordovician, shales of lower zones of Arenig Series. Well preserved graptolites.
Geol. Surv. O.S. 78 S.W. ; Ord. New Pop. 106 and 115.

**Criccieth.** Ogof Ddu, continuous section ¾ mile E. of Criccieth Castle.
Upper Cambrian (Dolgelly Beds), with trilobites at various levels (see reference for details).
Fearnsides, W. G. 1910a, pp. 153-156, with geol. map.
Geol. Surv. O.S. 75 S.W. ; Ord. New Pop. 116.

**Deganwy.** Llandudno. Deganwy Quarry, ⅜ mile E. of Deganwy station.
Ordovician, Ashgill Series, Deganwy Mudstones ; heads and tails of the trilobite *Phacops mucronatus,* with graptolites (*Orthograptus*).
Elles, G. L. 1909, p. 182, with geol. map.
Geol. Surv. 78 N.E. ; Ord. New Pop. 107.

**Dolwyddelan,** 6½ miles N. of Blaenau Ffestiniog. Quarry at Chwarel ddu, below Dolwyddelan Castle, ⅜ mile W. of cross-roads at Dolwyddelan village.
Ordovician, Caradoc (sooty, black, pyritous slates of *Dicranograptus clingani* zone overlying Snowdon Volcanic Series) ; graptolites, somewhat sheared.
Fearnsides, W. G. 1910b, p. 779. Williams, H. and Bulman, O. M. B. 1931, p. 443, with geol. map.
Geol. Surv. 75 N.E. ; Ord. New Pop. 107 and 116.

**Dolwyddelan.** Crags adjoining road from Dolwyddelan over Crimea Pass S. to Blaenau Ffestiniog about ½ mile S. of Roman Bridge.
Ordovician, Caradoc (sandy, calcareous beds of the Glanrafon Series under-lying main Snowdon Volcanic Series). Brachiopods, with some crinoid remains, lamellibranchs and trilobites.
Williams, H. and Bulman, O. M. B. 1931, p. 431, with geol. map.
Geol. Surv. O.S. 75 N.E. ; Ord. New Pop. 107 and 116.

**Llandegai,** 1½ miles S.E. of Bangor. Disused ironstone workings S.W. of village.
Ordovician, Llandeilo (zone of *Glyptograptus teretiusculus,* ironstone and fibrous shales). Graptolites fairly common and well preserved.
Geol. Surv. O.S. 78 S.E. ; Ord. New Pop. 106 and 107.

**Llandudno.** Quarries and natural exposures on Great Orme and Little Orme.
Carboniferous Limestone (D zone). A varied succession of limestones and shales with corals and brachiopods. Fauna varies with lithology. $D_3$ not present on Little Orme. " Posidonomya " beds intercalated with $D_2$ limestones at top of Great Orme.
Smyth, L. B. 1925, pp. 141-164, with geol. map. Neaverson, E. 1937, pp. 115-135 with geol. maps.
Geol. Surv. O.S. 78 N.E. ; Ord. New-Pop. 107.

**Llangwstenin,** 2 miles W. of Colwyn Bay. Large quarry 600 yds. S.S.W. of Llangwstenin Church, 300 yds. W. by N. of Mochdre station (L.M.S.). Ask at adjoining farm for permission.

Silurian, Lower Ludlow Shales, flags and sandstones with *Monograptus colonus, M. dubius* (long var.), *M. nilssoni, M. varians,* and other graptolites plentiful.

Geol. Surv. 79 N.W. ; Ord. New Pop. 107.

**Penmorfa,** 2 miles N.W. of Portmadoc. Stream section E. of Penmorfa Church, W. of village below 200 ft. contour.

Cambrian, Tremadoc (Tynllan Beds), with the trilobites *Niobe homfrayi* and *Psilocephalus.*

Fearnsides, W. G. 1910a, p. 156 with geol. map.

Geol. Surv. 75 N.E. ; Ord. New Pop. 116 and 107.

**Portmadoc.** Hillside above and E. of Tyddyn-dicwm-uchaf Farm, 2 miles N.W. of Portmadoc.

Ordovician, Caradoc. Slates with graptolites, including *Climacograptus, Orthograptus, Dicellograptus, Dicranograptus,* to be collected from screes. Thrust over Cambrian, Tremadoc.

Fearnsides, W. G. 1910a, pp. 166-168, with geol. map.

Geol. Surv. O.S. 75 N.E. ; Ord. New Pop. 116 and 107.

**Portmadoc.** Moelfre Crag, ¾ mile S.W. of Portmadoc.

Cambrian, Lower Tremadoc (*Dictyonema* band 50 ft. above white weathering cherty *Obolus* beds of Tynllan (*Niobe*) Beds). Trilobites (*Niobe, Psilocephalus,* etc.) and dendroid graptolites.

Fearnsides, W. G. 1910a, p. 156 with geol. map.

Geol. Surv. O.S. 75 N.E. ; Ord. New Pop. 116.

**Portmadoc.** Cefn-cefanydd, in roadway about 200 ft. contour, 1⅝ miles W.N.W. of Portmadoc.

Cambrian, Lower Tremadoc (*Dictyonema* band). The dendroid graptolite *Dictyonema flabelliforme sociale* abundant in stone wall by keeper's house. Salter's type-locality for this fossil.

Salter, J. W. 1866, p. 331. Fearnsides, W. G. 1910a, p. 157, with geol. map.

Geol. Surv. O.S. 75 N.E. ; Ord. New Pop. 116.

**Portmadoc.** Ynys-towyn, Portmadoc.

Cambrian, Tremadoc (Garth Hill Beds). Top 6 in. of slates yield the trilobite *Angelina sedgwicki.* Overlying grits of Arenig age contain *Bolopora.*

Fearnsides, W. G. 1910a, p. 163, with geol. map.

Geol. Surv. O.S. 75 N.E. ; Ord. New Pop. 116.

**Portmadoc.** Coed-y-Chwarel Quarry, 2 miles W. of Portmadoc adjoining and S. of railway track.

Upper Cambrian (Ffestiniog Beds) crowded with the horny brachiopod *Lingulella davisi.*

Fearnsides, W. G. 1910a, p. 152, with geol. map.

Geol. Surv. O.S. 75 N.E. ; Ord. New Pop. 116.

# DENBIGHSHIRE

**Bersham,** 2 miles W.S.W. of Wrexham. Tip heaps at Bersham Colliery (permission at Colliery Office).

Carboniferous, Coal Measures (*similis-pulchra* zone, shales from roofs of Main, Two Yard and Brassy seams). Seed-fern stems (*Lyginodendron*), and solid non-marine lamellibranchs (" Carbonicola ") in grey shale from Main seam. " *Carbonicola* " and *Naiadites* in black shale from Brassy seam. Stigmarian rootlets in dark grey shale from Two Yard seam.

Wood, A. 1937a, pp. 10-11.

Geol. Surv. N.S. 121 ; Ord. New Pop. 109.

**Brymbo,** 3½ miles N.W. of Wrexham.   Tip heaps of Old Black Lane Colliery.

Carboniferous, Coal Measures (*similis-pulchra* zone, shales from above Drowsell seam).   Abundant good specimens of the non-marine lamellibranch *Anthracosia atra.*

Wood, A. 1937a, p. 12.

Geol. Surv. N.S. 121 ;   Ord. New Pop. 109.

**Clocaenog,** 3½ miles S.W. of Ruthin.   Roadside quarry, E. side of Ruthin-Clocaenog road, about 750 yds. E. by N. of Clocaenog Church, and nearly a mile S.W. of Pool Park House.

Silurian, Lower Ludlow flags and sandstones of the *Monograptus leint-wardinensis* zone).   Graptolites such as *M. leintwardinensis* and its var. *incipiens*, *M.* cf. *ultimus*, etc., well preserved and plentiful.

Boswell, P. G. H. 1928, pp. 701-702, with geol. map.

Geol. Surv. O.S. 74 N.W. ;   Ord. New Pop. 108.

**Denbigh.**   Large quarry (in work) at the Graig, ¾ mile W.N.W. of Denbigh railway station.

Carboniferous Limestone (D₁ subzone showing lithological variations).   Corals and brachiopods.   A pink limestone in middle of section yields well-preserved lamellibranchs.   Abundant carbonized twigs of *Archaeosigillaria vanuxemi* in shaly limestone at S. end of quarry.

Neaverson, E. 1945, p. 52, with geol. map.

Geol. Surv. O.S. 79 S.W. ;   Ord. New Pop. 108.

**Eglwys-fach,** 6 miles N. of Llanrwst.   Quarry ¼ mile W. of Pennant (where permission should be obtained), rather more than 2 miles S.S.E. of Eglwys-fach Church, and 2 miles E.N.E. of Dolgarrog station.

Silurian, Wenlock (mudstones and flags of *Cyrtograptus lundgreni* zone).   Graptolites : *C. lundgreni, Monograptus flemingii* ;   large specimens in relief.   Both plentiful.

Boswell, P. G. H. and Double, I. S. 1940, p. 177, with geol. map.

Geol. Surv. O.S. 78 S.E. ;   Ord. New Pop. 107.

**Eglwys-fach.**   Roadside section on W. side of lane at top of steep hill, almost 1 mile S. of Eglwys-fach Church, and 200 yds. S.W. of Rhiw.

Silurian, Wenlock flags (Berllan Beds, npper division of *Cyrtograptus rigidus* zone).   Graptolites : *Monograptus retroflexus* relatively abundant in a band about 9 ins. below top of section, with other monograptids and *Cyrtograptus rigidus.*

Boswell, P. G. H. 1943, pp. 103, 109 ;   1945, pp. 88-90.

Geol. Surv. O.S. 78 S.E. ;   Ord. New Pop. 107.

**Eglwys-fach.**   Quarry in lane approach to Ty'n-y-coed Farm, 1¼ miles N. by E. of Eglwys-fach Church, and ½ mile E. by N. of Bodnant.   Apply at farm for permission.

Silurian, Wenlock flags (Berllan beds, upper division of *Cyrtograptus rigidus* zone).   Graptolites : *Cyrtograptus rigidus* (good specimens), *Monograptus dubius* (small form), etc.

Boswell, P. G. H. 1945, p. 92.

Geol. Surv. O.S. 78 S.E. ;   Ord. New Pop. 107.

**Glan Conway,** 2½ miles S.E. of Conway.   Roadside cutting 400 yds. S.S.W. of Pensarn corner, ½ mile N. by E. of Glan Conway Church.

Silurian, Wenlock mudstones (*Cyrtograptus murchisoni* zone).   Graptolites : *Cyrtograptus murchisoni, Monograptus priodon, M. vomerinus.*

Boswell, P. G. H. 1943, p. 108, with geol. map.

Geol. Surv. O.S. 78 N.E. ;   Ord. New Pop. 107.

**Glyn Ceiriog,** 6½ miles W. of Chirk.   Screes and crags on E. side of road, 300 yds. S. of Glyn Ceiriog.

Ordovician, Ashgill (Dolhir Beds, *Flexicalymene quadrata* zone). Trilobites, bryozoa and brachiopods abundant.

Wills, L. J. and Smith, B. 1922, p. 187, with geol. map.
Geol. Surv. N.S. 121 ; Ord. New Pop. 117.

**Gwytherin,** 5½ miles E. of Llanrwst. Section in gorge 600 yds. S.W. of Pant-y-fotty, just over 1½ miles S. by E. of Gwytherin Church.

Silurian, Wenlock flags and shales (*Cyrtograptus lundgreni* zone above the waterfall ; flags of the *C. rigidus* zone below the waterfall). *C. lundgreni* plentiful and well preserved in a band a few yds. above the top of the waterfall, accompanied by *Monograptus flemingii* and *M. dubius* (small var.). In the *rigidus* beds *C. rigidus, M. flemingii* and vars., and *M. basilicus.*

Boswell, P. G. H. 1942, p. 98, with geol. map.
Geol. Surv. O.S. 79 S.W. ; Ord. New Pop. 108.

**Gyffylliog,** 5 miles W. of Ruthin. Section on W. side of track, 500 yds. S. by W. of Porth Farm, a little more than a mile N.W. of Gyffylliog Church.

Silurian, Lower Ludlow (flags and sandstones, *Monograptus tumescens* zone. Also a good section in fossiliferous flags of the *M. scanicus* zone by the side of the track ½ mile further S.). *M. tumescens, M. tumescens* var. *minor* both plentiful, *M. scanicus* rare.

Boswell, P. G. H. 1926, pp. 570-572, with geol. map.
Geol. Surv. O.S. 79 S.W. ; Ord. New Pop. 108.

**Llanddulas,** 2½ miles W. by N. of Abergele. Large disused quarry 1 mile S. of Llanddulas Church. Also natural exposures in sides of Dulas valley.

Carboniferous Limestone (D₁ subzone, chiefly calcite mudstone). Typical fauna, with the large brachiopod *Daviesiella llangollensis* as the chief fossil.

Neaverson, E. 1935, p. 226.
Geol. Surv. O.S. 79 N.W. ; Ord. New Pop. 108.

**Llanelidan,** 5 miles S. of Ruthin. Disused quarries at Melin-y-coed, Tynllanfair, and Faenòl, about 2½ miles N.E. of Llanelidan Church.

Carboniferous Limestone (D₂ subzone). Abundant well-preserved reef corals including *Orionastraea phillipsi*, associated with brachiopods.

Neaverson, E. 1929, pp. 125-126.
Geol. Surv. N.S. 121 ; Ord. New Pop. 108.

**Llanfair Dyffryn Clwyd,** Ruthin. Quarry at Pwll Glas, and natural exposures on the escarpment of Craig adwy wynt, 1½ miles S.W. of Llanfair Dyffryn Clwyd.

Carboniferous Limestone (D₁ subzone). Lower beds are calcite mudstones with the brachiopod *Daviesiella llangollensis*. A quarry at the top of the escarpment near Tan-y-graig has yielded a more varied fauna of brachiopods and simple corals.

Neaverson, E. 1929, p. 118.
Geol. Surv. N.S. 108 ; Ord. New Pop. 108.

**Llanfair Dyffryn Clwyd,** Ruthin. Quarry and natural exposures at Graigfechan ¾ mile E. of village.

Carboniferous Limestone (D₂ subzone). Quarry worked in *Saccaminopsis* limestone which yields simple corals and brachiopods. Hillside exposures with well-preserved reef corals.

Neaverson, E. 1929, p. 125.
Geol. Surv. N.S. 108 ; Ord. New Pop. 108.

**Llangollen.** Numerous quarries and natural exposures along the Eglwyseg and Trevor escarpments, about 1 mile N. of the town.

Carboniferous Limestone (full succession of D zone, estimated thickness 1250 ft.). Abundant brachiopods, reef corals and molluscs. Type-locality of *Daviesiella llangollensis.*

Wedd, C. B. and others 1927, pp. 108-152.
Geol. Surv. N.S. 121 ; Ord. New Pop. 108 and 117.

**Llanrwst.** Lane section 300 yds. S. by W. of Bryn-sylldy Farm, about 1¼ miles E. of Llanrwst.

Silurian, Lower Ludlow (mudstones and flags, *Monograptus dubius*, *M. vulgaris*, and *M. nilssoni* zones, the last at lane junction). Graptolites : large specimens of *M. vulgaris* abundant in the *vulgaris* zone ; the small form of *M. dubius* is gregarious in the beds below, and *M. colonus*, *M. dubius* (long var.) and *M. nilssoni*, etc., in the beds above.

Boswell, P. G. H. and Double, I. S. 1940, p. 174, with geol. map.
Geol. Surv. O.S. 78 S.E. and 79 S.W. ; Ord. New Pop. 107.

**Llanrwst.** On side of farm track extending for ¼ mile S.E. from Llwyn-Goronwy (where permission should be obtained), ½ mile E. of Llanrwst.

Silurian, Wenlock Flags (shales and mudstones of *Cyrtograptus lundgreni* zone). Graptolites : *Cyrtograptus carruthersi*, *Monograptus dubius* small form, and other monograptids.

Boswell, P. G. H. 1943, p. 145, with geol. map.
Geol. Surv. O.S. 79 S.W. ; Ord. New Pop. 107.

**Llansannan,** 8 miles W. of Denbigh. Road cuttings on new road from Llanfair Talhaiarn to Llansannan, E.S.E. of Cil-Owen and S.E. of Foel Cottage, 1½ miles N. of Llansannan Church.

Silurian, Lower Ludlow (flags and grits of the *Monograptus scanicus* zone). Graptolites abundant : *M. scanicus*, *M. chimaera*, *M. dubius*, *M. micropoma*, *M. varians*, etc.

Boswell, P. G. H. and Double, I. S. 1938, p. 298, with geol. map.
Geol. Surv. O.S. 79 S.W. ; Ord. New Pop. 108.

**Melin-y-coed,** 1 mile S.E. of Llanrwst. Section on N. bank of Nant-y-Goron, 580 yds. N.W. of Melin-y-coed. Access from Coed-llydan-mawr Farm, 370 yds. N.W. of village (apply for permission). Also by footpath from road at Pont Cae-Melwr, ¼ mile to E.S.E.

Silurian, Wenlock (mudstones and shales of *Cyrtograptus murchisoni* zone). Graptolites : *Cyrtograptus murchisoni*, *C. symmetricus*, etc.

Boswell, P. G. H. and Double, I. S. 1940, p. 154, with geol. map
Geol. Surv. O.S. 78 S.E. ; Ord. New Pop. 107.

**Nantglyn,** 4 miles S.W. of Denbigh. Large quarries 2¼ miles S.W. of Nantglyn Church.

Silurian, Lower Ludlow Flags. (Type-locality for Nantglyn Flags, *Monograptus nilssoni* zone). *Monograptus bohemicus* (large form), *M. colonus*, *M. dubius* (long var.), *M. nilssoni*, and other graptolites plentiful. Also good specimens of the crinoid *Periechocrinus pulcher*.

Boswell, P. G. H. 1926, pp. 562-563, with geol. map.
Geol. Surv. O.S. 79 S.W. ; Ord. New Pop. 108.

**Old Colwyn,** E. of Colwyn Bay. Stream section at Ffernant Dingle, 2 miles S.E. of Old Colwyn.

Red sandstones and conglomerates forming the local base of the Carboniferous Limestone (D₁ subzone). Derived pebbles in conglomerate contain numerous fossils of Silurian (Upper Ludlow) age.

Strahan, A. and Walker, A. O. 1879, pp. 268-274. Neaverson, E. 1935, p. 224, with geol. map.
Geol. Surv. O.S. 79 N.W. ; Ord. New Pop. 108.

**Pen-y-cae,** 1½ miles N.W. of Ruabon. Newton Mountain, section in northernmost branch of Trefechan Brook, 300 yds. N.W. of footbridge.

Carboniferous, Millstone Grit (R zone, shale above limestone in Cefn-y-Fedw Sandstone). The goniatites *Reticuloceras inconstans* and *Homoceras striolatum* occur in the shale. Brachiopods are abundant in the limestone.

Wood, A. 1937b, p. 18.
Geol. Surv. N.S. 121 ; Ord. New Pop. 108 and 109.

**Plas Power,** 2½ miles N.W. of Wrexham. Tip heaps of the Plas Power Colliery.

Carboniferous, Coal Measures (*similis-pulchra* zone ; dull black shales from immediately above Powell seam, succeeded by light grey shales). Abundant specimens of the marine brachiopod *Lingula* from the black shale ; non-marine lamellibranchs from the light grey shale (*Anthracosia planitumida* and *Naiadites*).

Wood, A. 1937a, pp. 11-12.
Geol. Surv. N.S. 121 ; Ord. New Pop. 109.

**Pwll-glas,** 3 miles S. of Ruthin. Quarry at Pen-y-bryn Farm (where permission should be obtained), 300 yds. W.S.W. of Chapel and N. of Inn.

Silurian, Lower Ludlow (sandy flags and mudstones of the *Monograptus leintwardinensis* zone), with the zone fossil and other graptolites.

Boswell, P. G. H. 1928, pp. 697-698, with geol. map.
Geol. Surv. N.S. 121 ; Ord. New Pop. 108.

**Rhosllanerchrugog,** 3½ miles S.W. of Wrexham. Llwyneinion Brickpit, ½ mile N.N.W. of Rhos.

Carboniferous, Coal Measures (*ovalis* zone, roof of Wall and Bench Coal). A thin band full of small fish scales of e.g. *Elonichthys*, and shagreen scales of Elasmobranchs.

Wood, A. 1936, p. 485. Wedd, C. B. and others 1928, p. 69.
Geol. Surv. N.S. 121 ; Ord. New Pop. 109.

**Tal-y-cafn,** 3½ miles S. of Conway. Knob of rock by side of lane running S. from road to Graig, ⅓ mile E. by S. of Tal-y-cafn station.

Silurian, Wenlock Flags (Lletty Beds, lower division of *Cyrtograptus rigidus* zone). Graptolites : *Cyrtograptus* and *Monograptus* spp.

Boswell, P. G. H. 1945, p. 92.
Geol. Surv. O.S. 78 S.E. ; Ord. New Pop. 107.

**Trevor,** 2½ miles S.W. of Ruabon. Exposure on N.N.W. side of road leading to Cysylltan Bridge across R. Dee, 100 yds. N.E. of turning to bridge.

Carboniferous, Coal Measures (shales above Aqueduct Grit). The goniatite *Gastrioceras subcrenatum* and lamellibranchs.

Wood, A. 1937b, p. 22.
Geol. Surv. N.S. 121 ; Ord. New Pop. 117.


## FLINTSHIRE

**Bryn Celyn,** N.E. of Holywell. Moor Quarries (disused), 1 mile E. of Holywell.

Carboniferous, Coal Measures (*lenisulcata* zone, siltstone partings near top of Gwespyr Sandstone). Non-marine lamellibranchs (*Carbonicola* and *Anthraconaia*) ; shells not well preserved but best exposure of this zone in N. Wales.

Wood, A. 1937a, p. 3.
Geol. Surv. N.S. 96 ; Ord. New Pop. 108.

**Caergwrle,** 9 miles S.W. of Chester. Llay Hall Colliery tips 1½ miles S.S.W. of Caergwrle.

Carboniferous, Coal Measures (*ovalis* zone, shales from above Wall and Bench Coal). Non-marine lamellibranchs (*Carbonicola* and *Naiadites*).

Wood, A. 1937a, p. 5.
Geol. Surv. N.S. 108 ; Ord. New Pop. 109.

**Caerwys,** 9½ miles N.W. of Mold. Large quarry at Afonwen, on main Mold-Denbigh road, ½ mile S. of Caerwys.

Post-glacial calcareous tufa, more than 20 ft. thick, with well-preserved land and freshwater mollusca, species of *Helix, Zonites, Lymnaea,* etc.

Strahan, A. 1890, p. 150.
Geol. Surv. N.S. 108 ; Ord. New Pop. 108.

**Cilcain,** 5 miles W. by N. of Mold. In wide gully N. by E. from summit of Moel Fammau, about 1 mile from summit along old path.

Silurian, Wenlock Shale at sides of gully and old quarry tip near bottom of gully. Occasional trilobites with numerous brachiopods in limestone.

Geol. Surv. N.S. 108 ; Ord. New Pop. 108.

**Dyserth,** 3½ miles S.E. of Rhyl. Large quarry (in work) and natural exposures on slopes of Moel Hiraddug, S. of village.

Carboniferous Limestone ($D_1$ subzone), typical fauna, mainly corals and brachiopods.

Neaverson, E. 1930, pp. 186-190, with geol. map.

Geol. Surv. O.S. 79 N.W. ; Ord. New Pop. 108.

**Gwaenysgor,** 1½ miles S.S.E. of Prestatyn. Abandoned quarry 100 yds. N. of Gwaenysgor Church.

Carboniferous Limestone ($D_2$ subzone). Plentiful brachiopods and good specimens of the alga *Koninckopora.*

Neaverson, E. 1930, pp. 197-198, with geol. map.

Geol. Surv. O.S. 79 N.W. ; Ord. New Pop. 108.

**Gwaenysgor.** Disused quarry at Teilia Farm, ½ mile N.E. of Gwaenysgor Church.

Carboniferous Limestone (*Posidonomya* beds in upper part of $D_2$ subzone). The quarry has yielded, chiefly by excavation made for the purpose, a famous series of Lower Carboniferous plants associated with marine lamellibranchs (*Posidonia* and *Dunbarella* [*Pterinopecten*]) and goniatites.

Hind, W. and Stobbs, J. T. 1906, pp. 452-453. Walton, J. 1926, 1931.

Geol. Surv. O.S. 79 N.W. ; Ord. New Pop. 108.

**Gwespyr,** 4 miles E. of Prestatyn. Tip heaps of Point of Ayr Colliery, ½ mile E. of Talacre Station. Permission from Colliery Office.

Carboniferous, Coal Measures (*modiolaris* zone, shales from above Durbog Coal). Solid specimens of non-marine lamellibranchs (*Anthracosia phrygiana, Anthraconaia modiolaris, Naiadites* spp.).

Wood, A. 1937a, p. 8.

Geol. Surv. N.S. 96 ; Ord. New Pop. 108.

**Halkyn,** 3½ miles S.E. of Holywell. Stream section in Coed-y-cra-Uchaf, 1½ miles S.E. of Halkyn.

Carboniferous, Millstone Grit (R zone). A band of limy shale just below the waterfall contains the goniatite *Reticuloceras reticulatum* in masses.

Wood, A. 1937b, p. 19.

Geol. Surv. N.S. 108 ; Ord. New Pop. 108 and 109.

**Halkyn.** Natural limestone cleft with disused quarries, on path from Moel-y-Crio to Catch, S.W. of Halkyn, midway between the two.

Carboniferous Limestone, with chert in the joints. *Productus* spp. and other brachiopods, large corals, well weathered.

Geol. Surv. N.S. 108 ; Ord. New Pop. 108 and 109.

**Higher Kinnerton,** 6 miles S.W. of Chester. Warren Dingle, 1¼ miles N.W. of Higher Kinnerton, by reservoir at head of dingle.

Carboniferous, Millstone Grit (passage beds between R and G zones). Goniatites, including *Gastrioceras* ? *sigma, Reticuloceras superbilingue.*

Wood, A. 1937b, p. 19.

Geol. Surv. N.S. 108 ; Ord. New Pop. 109.

**Higher Kinnerton.** Warren Dingle, 1¼ miles N.W. of Higher Kinnerton, and 250 yds. N.N.E. of Bramley Farm.

· Carboniferous, Millstone Grit (R zone). The goniatite *Reticuloceras bilingue,* the lamellibranch *Sanguinolites,* and the brachiopod *Lingula* all occur, but specimens are not abundant.

Wood, A. 1937b, p. 19.

Geol. Surv. N.S. 108 ; Ord. New Pop. 109.

**Holywell.** Panton Hall Dingle, 1 mile E.S.E. of Holywell.
Carboniferous, Millstone Grit (G zone, just below the Gwespyr Sandstone), with the goniatites *Gastrioceras cancellatum* and *G. crenulatum*.
Wood, A. 1937b, p. 21.
Geol. Surv. N.S. 96 ; Ord. New Pop. 108.

**Holywell.** Several large quarries, especially that near Waenbrodlas, on Holywell Common, about 2 miles S. of Holywell station.
Carboniferous Limestone, $D_2$ subzone, with abundant brachiopods, especially of the *Productus giganteus* group, reef corals, fish-teeth, etc.
Hind, W. and Stobbs, J. T. 1906, pp. 395-397.
Geol. Surv. N.S. 108 ; Ord. New Pop. 108.

**Llanasa,** 7 miles E. of Rhyl. Disused quarries and natural outcrops on Axton Common, 1 mile S. of Llanasa Church.
Carboniferous Limestone ($D_2$ subzone, knoll-reef facies). Abundant and well-preserved brachiopods and molluscs.
Neaverson, E. 1930, pp. 200-201, with geol. map.
Geol. Surv. N.S. 96 ; Ord. New Pop. 108.

**Meliden,** 1½ miles S.S.W. of Prestatyn. Disused quarry adjacent to railway station.
Carboniferous Limestone ($D_2$ subzone, knoll-reef facies), with typical fauna of abundant brachiopods and molluscs, and a few corals and goniatites.
Neaverson, E. 1930, pp. 192-194.
Geol. Surv. O.S. 79 N.W. ; Ord. New Pop. 108.

**Mold.** Series of quarries at Gwernymynydd, 2 miles S.W. of Mold.
Carboniferous Limestone (chiefly $D_2$ subzone, becoming sandy in upper part). Many brachiopods and corals. Some bands show interesting variations in lithology and fauna. Fish-teeth sometimes abundant.
Hind, W. and Stobbs, J. T. 1906, p. 398. Wedd, C. B. and King, W. B. R. 1924, p. 28.
Geol. Surv. N.S. 108 ; Ord. New Pop. 108 and 109.

**Prestatyn.** Series of quarries and natural exposures along hillside ¾ mile S.W. of Prestatyn railway station.
Carboniferous Limestone (D zone), four horizons with distinct lithology and faunas. Limestones contain abundant brachiopods and corals, rarely goniatites. Calcareous mudstones with large lamellibranchs (*Posidonia, Dunbarella* [*Pterinopecten*]) and crushed goniatites.
Neaverson, E. 1930, pp. 194-197 ; 1944, pp. 135-142.
Geol. Surv. O.S. 79 N.W. ; Ord. New Pop. 108.

**Rhydymwyn,** 3 miles N.W. of Mold. In W. bank of stream, Nant-y-Figillt, 1½ miles N. of Rhydymwyn.
Carboniferous, Millstone Grit (R and G zones). The goniatites *Gastrioceras cancellatum* and *Reticuloceras superbilingue.*
Wood, A. 1937b, p. 20.
Geol. Surv. N.S. 108 ; Ord. New Pop. 108 and 109.

**Rhydymwyn.** Large quarries (in work) at Hendre, ¾ mile N.W. of Rhydymwyn Church.
Carboniferous Limestone ($D_2$ subzone, rather argillaceous in character), with abundant reef corals and brachiopods, many of the latter weathered out to show interior of valves. Many clisiophyllid corals have been collected from old mine tips S. of the village.
Hind, W. and Stobbs, J. T. 1906, p. 398.
Geol. Surv. N.S. 108 ; Ord. New Pop. 108.

# GLAMORGAN

**Abercanaid,** 1 mile S. of Merthyr Tydfil. Tip from level on W. side of Taff valley. In side valley of Nant Graig, S. of Graig Farm, ½ mile S.W. of Abercanaid station.
Carboniferous, Coal Measures (Floral Zone G, roof shales of Castell Weiver seam). Abundant plants.
Moore, L. R. and Cox, A. H. 1943, p. 215.
Geol. Surv. N.S. 231 ; Ord. New Pop. 154.

**Abercanaid.** Tip from crop working on W. side of Taff valley, 150 yds. due W. of Abercanaid station.
Carboniferous, Coal Measures (Upper *similis-pulchra* zone, roof shales of Middle Gorllwyn seam). Non-marine lamellibranchs (*Anthraconaia adamsi*).
Moore, L. R. and Cox, A. H. 1943, p. 210, with geol. map.
Geol. Surv. N.S. 231 ; Ord. New Pop. 154.

**Caerphilly.** Wernddu Clay Pit, S.E. of Caerphilly.
Carboniferous, Coal Measures (Lower Coal Series, entire section from top of Farewell Rock to base of Pennant Sandstone (*lenisulcata* to *phillipsi* zones). Plants, non-marine lamellibranchs, and marine fossils of the Amman, Cefn Coed, and (?) Cwmgorse marine bands.
Moore, L. R. 1945, p. 151, with geol. map.
Geol. Surv. N.S. 249 ; Ord. New Pop. 154.

**Cilfynydd,** 2½ miles N.N.E. of Pontypridd. Tip from levels behind chapel at end of Cross Street, Cilfynydd.
Carboniferous, Coal Measures (roof of Cefn Glas seam, *tenuis* zone). Abundant non-marine lamellibranchs : *Anthraconauta tenuis, A. phillipsi.*
Geol. Surv. N.S. 249 ; Ord. New Pop. 154.

**Cwmdare,** 1½ miles N.W. of Aberdare. Tips from old levels by inclined tramway on N. side of road from Cwmdare to Bwllfa Dare and immediately E. of Bwllfa Terrace.
Carboniferous, Coal Measures (*similis-pulchra* and *phillipsi* zones, shales from above Gorllwyn (in tramway foundation 70 yds. from road), Graig (large tips) and Bwlch (small tips) coal seams). Non-marine shells (*Anthraconaia adamsi,* etc.) from Gorllwyn ; plants from Graig and Bwlch.
Robertson, T. 1932, p. 160.
Geol. Surv. N.S. 231 ; Ord. New Pop. 154.

**Cwmllynfell,** 2½ miles S.E. of Brynamman. Right bank of stream 20 ft. below culvert beneath road, 1½ miles S. of Cwmllynfell at extreme end of Penrhiwfawr hamlet.
Carboniferous, Coal Measures (*phillipsi* zone, finely laminated shales above underclay) with non-marine shells (*Anthraconauta phillipsi*) and plants (*Lepidodendron* sp.).
Geol. Surv. N.S. 230 ; Ord. New Pop. 153.

**Cwmtwrch,** N.N.W. of Ystalyfera. Old tips along S. bank of R. Twrch, narrow opening in hillside 100 yds. S. of well and 350 yds. W. of mill ; and various points along Gurnos Patches, alongside and overlooking river.
Carboniferous, Coal Measures (*similis-pulchra* zone, roof of Stwrin Vein). Non-marine shells : *Anthracosia* [*Carbonicola*] *fulva* and *A. atra.*
Davies, J. H. and Trueman, A. E. 1927, p. 227. Trueman, A. E. 1929, p. 84.
Geol. Surv. N.S. 230 ; Ord. New Pop. 153.

**Cymmer** (Porth Rhondda), 3 miles W.N.W. of Pontypridd. Tips from coal levels S. of St. John's Church, Cymmer.
Carboniferous, Coal Measures (*phillipsi* zone, roof of No. 1 Rhondda seam), with many non-marine lamellibranchs and plants.
Moore, L. R. and Cox, A. H. 1943, p. 243, with geol. map.
Geol. Surv. N.S. 248 ; Ord. New Pop. 154.

**Deri,** 5 miles S. by E. of Rhymney. Tips from levels in Bargoed-Rhymney valley, on W. side of road where stream (Nant Hir) crosses road.

Carboniferous, Coal Measures (Floral Zone H, roof shales of Brithdir seam) with abundant plants.

Moore, L. R. and Cox, A. H. 1943, p. 218, with geol. map.

Geol. Surv. N.S. 232 ; Ord. New Pop. 154.

**Ferndale,** 6 miles N.W. of Pontypridd. Tips from coal levels on side of Cwm-Rhondda-Fach at Ferndale, S. of No. 2 and No. 4 Ferndale Collieries.

Carboniferous, Coal Measures (Floral Zone G, roof shales of No. 2 Rhondda seam) with abundant plants.

Moore, L. R. and Cox, A. H. 1943, with geol. map.

Geol. Surv. N.S. 248 ; Ord. New Pop. 154.

**Glanrhyd, Ystradgynlais,** 1½ miles N.E. of Ystalyfera. Section in small stream on N. end of Varteg Hill, 100 yds. W. of Penrhiwvarteg Farm, above waterfall near railway bridge, 1¼ miles S.S.E. of Ystradgynlais (now much obscured by building).

Carboniferous, Coal Measures (*similis-pulchra* zone, shales, mudstones and calcareous ironstones of Cefn Coed Marine Band). Fauna varied but poorly preserved : goniatites, lamellibranchs, brachiopods and gastropods.

Geol. Surv. N.S. 230 ; Ord. New Pop. 153.

**Kenfig Hill,** 4½ miles W. of Bridgend. Small quarry on S. slope of Cefn Cribbwr Hill, 300 yds. E. of Kenfig Hill.

Triassic (littoral conglomerate), banked against Carboniferous, Millstone Grit, and containing crinoids and brachiopods (*Spirifer, Productus*) derived from the Carboniferous Limestone.

Strahan, A. and Cantrill, T. C. 1904, p. 20.

Geol. Surv. N.S. 248 ; Ord. New Pop. 153.

**Lavernock,** 2 miles S. of Penarth. Coast section from Lavernock Point S.W. to St. Mary's Well Bay.

Triassic, Rhaetic Beds, and Jurassic, Lower Lias (zones of *Psiloceras planorbis* and *Scamnoceras angulatum*). Fish remains in bone bed at base of Rhaetic, lamellibranchs in overlying black shales and " White Lias." Many ammonites (*Psiloceras, Waehneroceras,* etc.) and an evolutionary sequence of grypheate oysters in the Lower Lias.

Richardson, L. 1905, pp. 289-293, 385. Trueman, A. E. 1920, pp. 96-103.

Geol. Surv. N.S. 263 ; Ord. New Pop. 154.

**Llantwit Major,** 4½ miles S.S.W. of Cowbridge. Foreshore reefs about 100 yds. W. of Summerhouse Point, 2 miles S.E. of Llantwit Major.

Jurassic, Lower Lias (zone of *Coroniceras bucklandi*). Abundant ammonites (especially *Arnioceras* and *Gryphaea*).

Trueman, A. E. 1922, p. 267, with geol. map.

Geol. Surv. N.S. 261-262 ; Ord. New Pop. 154.

**Llanwonno,** 3½ miles S.W. of Mountain Ash. Tip from level into bank of stream at waterfall Pistyll-Goleu, ½ mile N.N.E. of Llanwonno.

Carboniferous, Coal Measures (*tenuis* zone, roof shales of Cefn Glas seam). Abundant non-marine shells (*Anthraconauta tenuis, A. phillipsi*), with ostracods and poorly preserved insect wings.

Moore, L. R. and Cox, A. H. 1943, p. 221, with geol. map.

Geol. Surv. N.S. 248 ; Ord. New Pop. 154.

**Oystermouth,** 5 miles S.S.W. of Swansea. Cliff slopes immediately W. of Bracelet Bay, W. side of Mumbles Head.

Carboniferous Limestone (D zone pseudobreccias). Numerous corals (*Dibunophyllum, Palaeosmilia,* etc.).

George, T. N. and Trueman, A. E. 1924, p. 312, with geol. map.

Geol. Surv. N.S. 247 ; Ord. New Pop. 153.

**Oystermouth.** Old quarry near Oystermouth Castle, W. of main road from Swansea.
Carboniferous Limestone (D zone). Many brachiopods and simple corals.
Dixon, E. E. L. and Vaughan, A. 1911, pp. 494, 550, with geol. map.
Geol. Surv. N.S. 247 ; Ord. New Pop. 153.

**Rudry,** 3 miles E.S.E. of Caerphilly. Roadside cutting on road from Cefn-on Farm past E. side of Wernddu Wood.
Carboniferous, basal beds of Farewell Rock, " Millstone Grit " shales, *lenisulcata* zone. Non-marine lamellibranchs : *Anthraconaia lenisulcata, Carbonicola*. Marine shales with goniatites : *Gastrioceras* cf. *crenulatum* and *G. cumbriense*.
Moore, L. R. 1945, pp. 149-150, with geol. map.
Geol. Surv. N.S. 249 ; Ord. New Pop. 154.

**Rudry.** Tip from level on bank of stream, 300 yds. N.W. from Pen-y-Waun Farm, 150 yds. N.E. of Ynys-Dawel, ½ mile N.N.E. from Rudry.
Carboniferous, " Millstone Grit " (Floral Zone C, roof shales of Sun Vein). Abundant plants.
Moore, L. R. 1945, p. 150, with geol. map.
Geol. Surv. N.S. 249 ; Ord. New Pop. 154.

**St. Donats,** 4½ miles S.S.W. of Cowbridge. Foreshore reefs at St. Donats.
Jurassic, Lower Lias (zone of *Coroniceras bucklandi*). Abundant oysters (type-locality of *Gryphaea obliquata*).
Trueman, A. E. 1922, p. 266, with geol. map.
Geol. Surv. N.S. 261-262 ; Ord. New Pop. 154.

**Southerndown,** 4 miles S.S.W. of Bridgend. Exposure at eastern corner of Southerndown Beach, under Dunraven Castle.
Jurassic, Lower Lias (*bucklandi* zone), very fossiliferous shales (exposed near faulted junction of Lower Lias and Carboniferous Limestone with oysters (*Ostrea, Gryphaea*) and rare ammonites (*Arnioceras bodleyi*).
Trueman, A. E. 1922, p. 260.
Geol. Surv. N.S. 261-262 ; Ord. New Pop. 154.

**Sutton,** 4 miles S.W. of Bridgend. Foreshore slightly W. of Black Rocks.
Carboniferous Limestone (C zone), with well-preserved corals (*Caninia gigantea, Syringopora*) and brachiopods (*Productus giganteus*).
George, T. N. 1933, p. 243, with geol. map.
Geol. Surv. N.S. 261-262 ; Ord. New Pop. 154.

**Tongwynlais,** 3 miles N.W. of Llandaff. Hillside excavation due E. of the Wyndham Arms.
Carboniferous Limestone (Km zone), very fossiliferous in places, resting on ironstone with crinoids and bryozoa. An undescribed flora occurs about 35 ft. below the base of the Carboniferous Limestone, in the underlying Old Red Sandstone.
Geol. Surv. N.S. 249 or 263 ; Ord. New Pop. 154.

**Tonyrefail,** 5 miles N.W. of Llantrisant. Tip from coal level, 600 yds. W. of Cilely Colliery.
Carboniferous, Coal Measures (marine shales in roof of Hafod seam). Brachiopods (*Lingula mytiloides, Orbiculoidea*), goniatites (*Gastrioceras*) and fish remains.
Moore, L. R. and Cox, A. H. 1943, pp. 240-241, with geol. map.
Geol. Surv. N.S. 248 ; Ord. New Pop. 154.

**Tonyrefail.** Tip from coal levels in Nant Caer-Gwerlas, N.W. of Tonyrefail.
Carboniferous, Coal Measures (*phillipsi* zone and Floral Zone G, roofs of Nos. 2 and 3 Rhondda seams). No. 3 Rhondda contains non-marine shells

(*Anthraconauta phillipsi*) and marine brachiopods (*Lingula mytiloides,* *Orbiculoidea* sp.) with fish remains. No. 2 Rhondda contains plants and *A. phillipsi.*
Moore, L. R. and Cox, A. H. 1943, p. 241, with geol. map.
Geol. Surv. N.S. 248 ; Ord. New Pop. 154.

**Troed-y-Rhiw,** 3 miles S.S.E. of Merthyr Tydfil. Tips from levels on E. side of Taff Valley.
Carboniferous, Coal Measures (Floral Zone H, roof shales of Brithdir seam). Abundant plants.
Moore, L. R. and Cox, A. H. 1943, p. 218, with geol. map.
Geol. Surv. N.S. 231 ; Ord. New Pop. 154.

**Wick,** 5 miles S.S.E. of Bridgend. Old quarries about 350 yds. W. of Beacon Tower, about ½ mile W.N.W. of Wick.
Jurassic, Lower Lias (zones of *Scamnoceras angulatum* and *Coroniceras bucklandi*). Numerous compound corals forming a reef-like mass.
Strahan, A. and Cantrill, T. C. 1904, p. 88. Trueman, A. E. 1922, p. 272.
Geol. Surv. N.S. 261-262 ; Ord. New Pop. 154.

**Ynys-Boeth,** 3 miles S.E. of Mountain Ash. Tips from coal levels, Cwm Cynon, along new road from Abercynon to Aberdare, on N.E. side of valley, ¼ mile N.N.E. of 16th. milestone from Cardiff.
Carboniferous, Coal Measures (*tenuis* zone, roof shales of Cefn Glas seam). Non-marine shells abundant : *Anthraconauta tenuis, A. phillipsi.*
Moore, L. R. and Cox, A. H. 1943, pp. 219-220.
Geol. Surv. N.S. 248 ; Ord. New Pop. 154.

**Ystalyfera.** White's Quarry on Varteg Hill, ¾ miles E. of Ystalyfera, directly above Yniscu Colliery.
Carboniferous, Coal Measures (base of *phillipsi* zone, Upper Cwmgorse Marine Band). Large, well-preserved brachiopods (*Lingula* and *Orbiculoidea*) fairly common in black shale. Lamellibranchs rarer in blue grey shales and mudstones.
Geol. Surv. N.S. 230 ; Ord. New Pop. 153.

## MERIONETHSHIRE

**Aberllefenni,** 7 miles N. of Machynlleth. Outcrop on path near Nant-y-Aur, 1¼ miles N.N.E. of Aberllefenni slate-dressing sheds, and 250 yds. N.W. of Capel Ratgoed, Ceiswyn Valley.
Ordovician, Caradoc (" Nod Glas," black highly pyritous mudstones and shales). Abundant graptolites at this important mapping horizon (*Dicranograptus clingani* zone).
Pugh, W. J. 1923, pp. 517-518, with geol. map.
Geol. Surv. O.S. 59 N.E. ; Ord. New Pop. 116.

**Arenig Station,** 8 miles W.N.W. of Bala. Llechwedd Erwent, western and eastern slopes, 3 miles S.S.W. of Arenig Station.
Ordovician, Arenig (Erwent Limestone), a streaky rock 10 or 12 ft. thick with many brachiopods, molluscs and trilobites.
Fearnsides, W. G. 1905, p. 620, with geol. map.
Geol. Surv. O.S. 75 S.E.-74 S.W. ; Ord. New Pop. 116.

**Arenig Station.** Sections in east-west streams S. of Amnodd Wen Farm, 1¾ miles S.S.W. of Arenig Station.
Cambrian, Tremadoc (*Shumardia* Shales) with rich trilobite fauna.
Fearnsides, W. G. 1905, p. 617, with geol. map. Lake, P. 1906-1946.
Geol. Surv. O.S. 75 S.E. ; Ord. New Pop. 116.

**Arenig Station.** N. slope of Moel Llyfnant, 2½ miles S.W. of Arenig Station.
Ordovician, Arenig (*Calymene* Ashes). Grey ashy limestones on scree containing calymenid trilobites.
Fearnsides, W. G. 1905, p. 620, with geol. map.
Geol. Surv. O.S. 75 N.E.-S.E. ; Ord. New Pop. 116.

**Arenig Station.** Old quarries and stream adjoining, ⅓ mile S. of Hafotty Filltirgerig Farm and 1¼ miles S.W. of Arenig Station.
Ordovician, Arenig (*extensus* flags) with graptolites (*Didymograptus*).
Fearnsides, W. G. 1905, p. 619, with geol. map.
Geol. Surv. O.S. 75 N.E. ; Ord. New Pop. 116.

**Arenig Station.** Nant Rhydau Glerwon, W. of Pont tai-herion Farm, 2 miles W. of Arenig Station.
Ordovician, Lower Llanvirn (Olchfa (*bifidus*) Shales) with " tuning-fork " graptolites as slabs in glacial drift.
Fearnsides, W. G. 1905, p. 623, with geol. map.
Geol. Surv. O.S. 75 N.E. ; Ord. New Pop. 116.

**Arenig Station.** Nant-y-Gis-faen (a tributary of Afon Tryweryn), 100 yds. S. of confluence with its lowest eastern tributary, 2¼ miles S.W. of Arenig Station, and ⅔ mile S.E. of effluent from Llyn Trywern.
Upper Cambrian ( Dolgelly Beds, *O. lenticularis* band) with plentiful brachiopods (*Orusia lenticularis*).
Fearnsides, W. G. 1905, p. 613, with geol. map.
Geol. Surv. O.S. 75 S.E. ; Ord. New Pop. 116.

**Arenig Station.** Old quarries and lowest eastern stream, tributary to Nant-y-Gis-faen, 2¼ miles S.W. of Arenig Station, and ⅔ mile S.E. of effluent of Llyn Trywern.
Upper Cambrian (Dolgelly Beds), with the trilobite *Peltura scarabaeoides*.
Fearnsides, W. G. 1905, p. 614, with geol. map.
Geol. Surv. O.S. 74 N.W. ; Ord. New Pop. 116.

**Bala.** Moel Fryn quarries, 2¼ miles S.E. of Bala station, rather over 1 mile uphill from S.E. shore of Bala Lake.
Ordovician, Caradoc, calcareous ashes and limestones with brachiopods and trilobites.
Elles, G. L. 1922, pp. 150-151, with geol. map.
Geol. Surv. O.S. 74 S.W. ; Ord. New Pop. 117.

**Bala.** Old quarry on Pen-y-Dallgwm, due W. of shepherd's hut in Cwm-yr-Aethen, on W. side of Lake Vyrnwy road, 4 miles S.E. of Bala Station.
Ordovician, Ashgill (Hirnant Limestone, pisolite), with well-preserved brachiopods (*Orthis hirnantensis*, *Platystrophia biforata*, *Orthis sagittifera*, etc.).
Elles, G. L. 1922, pp. 156-157, with geol. map.
Geol. Surv. O.S. 74 S.W. ; Ord. New Pop. 117.

**Brithdir.** 2½ miles E. of Dolgelly. W. bank of Nant Helygog, 1600 yds. S.E. of Helygog Farm, and 1600 yds. E. of Gorwyr, ½ mile E.S.E. of Brithdir.
Ordovician, Llanvirn (*Ogyginus corndensis* Beds, tough, blue, calcareous and pyritous flags, following *Didymograptus bifidus* mudstones). Fauna of trilobites, crinoids and molluscs, rarely seen at this horizon in N. Wales.
Cox, A. H. and Lewis, H. P. 1945, p. 80.
Geol. Surv. O.S. 59 N.E. ; Ord. New Pop. 116.

**Corwen.** Quarry (in work) at Hafod-y-calch, 1½ miles S.W. of Corwen Station.
Carboniferous Limestone (limestone and shales high in D₂ subzone). Quarry famous for reef corals and numerous species of brachiopods. Type-locality of *Orionastraea phillipsi* and *Corwenia rugosa*.
Morton, G. H. 1879, pp. 306-316.
Geol. Surv. O.S. 74 N.W. ; Ord. New Pop. 117.

**Dolgelly.** Pont Gamlan, 2 miles N. of Dolgelly.

Middle Cambrian (Clogau Beds), with the trilobite *Paradoxides hicksi*, and brachiopods.

Lake, P. 1935 (in 1906-1946). Matley, C. A. and Wilson, T. S. 1946, p. 14, with geol. map.

Geol. Surv. O.S. 75 S.E. ; Ord. New Pop. 116.

**Dolgelly.** Near Dol-y-melynllyn and Tyn-y-groes, in Mawddach stream above junction with Eden.

Upper Cambrian (Maentwrog Flags) with trilobites (*Olenus gibbosus* and agnostids).

Belt, T. 1867, pp. 295, 538. Lake, P. 1906, 1931 (in 1906-1946). Matley, C. A. and Wilson, T. S. 1946, p. 15, with geol. map.

Geol. Surv. O.S. 75 S.E. ; Ord. New Pop. 116.

**Llan Ffestiniog,** 2½ miles S. of Blaenau Ffestiniog. Slate quarry and tips Croes-y-Ddwy-Afon, 3 miles E. of Llan Ffestiniog, and ½ mile N.E. of Pont-ar-Afon Gam.

Ordovician, Arenig (flags, grit and conglomerate, basal beds " Garth Grit," with phosphatic nodules). This quarry and that at Bryn Glas, 1 mile to the W., are good localities for the basal Arenig guide-fossil *Bolopora undosa*.

Lewis, H. P. 1926, pp. 411-427.

Geol. Surv. O.S. 75 N.E. ; Ord. New Pop. 107 and 116.

**Llangower,** 2½ miles S.W. of Bala. Bryn Pig, 2⅝ miles S.S.W. of Bala Station, over 1½ miles uphill from Llangower.

Ordovician, Caradoc and Ashgill (Rhiwlas and Gelli Grin (=Bala) limestones) with brachiopods and trilobites.

Elles, G. L. 1922, pp. 152-153, with geol. map.

Geol. Surv. O.S. 74 S.W. ; Ord. New Pop. 117.

**Maentwrog,** 2½ miles W.S.W. of Ffestiniog. Rhaiadr Du on the Ceunant Llenyrch stream near fallen bridge, Llenyrch, 1¼ miles S. of Maentwrog.

Middle Cambrian (Clogau Shales). Rich in *Paradoxides davidis* and other trilobites.

Lake, P. 1906-1946. Matley, C. A. and Wilson, T. S. 1946, p. 14, with geol. map.

Geol. Surv. O.S. 75 N.E. ; Ord. New Pop. 116.

**Maentwrog.** Caen-y-coed slate quarries (disused), about 1 mile S. of Maentwrog.

Upper Cambrian (Maentwrog Beds), top beds of quarry yielded Homfray's best specimens of *Olenus cataractes*.

Belt, T. 1867, p. 539. Lake, P. 1913 (in 1906-1946). Matley, C. A. and Wilson, T. S. 1946, p. 16, with geol. map.

Geol. Surv. O.S. 75 N.E. ; Ord. New Pop. 116.

**Rhos-y-gwaliau,** near Bala. Quarry and cliff face (much overgrown) W.S.W. of Gelli Grin and farm house, 1¼ miles E.S.E. of Bala Station, 1 mile uphill from N.E. end of Bala Lake, 1 mile S.E. of Rhos-y-gwaliau.

Ordovician, Caradoc (Gelli Grin (=Bala) Limestone, massive and crystalline). A classic locality for brachiopods (*Plectambonites rhombica*) and trilobites (*Pterygometopus jukesi*).

Elles, G. L. 1922, pp. 148-150.

Geol. Surv. O.S. 74 S.W. ; Ord. New Pop. 117.

**Rhydymain,** 6 miles N.E. of Dolgelly. Outcrops in field between lane. and E. bank of Afon Celynog, 400 yds. S.S.W. of St. Paul's Church and 80 yds. N.W. of Pont-y-Sel.

Ordovician, Llanvirn (*Didymograptus bifidus* zone, dark pyritous mudstones with thin bands of ash). Characteristic " tuning-fork " graptolites very common, with rare trilobites.

Cox, A. H. and Lewis, H. P. 1945, p. 71.

Geol. Surv. O.S. 75 S.E. ; Ord. New Pop. 116.

## MONTGOMERYSHIRE

**Alberbury** (Salop.), 8½ miles W. of Shrewsbury. Right bank of R. Severn, 1900 ft. N.W. of Bausley House, 2 miles W. of Alberbury.

Ordovician, Caradoc (*Nemagraptus gracilis* zone).

Wedd, C. B. 1932, pp. 51-52, with geol. map.

Geol. Surv. O.S. 60 N.W. ; Ord. New Pop. 118.

**Derwenlas,** 2 miles S.W. of Machynlleth. S. side of old coach road branching S. from main Machynlleth road at Derwenlas. Section begins just above covered well about 150 yds. W. of village inn.

Silurian, Middle Llandovery (Derwen Group, mainly mudstones with dark, graptolite-bearing shale bands). Graptolites of *Mesograptus magnus* and *Monograptus regularis* zones common in lower 100 ft.

Jones, O. T. and Pugh, W. J. 1916, pp. 355-360, with geol. map.

Geol. Surv. 59 S.E. ; Ord. New Pop. 127.

**Derwenlas.** Morben Slate Quarry (disused), cuttings at top edge of quarry on N. side and adjacent tip heap, 400 yds. E. of Morben Hall, 600 yds. W. of Derwenlas.

Silurian, Upper Llandovery (Derwen Group (upper part), slates with some grits forming inverted anticline). Graptolites of *Monograptus sedgwicki* and *M. halli* zones common.

Jones, O. T. and Pugh, W. J. 1916, pp. 362-365, with geol. map.

Geol. Surv. O.S. 59 S.E. ; Ord. New Pop. 127.

**Llanfyllin.** Lluest Quarry, W. side of Allt-y-Gadw, 1¼ miles S.S.E. of Llanfyllin.

Ordovician, Caradoc (*Wattsella horderleyensis* zone). Brachiopods, gastropods and trilobites as casts and moulds.

Whittington, H. B. 1938a.

Geol. Surv. N.S. 137 ; Ord. New Pop. 117.

**Llanfyllin.** Crags on crest of Allt Goch, 1½ miles S.W. of Llanfyllin.

Ordovician, Upper Ashgill (*Calymene quadrata* horizon). Many excellent fossils generally in somewhat phosphatized nodules. Type area of *C. quadrata*.

King, W. B. R. 1923, p. 499. Wedd, C. B. and others 1929, p. 63.

Geol. Surv. N.S. 137 ; Ord. New Pop. 117.

**Llangyniew,** 9 miles W. of Welshpool. Outcrops on W. side of road 4 miles S.W. of Meifod, 1¾ miles W. of Llangyniew. Section overgrown.

Silurian, Basal Llandovery (limestone masses in the *Meristina crassa* Sandstone). Calcareous algae with other shelly fossils, chiefly brachiopods, corals and bryozoa.

King, W. B. R. 1928, pp. 685-687, with geol. map. Lewis, H. P. 1937, pp. 617-623.

Geol. Surv. O.S. 60 N.E. ; Ord. New Pop. 117.

**Llangyniew.** Graig Wen Quarry, ⅔ mile N.E. of Neuadd Bridge, on roadside 2 miles W. of Llangyniew.

Ordovician, Highest Ashgill, and Silurian, Basal Llandovery. The unconformity is well seen. Excellent Ashgill fossils in phosphatic nodules ; basal Llandovery is decalcified sandstone.

King, W. B. R. 1928, p. 68, with geol. map.

Geol. Surv. O.S. 60 N.E. ; Ord. New Pop. 117.

**Llangyniew.** Pen-y-graig Quarry, by roadside on W. of bridge over stream, 1 mile N.W. of Llangyniew.

Silurian, Upper Llandovery, fairly rich in brachiopods and trilobites. Exposures in adjoining fields equally good. A locality examined by Sedgwick and Salter.

King, W. B. R. 1928, p. 689, with geol. map.

Geol. Surv. O.S. 60 N.E. ; Ord. New Pop. 117.

**Llanrhaiadr-ym-Mochnant.** W. side of disused Pen-y-garnedd lime-
stone and phosphate quarry, 1¾ miles S.W. of Llanrhaiadr Church, 1½ miles
E.S.E. of Pen-y-bont Fawr Church.
Ordovician, Upper Caradoc, 18 in. band of phosphatic shale, with many
nodules containing a rich fauna of sponge spicules and other microfossils,
succeeded by shale; with graptolites of the *Pleurograptus* zone. Dip inverted.
Lewis, H. P. 1940. King, W. B. R. 1923, p. 492, with geol. map. Wedd,
C. B. and others 1929, pp. 42-43.
Geol. Surv. N.S. 137 ; Ord. New Pop. 117.

**Llansaintffraid-ym-Mechain,** 6 miles E. of Llanfyllin. Quarry on
S.E. side of Bryngwyn Hill, 3 miles S.W. of Llansaintffraid. Locality 38 of
Whittington.
Ordovician, Caradoc (lower part including Pen-y-garnedd Limestone).
Numerous brachiopods and trilobites.
Whittington, H. B. 1938b, p. 429, with geol. map.
Geol. Surv. N.S. 137 ; Ord. New Pop. 117.

**Llanwddyn.** At S.E. end of Lake Vyrnwy. Stream banks near Aber
Marchnant Farm, ⅝ mile due E. of St. Wddyn's Church.
Ordovician, base of Ashgill (=Rhiwlas Limestone), uncleaved, calcareous
mudstones, extremely fossiliferous. Probably one of the best exposures for the
*Phillipsinella parabola* horizons in England and Wales.
King, W. B. R. 1923, p. 494, with geol. map.
Geol. Surv. O.S. 74 S.W. ; Ord. New Pop. 117.

**Llanyblodwel.** Old quarry at roadside, ⅓ mile W. of Llanyblodwel Church.
Ordovician, Caradoc (*Heterorthis retrorsistria* zone). The zone fossil and other
brachiopods occur abundantly.
Whittington, H. B. 1938b, p. 425, with geol. map.
Geol. Surv. N.S. 137 ; Ord. New Pop. 117.

**Llanyblodwel.** Dingle 400 yds. N.W. of farm, 1 mile N.W. of Llanyblodwel.
Ordovician, Ashgill (*Phillipsinella parabola* zone), blue-black mudstones
with brachiopods and trilobites.
Whittington, H. B. 1938b, p. 433, with geol. map.
Geol. Surv. N.S. 137 ; Ord. New Pop. 117.

**Meifod,** 17 miles S.W. of Oswestry. Crags and old quarries in wood,
⅔ mile W. and W.S.W. of Lion Hotel, Meifod.
Ordovician, Caradoc, highly fossiliferous sandstones. Probably this is the
Allt-yr-aner locality of M'Coy and Sedgwick.
King, W. B. R. 1928, p. 676, with geol. map.
Geol. Surv. O.S. 60 N.E. ; Ord. New Pop. 117.

## PEMBROKESHIRE

**Abereiddy,** 4½ miles N.E. of St. Davids. Black shales, mudstones and
thin ash beds on S. side of Abereiddy Bay.
Ordovician, Llanvirn (*Didymograptus murchisoni* zone), with abundant
graptolites (*D. murchisoni, D. murchisoni* var. *geminus*) in shales.
Cox, A. H. 1916, p. 304, with geol. map. Cox, A. H. and others 1930, p. 264,
with geol. map.
Geol. Surv. O.S. 40 ; Ord. New Pop. 138 and 151.

**Amroth,** 6 miles S.E. of Narberth. Cliffs and foreshore 1 mile E. of Amroth
Castle, immediately below sandstones of Telpyn Point, just E. of cave.
Carboniferous, Millstone Grit (Shale Group, G zone). Two bands of shale
(the upper with a calcareous band) separated by 70 ft. of sandstones. Goniatites :
*Gastrioceras cancellatum* in the upper bed, *Anthracoceras* in the lower.
Geol. Surv. N.S. 228 ; Ord. New Pop. 152.

**Angle,** 8 miles W.N.W. of Pembroke. Cliffs on N. and S. sides of West Angle Bay.
Upper Devonian. Brachiopods and lamellibranchs abundant.
Dixon, E. E. L. 1921, pp. 47-49.
Geol. Surv. N.S. 226-227 ; Ord. New Pop. 151.

**Angle.** S. side of West Angle Bay.
Carboniferous Limestone (Lower Limestone Shales, *Cleistopora* zone, Km and K₁). Abundant ostracods and lamellibranchs, with brachiopods and fish remains above. Corals enter at the top.
Dixon, E. E. L. 1921, pp. 115-118.
Geol. Surv. N.S. 226-227 ; Ord. New Pop. 151.

**Bletherston,** 5 miles N.N.W. of Narberth. Spring Hill, quarry and exposure in lane, ¼ mile N.E. of Bullhook, 1 mile S.W. of Bletherston.
Ordovician, Caradoc (Mydrim Shales). Abundant graptolites (*Climaco-graptus, Dicranograptus,* etc.) with rare trinucleid trilobites.
Strahan, A. and others 1914, p. 47.
Geol. Surv. N.S. 228 ; Ord. New Pop. 151.

**Bosherston,** 4½ miles S.S.W. of Pembroke. Cliff sections and stacks S. of Stackpole Quay, and near Stackpole Quay Farm, 1¾ miles N.E. of Bosherston.
Carboniferous Limestone (Z zone just E. of farm ; Upper *Syringothyris* zone (C₂) near 5th point S. of Quay ; S zone S. of 5th point and in middle cove). A representative sequence of coral and brachiopod faunas.
Dixon, E. E. L. 1921, pp. 73-86, 138-140, with geol. map.
Geol. Surv. N.S. 245 ; Ord. New Pop. 151.

**Bosherston.** Cliff top, N. end of The Green Bridge of Wales, 2½ miles W. of Bosherston, near Elegug Stacks.
Carboniferous Limestone (S₂ subzone). Corals and brachiopods.
Dixon, E. E. L. 1921, pp. 73-86, 141.
Geol. Surv. N.S. 245 ; Ord. New Pop. 151.

**Bosherston.** Trevalen, cliff S. side of New Quay, 1¼ miles S. of Bosherston.
Carboniferous Limestone (S₂ subzone). Corals and brachiopods.
Dixon, E. E. L. 1921, pp. 73-86, 133.
Geol. Surv. N.S. 245 ; Ord. New Pop. 151.

**Bosherston.** Cliff tops, St. Gowan's Head and between St. Gowan's Chapel and Stennis Ford, 1¼-1½ miles S. of Bosherston.
Carboniferous Limestone (D₁ subzone, limestones with many " pseudo-breccias "). Corals and large brachiopods.
Dixon, E. E. L. 1921, pp. 73-86, 142-143.
Geol. Surv. N.S. 245 ; Ord. New Pop. 151.

**Bosherston.** Cliff tops N. of Crocksydam and various points in Bull-slaughter Bay, W.S.W. of Bosherston, viz. cliff top and E. side of hollow; cliffs at W. end ; foreshore S. of 3rd cove ; 2nd cove S. of footpath.
Carboniferous Limestone (D₂ subzone). Corals and brachiopods, with gastropods and trilobites in certain beds.
Dixon, E. E. L. 1921, pp. 73-86, 143-144, 135-137, and fig. 11, p. 136.
Geol. Surv. N.S. 245 ; Ord. New Pop. 151.

**Boulston,** 2¾ miles S.S.E. of Haverfordwest. Left bank of R. Western Cleddau, 600 yds. N.W. of Picton Point ; and several outcrops further W. between Landshipping Ferry and the creek.
Carboniferous, Coal Measures (*similis-pulchra* zone), black mudstones 2 ft. (Cefn Coed marine band), overlain by shales and non-marine measures. Chonetid brachiopods and lamellibranchs in black mudstones. Small crustacea (*Euestheria*) in overlying shales. Plants and non-marine lamellibranchs in non-marine measures.
Strahan, A. and others 1914, p. 193.
Geol. Surv. N.S. 228 ; Ord. New Pop. 138 and 151.

**Castlemartin.** Foreshore at N. end of Freshwater West, 7 miles W. of Pembroke.

Silurian, Ludlow, abundant brachiopods (*Camarotoechia nucula*, etc.). Liable to concealment by blown sand.

Dixon, E. E. L. 1921, pp. 16-22.

Geol. Surv. N.S. 244 ; Ord. New Pop. 151.

**Castlemartin.** Cliffs at Bluck's Pool, 1¾ miles S.W. of Castlemartin.

Carboniferous Limestone ($Z_2$ subzone). Corals abundant and well preserved, with many brachiopods, bryozoa, crinoid cups, etc.

Dixon, E. E. L. 1921, pp. 73-86, 123-126.

Geol. Surv. N.S. 244 ; Ord. New Pop. 151.

**Castlemartin.** Cliffs between Wind Bay and Pen-y-holt Bay, and around Linney Head, 2½ miles S.W. of Castlemartin.

Carboniferous Limestone ($C_2$ subzone). Many caninoid, zaphrentid and other corals, and large brachiopods.

Dixon, E. E. L. 1921, pp. 73-86, 130-133, 141, and fig. 10, p. 124.

Geol. Surv. N.S. 245 ; Ord. New Pop. 151.

**Castlemartin.** Cliffs, 760 yds. E. of Pen-y-holt Stack, $1\frac{9}{10}$ miles W.S.W. of Castlemartin. Also from 100 yds. W. of Harness Slade, E. to the Wash (1¾-2½ miles S.E. of Linney Head).

Carboniferous Limestone ($S_1$ subzone.) *Lithostrotion* and zaphrentid-phase corals, and gastropods.

Dixon, E. E. L. 1921, pp. 73-86, 130-133, and fig. 10, p. 124.

Geol. Surv. N.S. 244 ; Ord. New Pop. 151.

**Clarbeston,** 6¼ miles N.E. of Haverfordwest. Pwll-y-gors Hill, small quarry by pathway in wood, on right bank of R. Syfynwy, opposite New Mill, ½ mile E. of Clarbeston.

Ordovician, Caradoc (Mydrim Limestone). Well-preserved graptolites (*Climacograptus, Dicranograptus, Glyptograptus*, etc.).

Strahan, A. and others 1914, pp. 38-39, 47-48.

Geol. Surv. N.S. 228 ; Ord. New Pop. 138 and 151.

**Cosheston,** 2 miles N.E. of Pembroke. Cliffs of Milford Haven, in Mill Bay, 1 mile N.W. of Cosheston.

Lower Old Red Sandstone, Cosheston Group, with plentiful plant fragments (*Psilophyton*).

Murchison, R. I. 1839, pp. 385-386. Strahan, A. and others 1914, p. 120

Geol. Surv. N.S. 228 ; Ord. New Pop. 151.

**Cresswell,** 5½ miles N.E. of Pembroke. S. shore of R. Cresswell, 300 yds. N.W. of Newpark Farm, ¾ mile W. of Cresswell.

Carboniferous, Millstone Grit. Shales and mudstones with goniatites and lamellibranchs (*Dunbarella*).

Strahan, A. and others 1914, p. 152.

Geol. Surv. N.S. 228 ; Ord. New Pop. 138 and 151.

**Crymmych Arms,** 7½ miles S. of Cardigan. Roadside quarry ½ mile along the Mynochlog-ddu road from Pwllglas House, S.W. of Crymmych Arms.

Ordovician, Llanvirn (*Didymograptus murchisoni* zone, with dense black mudstones). Graptolites (*D. murchisoni, Pleurograptus*, etc.) and fragmentary remains of trilobites (*Trinucleus*).

Evans, W. D. 1945, p. 99, with geol. map.

Geol. Surv. O.S. 40 ; Ord. New Pop. 139.

**Fishguard.** Brickyard quarry, Goodwick, 1 mile N.W. of Fishguard.

Ordovician, Bala, black shales and mudstones with numerous specimens of *Diplograptus* (*Mesograptus*) *multidens*.

Geol. Surv. O.S. 40 ; Ord. New Pop. 138.

**Gumfreston,** 1½ miles W. of Tenby. Roadside cutting (much overgrown), N. side of road, 100 yds. E. of farm near Gumfreston Church.

Carboniferous, Millstone Grit ($E_2$ and $R_2$ subzones). Goniatites : *Eumorphoceras, Nuculoceras, Reticuloceras*.

Geol. Surv. N.S. 245 ; Ord. New Pop. 152.

**Haroldston West,** 5½ miles W. of Haverfordwest. Cliff top N. of Settling Nose, and foreshore N. of Black Point, 1¼-1½ miles N. of Broadhaven.

Carboniferous, Millstone Grit (G zone, shales just above Farewell Rock). North of the Nose : orthotetid brachiopods and the goniatite *Gastrioceras cancellatum* in 30 ft. ironstained shales below pale sandstone. S. of the Nose : *Gastrioceras subcrenatum* in 3 ft. dark shale below sandstone.

Cantrill, T. C. and others 1916, pp. 116-117.

Geol. Surv. N.S. 226/227 ; Ord. New Pop. 138 and 151.

**Haverfordwest.** Trefgarn Bridge, quarry by roadside at 4th milestone N. of Haverfordwest on Fishguard road.

Upper Cambrian (*Lingula* Flags, shales with interbedded grits). The brachiopod *Lingullela davisi* numerous, associated with the trilobites *Olenus* and *Agnostus*.

Strahan, A. and others 1914, p. 12.

Geol. Surv. N.S. 228 ; Ord. New Pop. 138 and 151.

**Haverfordwest.** Shoalshook, railway cutting ½ mile S.W. 'of Crundale House and 1 mile N.E. of Haverfordwest Station, on left bank of Cartlett Brook. Permission required from railway authorities.

Ordovician, Ashgill (Shoalshook Limestone). Many brachiopods and trilobites, with rare graptolites.

Strahan, A. and others 1914, pp. 59-64.

Geol. Surv. N.S. 228 ; Ord. New Pop. 138 and 151.

**Haverfordwest.** Old quarry behind Prendergast Place, Haverfordwest. Ordovician, Ashgill (Shoalshook Limestone). Brachiopods and trilobites.

Strahan, A. and others 1914, pp. 59-64.

Geol. Surv. N.S. 228 ; Ord. New Pop. 138 and 151.

**Haverfordwest.** Redhill Quarry, large roadside quarry 1½ miles N.W. of Haverfordwest.

Ordovician, Ashgill (Redhill Beds, type-locality). Numerous trilobites.

Marr, J. E. and Roberts, T. 1885, p. 482, with geol. map. Strahan, A. and others 1914, pp. 74-75.

Geol. Surv. N.S. 228 ; Ord. New Pop. 138 and 151.

**Haverfordwest.** North Gate of Haverfordwest, roadside exposures at Hobby-bach and Crowhill Road.

Ordovician, Ashgill (Slade Beds, type-locality). Orthid and other brachiopods numerous.

Marr, J. E. and Roberts, T. 1885, p. 483, with geol. map. Strahan, A. and others 1914, pp. 74-75.

Geol. Surv. N.S. 228 ; Ord. New Pop. 138 and 151.

**Haverfordwest.** Quarry E. of Black Backs Bridge over Millin Brook, 3 miles E. of Haverfordwest on road to Rhos.

Silurian, Lower Llandovery (*Pentamerus undatus* Beds = Cartlett Beds). Abundant brachiopods.

Strahan, A. and others 1914, pp. 98-99.

Geol. Surv. N.S. 228 ; Ord. New Pop. 138 and 151.

**Haverfordwest.** Old quarry 130 yds. S.W. of Black Backs Bridge over Millin Brook, 3 miles E. of Haverfordwest on road to Rhos.

Silurian, Lower Llandovery (Cartlett Beds, slightly above *Pentamerus undatus* Beds). Abundant brachiopods.

Strahan, A. and others 1914, p. 100.

Geol. Surv. N.S. 228 ; Ord. New Pop. 138 and 151.

**Haverfordwest.** Clarborough, old quarry in dingle 300 yds. S.W. of Deep Lake, 2¼ miles E. of Haverfordwest.
Silurian, Lower Llandovery (Gasworks Mudstones). Corals and brachiopods abundant.
Strahan, A. and others 1914, p. 88.
Geol. Surv. N.S. 228 ; Ord. New Pop. 138 and 151.

**Haverfordwest.** Section between Cambrian Place and Gasworks, along E. bank of R. Cleddau, Haverfordwest.
Silurian, Lower Llandovery (Gasworks Mudstones and Sandstones). Brachiopods and trilobites. See reference for measured section.
Strahan, A. and others 1914, pp. 89-91.
Geol. Surv. N.S. 228 ; Ord. New Pop. 138 and 151.

**Haverfordwest.** The Frolic Section, S.E. of Higgon's Well along left bank of Cleddau river S. of the town.
Silurian, Lower Llandovery (Gasworks Mudstones), with corals, brachiopods and trilobites. See reference for measured section.
Strahan, A. and others 1914, pp. 92-96.
Geol. Surv. N.S. 228 ; Ord. New Pop. 138 and 151.

**Haverfordwest.** Frolic path, on left bank of Cleddau river, exposures at various points along riverside at Higgon's Well, S. of Haverfordwest.
Silurian, Lower Llandovery (Uzmaston Beds), with a typical brachiopod fauna.
Strahan, A. and others 1914, pp. 105-106.
Geol. Surv. N.S. 228 ; Ord. New Pop. 138 and 151.

**Johnston,** 4 miles S.S.W. of Haverfordwest. Old quarry in field, 500 yds. E. of Harmeston Cross, ¾ mile S. of Johnston Church.
Silurian, Upper Llandovery (Rosemarket Beds). *Pentamerus oblongus* and other brachiopods abundant in sandy mudstones.
Strahan, A. and others 1914, p. 111.
Geol. Surv. N.S. 228 ; Ord. New Pop. 138 and 151.

**Keeston,** 4 miles N.W. of Haverfordwest. Large quarry in village.
Ordovician, Ashgill, Redhill Beds. Numerous brachiopods and trilobites.
Cantrill, T. C. and others 1916, p. 49.
Geol. Surv. N.S. 226/227. Ord. New Pop. 138 and 151.

**Little Haven,** 6 miles W.S.W. of Haverfordwest. Rooks Bay and coast section about ¼ mile S. of Little Haven ; also N. and S. of the harbour.
Carboniferous, Coal Measures (*lenisulcata* zone). Plants and non-marine lamellibranchs.
Cantrill, T. C. and others 1916, p. 122. Dix, E. 1933, p. 170.
Geol. Surv. N.S. 226/227 ; Ord. New Pop. 138 and 151.

**Little Haven.** The Settlands (Settlings), cliffs between Broad Haven and Little Haven ; and at Falling Cliffs, ¼ mile S.S.W. of Little Haven.
Carboniferous, Coal Measures (base of *ovalis* zone). Plants and molluscan shells abundant at various spots.
Cantrill, T. C. and others 1916, p. 119.
Geol. Surv. N.S. 226/227 ; Ord. New Pop. 138 and 151.

**Llanglydwen,** 12 miles S. of Cardigan. On E. side of Carn Wen Hill, small quarry on E. side of farm road, 1½ miles N. 10° W. of Llanglydwen Church.
Ordovician, Llanvirn (mudstones and thin bands of felspathic ash). Mixed graptolite and trilobite facies. *Didymograptus murchisoni* var. *geminus, Trinucleus* sp., unidentified brachiopods.
Geol. Surv. O.S. 40 ; Ord. New Pop. 139.

**Lydstep,** $3\frac{1}{4}$ miles S.W. of Tenby.  Cliff 350 yds. W. of Draught, and the headland of Black Mixen, $\frac{1}{2}$ mile S. of Lydstep.
Carboniferous Limestone ($C_1$ subzone).  Crinoidal limestones and abundant corals (*Zaphrentoides* and *Caninia*).
Dixon, E. E. L. 1921, pp. 73-86, 100, 111 and fig. 8, p. 110.
Geol. Surv. N.S. 245 ;  Ord. New Pop. 152.

**Lydstep.**  Cliffs S. of Lydstep, neck of Black Mixen and cliff-foot W. of Skomer ;  also S. face and N.W. corner of Whitesheet Rock.
Carboniferous Limestone ($C_2$-$S_1$ zone) with many corals and brachiopods.
Dixon, E. E. L. 1921, pp. 73-86, 101-102, 112, and fig. 8, p. 110.
Geol. Surv. N.S. 245 ;  Ord. New Pop. 152.

**Lydstep.**  Lydstep Quarry, N. part and adjacent foreshore ;  quarry 450 yds. E.N.E. of Lydstep Cottage ;  quarry 100 yds. N.E. of Lydstep Farm.
Carboniferous Limestone ($D_1$ subzone).  Many corals and brachiopods.
Dixon, E. E. L. 1921, pp. 76-83, 103, 114-115, and fig. 8, p. 110.
Geol. Surv. N.S. 245 ;  Ord. New Pop. 152.

**Lydstep.**  Lydstep Quarry, cliffs facing N., S.E. of Lydstep House.
Carboniferous Limestone ($S_2$ subzone).  Corals, brachiopods and gastropods abundant in certain beds.
Dixon, E. E. L. 1921, pp. 76-83, 103, 114-115, and fig. 8, p. 110.
Geol. Surv. N.S. 245 ;  Ord. New Pop. 152.

**Manorbier,** $4\frac{1}{2}$ miles S.W. of Tenby.  Cliffs at N.W. corner of Swanlake Bay, $1\frac{1}{2}$ miles W. of Manorbier.
Lower Old Red Sandstone, red marls with Ostracoderms (*Pteraspis*, *Cephalaspis*).
Dixon, E. E. L. 1921, pp. 35-36.
Geol. Surv. N.S. 245 ;  Ord. New Pop. 151.

**Manorbier.**  Cliff sections at Skrinkle Haven.
Carboniferous Limestone ;  K zone, with ostracods and lamellibranchs below and brachiopods above, in S. cove and W. side of middle cove.  Horizon $\beta$, Z zone, and horizon $\gamma$ at back and E. sides of E. cove, with corals, brachiopods, gastropods and bryozoa, and crinoidal limestones.
Dixon, E. E. L. 1921, pp. 73-86, 96-100, 105-109, and fig. 8, p. 110.
Geol. Surv. N.S. 245 ;  Ord. New Pop. 151 and 152.

**Marloes,** $7\frac{1}{2}$ miles W.N.W. of Milford Haven.  Marloes Bay, coast section extending from Gateholm to Hoopers Point, S.W. of Marloes.
Silurian, Upper Llandovery, Wenlock and Ludlow.  Abundant corals, brachiopods and trilobites.  Section famous through the writings of de la Beche, Murchison, Phillips, Salter and W. S. Symonds.
Cantrill, T. C. and others 1916, pp. 57-67.
Geol. Surv. N.S. 226/227 ;  Ord. New Pop. 138 and 151.

**Marloes.**  Wooltack Bay, section extending from Renney Slip to Gateholm, W.S.W. of Marloes.
Silurian, Upper Llandovery, Wenlock and Ludlow.  Corals, brachiopods and trilobites.
Cantrill, T. C. and others 1916, pp. 68-77.
Geol. Surv. N.S. 226/227 ;  Ord. New Pop. 138 and 151.

**Narberth.**  Kilnpark, N. of Narberth station.
Ordovician, Llanvirn (shales high in the *Didymograptus bifidus* zone).
Abundant " tuning-fork " and diplograptid graptolites.
Strahan, A. and others 1914, p. 26.
Geol. Surv. N.S. 228 ;  Ord. New Pop. 152.

**Narberth.** Lane leading to Whitley Farm, ½ mile N.E. of Narberth Station.
Ordovician, Llandeilo, sandy shales and flags with numerous brachiopods
and trilobites.
Strahan, A. and others 1914, p. 32.
Geol. Surv. N.S. 228 ; Ord. New Pop. 152.

**Narberth.** Small quarry near path, 120 yds. S.E. of Brynglas, ¼ mile
E. of bridge, Llan Mill, 2 miles E.S.E. of Narberth.
Ordovician, Llandeilo (limestones and calcareous flags) with brachiopods,
trilobites, etc.
Strahan, A. and others 1914, p. 33.
Geol. Surv. N.S. 228 ; Ord. New Pop. 152.

**Narberth.** Road section S. of Lampeter Velfrey, and W. of the bridge at
Llan Mill, 2 miles E.S.E. of Narberth.
Ordovician, Llanvirn (highest beds of *Didymograptus bifidus* zone). Abundant
" tuning-fork " graptolites in excellent preservation, associated with trilobites
(*Ogygiocaris buchi, Flexicalymene cambrensis,* etc.).
Strahan, A. and others 1914, pp. 26-27.
Geol. Surv. N.S. 228 ; Ord. New Pop. 152.

**Narberth.** Quarry at Trewern, 400 yds. N. of Fron, 2 miles W. of Whitland,
6 miles E.N.E. of Narberth.
Ordovician, Caradoc (Robeston Wathen Limestone) with abundant corals.
Strahan, A. and others 1914, pp. 56, 62-64.
Geol. Surv. N.S. 228 ; Ord. New Pop. 152.

**Narberth.** Roadside quarry 50 yds. N.E. of Banc-Saeson, ¼ mile N.W. of
Fron, 2 miles W. of Whitland, 6 miles E.N.E. of Narberth.
Ordovician, Ashgill Series (Redhill and Slade beds a few feet above junction
with Shoalshook limestone). Numerous corals, brachiopods and trilobites.
Strahan, A. and others 1914, pp. 68-69.
Geol. Surv. N.S. 228 ; Ord. New Pop. 152.

**Narberth.** In farmyard, Pant-y-gorphwys, ¼ mile N. of Stonyford, 1 mile
N.N.E. of Narberth.
Ordovician, Caradoc (Mydrim Shales). Abundant graptolites in shales
overlying the Llandeilo Limestone.
Strahan, A. and others 1914, p. 41.
Geol. Surv. N.S. 228 ; Ord. New Pop. 152.

**Narberth.** Cilrath-fawr, 1½ miles N. of Narberth, N. bank of Whitland-
Robeston Wathen road, S.W. of lane and also in lane.
Ordovician, Ashgill (Redhill-Slade Beds) with orthid brachiopods and
trilobites.
Strahan, A. and others 1914, pp. 66-67.
Geol. Surv. N.S. 228 ; Ord. New Pop. 152.

**Narberth.** Old quarry 40 yds. from junction of Lampeter Velfrey and
Ludchurch roads, 1¼ miles S.E. of Narberth.
Ordovician, Ashgill (Slade Beds). Numerous brachiopods and trilobites.
Strahan, A. and others 1914, p. 65.
Geol. Surv. N.S. 228 ; Ord. New Pop. 152.

**Nolton,** 6 miles W.N.W. of Haverfordwest. Cliffs of Druidston Haven,
1 mile S.W. of Nolton.
Ordovician, Caradoc (Mydrim Shales). Graptolites abundant, mainly
diplograptids.
Cantrill, T. C. and others 1916, pp. 47-48.
Geol. Surv. N.S. 226/227 ; Ord. New Pop. 138 and 151.

**Nolton.** Cliff at Rickets Head, 1 mile N.W. of Nolton.
Carboniferous, Coal Measures, shales associated with Rickets Head Vein.
Abundant plants.
Cantrill, T. C. and others 1916, p. 135.
Geol. Surv. N.S. 226/227 ; Ord. New Pop. 138 and 151.

**Nolton.** Cliffs at Druidston Haven, ¾ mile S.S.W. of Nolton.
Pleistocene, shelly boulder clay with arctic species of marine lamellibranchs
and gastropods.
Cantrill, T. C. and others 1916, p. 157.
Geol. Surv. N.S. 226/227 ; Ord. New Pop. 138 and 151.

**Pembroke.** Cliffs on N. and S. sides of Freshwater East, 3 miles S.E. of
Pembroke.
Silurian, Wenlock-Ludlow. Some corals with many brachiopods and
pockets of lamellibranchs and gastropods.
Dixon, E. E. L. 1921, pp. 13-16, 19-22.
Geol. Surv. N.S. 245 ; Ord. New Pop. 151.

**Robeston Wathen,** 1¾ miles N.W. of Narberth. Old quarry in dingle
N. of the village of Robeston Wathen.
Ordovician, Caradoc (Robeston Wathen Limestone, type-locality). Abun-
dant corals.
Strahan, A. and others 1914, pp. 57-58.
Geol. Surv. N.S. 228 ; Ord. New Pop. 152.

**Robeston Wathen.** Slebech, cart road near edge of wood 450 yds. S.S.E.
of New Church ; also small pit 150 yds. S. of Haverfordwest road, 200 yds.
E. of the 5th mile-post. Both about 3 miles W.S.W. of Robeston Wathen.
Ordovician, Ashgill (Slade Beds). Abundant brachiopods and trilobites.
Strahan, A. and others 1914, pp. 71-72.
Geol. Surv. N.S. 228 ; Ord. New Pop. 138 and 151.

**Robeston Wathen.** On left bank of Eastern Cleddau, ⅝ mile S.W. of
Blackpool, 1¼ miles S.W. of Robeston Wathen.
Silurian, Lower Llandovery (Canaston Shales). Brachiopods abundant in
mudstones.
Strahan, A. and others 1914, pp. 108-109.
Geol. Surv. N.S. 228 ; Ord. New Pop. 138 and 151.

**St. David's.** E. side of Ogof Velvet, N.E. corner of Ramsey Island.
Upper Cambrian (Lingula Flags), shales and thin-bedded quartzites with
the brachiopod *Lingulella davisi* abundant.
Pringle, J. 1930, p. 9, with geol. map.
Geol. Surv. O.S. 40 ; Ord. New Pop. 138 and 151.

**St. David's.** Aber Mawr, W. side of Ramsey Island.
Ordovician, Arenig (*Didymograptus hirundo* zone). Extensiform graptolites
abundant.
Pringle, J. 1930, p. 16, with geol. map.
Geol. Surv. O.S. 40 ; Ord. New Pop. 138 and 151.

**St. David's.** Cliffs forming E. wall of Ogof Hen Bay, N. end of Ramsey
Island.
Ordovician, Arenig (Porth Gain Beds), with brachiopods, lamellibranchs
and trilobites abundant and well-preserved.
Pringle, J. 1930, pp. 11-12, with geol. map.
Geol. Surv. O.S. 40 ; Ord. New Pop. 138 and 151.

**St. David's.** Cliffs at Road Uchaf, E. side of Ramsey Island. Approached
by boat.
Ordovician, Arenig (*Didymograptus extensus* zone). The graptolites *Dendro-
graptus*, and *Didymograptus* of the extensiform group, abundant.
Pringle, J. 1930, pp. 13-14, with geol. map.
Geol. Surv. O.S. 40 ; Ord. New Pop. 138 and 151.

**St. David's.** Porth Llavog, W. side of Ramsey Island.
Ordovician, Llanvirn (highest beds of *Didymograptus bifidus* zone). " Tuning-fork " graptolites abundant, associated with the trilobite *Ogygiocaris buchi.*
Pringle, J. 1930, p. 18, with geol. map.
Geol. Surv. O.S. 40 ; Ord. New Pop. 138 and 151.

**St. David's.** Llanvirn-y-Fran, quarry below path to Abereiddy Bay, 4 miles N.N.E. of St. David's.
Ordovician, Llanvirn (type-locality), *Didymograptus bifidus* zone. Trilobites and " tuning-fork " graptolites abundant.
Hicks, H. 1875, pp. 173, 177 with geol. map. Cox, A. H. and others 1930, pp. 261-262, with geol. map.
Geol. Surv. O.S. 40 ; Ord. New Pop. 138 and 151.

**St. David's.** Cliff at N. end of Whitesand Bay, N.W. of St. David's.
Upper Cambrian (Lingula Flags), shales with inter-bedded flaggy quartzites with the brachiopod *Lingulella davisi* numerous.
Cox, A. H. and others 1930, p. 256, with geol. map.
Geol. Surv. O.S. 40 ; Ord. New Pop. 138 and 151.

**St. Ishmael's.** Cliffs of Lindsway Bay, S.E. of St. Ishmael's.
Silurian, Wenlock-Ludlow. Fossils, mainly brachiopods, abundant.
Cantrill, T. C. and others 1916, pp. 77-81.
Geol. Surv. N.S. 226/227 ; Ord. New Pop. 138 and 151.

**Solva,** 3½ miles E. of St. David's. Cliffs at Porthyrhaw, 1 mile S.W. of Solva.
Middle Cambrian, flags and shales with *Paradoxides davidis.* Hicks and Salter's type-locality for the Menevian Series. Trilobites fairly numerous, but good specimens of *P. davidis* are rare.
Hicks, H. 1866, p. 284. Cox, A. H. and others 1930, p. 254.
Geol. Surv. O.S. 40 ; Ord. New Pop. 138 and 151.

**Tenby.** Cliff ¼ mile W. of Giltar Point, 1½ miles S. of Tenby.
Carboniferous Limestone (S zone). Corals, brachiopods and gastropods.
Dixon, E. E. L. 1921, pp. 111, 112, and fig. 7, p. 107.
Geol. Surv. N.S. 245 ; Ord. New Pop. 152.

**Tenby.** Cliffs E. of lifeboat-slip, and also S.E. of pier.
Carboniferous Limestone ($Z_2$ subzone), corals and brachiopods.
Dixon, E. E. L. 1921, pp. 73-86, 88, 91, and fig. 6, p. 92.
Geol. Surv. N.S. 245 ; Ord. New Pop. 152.

**Tenby.** Cliffs 200-300 yds. S. of Monkstone Point.
Carboniferous, Coal Measures (*lenisulcata* zone). Two plant beds with *Neuropteris,* and two horizons with the brachiopod *Lingula.*
Geol. Surv. N.S. 228 ; Ord. New Pop. 152.

**Tenby.** Bowman's Point and small cove 220 yds. N. of Waterwynch Bay.
Carboniferous, Millstone Grit (G zone). The goniatites *Gastrioceras cancellatum* and *G. subcrenatum.*
Dixon, E. E. L. 1933, p. 410. Bisat, W. S. 1933, p. 412.
Geol. Surv. N.S. 228 ; Ord. New Pop. 152.

**Tenby.** North Sands Bay (First Point) and foreshore at low tide near S. end of promenade.
Carboniferous, Millstone Grit (H and G zones). Goniatites (*Anthracoceras*) and lamellibranchs in shales below sandstone near First Point. Goniatites (*Homoceras*) in large bullions at S. end of promenade.
Bisat, W. S. 1933, p. 412.
Geol. Surv. N.S. 228 ; Ord. New Pop. 152.

**Tenby.** Many caves and fissures in Carboniferous Limestone (especially Hoyles Mouth and Longbury Bank, 1 mile W. of Tenby) have yielded interesting Pleistocene deposits with bones of mammals and human implements. Most of these deposits have been quarried away, and the finds are to be seen in the Tenby Museum.

**Tiers Cross,** 3 miles N. of Milford Haven. Old quarry 700 yds. S. of Bullford, ½ mile E. of Tiers Cross.
Silurian, Upper Llandovery (Rosemarket Stage). Corals, brachiopods and trilobites abundant.
Cantrill, T. C. and others 1916, p. 84.
Geol. Surv. N.S. 226/227 ; Ord. New Pop. 138 and 151.

**Walwyn's Castle,** 6 miles S.W. of Haverfordwest. Syke quarry, ¼ mile S. of Church at Walwyn's Castle.
Silurian, Upper Llandovery (Rosemarket Stage). The brachiopods *Pentamerus oblongus* and *Stricklandia lirata* are common.
Cantrill, T. C. and others 1916, p. 84.
Geol. Surv. N.S. 226/227 ; Ord. New Pop. 138 and 151.

# RADNORSHIRE

**Builth Wells.** Stream sections in tributary to Dulas Brook, near Trecoed Springs, 2½ miles N.N.E. of Builth Wells Station and ½ mile N.E. of crossroads N. of Pencerrig.
Ordovician, Llandeilo (flags and shales of *Glyptograptus teretiusculus* zone). Trilobites (*Ogygiocaris buchi*, etc.) and graptolites (*Diplograptus foliaceus, G. teretiusculus*).
Elles, G. L. 1940, p. 410.
Geol. Surv. O.S. 56 S.W. ; Ord. New Pop. 128 and 141.

**Builth Wells.** Maesgwynne Old Quarry, 3¼ miles N.E. of Builth Wells station, and ⅞ mile N.E. of crossroads N. of Pencerrig.
Ordovician, Llandeilo (flags and shales of *Glyptograptus teretiusculus* zone), containing various trilobites and graptolites, including *Diplograptus foliaceus*.
Elles, G. L. 1940, pp. 409–410.
Geol. Surv. O.S. 56 S.W. ; Ord. New Pop. 128.

**Builth Wells.** Pencerrig, 1 mile N. of Builth Wells station, bottom of stream flowing out of Pencerrig Lake.
Silurian, Wenlock Shales (*Cyrtograptus murchisoni* zone) with the zonal graptolite well preserved.
Elles, G. L. 1900, p. 374.
Geol. Surv. O.S. 56 S.W. ; Ord. New Pop. 141.

**Llandrindod Wells.** Section just above junction of streams N.E. of Hillside (Bach-y-Graig), ¾ mile E.S.E. of Llandrindod, on E. side of main road.
Ordovician, Llanvirn (*Didymograptus murchisoni* zone) with the zonal graptolite and others well-preserved ; also brachiopods.
Elles, G. L. 1940, pp. 404–405, with geol. map.
Geol. Surv. O.S. 56 S.W. ; Ord. New Pop. 128.

**Llandrindod Wells.** Section in chief tributary to Howey (Howddy) Brook where footpath crosses stream below waterfalls. Near source of Howey Brook, 2⅜ miles S.E. of Llandrindod Wells.
Ordovician, Llanvirn (*Didymograptus murchisoni* zone). This section, the type-locality of *D. murchisoni*, was known to Murchison.
Elles, G. L. 1940, pp. 401–403, with geol. map.
Geol. Surv. O.S. 56 S.W. ; Ord. New Pop. 128.

**Llandrindod Wells.** Llanfawr Quarry, ½ mile N.E. of Llandrindod station on E. side of road.

Ordovician, Caradoc (flags and shales of *Nemagraptus gracilis* zone). Abundant and well-preserved graptolites in thin shaly partings, trilobites (*Ogygiocaris buchi*, etc.), and brachiopods in flags.

Elles, G. L. 1940, pp. 447-448, with geol. map.

Geol. Surv. O.S. 56 S.W. ; Ord. New Pop. 128.

**Old Radnor,** 3 miles W.N.W. of Kington. Dolyhir Quarries, ⅔ mile S.W. of Old Radnor.

Silurian, Wenlock (Woolhope Limestone, reef-facies with thin shale band and concretions, resting on Pre-Cambrian grits and conglomerates). Algae (*Solenopora*), corals and bryozoa abundant in the limestone ; trilobites, brachiopods and gastropods in shale and concretions. A band of cephalopods (*Orthoceras*) near top of limestone.

Garwood, E. J. and Goodyear, E. 1919, with geol. map.

Geol. Surv. O.S. 56 S.E. ; Ord. New Pop. 128.

## LIST OF WORKS REFERRED TO

N.B.—Papers written jointly by more than two authors are referred to in the text as by the first author " and others." An asterisk indicates that the work includes plates of fossils.

BECHE, H. T. DE LA. 1846. " On the Formation of the Rocks of South Wales and South-Western England." *Mem. Geol. Surv.*, vol. i, pp. 1-296.

BELT, T. 1867. " On some New Trilobites from the Upper Cambrian Rocks of North Wales." *Geol. Mag.*, vol. iv, pp. 294-295.*

BISAT, W. S. 1933. " The Carboniferous Goniatites of the Neighbourhood of Tenby." *Proc. Geol. Assoc.*, vol. xliv, pp. 412-414.

BOSWELL, P. G. H. 1926. "A Contribution to the Geology of the Eastern Part of the Denbighshire Moors." *Quart. Journ. Geol. Soc.*, vol. lxxxii, pp. 556-585, with geol. map.

——. 1928. " The Salopian Rocks and Tectonics of the District South-West of Ruthin (Denbighshire)." *Quart. Journ. Geol. Soc.*, vol. lxxxiii, pp. 689-710, 735-736, with geol. map.

——. 1942. " The Wenlock and Ludlow Rocks of the District around Gwytherin, North-Western Denbighshire." *Proc. Liverpool Geol. Soc.*, vol. xviii, pp. 86-100, with geol. map.

——. 1943. " The Salopian Rocks and Geological Structure of the Country around Eglwys-Fach and Glan Conway, North-Western Denbighshire." *Proc. Geol. Assoc.*, vol. liv, pp. 93-112, with geol. map.

——. 1945. " The Occurrence of the Zone of *Cyrtograptus rigidus* (Wenlock Series) in North Wales, with notes on the age of the Denbigh Grit Series." *Proc. Liverpool Geol. Soc.*, vol. xix, pp. 72-96, maps.

——. 1949. " The Middle Silurian Rocks of North Wales." *London*, with geol. maps.

—— and DOUBLE, I. S. 1938. " The Ludlow Rocks and Structure of the Country in the Neighbourhood of Llanfair Talhaiarn and Llansannan, Denbighshire." *Proc. Liverpool Geol. Soc.*, vol. xvii, pp. 277-311, with geol. map.

—— and DOUBLE, I. S. 1940. " The Geology of an Area of Salopian Rocks West of the Conway Valley, in the Neighbourhood of Llanrwst, Denbighshire." *Proc. Geol. Assoc.*, vol. li, pp. 151-187, with geol. map.

CANTRILL, T. C., DIXON, E. E. L., THOMAS, H. H. and JONES, O.T. 1916. " The Geology of the South Wales Coalfield. Part XII. The Country around Milford." *Mem. Geol. Surv.*

CHALLINOR, J. 1928. "A Shelly Band in Graptolitic Shales." *Geol. Mag.*, vol. lxv, pp. 364-368.

COX, A. H. 1916. " The Geology of the District between Abereiddy and Abercastle (Pembrokeshire)." *Quart. Journ. Geol. Soc.*, vol. lxxi, pp. 273-342, with geol. map.

——, GREEN, J. F. N., JONES, O. T. and PRINGLE, J. 1930. " The Geology of the St. David's District, Pembrokeshire." *Proc. Geol. Assoc.*, vol. xli, pp. 241-289, with geol. map.

—— and LEWIS, H. P. 1945. " Summer Field Meeting, 1944. The Dolgelley District." *Proc. Geol. Assoc.*, vol. lvi, pp. 59-81.

CROSFIELD, M. C. and SKEAT, E. G. 1896. " On the Geology of the Neighbourhood of Carmarthen." *Quart. Journ. Geol. Soc.*, vol. lii, pp. 523-541, with geol. map.*

DAVIES, J. H. and TRUEMAN, A. E. 1927. "A Revision of the Non-Marine Lamellibranchs of the Coal Measures, and a Discussion of their Zonal Sequence." *Quart. Journ. Geol. Soc.*, vol. lxxxiii, pp. 210-259.*

Dix, E. 1933. " The Succession of Fossil Plants in the Millstone Grit and the Lower Portion of the Coal Measures in the South Wales Coalfield (near Swansea) and a Comparison with other Areas." *Palaeontographica*, vol. lxxvii B.

Dixon, E. E. L. 1921. " The Geology of the South Wales Coalfield. Part XIII. The Country around Pembroke and Tenby." *Mem. Geol. Surv.*

——. 1933. " Notes on the Geological Succession in South Pembroke-shire." *Proc. Geol. Assoc.*, vol. xliv, pp. 402-411.

—— and Vaughan, A. 1911. " The Carboniferous Succession in Gower (Glamorganshire), with notes on its Fauna and Conditions of Deposition." *Quart. Journ. Geol. Soc.*, vol. lxvii, pp. 477-571, with geol. map.*

Elles, G. L. 1900. " The Zonal Classification of the Wenlock Shales of the Welsh Borderland." *Quart. Journ. Geol. Soc.*, vol. lvi, pp. 370-414.*

——. 1909. " The Relation of the Ordovician and Silurian Rocks of Conway (North Wales)." *Quart. Journ. Geol. Soc.*, vol. lxv, pp. 169-194, with geol. map.

——. 1922. " The Bala Country : its Structure and Rock-Succession." *Quart. Journ. Geol. Soc.*, vol. lxxviii, pp. 132-175, with geol. map.

——. 1940. " The Stratigraphy and Faunal Succession in the Ordovician Rocks of the Builth-Llandrindod Inlier, Radnorshire." *Quart. Journ. Geol. Soc.*, vol. xcv, pp. 383-445, with geol. map.*

Evans, D. C. 1906. " The Ordovician Rocks of Western Caermarthenshire." *Quart. Journ. Geol. Soc.*, vol. lxii, pp. 597-643, with geol. map.

Evans, D. G. and Jones, R. O. 1929. " Notes on the Millstone Grit of the North Crop of the South Wales Coalfield." *Geol. Mag.*, vol. lxvi, pp. 164-177.

Evans, W. D. 1945. " The Geology of the Prescelly Hills, North Pembroke-shire." *Quart. Journ. Geol. Soc.*, vol. ci, pp. 89-110, with geol. map.

Fearnsides, W. G. 1905. " On the Geology of Arenig Fawr and Moel Llyfnant." *Quart. Journ. Geol. Soc.*, vol. lxi, pp. 608-640, with geol. map.

——. 1910a. " The Tremadoc Slates and Associated Rocks of South-East Carnarvonshire." *Quart. Journ. Geol. Soc.*, vol. lxvi, pp. 142-188, with geol. map.

——. 1910b. " North and Central Wales." " Geology in the Field " (*Geol. Assoc.*), Pt. IV, pp. 786-825, with geol. map.

Garwood, E. J. and Goodyear, E. 1919. " On the Geology of the Old Radnor District, with special reference to an Algal Development in the Woolhope Limestone." *Quart. Journ. Geol. Soc.*, vol. lxxiv (for 1918), pp. 1-31.*

George, T. N. 1933. " The Carboniferous Limestone Series in the West of the Vale of Glamorgan." *Quart. Journ. Geol. Soc.*, vol. lxxxix, pp. 221-272, with geol. map.

—— and Trueman, A. E. 1924. " Excursion to the Swansea District." *Proc. Geol. Assoc.*, vol. xxxv, pp. 308-315, with geol. map.

Greenly, E. 1919. " The Geology of Anglesey." *Mem. Geol. Surv.*, 2 vols. (Palaeontology only in vol. ii).

——, Smith, S. and others. 1928. " The Lower Carboniferous Rocks of the Menaian Region of Carnarvonshire : their Petrology, Succession and Physiography." *Quart. Journ. Geol. Soc.*, vol. lxxxiv, pp. 382-439.

Hicks, H. 1866. " Report on further Researches in the Lingula-Flags of South Wales." *Rep. Brit. Assoc.*, Birmingham, 1865, pp. 281-286.

HICKS, H.    1875.    " On the Succession of the Ancient Rocks in the Vicinity of St. David's, Pembrokeshire, with special reference to the Arenig and Llandeilo Groups and their Fossil Contents." *Quart. Journ. Geol. Soc.*, vol. xxxi, pp. 167-195, with geol. map.*

HIND, W. and STOBBS, J. T.    1906.    " The Carboniferous Succession below the Coal Measures in North Shropshire, Denbighshire and Flintshire." *Geol. Mag.*, Dec. 5, vol. iii, pp. 385-400, 445-459, 496-507.

JONES, O. T.    1909.    " The Hartfell-Valentian Succession in the District around Plynlimon and Pont Erwyd (North Cardiganshire)." *Quart. Journ. Geol. Soc.*, vol. lxv, pp. 463-537, and maps.

—— and PUGH, W. J.    1916.    " The Geology of the District around Machynlleth and the Llyfnant Valley." *Quart. Journ. Geol. Soc.*, vol. lxxi (1915), pp. 343-385, with geol. map.

KING, W. B. R.    1923.    " The Upper Ordovician Rocks of the South-Western Berwyn Hills." *Quart. Journ. Geol. Soc.*, vol. lxxix, pp. 487-507.*

——.    1928.    " The Geology of the District around Meifod (Montgomeryshire)." *Quart. Journ. Geol. Soc.*, vol. lxxxiv, pp. 671-702, with geol. map.

LAKE, P.    1906-1946.    "A Monograph of British Cambrian Trilobites." Part IX, 1935.    *Palaeont. Soc.*

LEWIS, H. P.    1926.    " On *Bolopora undosa* gen. et sp. nov. : a Rock-building Bryozoan with Phosphatized Skeleton, from the Basal Arenig Rocks of Ffestiniog (North Wales)." *Quart. Journ. Geol. Soc.*, vol. lxxxii, pp. 411-427.*

——.    1937.    " Calcareous Algae (*Ortonella* and *Rhabdoporella*) in the Llandoverian Rocks of Wales." *Ann. Mag. Nat. Hist.*, Ser. 10, vol. xx, pp. 617-623.*

——.    1940.    " The Microfossils of the Upper Caradocian Phosphate Deposits of Montgomeryshire, North Wales." *Ann. Mag. Nat. Hist.*, Ser. 10, vol. v, pp. 1-39.*

MARR, J. E. and ROBERTS, T.    1885.    " The Lower Palaeozoic Rocks of the Neighbourhood of Haverfordwest." *Quart. Journ. Geol. Soc.*, vol. xli, pp. 476-491, with geol. map.

MATLEY, C. A. and WILSON, T. S.    1946.    " The Harlech Dome, North of the Barmouth Estuary." *Quart. Journ. Geol. Soc.*, vol. cii, pp. 1-40, with geol. map.

MOORE, L. R.    1945.    " The Geological Sequence of the South Wales Coalfield : the ' South Crop ' and Caerphilly Basin and its Correlation with the Taff Valley Sequence." *Proc. S. Wales Inst. Eng.*, vol. lx, pp. 141-252, with geol. map.

—— and COX, A. H.    1943.    " The Coal Measure Sequence in the Taff Valley, Glamorgan, and its Correlation with the Rhondda Valley Sequence." *Proc. S. Wales Inst. Eng.*, vol. lix, pp. 189-304, with geol. map.*

MORTON, G. H.    1879.    " The Carboniferous Limestone and Millstone Grit of Llangollen." *Proc. Liverpool Geol. Soc.*, vol. iii, pp. 299-325, 371-428.

MURCHISON, R. I.    1839.    " The Silurian System." 2 vols., *London.*

NEAVERSON, E.    1929.    " Faunal Horizons in the Carboniferous Limestone of the Vale of Clwyd." *Proc. Liverpool Geol. Soc.*, vol. xv, pp. 111-133.

——.    1930.    " The Carboniferous Rocks around Prestatyn, Dyserth and Newmarket (Flintshire)." *Proc. Liverpool Geol. Soc.*, vol. xv, pp. 181-212, with geol. map.

——.    1935.    " The Carboniferous Limestone between Colwyn and Abergele (Denbighshire)." *Proc. Liverpool Geol. Soc.*, vol. xvi, pp. 221-233, with geol. map.

——. 1937. " The Carboniferous Rocks between Llandudno and Colwyn Bay, North Wales." *Proc. Liverpool Geol. Soc.*, vol. xvii, pp. 115-135, with geol. maps.*

——. 1944. " Goniatites from the Carboniferous Limestone of Prestatyn and Newmarket (Flintshire)." *Proc. Liverpool Geol. Soc.*, vol. xviii, pp. 135-143.*

——. 1945. " The Carboniferous Rocks between Abergele and Denbigh." *Proc. Liverpool Geol. Soc.*, vol. xix, pp. 52-68, with geol. map.

NORTH, F. J. 1931. " Coal and the Coalfields in Wales." 2nd ed. *Publ. Nat. Mus. Wales.*

PHILLIPS, J. 1848. " The Malvern Hills, compared with the Palaeozoic Districts of Abberley, etc." *Mem. Geol. Surv.*, vol. ii.

—— and SALTER, J. W. 1848. (In Phillips, J., 1848.) " Palaeontological Appendix to Professor John Phillips' Memoir on the Malvern Hills, compared with the Palaeozoic Districts of Abberley, etc." *Mem. Geol. Surv.*, vol. ii, pt. I, pp. 331-386.*

PRINGLE, J. 1930. " The Geology of Ramsey Island, Pembrokeshire." *Proc. Geol. Assoc.*, vol. xli, pp. 1-31, with geol. map.

PUGH, W. J. 1923. " The Geology of the District around Corris and Aberllefenni (Merionethshire)." *Quart. Journ. Geol. Soc.*, vol. lxxix, pp. 508-541, with geol. map.

RICHARDSON, L. 1905. " The Rhaetic and Contiguous Deposits of Glamorganshire." *Quart. Journ. Geol. Soc.*, vol. lxi, pp. 385-424.

ROBERTS, T. (the late). 1893. " Notes on the Geology of the District West of Caermarthen. Compiled from the Notes of the late T. Roberts, Esq., M.A., F.G.S." *Quart. Journ. Geol. Soc.*, vol. xlix, pp. 166-170, with map.

ROBERTSON, T. 1932. " The Geology of the South Wales Coalfield. Part V. The Country around Merthyr Tydfil. 2nd ed." *Mem. Geol. Surv.*

SALTER, J. W. 1866. " The Geology of North Wales : Palaeontological Appendix." *Mem. Geol. Surv.*, vol. iii.*

SHIRLEY, J. 1936. " Some British Trilobites of the Family Calymenidae." *Quart. Journ. Geol. Soc.*, vol. xcii, pp. 384-422.*

SMYTH, L. B. 1925. "A Contribution to the Geology of Great Orme's Head." *Sci. Proc. Roy. Dublin Soc.*, N.S. vol. xviii, pp. 141-164, with map.*

STRAHAN, A. 1890. " The Geology of the Neighbourhoods of Flint, Mold and Ruthin." *Mem. Geol. Surv.*

—— and WALKER, A. O. 1879. " On the Occurrence of Pebbles with Upper Ludlow Fossils in the Lower Carboniferous Conglomerates of North Wales." *Quart. Journ. Geol. Soc.*, vol. xxxv, pp. 268-274.

—— and CANTRILL, T. C. 1904. " The Geology of the South Wales Coalfield. Part IV. The Country around Bridgend." *Mem. Geol. Surv.*

—— and others. 1907. " The Geology of the South Wales Coalfield. Part VII. The Country around Ammanford." *Mem. Geol. Surv.*

—— and others. 1909. " The Geology of the South Wales Coalfield. Part X. The Country around Carmarthen." *Mem. Geol. Surv.*

—— and others. 1914. " The Geology of the South Wales Coalfield. Part XI. The Country around Haverfordwest." *Mem. Geol. Surv.*

TRUEMAN, A. E. 1920. " The Liassic Rocks of the Cardiff District." *Proc. Geol. Assoc.*, vol. xxxi, pp. 93-103, with geol. map.

——. 1922. " The Liassic Rocks of Glamorgan." *Proc. Geol. Assoc.*, vol. xxxiii, pp. 245-284, with geol. map.

——. 1929. " Some New Carboniferous Lamellibranchs." *Ann. Mag. Nat. Hist.*, Ser. 10, vol. iv, pp. 82-95.

TRUEMAN, A. E. and WARE, W. D. 1932. "Additions to the Fauna of the Coal Measures of South Wales." *Trans. S. Wales Inst. Eng.*, vol. xlviii, pp. 67-85.

WALTON, J. 1926. "Contributions to the knowledge of Lower Carboniferous Plants. I and II." *Phil. Trans. Roy. Soc.*, Ser. B, vol. ccxv, pp. 201-224.*

——. 1931. "Contributions to the knowledge of Lower Carboniferous Plants. III." *Phil. Trans. Roy. Soc.*, Ser. B, vol. ccxix, pp. 347-379.*

WARE, W. D. 1939. "The Millstone Grit of Carmarthenshire." *Proc. Geol. Assoc.*, vol. l, pp. 168-204, with geol. map.*

WEDD, C. B. 1932. "Notes on the Ordovician Rocks of Bausley, Montgomeryshire." *Summ. Prog. Geol. Surv. for 1931*, Pt. II, pp. 49-55, with geol. map.

—— and KING, W. B. R. 1924. "The Geology of the Country around Flint, Hawarden and Caergwrle." *Mem. Geol. Surv.*

——, SMITH, B. and WILLS, L. J. 1927. "The Geology of the Country around Wrexham. Part I. Lower Palaeozoic and Lower Carboniferous Rocks." *Mem. Geol. Surv.*

——, SMITH, B. and WILLS, L. J. 1928. "The Geology of the Country around Wrexham. Part II. Coal Measures and Newer Formations." *Mem. Geol. Surv.*

——, SMITH, B., KING, W. B. R. and WRAY, D. A. 1929. "The Country around Oswestry." *Mem. Geol. Surv.*

WHITE, E. I. 1938. "New Pteraspids from South Wales." *Quart. Journ. Geol. Soc.*, vol. xciv, pp. 85-115.*

WHITTINGTON, H. B. 1938a. "The Fauna of the Lluest Quarry, Llanfyllin (*Wattsella horderleyensis* Superzone), and its Correlation." *Proc. Geol. Assoc.*, vol. xlix, pp. 49-54.*

WHITTINGTON, H. B. 1938b. "The Geology of the District around Llansantffraid ym Mechain, Montgomeryshire." *Quart. Journ. Geol. Soc.*, vol. xciv, pp. 423-457, with geol. map.

WILLIAMS, H. and BULMAN, O. M. B. 1931. "The Geology of the Dolwyddelan Syncline (North Wales)." *Quart. Journ. Geol. Soc.*, vol. lxxxvii, pp. 425-458, with geol. map.

WILLS, L. J. and SMITH, B. 1922. "The Lower Palaeozoic Rocks of the Llangollen District, with special Reference to the Tectonics." *Quart. Journ. Geol. Soc.*, vol. lxxviii, pp. 176-226, with geol. map.

WOOD, A. 1936. "Fish Remains from the North Wales Coalfield." *Geol. Mag.*, vol. lxxiii, pp. 481-488.

——. 1937a. "The Non-Marine Lamellibranchs of the North Wales Coalfield." *Quart. Journ. Geol. Soc.*, vol. xciii, pp. 1-22.

——. 1937b. "Goniatite Zones of the Millstone Grit Series in North Wales." *Proc. Liverpool Geol. Soc.*, vol. xvii, pp. 10-28.

# Scotland

## ABERDEEN

**Rhynie.** Dryden, 1½ miles S. of Rhynie. ¼ mile S.S.W. of Dryden Farm near top of hollow in old quarry-hole under a rowan-tree.
Middle Old Red Sandstone, Rhynie Chert (a fossilized peat), with remains of woody plants showing microstructure ; also crustacea and air-breathing arthropods (the earliest known insects).
Kidston, R. and Lang, W. H. 1917, 1920, 1921. Scourfield, D. J. 1926, 1940.
Geol. Surv. 76 ; Ord. Pop. 39.

## ARGYLL

**Campbelltown.** Tirfergus Glen, 4 miles S.W. of Campbelltown.
Carboniferous, Lower Limestone Series, with plants, brachiopods, molluscs and trilobites.
Geol. Surv. 12 ; Ord. Pop. 76.

## ARGYLL (ARDNAMURCHAN)

**Kilchoan.** Rocks at headland and on shore near high water mark N. of Rudha a Mhile, Mingay, Kilchoan.
Jurassic, Lower Lias, with lamellibranchs and rhynchonellid brachiopods.
Richey, J. E. and Thomas, H. H. 1930, p. 38.
Geol. Surv. 52 ; Ord. Pop. 46.

**Kilchoan.** Rudha Aird an Iasgaich, on shore just S. of pier.
Jurassic, Lower Lias (Broadford Beds, ? *planorbis* zone), with lamellibranchs.
Richey, J. E. and Thomas, H. H. 1930, p. 39.
Geol. Surv. 52 ; Ord. Pop. 46.

**Kilchoan.** On shore at Mingary Castle and also 40 yds. and 90-165 yds. E. 21° S. of castle.
Jurassic, Lower Lias (Broadford Beds, *Gryphaea* Limestone), with rhynchonellid brachiopods, lamellibranchs and ammonites.
Richey, J. E. and Thomas, H. H. 1930, p. 39.
Geol. Surv. 52 ; Ord. Pop. 46.

**Kilchoan.** Shore S.W. of Mingary Castle and below sill on which the castle stands.
Jurassic, Lower Lias (Broadford Beds), with rhynchonellid brachiopods, lamellibranchs and ammonites.
Richey, J. E. and Thomas, H. H. 1930, p. 39.
Geol. Surv. 52 ; Ord. Pop. 46.

**Kilchoan.** Shore below Ormsaigbeg.
Jurassic, Lower Lias (? *oxynotum* zone), with belemnites, lamellibranchs and crinoids.
Richey, J. E. and Thomas, H. H. 1930, p. 42.
Geol. Surv. 51 ; Ord. Pop. 46.

**Kilchoan.** W. shore of Kilchoan Bay, 1500 yds. S.W. of landing-jetty
Jurassic, Upper Lias (ironstone of *jurense* zone resting on black shales of *serpentinum* zone), with brachiopods, lamellibranchs and ammonites.
Richey, J. E. and Thomas, H. H. 1930, pp. 34, 43.
Geol. Surv. 52 ; Ord. Pop. 46.

**Kilchoan.** Shore 500 yds. E. 6° S., 450 yds. E. 15° S. and 390 yds. E. 25° S. of Maol Buidhe trigonometrical station.
Jurassic, Inferior Oolite (*opalinum* and *murchisonae* zones), with rhynchonellid brachiopods, lamellibranchs and ammonites.
Richey, J. E. and Thomas, H. H. 1930, pp. 34, 45-47.
Geol. Surv. 51 ; Ord. Pop. 46.

**Kilchoan.** 390 yds. E. 25° S. and in cliffs 358 yds. E. 25° S. of Maol Buidhe trigonometrical station.
Jurassic, Inferior Oolite (*sowerbyi* zone), with brachiopods and ammonites.
Richey, J. E. and Thomas, H. H. 1930, pp. 34, 47-48.
Geol. Surv. 51 ; Ord. Pop. 46.

**Kilmory.** Ockle Point, Ockle.
Jurassic, Lower Lias (Broadford Beds), with lamellibranchs.
Richey, J. E. and Thomas, H. H. 1930, p. 40.
Geol. Surv. 52 ; Ord. Pop. 46.

**Kilmory.** Shore ½ miles N. of Kilmory.
Jurassic, Lower Lias (Broadford Beds, top of *semicostatum* zone, in a volcanic vent), with lamellibranchs.
Richey, J. E. and Thomas, H. H. 1930, p. 40.
Geol. Surv. 52 ; Ord. Pop. 46.

**Kilmory.** Shore of bay on W. side of Garbh Rudha.
Jurassic, Lower Lias, with corals and lamellibranchs.
Richey, J. E. and Thomas, H. H. 1930, p. 40.
Geol. Surv. 52 ; Ord. Pop. 46.

# ARGYLL (MULL)

**Ardmeanach,** Shore 300 yds. S.S.E., 200 yds. S.S.E. and 200 yds. N. of Ard na h'-Iolaire, The Wilderness.
Jurassic, Lower Lias (*planorbis* zone, oyster bed facies), with lamellibranchs and ammonites.
Bailey, E. B. and Anderson, E. M. 1925, pp. 47-49.
Geol. Surv. 43 ; Ord. Pop. 59.

**Bunessan.** E. side of Carsaig Bay at low water.
Jurassic, Lower Lias (*raricostatum* zone), with brachiopods, lamellibranchs and ammonites.
Lee, G. W. and Bailey, E. B. 1925, pp. 84-85.
Geol. Surv. 44 ; Ord. Pop. 59.

**Bunessan.** W. side of Carsaig Bay at low water.
Jurassic, Lower Lias (*jamesoni* zone), with lamellibranchs, belemnites and ammonites.
Lee, G. W. and Bailey, E. B. 1925, pp. 85-86.
Geol. Surv. 44 ; Ord. Pop. 59.

**Bunessan.** Ardtun, peninsula between Loch na Lathaich and Loch Sciolain.
Eocene, leaf beds, with plant-remains and elytra of beetles.
Bailey, E. B. and others 1924, chap. 4.
Geol. Surv. 43 ; Ord. Pop. 59.

**Carsaig.** Exposure just above old quarries below the Nun's Pass.
Jurassic, Upper Lias (*serpentinum* zone), with ammonites, lamellibranchs, etc.
Lee, G. W. and Bailey, E. B. 1925, p. 97.
Geol. Surv. 44 ; Ord. Pop. 59-60.

**Gribun.** Allt na Teangaidh, between 400 yds. E. 7° N. and 450 yds.
E. 12° S. of Balmeanach Farm.
Triassic, Rhaetic (*Pteria contorta* beds), with lamellibranchs and fish-scales.
Bailey, E. B. and Anderson, E. M. 1925, pp. 45-47.
Geol. Surv. 43 ; Ord. Pop. 59.

**Gribun.** Escarpment exposures just over ½ mile S.W. of Balmeanach Farm.
Triassic, Rhaetic (*Pteria contorta* beds), with lamellibranchs.
Bailey, E. B. and Anderson, E. M. 1925, pp. 45-47.
Geol. Surv. 43 ; Ord. Pop. 59.

**Gribun.** Bank of small stream above waterfall 275 yds. W. of Gribun School.
Triassic, Rhaetic, with lamellibranchs.
Bailey, E. B. and Anderson, E. M. 1925, p. 47.
Geol. Surv. 43 ; Ord. Pop. 53.

**Gribun.** Sloc nan Con, section in small stream midway between Sloc nan
Con and Caisteal Sloc nan Ban, 1¼ miles S.W. of Balmeanach Farm.
Triassic, Rhaetic, with lamellibranchs.
Bailey, E. B. and Anderson, E. M. 1925, p. 46.
Geol. Surv. 43 ; Ord. Pop. 59.

**Gribun.** Allt na Teangaidh, below road in bank.
Cretaceous, Cenomanian Greensand, with lamellibranchs.
Bailey, E. B. and Anderson, E. M. 1925, p. 51.
Geol. Surv. 43 ; Ord. Pop. 59.

**Gribun.** Below road 350 yds. E. 35° N. of Balmeanach Farm.
Cretaceous, Cenomanian Greensand, with rhynchonellid brachiopods and
lamellibranchs.
Bailey, E. B. and Anderson, E. M. 1925, p. 51.
Geol. Surv. 43 ; Ord. Pop. 53.

**Lochbuie.** Port Donain, S. shore on W. side of small sandy bay.
Jurassic, Inferior Oolite (*opalinum* zone), with brachiopods, lamellibranchs,
belemnites and ammonites.
Lee, G. W. and Bailey, E. B. 1925, pp. 62, 108-110.
Geol. Surv. 44 ; Ord. Pop. 60.

**Lochbuie.** Port nam Marbh, coast-section immediately S.W. of little bay.
Jurassic, Inferior Oolite (*murchisonae* zone), with bryozoa, brachiopods,
lamellibranchs, gastropods, belemnites and ammonites common in 6 ft. of
grey, siliceous limestone some 30 ft. above Lias shales.
Lee, G. W. and Bailey, E. B. 1925, pp. 62, 99, 103.
Geol. Surv. 44 ; Ord. Pop. 60.

**Lochdonhead.** Right bank of stream in Ardnadrochet Glen, 1 mile S.S.E.
of Ardnadrochet Farm and 700 yds. N.N.W. of Auchnacraig Farm.
Jurassic, Inferior Oolite (*opalinum* and *murchisonae* zones), with bryozoa,
brachiopods, lamellibranchs and ammonites.
Lee, G. W. and Bailey, E. B. 1925, pp. 62, 100-103.
Geol. Surv. 44 ; Ord. Pop. 60.

## AYRSHIRE

**Annbank.** Left bank of R. Ayr opposite Annbank and just S. of piers of
old bridge 1 mile N. of Tarholm Bridge.
Carboniferous, Coal Measures (*similis-pulchra* zone, measures between Ell
Coal and base of Barren Red Measures), with a rich plant-bed.
Geol. Surv. 14 ; Ord. Pop. 78.

**Ballantrae.** Bennane Head, S. of Bennane Cave ; section begins 50 yds. N. of mouth of Bennane Burn.
Ordovician, Arenig, with graptolites.
Peach, B. N. and Horne, J. 1899, pp. 433, 435.
Geol. Surv. 7 ; Ord. Pop. 82.

**Ballantrae.** N. side of Portandea Bay, 2 miles N. of Glen App.
Ordovician, Caradoc (Glenkiln shale), with graptolites and small brachiopods.
Peach, B. N. and Horne, J. 1899, pp. 421-423.
Geol. Surv. 7 ; Ord. Pop. 82.

**Barr.** Kirriemore Burn, in bank about 1 mile E. of Kirriereoch Loch, 8 miles E.S.E. of Barr.
Ordovician, Caradoc (Glenkiln shales), with graptolites.
Peach, B. N. and Horne, J. 1899, p. 418.
Geol. Surv. 8 ; Ord. Pop. 87.

**Barr.** Balclatchie Bridge, about 200 yds. W. of waterworks on roadside and exactly opposite on left bank of Penwhapple Burn.
Ordovician, Caradoc (Balclatchie Mudstones), with graptolites, brachiopods, molluscs and trilobites.
Peach, B. N. and Horne, J. 1899, pp. 508-509.
Geol. Surv. 8 ; Ord. Pop. 82.

**Barr.** Section in Penwhapple Burn by roadside, in bed of stream and in cliff on S. Bank, about 2 miles N.W. of Barr.
Ordovician, Caradoc (Balclatchie Mudstones), with graptolites, brachiopods, molluscs, etc.
Peach, B. N. and Horne, J. 1899, pp. 508-510.
Geol. Surv. 8 ; Ord. Pop. 83.

**Barr.** W. branch of Benan Burn (tributary to R. Stinchar 2½ miles S.W. of Barr), W. of limestone quarry.
Ordovician, Caradoc (Stinchar Limestone group), with graptolites and brachiopods.
Peach, B. N. and Horne, J. 1899, pp. 487-488.
Geol. Surv. 8 ; Ord. Pop. 82.

**Barr.** Trochraigue, wood N. of house and near little pond near old toll-bar, 4¾ miles N.W. of Barr.
Ordovician, Caradoc (Stinchar Limestone group), with graptolites, brachiopods, lamellibranchs and trilobites.
Peach, B. N. and Horne, J. 1899, pp. 504-505.
Geol. Surv. 8 ; Ord. Pop. 82-83.

**Barr.** Tormitchell (Tramitchell) limestone quarries, S.S.E. of Tormitchell, 3 miles W. of Barr.
Ordovician, Caradoc (Stinchar Limestone group), with brachiopods, molluscs, etc. Type-locality of the calcareous alga *Girvanella*.
Peach, B. N. and Horne, J. 1899, pp. 493-494.
Geol. Surv. 8 ; Ord. Pop. 82.

**Barr.** Section at prominent bend of Penwhapple Glen, 300 yds. N. of foot of Penkill Burn, 4 miles N.W. of Barr.
Silurian, Llandovery (Tarannon Series), with graptolites, brachiopods, lamellibranchs and cephalopods.
Peach, B. N. and Horne, J. 1899, pp. 545-546.
Geol. Surv. 8 ; Ord. Pop. 82.

**Barr.** Head of Bargany Pond Burn, which rises on W. slope of Hadyard Hill, near Littlelane, 3 miles N.N.W. of Barr.
Silurian, Llandovery (Carnregan Group), with brachiopods, trilobites, etc.
Peach, B. N. and Horne, J. 1899, pp. 537-538.
Geol. Surv. 8 ; Ord. Pop. 83.

**Barr.** Section at foot of rivulet 100 yds. S. of E. limit of Blackwood Head Plantation, 3½ miles N.N.W. of Barr.

Silurian, Llandovery (Bargany Group), 100 yds. S. of faulted junction with Carboniferous, yields corals, trilobites, brachiopods and plants.

Peach, B. N. and Horne, J. 1899, p. 546.

Geol. Surv. 8 ; Ord. Pop. 82.

**Barrhill.** Cross Water (which joins Duisk Water at Barrhill), at a point above Linn Dubh, ¾ mile S.W. of Barrhill and 400 yds. S.S.E. of Ward.

Ordovician, Caradoc (Glenkiln shales) with graptolites.

Peach, B. N. and Horne, J. 1899, p. 417.

Geol. Surv. 8 ; Ord. Pop. 82.

**Beith.** Broadstone Quarry, 1 mile E.S.E. of Beith.

Carboniferous, Lower Limestone Series (Broadstone or Blackbyre Limestone), with corals, brachiopods, lamellibranchs, arthropods and fish-remains.

Richey, J. E. and others 1930, pp. 144-145. Hill, D. 1937-1941, p. 21.

Geol. Surv. 22 ; Ord. Pop. 72.

**Beith.** Quarry a little N. of Trearne House, Gateside, 1¼ miles E. of Beith.

Carboniferous, Lower Limestone Series (Broadstone Limestone), with corals, bryozoa, productid brachiopods, etc.

Richey, J. E. and others 1930, p. 146. Hill, D. 1937-1941, p. 23.

Geol. Surv. 22 ; Ord. Pop. 72.

**Beith.** Section in Dusk Water, 20 yds., 330 yds. and 440 yds. below Hessilhead Bridge, 2¼ miles E.S.E. of Beith.

Carboniferous, Lower Limestone Series (Dockra and Hosie Limestones) with productid and other brachiopods, and gastropods.

Richey, J. E. and others 1930, pp. 142, 146, 148.

Geol. Surv. 22 ; Ord. Pop. 72.

**Beith.** Dockra Quarry, 1¼ miles S.E. of Beith.

Carboniferous, Lower Limestone Series (Dockra Limestone), with corals, productid brachiopods and lamellibranchs.

Richey, J. E. and others 1930, pp. 146-147.

Geol. Surv. 22 ; Ord. Pop. 72.

**Benquhat.** Gully 1 mile, 300 yds. S.E. of E. end of Benquhat.

Carboniferous, Coal Measures (Skipsey's Marine Band), with *Lingula* and productid brachiopods, lamellibranchs and gastropods.

Geol. Surv. 14 ; Ord. Pop. 83.

**Beoch.** Black Water, 1¼ miles W. 5° N. of Beoch Cottages, at the Chalybeate Springs 5 miles S.W. of Ayr.

Carboniferous, Coal Measures, with non-marine shells.

Geol. Surv. 14 ; Ord. Pop. 83.

**Bowerhill.** Shore 100 yds., 150 yds. and 180 yds. N.W. of Bowerhill, 3½ miles W. 40° S. of Ayr ; also reefs 300 yds. N.E. of Bowerhill.

Carboniferous, Cementstone Series, with lamellibranchs, ostracods, fish-remains, etc.

Geol. Surv. 14 ; Ord. Pop. 78.

**Busby,** 7 miles S. of Glasgow. Thornton Quarry, 2 miles S.E. of Busby.

Carboniferous, Lower Limestone Series (Main = Hurlet Limestone), with corals, productid brachiopods, molluscs, etc.

Richey, J. E. and others 1930, pp. 165-167.

Geol. Surv. 22 ; Ord. Pop. 72.

**Carsphairn.** Garryhorn Burn, 150 yds. S.E. of Garryhorn Farm and a few yards further downstream, 1 mile W. of Carsphairn.

Ordovician, Caradoc (Glenkiln black shale), with graptolites.

Peach, B. N. and Horne, J. 1899, pp. 378-379.

Geol. Surv. 8 ; Ord. Pop. 83.

**Carsphairn.** Water of Deugh, ¼ mile below Knockingarroch, 2 miles N. of Carsphairn.
Ordovician, Caradoc (Glenkiln shales), with graptolites.
Peach, B. N. and Horne, J. 1899, pp. 377-378.
Geol. Surv. 8 ; Ord. Pop. 83.

**Carsphairn.** E. slope of Cairnsgarroch Hill ; head of middle of three rivulets which unite to form Halfmark Burn, 1 mile S.W. of Carsphairn.
Ordovician, Caradoc (Hartfell shales), with graptolites.
Peach, B. N. and Horne, J. 1899, p. 382.
Geol. Surv. 8 ; Ord. Pop. 83.

**Cronberry.** Gass Water ; (1) in banks and bed of stream 517 yds. S. 41° E. of, (2) 766 and 784 yds. S. 33° E. of, (3) left bank, 855, 883 and 1083 yds. S. 35° E. of Stonebriggs, Cronberry.
Carboniferous, Lower and Upper Limestone Series, with corals, sea-urchins, brachiopods, lamellibranchs and trilobites.
Geol. Serv. 15 ; Ord. Pop. 78.

**Dalblair.** (1) In bank of Dornal Burn entering Glenmuir Water ; (2) Base of high bank 63 yds. above confluence, 600 yds. E. 6° N. of Guelt Farm ; (3) In burn 700 yds. N. 11° W. of Low Dalblair.
Carboniferous, Lower Limestone Series, with sea-urchins, brachiopods and molluscs.
Geol. Surv. 15 ; Ord. Pop. 78.

**Dalblair.** Glenmuir Water. (1) Left bank 383-458 yds. E. 26° N. of Guelt Farm ; (2), 700 yds. E. 10° N. of farm ; (3) High up on bank in scaur 1066 yds. E. 42° N. and 507 yds. W. of Kyle Farm.
Carboniferous, Lower Limestone Series, with crinoids, productid brachiopods and molluscs.
Geol. Surv. 15 ; Ord. Pop. 78.

**Dalmellington.** E. bank of Water of Deugh, about 500 yds. S. of mouth of Pochriegavin Burn.
Ordovician, Caradoc (Glenkiln-Hartfell Series), with graptolites.
Geol. Surv. 14 ; Ord. Pop. 83.

**Dalmellington.** Tongue Glen, 1½ miles N. of Dalmellington.
Carboniferous, Coal Measures, marine bed a few yards upstream from outcrop of Craigmark Ironstone, with productid brachiopods, lamellibranchs and fish-remains.
Geol. Surv. 14 ; Ord. Pop. 83.

**Dalmellington.** Auldnaw Glen, Beoch, ¾ mile S.S.W. of Upper Beoch, 3½ miles N.W. of Dalmellington.
Carboniferous, Coal Measures (*communis* zone), a thick musselband of beds of shale and ironstone above Pennyvenie High Coal, with well-preserved non-marine shells (*Carbonicola*).
Weir, J. and Leitch, D. 1936, p. 725. MacLennan, R. M. 1946, pp. 92-93.
Geol. Surv. 14 ; Ord. Pop. 83.

**Dalmellington.** Cummock Burn, E. of Clawfin, 1¾ miles W.N.W. of Dalmellington.
Carboniferous, Coal Measures (*communis* zone), with well-preserved solid non-marine shells (*Carbonicola* aff. *pseudorobusta*).
MacLennan, R. M. 1946, p. 93. Trueman, A. E. and Weir, J. 1947, pl. ix, figs. 7-10.
Geol. Surv. 14 ; Ord. Pop. 83.

**Dalry.** Cunningham Baidland, in bank of Rye Water 660 yds. W. of Hindog Farm, 1 mile N. 27° W. of Dalry.

Carboniferous, Lower Limestone Series (base of Dockra Limestone), with brachiopods, lamellibranchs and gastropods.
Richey, J. E. and others 1930, p. 152. Hill, D. 1937-1941, p. 23.
Geol. Surv. 22 ; Ord. Pop. 72.

**Dalry.** Auchenskeith Quarry, 2¼ miles S.S.E. of Dalry.
Carboniferous, Lower Limestone Series (Dockra and Broadstone Limestones), with corals, productid and other brachiopods and lamellibranchs.
Richey, J. E. and others 1930, p. 150. Hill, D. 1937-1941, p. 20.
Geol. Surv. 22 ; Ord. Pop. 72.

**Dalry.** Caaf Water, 420-750 yds. upstream from Linn Spout and in gully opposite old mill at Linn Spout ; also Linn Spout Quarry, ¾ mile S. of Dalry.
Carboniferous, " Millstone Grit " (Linn = Calmy Limestone), with brachiopods, lamellibranchs and fish and plant remains.
Richey, J. E. and others 1930, pp. 176-177.
Geol. Surv. 22 ; Ord. Pop. 72.

**Dunlop.** Old quarry ¼ mile E. of Middleton Farm and just over 2 miles N.N.W. of Dunlop.
Carboniferous, Lower Limestone Series, with productid and other brachiopods.
Geol. Surv. 22 ; Ord. Pop. 72.

**Dunlop.** Gameshill Quarry, 1 mile N.N.W. of Stewarton.
Carboniferous, Lower Limestone Series (Dockra Limestone overlain by Hosie Limestone A), with athyrid and productid brachiopods, corals and fish-remains.
Richey, J. E. and others 1930, pp. 158-159. Hill, D. 1937-1941, p. 24.
Geol. Surv. 22 ; Ord. Pop. 72.

**Galston.** In bank of Killoch Burn, 590, 580 and 290 yds. above road bridge at Killoch ; in bed of burn 320 yds. W. 37° S. and 770 yds. W. of Killoch ; also tip of old quarry in bank of burn 220 yds. E. 11° S. of Killoch, 3 miles S.E. of Galston.
Carboniferous, Cementstone, Lower Limestone and Upper Limestone Series, with brachiopods, molluscs and crustacea.
Geol. Surv. 22 ; Ord. Pop. 78.

**Galston.** Bank of Polbaith Burn, 230 yds. N. 28° W. of Redding and bed of burn 220 yds. N. 38° W. of Redding, 2 miles N. of Galston.
Carboniferous, Lower Limestone Series, with corals and brachiopods.
Richey, J. E. and others 1930, p. 161.
Geol. Surv. 22 ; Ord. Pop. 78.

**Galston.** Bank and bed of Hag Burn, ½ mile N. of Hag Bridge, 1 mile N. of Galston.
Carboniferous, Lower Limestone Series, with productid and other brachiopods, lamellibranchs and gastropods.
Richey, J. E. and others 1930, pp. 160-163.
Geol. Surv. 22 ; Ord. Pop. 78.

**Galston.** Bed of Burn Anne, 100-700 yds. N.W. of Cessnock Castle, Galston.
Carboniferous, Limestone Coal Series, overlain by Coal Measures (*similis-pulchra* zone, from Wee Coal to Major Coal). Non-marine lamellibranchs, the horny brachiopod *Lingula* and plants occur.
Richey, J. E. and others 1930, pp. 161-163, 233. Weir, J. and Leitch, D. 1936, pp. 720, 723.
Geol. Surv. 22 ; Ord. Pop. 78.

**Girvan.** Minuntion Farm, exposure behind old limekiln W. of farm.
Ordovician, Caradoc (Barr Series, *Orthis confinis* beds), with brachiopods,
trilobites, etc.
Peach, B. N. and Horne, J. 1899, pp. 489–490.
Geol. Surv. 8 ; Ord. Pop. 82.

**Girvan.** Ardmillan Braes, old quarries ½ mile E.S.E. of Ardwell Farm.
Ordovician, Caradoc (Balclatchie Group), with brachiopods, molluscs and
trilobites.
Peach, B. N. and Horne, J. 1899, pp. 512–514.
Geol. Surv. 7 ; Ord. Pop. 82.

**Girvan.** Both sides of gorge of Laggan Gill, 400 yds. W. of Laggan Farm.
Ordovician, Caradoc (Balclatchie Group, resting on Benan Conglomerate).
Graptolites and brachiopods occur, the former in exquisite solid preservation
in limestone.
Peach, B. N. and Horne, J. 1899, p. 512. Bulman, O. M. B. 1944–1947.
Geol. Surv. 7 ; Ord. Pop. 82.

**Girvan.** Woodland Point and beach at low water, ¾ mile S. of Craigskelly.
Silurian, Lower Llandovery, with graptolites, corals, bryozoa, brachiopods,
trilobites and cephalopods.
Peach, B. N. and Horne, J. 1899, pp. 542–543.
Geol. Surv. 7 ; Ord. Pop. 82.

**Glenbuck.** (1) Large quarry 800 yds. S. 50° W. of Airdsgreen ; (2) In
banks of burn 1000 yds. W. 26° S. of Airdsgreen ; (3) Bed of small burn
¼ mile S. 12° W. of Airdsgreen, 1 mile S.W. of Glenbuck.
Carboniferous, Lower Limestone Series, with corals, brachiopods, lamellibranchs and gastropods.
Geol. Surv. 15 ; Ord. Pop. 79.

**House of Hill.** Crag on N.W. slope of Larg Hill, 3½ miles S.W. of Loch Dee.
Ordovician, Caradoc (Glenkiln Shales), with graptolites.
Peach, B. N. and Horne, J. 1899, pp. 388–389.
Geol. Surv. 8 ; Ord. Pop. 87.

**House of Hill.** Pulnabrick Burn, 500 yds. upstream from Loch Trool.
Ordovician, Caradoc (Glenkiln shales), with graptolites.
Peach, B. N. and Horne, J. 1899, pp. 395–396.
Geol. Surv. 8 ; Ord. Pop. 87.

**Kilbirnie.** Pitcon Burn, 150, 80 and 50 yds. upstream from and 100–390
yds. downstream from Gowkhouse Burn.
Carboniferous, Lower Limestone Series (Top Hosie Limestone, ? Johnstone
Shell Bed), with brachiopods and lamellibranchs.
Richey, J. E. and others 1930, p. 139.
Geol. Surv. 22 ; Ord. Pop. 72.

**Kilbirnie.** Paduff Burn, 610–810 yds. upstream from Largs road, Kilbirnie.
Carboniferous, Lower Limestone Series (Johnstone Shell Bed, Hosie and
Dockra Limestones), with brachiopods, molluscs, ostracods and plants.
Richey, J. E. and others 1930, pp. 151–154.
Geol. Surv. 22 ; Ord. Pop. 72.

**Kilbirnie.** S. Howrat Quarry, N. of Howrat, 2 miles W. of Kilbirnie.
Carboniferous, Lower Limestone Series, with brachiopods, lamellibranchs
and gastropods.
Richey, J. E. and others 1930, p. 153.
Geol. Surv. 22 ; Ord. Pop. 72.

**Kilmarnock.** Inchgotrick old quarries, ¼ mile S.S.E. of Inchgotrick Farm,
3 miles S. of Kilmarnock, also ¼ mile S.E. of this, E. of Braeside.

Carboniferous, Lower Limestone Series, with corals, brachiopods, lamelli-branchs and gastropods.

Richey, J. E. and others 1930, pp. 139, 162-164, 190-195.

Geol. Surv. 22 ; Ord. Pop. 78.

**Kilmarnock.** Fenwick Water, 210 yds. and 440 yds. S.E. of Meiklewood.

Carboniferous, " Millstone Grit," with brachiopods, lamellibranchs (*Schizodus wheeleri*), etc.

Richey, J. E. and others 1930, p. 205.

Geol. Surv. 22 ; Ord. Pop. 78.

**Kilmarnock.** Upstream and downstream from confluence of Fenwick and Craufurdland Waters to form Kilmarnock Water, ⅓ mile E. of Wardneuk, 1¼ miles N.N.E. of Kilmarnock.

Carboniferous, Coal Measures (*communis* to *similis-pulchra* zones, Kilwinning Main to Hurlford Main Coals).  Non-marine lamellibranchs occur at various levels, notably solid *Carbonicola pseudorobusta* at junction of right-bank tribu-tary below Wardneuk, and the same species, crushed, in beds of Craufurdland and Fenwick Waters, 500 yds. upstream from Dean Castle.

Weir, J. and Leitch, D. 1936, p. 719.

Geol. Surv. 22 ; Ord. Pop. 78.

**Kilmaurs.** Greenhill Quarry, 1 mile S.S.W. of Kilmaurs.

Carboniferous, Coal Measures (*similis-pulchra* zone, Darroch Coal), with plant and fish remains and arthropods.

Richey, J. E. and others 1930, pp. 233, 249. Weir, J. and Leitch, D. 1936, pp. 720, 723.

Geol. Surv. 22 ; Ord. Pop. 78.

**Lendalfoot.** Shore-section 1 mile N. of Lendalfoot, 50 yds. S. of mouth of Pinbain Burn and N. of burn where old cliff abuts on road.

Ordovician, Arenig, shales with graptolites.

Peach, B. N. and Horne, J. 1899, p. 442.

Geol. Surv. 7 ; Ord. Pop. 82.

**Lendalfoot.** Coast-section, W. of mouth of burn S. of Balcreuchan Port, ¾ mile N.N.E. of Bennane Head.

Ordovician, Middle and Lower Arenig, with radiolaria, graptolites and brachiopods.

Peach, B. N. and Horne, J. 1899, p. 440.

Geol. Surv. 7 ; Ord. Pop. 82.

**Lugton.** Quarries ¼ and ⅓ mile S.S.W. of Lugton Inn.

Carboniferous, Lower Limestone Series (Dockra Limestone), with corals, brachiopods, gastropods, trilobites and fish.

Richey, J. E. and others 1930, pp. 153-157.

Geol. Surv. 22 ; Ord. Pop. 72.

**Lugton.** Duniflat Burn ; 25-60 yds. below eastern railway bridge ; right branch 110 yds. E. of eastern railway line ; left branch 160 yds. above eastern railway bridge, and 30 and 90 yds. above western railway bridge.

Carboniferous, Lower Limestone Series, Edge Coals, with corals and brachiopods.

Richey, J. E. and others 1930, p. 155.

Geol. Surv. 22 ; Ord. Pop. 72.

**Muirkirk.** 200 yds. up Slot Burn from Seggholm, 3 miles N.N.W. of Muirkirk.

Silurian, Downton Series, with plant and fish remains and rare crustacea.

Peach, B. N. and Horne, J. 1899, p. 578.

Geol. Surv. 23 ; Ord. Pop. 78.

P

**Muirkirk.** (1), Bank of stream 608 yds. S. of, (2) bank of stream 541 yds. S. 7° E. of, (3) bank of stream 430 yds S.S.E. of Walkmill. Also old quarry 633 yds. S.S.W. of Walkmill.
Carboniferous, Lower Limestone Series, with corals, bryozoa, brachiopods and molluscs.
Geol. Surv. 15 ; Ord. Pop. 79.

**Muirkirk.** Bed and banks of Garpel Water, up to 750 yds. S.W. of Springhill.
Carboniferous, Lower and Upper Limestone Series, with corals, bryozoa, brachiopods, molluscs, trilobites, etc.
Geol. Surv. 15 ; Ord. Pop. 78.

**Muirkirk.** (1) Old quarry ½ mile S. 16° E. of, (2) old quarry 600 yds. S. 23° E. of, (3) bank and bed of burn 466 yds. S. 19° E. of, (4) old quarry 468 yds. E. 41° S. of, (5) banks and bed of burn 334 yds. S. 18° E. of Auldhouseburn.
Carboniferous, Lower Limestone Series, with corals, brachiopods, lamellibranchs and gastropods.
Geol. Surv. 15 ; Ord. Pop. 79.

**Muirkirk.** Bank of Ashawburn, 410 yds. S. 18° E. of Walkmill, 1½ miles E.N.E. of Muirkirk.
Carboniferous, Lower Limestone Series, with corals, brachiopods, molluscs and trilobites.
Hill, D. 1937-1941, p. 19.
Geol. Surv. 15 ; Ord. Pop. 79.

**Muirkirk.** Old quarries 733 yds. S. 27° E. and 616 yds. S. 40° E. of railway station.
Carboniferous, Lower Limestone Series, with corals, crinoids, brachiopods and gastropods.
Geol. Surv. 15 ; Ord. Pop. 78.

**New Cumnock.** Muirfoot Burn, 367 yds. S. 27° E., 466 yds. S. 18° E. and 900 yds. S. 10° E. of High Polquheys.
Carboniferous, Lower Limestone Series, with brachiopods and molluscs.
Geol. Surv. 15 ; Ord. Pop. 83.

**New Dailly.** Craighead Quarry, 2 miles W. of New Dailly.
Ordovician, Caradoc (Balclatchie Group, Craighead Limestone), with brachiopods, lamellibranchs, trilobites, etc.
Peach, B. N. and Horne, J. 1899, pp. 462, 501-504. Anderson, F. W. and Pringle, J. 1946.
Geol. Surv. 14 ; Ord. Pop. 82.

**New Dailly.** Section near head of Lady Burn, below waterfall and above junction with tributary from Quarrel Hill.
Ordovician, Ashgill (Drummuck Group, Starfish Beds, a few inches of hard calcareous mudstone), with graptolites, starfish, brachiopods, trilobites, etc.
Peach, B. N. and Horne, J. 1899, pp. 525-526. Lamont, A. 1935, with geol. map.
Geol. Surv. 14 ; Ord. Pop. 82.

**New Dailly.** E. brow of Quarrel Hill about 680 yds. S.W. of High Mains Farm. Locs. 3-5 of Lamont 1935.
Ordovician, Ashgill (Drummuck Group), with brachiopods, gastropods and trilobites.
Lamont, A. 1935, pp. 298-300, with geol. map.
Geol. Surv. 14 ; Ord. Pop. 83.

**New Dailly.** Lady Burn (Threave Glen), between Drummuck Farm and
S. Threave, 2 miles N.W. of New Dailly.
Ordovician, Ashgill (Drummuck Group), with trilobites.
Lamont, A. 1935, with geol. map.
Geol. Surv. 14 ; Ord. Pop. 82.

**New Dailly.** Quarry in wood 150 yds. W. of Rough Neuk Farm and 400
yds. N.E. of High Mains Farm.
Silurian, Llandovery (Mulloch Hill Group), with corals, brachiopods, mol-
luscs, trilobites, etc.
Peach, B. N. and Horne, J. 1899, p. 530.
Geol. Surv. 14 ; Ord. Pop. 83.

**New Dailly.** Section in Glenshalloch Burn.
Silurian, Lower Llandovery (*Monograptus gregarius* zone), with graptolites.
Geol. Surv. 14 ; Ord. Pop. 83.

**Newmilns.** Bank and bed of Huggin Craig Burn, 330 yds. E. 11° N. of
Clearmount, Newmilns.
Carboniferous, Lower Limestone and Limestone Coal Series, with brachio-
pods, lamellibranchs and fish-remains.
Richey, J. E. and others 1930, pp. 138, 163.
Geol. Surv. 22 ; Ord. Pop. 78.

**Ochiltree.** Pit bing at Burnockhill, 2 miles a little W. of S. of Ochiltree.
Carboniferous, Coal Measures, marine bed with brachiopods, lamellibranchs,
fish-remains and plants.
Geol. Surv. 14 ; Ord. Pop. 78.

**Old Cumnock.** Shield Old Quarries, about 3 miles S. of Old Cumnock.
Carboniferous, limestone with corals, productid brachiopods and
lamellibranchs.
Geol. Surv. 14 ; Ord. Pop. 78.

**Old Cumnock.** Old quarries ½ mile W.N.W. and ¼ mile S.W. of Benston,
3 miles S.S.E. of Old Cumnock.
Carboniferous, limestone with corals, brachiopods and fish-remains.
Geol. Surv. 14 ; Ord. Pop. 83.

**Old Cumnock.** Bank of small stream 88 yds. S. 20° W. of Glaisnock House.
Carboniferous, Upper Limestone Series, with brachiopods and molluscs.
Geol. Surv. 14 ; Ord. Pop. 83.

**Port Currarie.** Knockgown, shore-section 600 yds. N. of Port Currarie
and W. of Currarie Farm.
Ordovician, Caradoc (Glenkiln shales), with graptolites.
Peach, B. N. and Horne, J. 1899, pp. 428-429.
Geol. Surv. 7 ; Ord. Pop. 82.

**Saltcoats.** Old quarry 200 yds. N.E. of Diddup Farm and 2 miles N.N.E.
of Saltcoats ; also section along burn.
Carboniferous, Upper Limestone Series, with brachiopods (productids,
orthotetids, rhynchonellids, etc.) and trilobites.
Richey, J. E. and others 1930, pp. 176-177.
Geol. Surv. 22 ; Ord. Pop. 77.

**Saltcoats.** Shore opposite Seaview Road.
Carboniferous, Coal Measures (base of *similis-pulchra* zone), with two
bands of non-marine shells, the lower immediately overlying, and burnt by, a
sill of igneous rock (teschenite).
Weir, J. and Leitch, D. 1936, p. 721.
Geol. Surv. 22 ; Ord. Pop. 77.

**Sorn.** Bed of R. Ayr. N. of Upper Heilar and at confluence with small stream ½ mile W. 41° S. of Upper Heilar, 2¾ miles E. of Sorn.
Carboniferous, Lower Limestone Series, Johnstone Shell Bed and Limestone Coal Series, with bryozoa, brachiopods and lamellibranchs.
Geol. Surv. 14 ; Ord. Pop. 78.

**Sorn.** Bank of Cleugh Burn at disused quarry S.E. of Blairmulloch and in bank of Burn 500 yds. E. of Blairmulloch, 1¾ miles N. of Sorn.
Carboniferous, limestone with crinoids and brachiopods.
Geol. Surv. 14 ; Ord. Pop. 78.

**Sorn.** Bank and bed of R. Ayr, Glenlogan Bridge and 100 yds. above bridge in middle of Sorn.
Carboniferous, limestone with corals, brachiopods, lamellibranchs and trilobites.
Geol. Surv. 14 ; Ord. Pop. 78.

**Sorn.** Bank of burn 335 yds. S.E. and 665 yds. S. 34° E. of Nethershield and 554 yds. S. 42° E. of Nethershield ; also in bank of R. Ayr 716 yds. S. 37° W. and 780 yds. S. 30° E. of Nethershield, 2 miles E.N.E. of Sorn.
Carboniferous, Calciferous Sandstone and Lower Limestone Series, with corals, brachiopods, lamellibranchs and gastropods.
Geol. Surv. 14 ; Ord. Pop. 78.

**Stewarton.** Burn Annick Water at Laigh Clunch, 2¾ miles N.E. of Stewarton, and in bank of westmost stream 40 yds. above bridge and 110 yds. W. 24° N. of Laigh Clunch, 3 miles N. of Fenwick.
Carboniferous, Lower Limestone Series (Hosie Limestone), with brachiopods, lamellibranchs and cephalopods.
Richey, J. E. and others 1930, pp. 157-159.
Geol. Surv. 22 ; Ord. Pop. 72.

**Straiton.** Quarry just N. of road 700 yds. W. 10° N. from Knockgardner Farm and about 2½ miles W.S.W. of Straiton ; and quarry S. of road 400 yds. E. 10° N. of Knockgardner and about 2 miles W. 30° S. of Straiton.
Silurian, Wenlock (Blair, Knockgardner and Straiton Beds), with corals, brachiopods, lamellibranchs and trilobites.
Geol. Surv. 14 ; Ord. Pop. 83.

**Waterside.** At intake for small dam by prominent bend in Dunaskin Glen ; left bank 150 yds. below entrance of Corbie Craigs Burn ; bluff on right bank 130 yds. below Corbie Craigs Burn ; left bank 200 yds. below dam ; bluff on right bank of Corbie Craigs Burn 100 yds. above junction with Dunaskin Glen.
Carboniferous, Coal Measures, with plants and non-marine shells.
Geol. Surv. 14 ; Ord. Pop. 83.

**Waterside.** Keirs Limeworks, about 700 yds. S. 30° E. of Keirs Farm and ¼ mile S. 20° W. of Waterside ; about 860 yds. S. 38° E. of Farm and just E. of wall in old quarry ; old quarry 800 yds. S. 40° E. of Farm and just W. of wall ; 3½ miles W. 30° N. of Dalmellington.
Carboniferous, Upper Limestone Series (First Limestone), with corals and productid brachiopods.
Geol. Surv. 14 ; Ord. Pop. 83.


# BANFFSHIRE

**Fochabers.** Tynet Burn at double bend immediately below old sawmill 600 yds. N. of road bridge. Best locality in right bank at top of cliff, but fossils may be obtained in left bank about 100 yds. W. of sawmill.

Middle Old Red Sandstone (Tynet Fish-Bed), with well-preserved crossopterygian fish (*Osteolepis, Diplopterax, Glyptolepis*), acanthodians (*Diplacanthus, Cheiracanthus, Mesacanthus*) and placoderms (*Coccosteus, Pterichthyodes* and the very rare *Rhamphodopsis*).

Agassiz, L. 1844-1845.
Geol. Surv. 95 ; Ord. Pop. 29.

**Gardenstown of Gamrie.** Den of Findon, 200 yds. S.W. of Findon Farm, about 300 yds. N.W. of Dubford crossroads, on N.E. edge of ravine and in grassy slopes above.

Middle Old Red Sandstone, about 6 feet of clays and limestone-nodules resting on conglomerate. The nodules yield fish, including acanthodians (*Diplacanthus, Cheiracanthus*), placoderms (*Coccosteus decipiens, Pterichthyodes*), crossopterygians (especially *Glyptolepis*) and *Cheirolepis*.

Read, H. H. 1923, p. 171.
Geol. Surv. 96 ; Ord. Pop. 30.

# BERWICKSHIRE

**Allanton.** Blackadder Water above bridge at Allanton, 1¼-1½ miles S.S.W. of Chirnside.

Carboniferous, Cementstone and Calciferous Sandstone Series, with plants and fish-remains.

Geol. Surv. 34 ; Ord. Pop. 75.

**Allanton.** Whiteadder Water above and below Allanton bridge and on right bank ¾ and 1 mile E. of bridge, 1¼ miles S. of Chirnside.

Carboniferous, Cementstone Series, with lamellibranchs, arthropods and fish and plant remains.

Geol. Surv. 34 ; Ord. Pop. 75.

**Berwick-on-Tweed.** Shore between Needles Eye and St. John's Haven, N. of Berwick.

Carboniferous, limestone with productid brachiopods and corals.

Geol. Surv. 34 ; Ord. Pop. 75.

**Cockburnspath.** Siccar Point, E. side, and old slate quarry to the S.W., 250 yds. N.E. of farmhouse, E. of Cockburnspath.

Silurian, Llandovery (Tarannon flaggy shales) with graptolites and fossil tracks.

Peach, B. N. and Horne, J. 1899, p. 209.
Geol. Surv. 34 ; Ord. Pop. 75.

**Cockburnspath.** Landslip on shore W. of Old Cambus Burn, 2¾ miles E. of Cockburnspath.

Upper Old Red Sandstone with fish-remains.

Geol. Surv. 34 ; Ord. Pop. 75.

**Cockburnspath.** Shore from Coastguard Station to Meikle Poo Craig, 3 miles E. of Cockburnspath.

Upper Old Red Sandstone with fish-remains.

Geol. Surv. 34 ; Ord. Pop. 75.

**Cockburnspath.** Shore midway between Pease Burn and Greenheugh Point, 1½ miles E. of Cockburnspath.

Upper Old Red Sandstone with fish-remains.

Geol. Surv. 34 ; Ord. Pop. 75.

**Cockburnspath.** Sections 50, 230, 300 and 400 yds. E.S.E. of entrance to Cove Harbour, Cockburnspath.

Carboniferous, Calciferous Sandstone Series, with plant remains.

Geol. Surv. 34 ; Ord. Pop. 75.

**Cockburnspath.** Shore 16 and 66 yds. S. of entrance to Cove Harbour.
Carboniferous, Calciferous Sandstone Series, limestone with crinoids, bryozoa, productid brachiopods and molluscs.
Geol. Surv. 34 ; Ord. Pop. 75.

**Cockburnspath.** Shore N.W. of Cove Harbour.
Carboniferous, Calciferous Sandstone Series, with plant and fish remains in limy shale above black, bituminous shale.
Geol. Surv. 34 ; Ord. Pop. 75.

**Cockburnspath.** Section in Middle Cliff, Cove Harbour, and between Middle Cliff and West Cliff.
Carboniferous, Calciferous Sandstone Series, shale with crinoids, bryozoa, brachiopods, molluscs and plants.
Geol. Surv. 34 ; Ord. Pop. 75.

**Coldstream.** Right bank of R. Tweed, a little below Coldstream Bridge.
Carboniferous, Calciferous Sandstone Series, with lamellibranchs, gastropods, ostracods, etc.
Geol. Surv. 26 ; Ord. Pop. 81.

**Coldstream.** Leet Water, near Hirsel, from 1 to 3½ miles N.W. of Coldstream.
Carboniferous, Calciferous Sandstone Series, with lamellibranchs, arthropods, plant and fish remains and the worm *Spirorbis*.
Geol. Surv. 26 ; Ord. Pop. 81.

**Duns.** Blackadder Water, near Pathhead, 2½ miles S.S.E. of Duns.
Carboniferous, Calciferous Sandstone Series, with fish and crustacean fragments, ostracods, lamellibranchs and the worm *Spirorbis*.
Geol. Surv. 26 ; Ord. Pop. 75.

**Edrom.** Whiteadder Water near Broomhouse, 3-4½ miles W. of Chirnside.
Carboniferous, Calciferous Sandstone Series, with arthropods and coprolites.
Geol. Surv. 34 ; Ord. Pop. 75.

**Fala.** Section 600 yds. up tributary joining main stream ½ mile N. of Kershope shepherd's house, 5½ miles S.S.W. of Gifford.
Ordovician, Caradoc (Glenkiln black shales), with graptolites.
Peach, B. N. and Horne, J. 1899, p. 274.
Geol. Surv. 33 ; Ord. Pop. 74.

**Fala.** S. side of Headshaw Burn, 800 yds. from foot of Windycleuch, 7 miles S.E. of Pathhead.
Ordovician, Caradoc (Hartfell shales), with graptolites.
Peach, B. N. and Horne, J. 1899, p. 272.
Geol. Surv. 33 ; Ord. Pop. 74.

**Greenlaw.** Hexpethdean Quarry, 3 miles W. by N. of Greenlaw.
Upper Old Red Sandstone (resting on intrusive igneous rocks), with scales and fragments of fishes.
Geol. Surv. 25 ; Ord. Pop. 75.

**Lauder.** Earnscleugh Burn, 400 yds. N.E. of farmhouse at W. end of scar on N.W. bank, 2-3 miles N.N.E. of Lauder.
Ordovician, Caradoc (Glenkiln-Hartfell shales), with graptolites.
Peach, B. N. and Horne, J. 1899, p. 196.
Geol. Surv. 25 ; Ord. Pop. 74.

**Lennel.** Lennel Braes ; on footpath on scaur on left bank of R. Tweed, ¼ mile below Coldstream Bridge ; also 50 and 150 yds. further downstream, and in scaur on S.E. side of churchyard ¼ mile E. of Lennel.
Carboniferous, Cementstone Series, with lamellibranchs.
Geol. Surv. 26 ; Ord. Pop. 81.

**Polwarth.** Langton Burn, about ¾ mile above Langton House, 5 miles N.N.E. of Greenlaw.
Carboniferous, Calciferous Sandstone Series, with lamellibranchs, gastropods, ostracods and fish remains.
Geol. Surv. 25 ; Ord. Pop. 75.

**Spottiswoode.** Blythe Burn, N. of Heugh Farm and also in quarries near Blythe Farm, 3½ miles N.E. of Lauder.
Silurian, Llandovery, with graptolites.
Peach, B. N. and Horne, J. 1899, p. 207.
Geol. Surv. 25 ; Ord. Pop. 75.

**Spottiswoode.** Easter Burn (tributary of Blythe Burn), 150 yds. above junction of the two streams near Broadshawrig, 4¾ miles N.E. of Lauder.
Silurian, Llandovery, with corals, crinoids and brachiopods in conglomerate.
Peach, B. N. and Horne, J. 1899, p. 207.
Geol. Surv. 25 ; Ord. Pop. 75.

**Westruther.** Brunta Burn near mill W. of Spottiswoode, also above Bruntaburn Wood and in higher part of Pondheigh Burn, 4½ miles E.N.E. of Lauder.
Silurian, Llandovery, with graptolites, *Protovirgula* and other tracks, in flags and grits.
Peach, B. N. and Horne, J. 1899, p. 206.
Geol. Surv. 25 ; Ord. Pop. 75.

**Westruther.** Wedderlie Burn, near Wedderburn Farm, 7½ miles N.E. of Lauder.
Silurian, Llandovery, with graptolites and tracks in shales.
Peach, B. N. and Horne, J. 1899, p. 207.
Geol. Surv. 25 ; Ord. Pop. 75.


# BUTESHIRE (ARRAN)

**Corrie.** Lochrim Burn, ¼ mile S. of Corrie.
Carboniferous, limestone and shales with brachiopods, lamellibranchs, gastropods and plant remains.
Tyrrell, G. W. 1928, p. 66.
Geol. Surv. 21 ; Ord. Pop. 77.

**Corrie.** Lagantuin Bay, 300 yds. N. of Fallen Rocks, N. of Corrie.
Carboniferous, Calciferous Sandstone Series, with plants and fish remains.
Tyrrell, G. W. 1928, p. 49.
Geol. Surv. 21 ; Ord. Pop. 77.

**Corrie.** Shore-section between Corrie Post Office and the ferry.
Carboniferous, limestone and shale with brachiopods, molluscs, trilobites and fish.
Tyrrell, G. W. 1928, pp. 64-65.
Geol. Surv. 21 ; Ord. Pop. 77.

**Lochranza.** Sections N. and S. of Laggan, ½ mile and 1 mile N.W. of Millstone Point.
Carboniferous, Calciferous Sandstone Series and Lower Limestone Series (Hurlet Limestone), with corals, brachiopods, lamellibranchs and nautiloid cephalopods.
Tyrrell, G. W. 1928, pp. 49-52.
Geol. Surv. 21 ; Ord. Pop. 77.

## CAITHNESS

**Castletown.** Murkle Bay, S.E. side.
Middle Old Red Sandstone (Thurso Flagstone Group, probably Mey Beds, calcareous flags in shore and low cliffs near a calcareous spring). The fish *Coccosteus minor* and *Thursius pholidotus* are fairly common.
Crampton, C. B. and Carruthers, R. G. 1914, p. 66. Heintz, A. 1938, p. 1.
Geol. Surv. 116 ; Ord. Pop. 12.

**John o' Groats.** About 200 yds. W. of pier at John o' Groats Hotel.
Middle Old Red Sandstone (John o' Groats Beds, thin band of pale-weathering flagstone in false-bedded red and yellow sandstones), with the fish *Tristichopterus alatus, Microbrachius dicki, Pentlandia macropterus.*
Crampton, C. B. and Carruthers, R. G. 1914, pp. 56-57.
Geol. Surv. 116 ; Ord. Pop. 12.

**Scrabster.** " Holborn Head " Quarries on sea-cliff ¼ mile N. of Brims Hill and 1½ miles W.N.W. of Scrabster pier.
Middle Old Red Sandstone (probably Thurso Group), tough, flaggy, calcareous rock on floor of old quarry with the fish *Osteolepis* cf. *microlepidotus*, numerous, also *Glyptolepis, Cheiracanthus, Mesacanthus, Coccosteus* and *Dipterus.*
Geol. Surv. 116 ; Ord. Pop. 11.

**Spital.** Achanarras Quarry, about 500 yds. S.S.W. of Achanarras Farm.
Middle Old Red Sandstone (Thurso Flagstone Group, Achanarras " limestone," about 6 ft. of grey calcareous flags). A classic section, type-locality of *Palaeospondylus gunni* and *Rhamphodopsis thrieplandi*. About 15 species of fish occur in all, including *Dipterus, Coccosteus, Cheiracanthus, Mesacanthus* and *Pterichthyodes.*
Crampton, C. B. and Carruthers, R. G. 1914, pp. 6, 63. Forster-Cooper, C. 1937.
Geol. Surv. 116 ; Ord. Pop. 12.

**Spital.** Banniskirk Quarries, 1000 yds. S.W. of Banniskirk House. Quarries abandoned, but good specimens may be found on tip-heaps.
(?) Middle Old Red Sandstone (Thurso Flagstone Group). Type-locality of *Dipterus valenciennesi*, which is common. *Coccosteus, Pterichthyodes* and acanthodians are less frequent, crossopterygians are rare.
Sedgwick, A. and Murchison, R. I. 1829, pp. 141-144, Pls.
Geol. Surv. 116 ; Ord. Pop. 12.

**Thurso.** Thurso East Shore, from ½ mile N.E. of Thurso Castle to Clardon Haven.
Middle Old Red Sandstone (Thurso Flagstone Group, including calcareous flags), with scattered fish-remains, including *Dipterus, Diplopterax* and *Glyptolepis*, common and characteristic. *Homostius* is important but rare.
Crampton, C. B. and Carruthers, R. G. 1914, p. 65.
Geol. Surv. 116 ; Ord. Pop. 12.

## CLACKMANNANSHIRE

**Cambus.** Section in left bank of R. Devon, also between Cambus and river-mouth.
Carboniferous, " Millstone Grit," with corals, crinoids, brachiopods and ostracods.
Dinham, C. H. and Haldane, D. 1932, pp. 123-124.
Geol. Surv. 39 ; Ord. Pop. 67.

**Tillicoultry.** Harvieston Burn, 1 mile E.N.E. of Tillicoultry on lower side of gorge.
Carboniferous, Coal Measures, with plants.
Dinham, C. H. and Haldane, D. 1932, pp. 151-152.
Geol. Surv. 39 ; Ord. Pop. 67.


# DUNBARTONSHIRE

**Bowling.** Escarpment on S. side of Loch Humphrey Burn, about ½ mile E. of Loch Humphrey, 1¾ miles N.E. of Bowling.
Carboniferous, Cementstone Series, with plants.
Geol. Surv. 30 ; Ord. Pop. 72.

**Cumbernauld.** Luggie Water above Lenziemill, 2 miles S. of Cumbernauld.
Carboniferous, soft shale and limestone with brachiopods and gastropods.
Robertson, T. and Haldane, D. 1937, p. 9.
Geol. Surv. 31 ; Ord. Pop. 73.

**Cumbernauld.** Castlecary Limeworks, 1½ miles N.E. of Cumbernauld.
Carboniferous, Upper Limestone Series (Castlecary Limestone), with brachiopods and plant and fish remains.
Geol. Surv. 31 ; Ord. Pop. 73.

**Cumbernauld.** Stream nearly ¼ mile from Glencryan House, ¾ mile a little N. of E. of Cumbernauld station.
Carboniferous, " Millstone Grit," with brachiopods, lamellibranchs and plants.
Geol. Surv. 31 ; Ord. Pop. 73.

**Kilsyth.** Section in burn between Roman Road and railway, 500 yds. N.E. of Westerwood, 3 miles E. of Kilsyth.
Carboniferous, Upper Limestone Series (Calmy Limestone), with brachiopods, lamellibranchs and gastropods.
Robertson, T. and Haldane, D. 1937, p. 88.
Geol. Surv. 31 ; Ord. Pop. 73.


# DUMFRIESSHIRE

**Abington.** Glencaple Burn, 300 yds. S. of foot of Hortin Gill, S. of Abington.
Ordovician, Caradoc (Hartfell shales), with graptolites.
Peach, B. N. and Horne, J. 1899, p. 289.
Geol. Surv. 15 ; Ord. Pop. 79.

**Birkhill.** Dobb's Linn, head of Moffatdale, ⅝ mile W. of Birkhill and 9¼ miles N.E. of Moffat.
Ordovician, Caradoc (Hartfell shales), and Silurian, Llandovery (Tarannon and Birkhill greywackes and shales), both with graptolites.
Peach, B. N. and Horne, J. 1899, pp. 92-100.
Geol. Surv. 16 ; Ord. Pop. 85.

**Canonbie.** Section near Gilnockie Old Tower in R. Esk.
Carboniferous, Lower Limestone Series, limestone and shales with corals, brachiopods and molluscs.
Peach, B. N. and Horne, J. 1903, pp. 849-850.
Geol. Surv. 11 ; Ord. Pop. 89.

**Canonbie.** Penton Linns, Liddel Water, 1 mile E. of Rowanburn Colliery.
Carboniferous, Lower Limestone Series, with foraminifera, corals, crinoids,
brachiopods, molluscs, etc.
Peach, B. N. and Horne, J. 1903, p. 850.
Geol. Surv. 11 ; Ord. Pop. 89.

**Canonbie.** Left bank of R. Esk, from 200-300 yds. above Knottyholm
Farm, ¼ mile N. of Canonbie Bridge.
Carboniferous, Coal Measures (barren red measures). In a rhythmic suc-
cession of shales, sandy shales, sandstone, marl, non-marine lamellibranchs
(*Anthraconauta*), with ostracods, etc., occur near the base of the shale members ;
plants sometimes occur just above.
Barrett, B. H. and Richey, J. E. 1945, pp. 39, 42.
Geol. Surv. 11 ; Ord. Pop. 89.

**Dunscore.** Section 200 yds. from foot of March Cleuch, tributary of
Glenessland Burn, which rises on N. slope of Craigdasher Hill, 4 miles W. by S.
of Dunscore.
Ordovician, Caradoc (Hartfell black shales), with graptolites.
Peach, B. N. and Horne, J. 1899, pp. 157-158.
Geol. Surv. 9 ; Ord. Pop. 88.

**Dunscore.** S.E. bank of Glen Burn, in wood S.S.E. of Glen Farm and
200 yds. E. of W. edge of wood.
Ordovician, Caradoc (Glenkiln shales), with graptolites and brachiopods.
Peach, B. N. and Horne, J. 1899, pp. 163-164.
Geol. Surv. 9 ; Ord. Pop. 88.

**Dunscore.** Banks of the Bogrie Burn from N. of the Bogrie Tower to
Castramon Burn, 3½ miles W. of Dunscore.
Ordovician, Caradoc (Hartfell shales) and Silurian, Llandovery (Birkhill
shales), with graptolites.
Peach, B. N. and Horne, J. 1899, p. 156.
Geol. Surv. 9 ; Ord. Pop. 88.

**Dunscore.** Section ¼ mile S.S.E. of Upper Whiteside, 3¾ miles W. by S.
of Dunscore.
Silurian, Llandovery, black shales with graptolites.
Peach, B. N. and Horne, J. 1899, p. 159.
Geol. Surv. 9 ; Ord. Pop. 88.

**Ecclefechan.** Gowkhall Scar, left bank of Kirtle Water S.E. of Waterbeck,
4 miles N.E. of Ecclefechan.
Carboniferous, Calciferous Sandstone Series, red shales with crinoids,
brachiopods and lamellibranchs.
Geol. Surv. 10 ; Ord. Pop. 89.

**Ecclefechan.** Kirtle Water at Nether Albie, Waterbeck.
Carboniferous, Calciferous Sandstone Series, soft shale with brachiopods
and molluscs.
Geol. Surv. 10 ; Ord. Pop. 89.

**Ecclefechan.** Left bank of Annan Water opposite Hoddam Castle, 2 miles
S.W. of Ecclefechan.
Carboniferous, Calciferous Sandstone Series, pebbly limestone with brachio-
pods, lamellibranchs and gastropods.
Geol. Surv. 10 ; Ord. Pop. 89.

**Ecclefechan.** Cowthat Burn, ¾ mile N.E. of Ecclefechan.
Carboniferous, Calciferous Sandstone Series, thin limestone with ferruginous
band with brachiopods, lamellibranchs and gastropods.
Geol. Surv. 10 ; Ord. Pop. 89.

**Kirkconnel.** Polhote Burn, 200 yds. W. of fork and 30 yds. above bend in W. branch of burn where it flows E. and W.
Ordovician, Caradoc (Glenkiln shales), with graptolites.
Peach, B. N. and Horne, J. 1899, p. 371.
Geol. Surv. 15 ; Ord. Pop. 84.

**Kirkconnel.** Polneul Burn, ⅝ mile S. of Nether Cairn, near Kirkconnel.
Carboniferous, Coal Measures (*communis* to *similis-pulchra* zones). Ostracods, brachiopods and marine and non-marine lamellibranchs occur.
Simpson, J. B. and Richey, J. E. 1936, fig. 8, pp. 35-38, 83-84.
Geol. Surv. 15 ; Ord. Pop. 84.

**Kirkconnel.** Lagrae Burn : (1) at Lagrae Cleuch, 584 yds. N. 28° E. of Nether Glenmuchloch ; (2) 100 yds. below waterfall at Greystone Ford ; (3) 30-40 yds. below 2 ; (4) 167 yds. above tributary, 1034 yds. N. 34° W. of Lagrae.
Carboniferous, Coal Measures (*similis-pulchra* zone). Non-marine lamellibranchs occur at locs. 1-3. Cephalopods and marine lamellibranchs occur at loc. 4 (Skipsey's Marine Band).
Simpson, J. B. and Richey, J. E. 1936, pl. II and p. 82.
Geol. Surv. 15 ; Ord. Pop. 84.

**Kirkconnel.** Roger Burn, S. side of conduit below Lagrae Road, also 100 yds. downstream from conduit.
Carboniferous, Coal Measures with non-marine shells.
Simpson, J. B. and Richey, J. E. 1936, pl. II and p. 83.
Geol. Surv. 15 ; Ord. Pop. 84.

**Kirkmichael.** Glenkiln Burn, ¾ mile above Kirkmichael Manse, 8¾ miles N.N.E. of Dumfries.
Ordovician, Caradoc (Glenkiln shales, type-section, and Hartfell shales), and Silurian, Llandovery (Birkhill Shales), with graptolites and brachiopods.
Peach, B. N. and Horne, J. 1899, pp. 146-150.
Geol. Surv. 10 ; Ord. Pop. 84.

**Kirtle Bridge.** Streamlet N. from Berclees, about 4½ miles N.E. of Kirtle Bridge.
Carboniferous, Calciferous Sandstone Series, limestone bands with corals, brachiopods and gastropods.
Hill, D. 1937-1941, p. 25.
Geol. Surv. 10 ; Ord. Pop. 89.

**Kirtle Bridge.** Cadgill Burn, N. of Auchengyle, 4 miles N.E. of Kirtle Bridge.
Carboniferous, Calciferous Sandstone Series, soft shale with lamellibranchs and gastropods.
Geol. Surv. 10 ; Ord. Pop. 89.

**Langholm.** Rig Burn, near head of burn, 5 miles N.N.W. of Langholm.
Silurian, Wenlock, shales with graptolites, brachiopods and arthropods.
Peach, B. N. and Horne, J. 1899, p. 557.
Geol. Surv. 10 ; Ord. Pop. 85.

**Langholm.** Near head of and in N.E. branch of Wolfhope Burn, Ewes Water, about 6 miles N.N.W. of Langholm.
Silurian, Wenlock, shales with graptolites, brachiopods, cephalopods and arthropods.
Peach, B. N. and Horne, J. 1899, p. 557.
Geol. Surv. 10 ; Ord. Pop. 85.

**Langholm.** Streamlet E. of Nether Stennis Water, 6½ miles N.N.W. of Langholm.
Silurian, Wenlock, shales with graptolites, corals, brachiopods and cephalopods.
Peach, B. N. and Horne, J. 1899, p. 557.
Geol. Surv. 10 ; Ord. Pop. 85.

**Langholm.** Glencartholm, R. Esk, 3½ miles S.S.E. of Langholm.
Carboniferous, Calciferous Sandstone Series, shales with plants, brachiopods, molluscs, etc.
Peach, B. N. and Horne, J. 1903, pp. 844-847.
Geol. Surv. 11 ; Ord. Pop. 89.

**Langholm.** Harelaw Hill Quarry, 5 miles S.E. of Langholm.
Carboniferous, Lower Limestone Series, with corals, brachiopods, molluscs, etc.
Peach, B. N. and Horne, J. 1903, p. 849.
Geol. Surv. 11 ; Ord. Pop. 89.

**Langholm.** Section near foot of Tarras Water, 2½ miles S.S.E. of Langholm.
Carboniferous, Calciferous Sandstone Series, with arthropods, fish-remains and plants.
Peach, B. N. and Horne, J. 1903, p. 843.
Geol. Surv. 11 ; Ord. Pop. 89.

**Lochmaben.** Black Linn, above junction with Tuppark Linn and at big bend in Linn, 6½ miles N.W. of Lochmaben and ¾ mile N.N.E. of Mountstewart Manse.
Ordovician, Caradoc (Glenkiln-Hartfell shales), with graptolites.
Geol. Surv. 10 ; Ord. Pop. 84.

**Lockerbie.** Gimmenbie Burn, Milk Water, near Gimmenbie Mains, 3 miles S.E. of Lockerbie.
Silurian, Wenlock, shales with graptolites, etc.
Peach, B. N. and Horne, J. 1899, p. 558.
Geol. Surv. 10 ; Ord. Pop. 89.

**Lockerbie.** Link Mill at bend of R. Annan 4 miles S.S.W. of Lockerbie.
Silurian, Wenlock, shales with graptolites, brachiopods and cephalopods.
Peach, B. N. and Horne, J. 1899, p. 558.
Geol. Surv. 10 ; Ord. Pop. 88.

**Lockerbie.** W. bank of Corrie Water (tributary to Water of Milk), near S. Corrielaw.
Silurian, Wenlock, shale with graptolites, etc.
Peach, B. N. and Horne, J. 1899, p. 557.
Geol. Surv. 10 ; Ord. Pop. 89.

**Moffat.** Carrifran Burn at junction with Broomy Gutter, 1½ miles N. of the course of Moffat Water.
Ordovician, Caradoc (Glenkiln black shales), with graptolites.
Peach, B. N. and Horne, J. 1899, p. 132.
Geol. Surv. 16 ; Ord. Pop. 85.

**Moffat.** Hartfell Spa, N. branch of Auchencat Burn, 4 miles slightly E. of N. of Moffat.
Ordovician, Caradoc (Hartfell black shales), with graptolites.
Peach, B. N. and Horne, J. 1899, pp. 133-134.
Geol. Surv. 16 ; Ord. Pop. 84.

**Moffat.** Bellcraig Burn at junction of streams 3 miles S.S.E. of Moffat also in small branches, the Hodge Burn.
Ordovician, Caradoc (Glenkiln and Hartfell shales), and Silurian, Llandovery (Birkhill shales) with graptolites.
Peach, B. N. and Horne, J. 1899, pp. 114-116.
Geol. Surv. 16 ; Ord. Pop. 84.

**Moffat.** Craigmichan Scaurs, S.E. flank of Capel Fell at head of Seleoth Burn, 4½ miles E.N.E. of Moffat.
Ordovician, Caradoc (Glenkiln and Hartfell shales), and Silurian, Llandovery (Birkhill shales), with graptolites.
Peach, B. N. and Horne, J. 1899, pp. 100-107.
Geol. Surv. 16 ; Ord. Pop. 85.

**Moffat.** Garpol Water, 1½ miles S.W. of Moffat, W. of R. Annan.
Silurian, Llandovery (Lower Birkhill shales), with graptolites.
Peach, B. N. and Horne, J. 1899, pp. 131-132.
Geol. Surv. 16 ; Ord. Pop. 84.

**Moniaive.** Bank on S. side of Dibbin Lane, 120 yds. upstream from dyke crossing mouth of stream, 6¼ miles N.W. of Moniaive.
Ordovician, Caradoc (Glenkiln shales), with graptolites.
Peach, B. N. and Horne, J. 1899, pp. 340-341.
Geol. Surv. 9 ; Ord. Pop. 84.

**Moniaive.** Patie Cleuch, 300 yds. W. of Shinnelhead shepherd's house.
Ordovician, Caradoc (Glenkiln-Hartfell shales), with graptolites and brachiopods.
Peach, B. N. and Horne, J. 1899, pp. 338-339.
Geol. Surv. 9 ; Ord. Pop. 84.

**Moniaive.** Benbrack, ¼ mile from county boundary, S. side of Dibbin Lane, stream draining S. slope of Benbrack Hill, 7¼ miles N.W. of Moniaive.
Ordovician, Caradoc (Hartfell black shale), with graptolites and brachiopods.
Peach, B. N. and Horne, J. 1899, pp. 342-343.
Geol. Surv. 9 ; Ord. Pop. 83.

**Moniaive.** Near head of Clodderoch Burn (tributary to Shinnel Water 300 yds. above Tynron), about 400 yds. above footpath to Moniaive.
Ordovician, Caradoc (Hartfell shales), with graptolites.
Peach, B. N. and Horne, J. 1899, p. 348.
Geol. Surv. 9 ; Ord. Pop. 84.

**Moniaive.** Ballinie Burn, ¾ mile W. of Ballinie Farm and in burn on hillside S. of Ballinie (W. of Moniaive).
Ordovician, Caradoc (Hartfell shales), with graptolites.
Peach, B. N. and Horne, J. 1899, p. 349.
Geol. Surv. 9 ; Ord. Pop. 84.

**Moniaive.** Scar Water, N. from Corfardine Farm to mouth of the tributary Auchenhessnane Burn, 4 miles N.N.W. of Moniaive.
Ordovician, Caradoc (Hartfell shales), with graptolites and brachiopods.
Peach, B. N. and Horne, J. 1899, pp. 347-348.
Geol. Surv. 9 ; Ord. Pop. 84.

**Moniaive.** Near head of Glenjaan Burn and near county boundary, 6 miles W.N.W. of Moniaive.
Ordovician, Caradoc (Glenkiln-Hartfell shales), with graptolites and brachiopods.
Peach, B. N. and Horne, J. 1899, p. 346.
Geol. Surv. 9 ; Ord. Pop. 84.

**Moniaive.** On N. slope of Stroanfreggan Burn, in small burn about 350 yds. S.W. of shepherd's house near road leading to Manwhill, 7¼ miles W.N.W. of Moniaive.
Ordovician, Caradoc (Hartfell shales), with graptolites.
Peach, B. N. and Horne, J. 1899, p. 343.
Geol. Surv. 9 ; Ord. Pop. 83.

**Raehills.** Duffkinnel Water, upstream from foot and above Glenhall Cottage, 8 miles N.N.W. of Lochmaben.
Silurian, Llandovery (Birkhill Group), with graptolites.
Peach, B. N. and Horne, J. 1899, p. 150.
Geol. Surv. 10 ; Ord. Pop. 84.

**Raehills.** Pishnack Burn (tributary to W. bank of Water of Ae), 11 miles N.W. of Lochmaben.
Silurian, Llandovery (Birkhill group), with graptolites and brachiopods.
Peach, B. N. and Horne, J. 1899, pp. 152-154.
Geol. Surv. 10 ; Ord. Pop. 84.

**Raehills.** Footbridge near mouth of Linholm Burn (tributary to Duffkinnel Water) and for about 200 yds. upstream.
Silurian, Llandovery (Birkhill group), with graptolites.
Peach, B. N. and Horne, J. 1899, p. 151.
Geol. Surv. 10 ; Ord. Pop. 84.

**Raehills.** Broadshaw Water N. of Raehills and near junction with Kinnel Water, 8 miles slightly W. of N. of Lochmaben.
Silurian, Llandovery (Birkhill shales), with graptolites.
Geol. Surv. 10 ; Ord. Pop. 84.

**Sanquhar.** Westmost branch of Kiln Burn, N. of Bail Hill, 3 miles N.W. of Sanquhar.
Ordoviciain, Arenig, cherts with radiolaria ; and Caradoc (Glenkiln black shales) with graptolites.
Peach, B. N. and Horne, J. 1899, pp. 309-310.
Geol. Surv. 15 ; Ord. Pop. 84.

**Sanquhar.** Gorge on S. slope of Craignorth Hill below Corsebank, left bank of Crawick Water.
Ordovician, Caradoc (Glenkiln shales), with graptolites.
Peach, B. N. and Horne, J. 1899, p. 318.
Geol. Surv. 15 ; Ord. Pop. 84.

**Sanquhar.** Right fork (S. bank) of Catcleuch Burn, a short distance above junction, Bail Hill, 3 miles N.W. of Sanquhar.
Ordovician, Caradoc (Glenkiln shales), with graptolites.
Peach, B. N. and Horne, J. 1899, pp. 304-306.
Geol. Surv. 15 ; Ord. Pop. 84.

**Sanquhar.** Whing Burn, N. from the foot of its tributary the Tongue Burn and particularly about ¼ mile downstream from Tongue Burn, 1½-2 miles S.W. of Sanquhar.
Ordovician, Caradoc (Glenkiln shales), with graptolites.
Peach, B. N. and Horne, J. 1899, pp. 352-353.
Geol. Surv. 15 ; Ord. Pop. 84.

**Sanquhar.** Spotfore Burn, ½ mile above junction with Crawick Water.
Ordovician, Caradoc (Glenkiln shales), with graptolites.
Peach, B. N. and Horne, J. 1899, pp. 313-317.
Geol. Surv. 15 ; Ord. Pop. 84.

**Sanquhar.** Stoodfold Burn, 300 yds. upstream from junction with Kiln Burn.
Ordovician, Caradoc (Glenkiln shales), with graptolites.
Peach, B. N. and Horne, J. 1899, p. 312.
Geol. Surv. 15 ; Ord. Pop. 84.

**Sanquhar.** Cog Burn, 120 yds. above junction with Glenlosh Burn, 1 mile E. of Cogshead.
Ordovician, Caradoc (Glenkiln-Hartfell shales), with graptolites.
Peach, B. N. and Horne, J. 1899, p. 298.
Geol. Surv. 15 ; Ord. Pop. 84.

**Sanquhar.** Head of Polthistly Burn (tributary to Crawick Water at Corsebank) and below Corsebank up gorge of small stream.
Ordovician, Caradoc (Glenkiln-Hartfell shales), with graptolites.
Peach, B. N. and Horne, J. 1899, pp. 318-319.
Geol. Surv. 15 ; Ord. Pop. 84.

**Sanquhar.** N. bank of Cairn Burn, near and below fork, about 5 miles S.S.E. of Sanquhar.
Ordovician, Caradoc (Hartfell black shales), with graptolites and brachiopods.
Peach, B. N. and Horne, J. 1899, p. 336.
Geol. Surv. 15 ; Ord. Pop. 84.

**Sanquhar.** Glenrae Burn (joining Crawick Water ¾ mile above Spango Bridge) ½ mile upstream, about 6½ miles N.N.E. of Sanquhar.
Ordovician, Caradoc (Hartfell black shales), with graptolites.
Peach, B. N. and Horne, J. 1899, p. 320.
Geol. Surv. 15 ; Ord. Pop. 79.

**Sanquhar.** In Polcraig Burn, which joins Crawick Water above Meikle Carco, 2¼ miles from foot of stream, 2½ miles N. of Sanquhar.
Ordovician, Caradoc (Hartfell shales), with graptolites.
Peach, B. N. and Horne, J. 1899, p. 313.
Geol. Surv. 15 ; Ord. Pop. 84.

**Tynron.** In Appin Burn ½ mile W. of Upper Appin shepherd's house (burn flows into Shinnel Water).
Ordovician, Caradoc (Glenkiln shales), with graptolites and brachiopods.
Peach, B. N. and Horne, J. 1899, pp. 345-346.
Geol. Surv. 9 ; Ord. Pop. 84.

**Wanlockhead.** Duntercleugh Burn, 300 yds. above its junction with Wanlock Water.
Ordovician, Caradoc (Glenkiln black shales), with graptolites.
Peach, B. N. and Horne, J. 1899, p. 292.
Geol. Surv. 15 ; Ord. Pop. 84.


## EAST LOTHIAN

**Aberlady.** Coast-section, Aberlady Point.
Carboniferous, Lower Limestone Series, with corals, brachiopods and lamellibranchs.
Clough, C. T. and others 1910, p. 209. Hill, D. 1937-1941, p. 19.
Geol. Surv. 33 ; Ord. Pop. 74.

**Aberlady.** Aberlady Bay, near Peffer Burn.
Recent deposits of 25 ft. Raised Beach, with sea-shells (*Cardium, Littorina,* etc.).
Clough, C. T. and others 1910, p. 215.
Geol. Surv. 33 ; Ord. Pop. 74.

**Broxburn.** Shore opposite the Vaults, 2 miles E. of Dunbar.
Carboniferous, Lower Limestone Series, with corals, crinoids, brachiopods
and molluscs.
Clough, C. T. and others 1910, p. 138.
Geol. Surv. 33 ; Ord. Pop. 75.

**Cockburnspath.** Shore E. of and 90 yds. N.W. of mouth of Bilsdean
Creek, 7 miles S.E. of Dunbar.
Carboniferous, Calciferous Sandstone Series, with plants.
Clough, C. T. and others 1910, pp. 45-47.
Geol. Surv. 33 ; Ord. Pop. 75.

**Dunbar.** E. side of Belhaven Bay, W. of Dunbar.
Carboniferous, Calciferous Sandstone Series and Cementstone Series, with
lamellibranchs and phyllopod crustacea.
Clough, C. T. and others 1910, p. 89.
Geol. Surv. 33 ; Ord. Pop. 75.

**Dunbar.** Shore 130 yds. N.E. of Catcraig Houses.
Carboniferous, Lower Limestone Series, with foraminifera, corals, brachio-
pods, molluscs, etc.
Clough, C. T. and others 1910, pp. 135-137. Hill, D. 1937-1941, p. 22.
Geol. Surv. 33 ; Ord. Pop. 75.

**Dunbar.** East Barns Quarry, 2 miles E. of Dunbar.
Carboniferous, Lower Limestone Series, with corals, brachiopods, molluscs,
etc.
Geol. Surv. 33 ; Ord. Pop. 75.

**Dunbar.** Oxwell Mains Quarry, E. of Dunbar.
Carboniferous, Lower Limestone Series, with corals, brachiopods, molluscs,
etc.
Clough, C. T. and others 1910, pp. 137, 213.
Geol. Surv. 33 ; Ord. Pop. 75.

**East Salton.** N.W. bank of Lammerlaw Burn, 700 yds. N. of Friar's Nose.
Ordovician, Caradoc (Hartfell shales), with graptolites.
Clough, C. T. and others 1910, pp. 116-117.
Geol. Surv. 33 ; Ord. Pop. 74.

**East Salton.** Salton Limeworks Quarries, E. and W. of road at Middlemains
Farm, 1 mile N.W. of E. Salton.
Carboniferous, Lower Limestone Series, with corals, bryozoa, brachiopods,
lamellibranchs and ostracods.
Clough, C. T. and others 1910, p. 211.
Geol. Surv. 33 ; Ord. Pop. 74.

**East Salton.** Spilmersford Quarry, 2 miles W. of E. Salton.
Carboniferous, Lower Limestone Series, with brachiopods, bryozoa,
molluscs, etc.
Clough, C. T. and others 1910, p. 143.
Geol. Surv. 33 ; Ord. Pop. 74.

**East Salton.** Blanceburn Quarry, 1 mile N.E. of E. Salton.
Carboniferous, Lower Limestone Series, with corals, brachiopods, and
lamellibranchs.
Clough, C. T. and others 1910, p. 210.
Geol. Surv. 33 ; Ord. Pop. 74.

**East Salton.** Kidlaw Quarries, 3½ miles S.E. of E. Salton.
Carboniferous, Lower Limestone Series, with echinoderms, bryozoa, brachio-
pods, molluscs and ostracods.
Clough, C. T. and others 1910, p. 212.
Geol. Surv. 33 ; Ord. Pop. 74.

**Garvald.** Thorter Burn, 1¼ miles S.E. of Garvald.
Ordovician, Caradoc, with graptolites and brachiopods.
Peach, B. N. and Horne, J. 1899, p. 278.
Geol. Surv. 33 ; Ord. Pop. 75.

**Garvald.** Papana Water, 2 miles S. of Garvald.
Ordovician, Caradoc (Glenkiln shales), with graptolites.
Peach, B. N. and Horne, J. 1899, p. 276.
Geol. Surv. 33 ; Ord. Pop. 75.

**Gullane.** Shore of Cheese Bay, 2 miles N.E. of Gullane.
Carboniferous, Calciferous Sandstone Series, with plants, fish and arthropods.
Clough, C. T. and others 1910, p. 207.
Geol. Surv. 41 ; Ord. Pop. 68.

**Haddington.** Right bank of R. Tyne above and below Waterloo Bridge.
Carboniferous, Calciferous Sandstone Series, with plants, lamellibranchs and fish-remains.
Geol. Surv. 33 ; Ord. Pop. 74.

**Haddington.** Streamlet at roadside a few hundred yards E. of Sandersdean, 2 miles S.E. of Haddington.
Carboniferous, Calciferous Sandstone Series, with bryozoa, productid brachiopods and lamellibranchs.
Clough, C. T. and others 1910, p. 208.
Geol. Surv. 33 ; Ord. Pop. 74.

**Haddington.** Letham Burn, 500 yds. W. of and 700 yds. E. of Letham House, 1 mile W. of Haddington.
Carboniferous, Calciferous Sandstone Series, with bryozoa, brachiopods, molluscs, etc.
Clough, C. T. and others 1910, pp. 208-209.
Geol. Surv. 33 ; Ord. Pop. 74.

**Humbie.** Left bank of Humbie Water a few yards above Salton Railway Station bridge.
Carboniferous, Calciferous Sandstone Series, with lamellibranchs and gastropods.
Clough, C. T. and others 1910, p. 209.
Geol. Surv. 33 ; Ord. Pop. 74.

**Innerwick.** Below and ¼ mile E. of Linkhead, 2¼ miles E. by S. of Innerwick.
Carboniferous, Calciferous Sandstone Series, with plants, brachiopods, corals, molluscs, etc.
Clough, C. T. and others 1910, p. 208.
Geol. Surv. 33 ; Ord. Pop. 75.

**Innerwick.** Shore at and a few yards W. of Standalane, ½ mile S.E. of Linkhead and 2½ miles E. by S. of Innerwick.
Carboniferous, Calciferous Sandstone Series with abundant plants (*Telangium affine*).
Clough, C. T. and others 1910, p. 208.
Geol. Surv. 33 ; Ord. Pop. 75.

**Innerwick.** Shore at Torness Point, E. of Dunbar.
Carboniferous, Lower Limestone Series, with corals, echinoderms, bryozoa and productid brachiopods.
Clough, C. T. and others 1910, p. 210.
Geol. Surv. 33 ; Ord. Pop. 75.

**Innerwick.** Shore at Chapel Point, 4¼ miles E. of Dunbar.
Carboniferous, Lower Limestone Series, with corals, echinoderms and gastropods.
Clough, C. T. and others 1910, p. 213.
Geol. Surv. 33 ; Ord. Pop. 75.

Q

**Longniddry.** Harelaw Limeworks, quarries E. and W. of limekiln near Longniddry station.
Carboniferous, Lower Limestone Series, with bryozoa, brachiopods and lamellibranchs.
Clough, C. T. and others 1910, p. 209.
Geol. Surv. 33 ; Ord. Pop. 74.

**Pathhead.** Lampland Quarry, N. and S. of limekiln 3 miles N.E. of Pathhead.
Carboniferous, Lower Limestone Series, with bryozoa, brachiopods, molluscs and ostracods.
Clough, C. T. and others 1910, pp. 211-212.
Geol. Surv. 33 ; Ord. Pop. 74.

**Pathhead.** Magazine Quarry, 1 mile E. of Pathhead and 6 miles S.E. of Dalkeith.
Carboniferous, Lower Limestone Series, with brachiopods, molluscs, etc.
Clough, C. T. and others 1910, p. 212.
Geol. Surv. 33 ; Ord. Pop. 74.

**Pathhead.** Hope Quarry.
Carboniferous, Lower Limestone Series, with brachiopods, molluscs, etc.
Clough, C. T. and others 1910, p. 211.
Geol. Surv. 33 ; Ord. Pop. 74.

**Port Seton.** Harbour.
Carboniferous, Millstone Grit (E. of harbour, W. of Powder Magazine), with plants ; and Coal Measures (W. division of harbour), with plants and non-marine shells.
Clough, C. T. and others 1910, p. 214.
Geol. Surv. 33 ; Ord. Pop. 74.

**Prestonpans.** Shore opposite Prestongrange at Bankfoot, W. of Prestonpans.
Carboniferous, Upper Limestone Series (No. 5 limestone and shale), with foraminifera, echinoderms, bryozoa, brachiopods, molluscs and ostracods.
Peach, B. N. and others 1910a, pp. 382-405.
Geol. Surv. 32 ; Ord. Pop. 74.

**Skateraw.** Quarry at Skateraw harbour and shore E. of harbour.
Carboniferous, Lower Limestone Series, with foraminifera, corals, bryozoa, brachiopods and gastropods.
Clough, C. T. and others 1910, pp. 210, 213.
Geol. Surv. 33 ; Ord. Pop. 75.

**Skateraw.** Longcraig, 1 mile E. of Skateraw and E. of Dunbar.
Carboniferous, Lower Limestone Series, with corals, brachiopods and lamellibranchs.
Clough, C. T. and others 1910, pp. 134-138.
Geol. Surv. 33 ; Ord. Pop. 75.

# FIFESHIRE.

**Aberdour.** Old limestone quarry, ¼ mile S.E. of Easter Bucklyire, 2 miles N.N.W. of Aberdour.
Carboniferous, Lower Limestone Series. Brachiopods, corals, lamellibranchs and cephalopods.
Allan, J. K. and Knox, J. 1934, p. 27.
Geol. Surv. 40 ; Ord. Pop. 68.

**Anstruther.** Billow Ness (Anstruther), shore E. and W. of Billow Ness. Carboniferous, Calciferous Sandstone Series. Plants, molluscs, ostracods, etc.
Geikie, A. 1902, pp. 76, 93, 356-375.
Geol. Surv. 41 ; Ord. Pop. 68.

**Blairadam.** Nivingston Quarry, 500 yds. S. of Cleish Mill, 2 miles W. of Blairadam station.
Carboniferous, Calciferous Sandstone Series, *Lingula* and plant remains.
Haldane, D. and Allan, J. K. 1931, p. 12.
Geol. Surv. 40 ; Ord. Pop. 68.

**Blebocraigs.** Dura Den, 6 miles W.S.W. of St. Andrews.
Upper Old Red Sandstone, flaggy red and yellow sandstones with green clay partings. A classic locality for well-preserved fossil fish. The chief exposure is now filled up, but scales and fragments of fish may be found in the stream bed 150 yds. above Yoolfield Mill.
Geikie, A. 1902, pp. 57-8, 355, 358.
Geol. Surv. 49 ; Ord. Pop. 64.

**Ceres.** Wilkieston Quarry, 5 miles S.W. of St. Andrews.
Carboniferous, Lower Limestone Series, Hurlet Limestone. Foraminifera, corals, ostracods, brachiopods, molluscs, etc.
Geikie, A. 1902, pp. 156, 357-375.
Geol. Surv. 41 ; Ord. Pop. 64.

**Ceres.** Woodtop Quarry, the Den, Teasses.
Carboniferous, Lower Limestone Series. Foraminifera, crinoids, arthropods, bryozoa, brachiopods, molluscs, etc.
Geikie, A. 1902, pp. 357-375.
Geol. Surv. 41 ; Ord. Pop. 64.

**Charlestown.** Large quarry section near village.
Carboniferous, Lower Limestone Series, Charlestown Main Limestone and overlying shales. Corals and other fossils abundant.
Geikie, A. 1900, pp. 212-239. Haldane, D. and Allan, J. K. 1931, pp. 19-27. Hill, D. 1937-1941, p. 22.
Geol. Surv. 40 ; Ord. Pop. 67.

**Crail.** Shore 1 mile W. of Crail and E. of the Pans.
Carboniferous, Calciferous Sandstone Series. Crinoids, bryozoa and molluscs.
Geikie, A. 1902, pp. 110, 366-375.
Geol. Surv. 41 ; Ord. Pop. 64.

**Culross.** Shore W. of Culross and a few yds. E. of the old pier at Dunimarle Point.
Carboniferous, Upper Limestone Series, *Edmondia punctatella* shale under Calmy Limestone and shales above it. Brachiopods, lamellibranchs and ostracods.
Dinham C. H. and Haldane, D. 1932, pp. 106-7.
Geol. Surv. 39 ; Ord. Pop. 67.

**Culross.** Shore on W. side of point S. of Caviehall, S.E. of Blair Castle.
Carboniferous, " Millstone Grit," first limestone and second marine band above Castle Cary Limestone. Lamellibranchs, gastropods and brachiopods.
Dinham C. H. and Haldane, D. 1932, pp. 128-9.
Geol. Surv. 31 ; Ord. Pop. 67.

**Culross.** W. side of Longamet Sandstone Quarry, W. of Culross.
Carboniferous, " Millstone Grit." Brachiopods and gastropods.
Dinham, C. H. and Haldane, D. 1932, pp. 125, 128-9.
Geol. Surv. 39 ; Ord. Pop. 67.

**Cupar.** Drumdryan Quarry (disused), 1 mile S. of Cupar.
Upper Old Red Sandstone, yellow sandstones. In 1831 the first *Holopty-chius* (fish scales) from Fife were obtained by Fleming.
Geikie, A. 1902, p. 57.
Geol. Surv. 48 ; Ord. Pop. 64.

**Dollar.** Stream in North Shore Wood, 3½ miles S.E. of Dollar.
Carboniferous, " Millstone Grit." Brachiopods and lamellibranchs.
Dinham, C. H. and Haldane, D. 1932, p. 127.
Geol. Surv. 39 ; Ord. Pop. 67.

**Dunduff,** 3 miles N. of Dunfermline. Gask Glen, S. side of Slateford
Bridge, and 280 yds. S.E. from Slateford Bridge at Burn Edge.
Carboniferous, Lower Limestone Series. Lamellibranchs and brachiopods.
Haldane, D. and Allan, J. K. 1931, pp. 33-36.
Geol. Surv. 40 ; Ord. Pop. 67.

**Dunfermline.** Roscobie Quarry, 4 miles N. of Dunfermline.
Carboniferous, Lower Limestone Series, limestone and shales (Charlestown
Main Limestone = Seafield Tower Limestone). Brachiopods and other fossils
abundant in the limestone and the shales immediately overlying. Rare fossils
in shales include crinoid crowns and an occasional well-preserved goniatite.
Geikie, A. 1900, pp. 213-239. Haldane, D. and Allan, J. K. 1931, p. 34.
Wright, J. 1920, pp. 370-375.
Geol. Surv. 40 ; Ord. Pop. 67.

**Dunfermline.** Greenknowes Quarry E. of kiln houses, S.W. of Green-
knowes, 3½ miles N.N.E. of Dunfermline.
Carboniferous, Lower Limestone Series. Cup corals.
Haldane, D. and Allan, J. K. 1931, p. 34.
Geol. Surv. 40 ; Ord. Pop. 67.

**Dunfermline.** Brucefield Fens. In Lyne Burn at the Weir and on the
left bank of the stream, 100 yds. S.W. from the Water Meter House.
Carboniferous, Lower Limestone Series. Encrinites and corals.
Haldane, D. and Allan, J. K. 1931, pp. 28-29.
Geol. Surv. 40 ; Ord. Pop. 67.

**Dunfermline.** Linn old quarry section, 4 miles N.W. of Dunfermline.
Carboniferous, Lower Limestone Series, shales overlying Charlestown
Main Limestone. Fossils abundant, including gastropods (*Bellerophon,
Euomphalus*) and an occasional goniatite.
Geikie, A. 1900, pp. 213-239. Haldane, D. and Allan, J. K. 1931, p. 33.
Geol. Surv. 40 ; Ord. Pop. 67.

**Dunfermline.** E. end of Western Reservoir in right bank of stream,
340 yds. N.E. of Locharnie, 4½ miles N. of Dunfermline.
Carboniferous, Lower Limestone Series. Gastropods and lamellibranchs.
Haldane, D. and Allan, J. K. 1931, p. 35.
Geol. Surv. 40 ; Ord. Pop. 67.

**Dunfermline.** At bend of Lyne Burn below Woodmill Bleachfield,
1 mile S.E. of Dunfermline Lower Station.
Carboniferous, Lower Limestone Series. Brachiopods and molluscs.
Haldane, D. and Allan, J. K. 1931, pp. 24-32.
Geol. Surv. 40 ; Ord. Pop. 67.

**Dysart.** Shore in front of Dysart.
Carboniferous, Coal Measures, *communis* zone. *Carbonicola pseudo-robusta,*
etc., in mussel-band about 100 ft. above Dysart Main Coal.
Weir, J. and Leitch, D. 1936, p. 730.
Geol. Surv. 40 ; Ord. Pop. 68.

**Elie.** On shore below Ardross Castle and E. of cliff, between Elie and St. Monans.

Carboniferous, Calciferous Sandstone Series, limestone and shale (Ardross Limestone). Fossils abundant in shale overlying limestone ; occasional crinoid crowns in shale.

Geikie, A. 1902, pp. 112, 357-375. Wright, J. 1939.
Geol. Surv. 41 ; Ord. Pop. 68.

**Elie.** Tideway E. of Ardross Castle, E. of Elie.

Carboniferous, Calciferous Sandstone Series, limestone and shale (" shrimp bed " in Ardross Limestone). Crustaceans of various species in limestone, also fishes, occasional goniatites, lamellibranchs (*Posidonia becheri*, etc.). Ophiuroids (brittle stars) on weathered surfaces of limestone.

Geikie, A. 1902, pp. 113, 357-375. Spencer, W. K. 1925.
Geol. Surv. 41 ; Ord. Pop. 68.

**Inverkeithing.** Charlestown Limestone Quarry, 4 miles W. of Inverkeithing.

Carboniferous, Lower Limestone Series. Foraminifera, sponges, brachiopods, molluscs, etc.

Peach, B. N. and others 1910a, pp. 116, 373-403.
Geol. Surv. 32 ; Ord. Pop. 67.

**Kinghorn.** Abden shore E. of Kinghorn, between tide marks.

Carboniferous, Lower Limestone Series, 1st and 2nd Abden Limestones and bone bed. Fish remains in bone bed : lamellibranchs, brachiopods, ostracods and plant remains.

Allan, J. K. and Knox, J. 1934, pp. 25-7. Geikie, A. 1900, pp. 214-219.
Geol. Surv. 40 ; Ord. Pop. 68.

**Kinghorn.** King Alexander's Crag, quarry 1700 yds. W. 30° S. of railway station at Kinghorn.

Carboniferous, Calciferous Sandstone Series. Plants.

Allan, J. K. and Knox, J. 1934, p. 16.
Geol. Surv. 40 ; Ord. Pop. 68.

**Kingsbarns.** Shore immediately E. of Randerston Castle.

Carboniferous, Calciferous Sandstone Series, Orthoceras Limestone. Crinoids, molluscs, etc.

Geikie, A. 1902, pp. 356-375.
Geol. Surv. 41 ; Ord. Pop. 64.

**Kingsbarns.** Shore E. of Cambo Burn, E. of Cambo Ness.

Carboniferous, Calciferous Sandstone Series. Ostracods, molluscs, etc.

Geikie, A. 1902, pp. 356-375.
Geol. Surv. 41 ; Ord. Pop. 64.

**Kirkcaldy.** Invertiel old quarry, on Invertiel road, W. of Bridgeton, Kirkcaldy.

Carboniferous, Lower Limestone Series, Seafield Tower Limestone. Fossils abundant in limestone and overlying shales including corals and brachiopods. Crinoid cups and microcrinoids abundant in shale overlying limestone, but less common in the higher beds.

Geikie, A. 1902, pp. 215-239. Wright, J. 1939. Hill, D. 1937-1941, p. 24.
Geol. Surv. 40 ; Ord. Pop. 68.

**Kirkcaldy.** Immediately W. of Seafield Tower, on W. boundary of burgh of Kirkcaldy.

Carboniferous, Lower Limestone Series, Seafield Tower Limestone and shales with limestone bands. Crinoid-cups and brachiopods in shale immediately below limestone ; fossils abundant in upper layers of limestone

(corals, gastropods, cephalopods, etc.) ; crinoids and other fossils abundant in overlying shales.
Geikie, A. 1900, p. 91. Wright, J. 1939.
Geol. Surv. 40 ; Ord. Pop. 68.

**Kirkcaldy.** Shore section from old Tyrie Bleachfield, W. of Kirkcaldy, along tideway to opposite Seafield Tower.
Carboniferous, Lower Limestone Series, " Hosie Limestones," shales and sandstones. Specimens not abundant in the top two limestones, but the second limestone from top contains curious sponge-like organisms. The faulted limestone lower down contains an abundant fauna of crinoids, corals, brachiopods, etc., and specimens are common in overlying shale.
Geikie, A. 1900, pp. 94-96. Wright, J. 1925, pp. 284-296.
Geol. Surv. 40 ; Ord. Pop. 68.

**Kirkcaldy.** Shaws Mill Plantation, 4 miles N.W. of Kirkcaldy.
Carboniferous, Lower Limestone Series, Charlestown Main Limestone. Corals, echinoderms, brachiopods, molluscs, trilobites, etc.
Allan, J. K. and Knox, J. 1934, p. 29.
Geol. Surv. 40 ; Ord. Pop. 68.

**Kirkcaldy.** Balbougie Glen, just W. of Balbougie farm.
Carboniferous, Lower Limestone Series. Lamellibranchs and gastropods.
Allan, J. K. and Knox, J. 1934, pp. 32-33, 47.
Geol. Surv. 40 ; Ord. Pop. 68.

**Kirkcaldy.** Old quarry, near farm of Bogie Mains, on N.W. boundary of burgh of Kirkcaldy.
Carboniferous, Lower Limestone Series, Seafield Tower Limestone and overlying shales. Abundant corals and occasional trilobites in the shales.
Geikie, A. 1900, pp. 90, 213-239. Allan, J. K. and Knox, J. 1934, p. 29.
Geol. Surv. 40 ; Ord. Pop. 68.

**Kirkcaldy.** Quarry 50 yds. E. of Kirkcaldy Golf Club House, and 500 yds. N.E. of Invertiel Farm.
Carboniferous, Lower Limestone Series. Brachiopods and crinoids.
Allan, J. K. and Knox, J. 1934, p. 28.
Geol. Surv. 40 ; Ord. Pop. 68.

**Kirkcaldy.** Foulford Quarry (disused) 2000 ft. W. 40° N. of Raith House, Kirkcaldy.
Carboniferous, Limestone Coal Series. Brachiopods.
Allan, J. K. and Knox, J. 1934, pp. 90-104.
Geol. Surv. 40 ; Ord. Pop. 68.

**Kirkcaldy.** East Den, 1400 ft. due W. of Overton Farm (1000 yds. W. 20° S. of Galatown crossroads).
Carboniferous, Upper Limestone Series. Corals, brachiopods, molluscs, etc.
Allan, J. K. and Knox, J. 1934, p. 143.
Geol. Surv. 40 ; Ord. Pop. 68.

**Largo.** Teasses Limeworks old quarry, N. of Backbrass ; and new quarry S. of Teasses House, N. of Largo.
Carboniferous, Lower Limestone Series. Sponges, echinoderms and molluscs.
Geikie, A. 1902, pp. 157, 357-375.
Geol. Surv. 41 ; Ord. Pop. 64.

**Largo.** Viewforth shore, Largo.
Carboniferous, Upper Limestone Series, Index Limestone. Foraminifera, echinoderms, brachiopods, molluscs, ostracods, etc.
Geikie, A. 1902, pp. 180, 357-375.
Geol. Surv. 41 ; Ord. Pop. 64.

**Newburgh.** Parkhill Quarry (disused), $\frac{1}{2}$ mile E. of Newburgh on S. side of shore road to Wormit.

Lower Old Red Sandstone, grey shales. In 1831 Fleming found here certain organic forms subsequently named *Parka*. Powrie obtained arthropods (*Pterygotus anglicus*) from this locality.

Geikie, A. 1902, pp. 355, 358.
Geol. Surv. 48 ; Ord. Pop. 64.

**Oakley.** In bed of Comrie Burn, Comrie Dean, $\frac{1}{2}$ mile W. by N. of Oakley railway station.

Carboniferous, Upper Limestone Series. Lamellibranchs and brachiopods.
Haldane, D. and Allan, J. K. 1931, pp. 130-134.
Geol. Surv. 40 ; Ord. Pop. 67.

**Pittenweem.** Cliff E. of Pittenweem.

Carboniferous, Calciferous Sandstone Series, Encrinite bed. Plants, corals, brachiopods and molluscs.

Geikie, A. 1902, pp. 77, 378-379.
Geol. Surv. 41 ; Ord. Pop. 64.

**Pitlessie.** Cults Limestone Quarries, S.E. of Pitlessie.

Carboniferous, Lower Limestone Series, Seafield Tower Limestone and shales. Fossils abundant, including corals in limestone. A layer of *Myalina* in shales above limestone.

Geikie, A. 1900, pp. 215-239.
Geol. Surv. 40 ; Ord. Pop. 64.

**Randerston.** Shore opposite old limestone quarry in field E. of road to Randerston Farm ; also shore E. of this.

Carboniferous, Calciferous Sandstone Series, *Schizodus* Bed and *Sedgwickia* Limestone. Corals, brachiopods, ostracods, etc.

Geikie, A. 1902, pp. 356-375.
Geol. Surv. 41 ; Ord. Pop. 64.

**St. Andrews.** Shore section, E. side of castle (below Kitchen Tower).

Carboniferous, Calciferous Sandstone Series, *Myalina* Limestone ; about 20 ft. of blue shales and ironstones, underlying white sandstones and resting on a coal 18ins. thick. Lamellibranchs, including *Myalina sublamellosa* and *Naiadites crassa*.

Geikie, A. 1902, pp. 138-139, 355-375.
Geol. Surv. 49 ; Ord. Pop. 64.

**St. Andrews.** Shore section from St. Andrews E. for 4 miles to Buddo Ness.

Carboniferous, Calciferous Sandstone Series ; Encrinite Bed 300 yds. E. of Maiden Rock, E. of Rock and Spindle and at Buddo Ness ; *Myalina* Limestone 600 yds. E. of Maiden Rock and E. of Rock and Spindle. Echinoderms, bryozoa, brachiopods, molluscs and ostracods.

Geikie, A. 1902, pp. 136, 355-375.
Geol. Surv. 49 ; Ord. Pop. 64.

**St. Andrews.** Shore section at base of cliff from W. end of Witch Lake to below Bath House and thence to low tide mark.

Carboniferous, Calciferous Sandstone Series, Encrinite Bed, a grey compact lenticular limestone, here in three seams, overlain and underlain by grey shales. Abundant crinoids, echinoids, corals, bryozoa, molluscs, etc.

Geikie, A. 1902, pp. 138-139, 355-375. Wright, J. 1939.
Geol. Surv. 49 ; Ord. Pop. 64.

**St. Andrews.** Right bank of Kinness Burn, below New Mill, $\frac{3}{4}$ mile W. of St. Andrews.

Carboniferous, Calciferous Sandstone Series. Plants, bryozoa, brachiopods and lamellibranchs.

Geikie, A. 1902, pp. 142, 355-375.
Geol. Surv. 49 ; Ord. Pop. 64.

**St. Monans.** Shore under Round Tower, E. of St. Monans.
Carboniferous, Calciferous Sandstone Series, limestone nodules in shale.
Corals, bryozoa, brachiopods and molluscs.
Geikie, A. 1902, pp. 357-375.
Geol. Surv. 41 ; Ord. Pop. 64.

**St. Monans.** Shore under and E. of Coal Farm, midway between St. Monans
and Pittenweem.
Carboniferous, Calciferous Sandstone Series, 1st and 3rd limestones under
St. Monans White Limestone and shale above No. 2 limestone. Corals,
brachiopods, molluscs, etc.
Geikie, A. 1902, pp. 74-76, 357-375.
Geol. Surv. 41 ; Ord. Pop. 64.

**Saline.** Lethams Glen, 400 yds. S. of North Lethams Bridge, N.E. of
Saline.
Carboniferous, Lower Limestone Series. Lamellibranchs, brachiopods,
corals, gastropods, etc.
Haldane, D. and Allan, J. K. 1931, p. 37.
Geol. Surv. 40 ; Ord. Pop. 67.

**Strathkinness.** Knockhill and Nydie Quarries (disused but accessible),
1 mile W. of Strathkinness.
Carboniferous, Calciferous Sandstone Series, Encrinite Bed and *Myalina*
Limestone. Plants, brachiopods and molluscs.
Geikie, A. 1902, pp. 355-375.
Geol. Surv. 49 ; Ord. Pop. 64.

**Townhill.** N. shore of Loch Fitty at parish boundary.
Carboniferous, Limestone Coal Series. Lamellibranchs and brachiopods.
Haldane, D. and Allan, J. K. 1931, pp. 111-112.
Geol. Surv. 40 ; Ord. Pop. 67.

**Townhill.** Lilliehill Fireclay Pit, Townhill.
Carboniferous, Upper Limestone Series, Index Limestone. Bryozoa,
crinoids, brachiopods, lamellibranchs, trilobites, etc.
Haldane, D. and Allan, J. K. 1931, pp. 107, 144.
Geol. Surv. 40 ; Ord. Pop. 67.

**West Wemyss.** Shore in front of West Wemyss.
Carboniferous, Coal Measures, Lower *similis-pulchra* zone, shale and iron-
stone 50 ft. above Barncraig coal. Abundant non-marine shells (*Anthraconaia
cymbula, Anthracosia* spp.).
Weir, J. and Leitch, D. 1936, p. 731.
Geol. Surv. 40 ; Ord. Pop. 68.

**Wormit.** Wormit Bay, ¾ mile W. of Wormit station.
Lower Old Red Sandstone, band of dark grey shale intercalated with other
sediments between sheets of andesitic lava. Fishes, eurypterids, the myriapod
*Kamecaris forfarensis,* and plant remains.
Geikie, A. 1902, pp. 35, 37, 355, 358.
Geol. Surv. 49 ; Ord. Pop. 64.


# FORFARSHIRE

**Forfar.** Abandoned quarries on E. and S. flanks of Turin Hill, *c.* 3½ miles
N.E. by E. of Forfar ; from near Pitscandlie (2 miles N.E. of Forfar) to ¼ mile
W. of Tillywhandland (4¾ miles E.N.E. of Forfar).
Lower Old Red Sandstone, Cairncommon Gritty Series, bands of mud-
stones and sandy strata between coarse conglomerates. Fossils now scarce,
occasionally to be found in waste heaps. Numerous fishes (*Mesacanthus,*

*Ischnacanthus, Parexus, Climatius, Cephalaspis* spp.) have been obtained ; also
eurypterids (*Pterygotus, Stylonurus*), and the plants *Parka decipiens* and
*Zosterophyllum*.
　Hickling, G. 1912, p. 302.　Stensio, E. A. 1932, esp. p. 201.
　Geol. Surv. 57 ; Ord. Pop. 58.

## INVERNESS (EIGG)

**Eigg.** E. shore of Eigg, about midway between Rudha nan Tri Clach and
Kildonan.
Jurassic, Lower Estuarine Shales, beds between Fish Bed and Reptile Bed.
Lamellibranchs, gastropods, fishes and reptiles.
　Harker, A. 1908, pp. 19-23.
　Geol. Surv. 60 ; Ord. Pop. 46.

**Eigg.** N.W. corner of Eigg, N. side of Musical Sand Bay.
Jurassic, Lower Estuarine Shales.　Lamellibranchs, gastropods, crustaceans,
fish remains.
　Harker, A. 1908, p. 21.
　Geol. Surv. 60 ; Ord. Pop. 46.

**Eigg.** S. side of Laig Bay, E. side of Clach Alasdair between tide marks ;
and 50 yds. E. of this locality.
Jurassic, Upper Oxfordian Shales.　Plants, lamellibranchs, ammonites, and
crustacean remains.
　Harker, A. 1908, p. 28.
　Geol. Surv. 60 ; Ord. Pop. 46.

## INVERNESS (MUCK)

**Camas Mor.** S. coast of Island.
Jurassic, Upper Part of Great Estuarine Series, *Ostrea* Beds. Lamellibranchs,
gastropods, ostracods, phyllopods.
　Harker, A. 1908, pp. 31-3.
　Geol. Surv. 60 ; Ord. Pop. 46.

## INVERNESS (RAASAY)

**Hallaig.** W. side of bay W. of Rudha na Leac.
Jurassic, Lower Lias.　Lamellibranchs.
　Lee, G. W. 1920, pp. 12-14.
　Geol. Surv. 81 ; Ord. Pop. 25.

**Hallaig.** Allt Fearns, above the road.
Jurassic, Lower Lias, Pabba Shales, *raricostatum* zone.　Lamellibranchs and
ammonites, especially *Echioceras*.
　Lee, G. W. 1920, pp. 17-20.
　Geol. Surv. 81 ; Ord. Pop. 25.

**Hallaig.** Hallaig shore, between tidemarks E. and S.E. of fisherman's
hut, ⅜ mile N.W. of the waterfall ; also N. of hut.
Jurassic, Lower Lias, Pabba Shales, *raricostatum* zone S. of hut, *jamesoni*
zone N. of hut.　Lamellibranchs, ammonites, brachiopods and belemnites.
　Lee, G. W. 1920, pp. 21-22.
　Geol. Surv. 81 ; Ord. Pop. 25.

**Hallaig.** At high water mark, ⅞ mile N.E. of Dun Caan.
Jurassic, Lower Lias, *davoei* zone.　Ammonites and lamellibranchs.
　Lee, G. W. 1920, p. 24.
　Geol. Surv. 81 ; Ord. Pop. 25.

**Hallaig.** Path from Beinn na Leac to Dun Caan.
Jurassic, Middle Lias. Brachiopods, ammonites and lamellibranchs.
Lee, G. W. 1920, pp. 25-29.
Geol. Surv. 81 ; Ord. Pop. 25.

**Hallaig.** Cliff N.E. of Dun Caan.
Jurassic, Upper Lias, *serpentinum* zone. Ammonites and belemnites.
Lee, G. W. 1920, pp. 30-31.
Geol. Surv. 81 ; Ord. Pop. 25.

**Hallaig.** Foot of Dun Caan.
Jurassic, " Inferior Oolite " (Upper Lias), Dun Caan Shales, *jurense* zone.
Ammonites, belemnites, lamellibranchs.
Lee, G. W. 1920, pp. 42-43.
Geol. Surv. 81 ; Ord. Pop. 25.

**Hallaig.** Druim an Roinach.
Jurassic, Inferior Oolite (Upper Lias), *opalinum* zone. Ammonites.
Lee, G. W. 1920, p. 43.
Geol. Surv. 81 ; Ord. Pop. 25.

**Hallaig.** Path 1 mile S. of Dun Caan.
Jurassic, " Inferior Oolite " (Upper Lias), sandstones of *opalinum, murchisoni*
and *sowerbyi* zones. Ammonites, belemnites and lamellibranchs.
Lee, G. W. 1920, pp. 44-46.
Geol. Surv. 81 ; Ord. Pop. 25.

**Holoman.** North branch of Glam Burn, $1\frac{1}{10}$ mile N.E. of Storav's Grave,
900 and 1000 ft. below bend in stream.
Jurassic, Middle Lias. Brachiopods and lamellibranchs.
Lee, G. W. 1920, pp. 25-29.
Geol. Surv. 81 ; Ord. Pop. 25.

**Holoman.** Balachiurn, on shore below Carn Dearg.
Jurassic, Inferior Oolite, sandstone. Lamellibranchs, brachiopods.
Lee, G. W. 1920, pp. 46-47.
Geol. Surv. 81 ; Ord. Pop. 25.

**Holoman.** Right bank of stream at point $\frac{3}{16}$ mile N.E. of Storav's Grave.
Jurassic, Inferior Oolite, plastic clay of *parkinsoni* zone. Ammonites.
Lee, G. W. 1920, p. 47.
Geol. Surv. 81 ; Ord. Pop. 25.

**Inverarish.** Allt Fearns, N. of road and $1\frac{3}{4}$ miles E. of Inverarish.
Localities between road and where path to Dun Caan crosses the burn.
Jurassic, Lower Lias, Pabba Shales. Brachiopods, lamellibranchs, ammonites,
belemnites.
Lee, G. W. 1920, pp. 17-23.
Geol. Surv. 81 ; Ord. Pop. 25.

**Inverarish.** Opencast working at mouth of " Outcrop Mine," 1 mile N.E.
of Inverarish.
Jurassic, Upper Lias, *serpentinum* zone. Ammonites, belemnites.
Lee, G. W. 1920, pp. 30-31.
Geol. Surv. 81 ; Ord. Pop. 25.

**Screapadal,** 1 mile S.W. of Screapadal.
Jurassic, Estuarine Series. Lamellibranchs and gastropods.
Lee, G. W. 1920, p. 55.
Geol. Surv. 81 ; Ord. Pop. 25.

## INVERNESS (SCALPA)

**Scalpa.** S. shore, 20-50 yds. E. of mouth of Allt Stapaig.
Jurassic, Upper Oxford Clay, just E. of prominent dyke. Ammonites, belemnites and lamellibranchs.
Peach, B. N. and others 1910b, pp. 131, 190-192.
Geol. Surv. 71 ; Ord. Pop. 35.

**Scalpa.** Allt Stapaig in S. of Scalpa : by roadside close to Sgur Stapaig, E. of mouth of Allt Stapaig.
Upper Cretaceous, Calcareous Grit, *Pecten asper* beds. Corals, gastropods, lamellibranchs.
Peach, B. N. and others 1910b, pp. 132, 192.
Geol. Surv. 71 ; Ord. Pop. 35.

## INVERNESS (SKYE)

**Broadford,** ½ mile N. of Ben Suardal, 1½-2 miles S.S.W. of Broadford. A prominent limestone knoll on E. side of road.
Cambrian, Durness Limestone. Sponges, lamellibranchs, gastropods and cephalopods.
Peach, B. N. and others 1910b, pp. 70, 177-179.
Geol. Surv. 71 ; Ord. Pop. 35.

**Broadford.** W. slopes above Allt a' Mhiulinn, 2 miles S. of Broadford.
Cambrian, Durness Limestone. Sponges and molluscs.
Peach, B. N. and others 1910b, pp. 177-179.
Geol. Surv. 71 ; Ord. Pop. 35.

**Broadford.** W. side of Bealach a' Ghlinne, 1 mile S. of Broadford.
Cambrian, Durness Limestone. Sponges and molluscs.
Peach, B. N. and others 1910b, pp. 177-179.
Geol. Surv. 71 ; Ord. Pop. 35.

**Broadford.** Isle of Pabba, near Broadford.
Jurassic, Lower Lias, Pabba Shales, *jamesoni* zone on N.W. and N.E. shores, *raricostatum* zone on S.E. shore. Crinoids, brachiopods ; ammonites and other molluscs.
Peach, B. N. and others 1910b, pp. 111-112, 180-185.
Geol. Surv. 71 ; Ord. Pop. 35.

**Camastianavaig.** Cliff ¾ mile E. of Camastianavaig.
Jurassic, Estuarine Series, oil shale. Ammonites.
Lee, G. W. 1920, p. 56.
Geol. Surv. 81 ; Ord. Pop. 25.

**Elgol.** S.W. shore of Loch Slapin, ¾ mile N. of first burn N. of Dun Liath.
Jurassic, Middle Lias, *spinatum* zone. Brachiopods, lamellibranchs, belemnites and ammonites.
Peach, B. N. and others 1910b, pp. 114, 186.
Geol. Surv. 71 ; Ord. Pop. 35.

**Elgol.** E. shore of Rudha na h-Easgainne, S. end of Strathaird peninsula.
Jurassic, Inferior Oolite, Group I. Lamellibranchs, belemnites.
Peach, B. N. and others 1910b, pp. 117, 188.
Geol. Surv. 71 ; Ord. Pop. 35.

**Elgol.** 6-8 ft. above the bridge near the school, Elgol, and also 20 to 30 yds. above it.
Jurassic, Inferior Oolite, Group II, Lower *parkinsoni* zone. Crinoids, lamellibranchs, ostracods, fish remains.
Peach, B. N. and others 1910b, p. 188.
Geol. Surv. 71 ; Ord. Pop. 35.

**Elgol.** Shore and cliff, S. of Glen Scaladal, N. of Càrn Mòr, Elgol.
Jurassic, Great Estuarine Series, *Ostrea* beds and *Cyrena* limestones. Lamellibranchs, gastropods, fish.
Peach, B. N. and others 1910b, pp. 123-124, 159.
Geol. Surv. 71 ; Ord. Pop. 35.

**Elgol.** Shore between tidemarks, N. of Elgol, and cliff at high water mark at small promontory of limestone, about 100 yds. S. of Càrn Mòr.
Jurassic, Great Estuarine Series, *Paludina* limestones. Gastropods, ostracods, fish scales and reptilian fragments.
Peach, B. N. and others 1910b, pp. 123-125, 189.
Geol. Surv. 71 ; Ord. Pop. 35.

**Elgol.** Fallen blocks of calcareous sandstone on shore at Elgol, W. side of Ben Cleat and S. of Càrn Mòr.
Jurassic, Kellaways Rock. Brachiopods, lamellibranchs.
Peach, B. N. and others 1910b, pp. 128-129, 190.
Geol. Surv. 71 ; Ord. Pop. 35.

**Elgol.** On shore between tidemarks at Rudha h'-Airidh Baine, W. of Beinn Leacach, N. of Elgol.
Jurassic, Upper Oxford Clay, sandstones. Ammonites.
Peach, B. N. and others 1910b, pp. 130, 190-191.
Geol. Surv. 71 ; Ord. Pop. 35.

**Elgol.** Blocks on slope of Càrn Mòr.
Jurassic, Upper Oxford Clay, sandstones. Ammonites, belemnites, lamellibranchs.
Peach, B. N. and others 1910b, pp. 130, 190-192.
Geol. Surv. 71 ; Ord. Pop. 35.

**Faoilean.** W. shore of Loch Slapin, ½ mile S.S.E. of Faoilean.
Jurassic, Middle Lias, *spinatum* zone. Brachiopods, lamellibranchs, belemnites.
Peach, B. N. and others 1910b, pp. 113-114.
Geol. Surv. 71 ; Ord. Pop. 35.

**Heast,** 2 ft. from top of main leap of Heast Cascade, N.E. of Heast.
Rhaetic. Lamellibranchs, fish scales, (?) plant remains.
Peach, B. N. and others 1910b, pp. 95-96, 180.
Geol. Surv. 71 ; Ord. Pop. 35.

**Holm.** Section in cliff ¾ mile S. of Holm, 5½ miles N.N.E. of Portree.
Jurassic, base of Inferior Oolite and Upper Lias, *bifrons* and *serpentinum* zones. Ammonites and belemnites.
Lee, G. W. 1920, pp. 39, 48.
Geol. Surv. 81 ; Ord. Pop. 24.

**Holm,** 1 mile N. of Prince Charles' Cave.
Jurassic, Estuarine Series, oil shale below limestone. Belemnites, lamellibranchs (*Inoceramus*), brachiopods, and plant remains.
Lee, G. W. 1920, p. 56.
Geol. Surv. 81 ; Ord. Pop. 24.

**Kirkibost,** 100-200 yds. N. of Rudha Cruaidhlinn, on W. side of Loch Slapin.
Jurassic, Middle Lias, *spinatum* zone. *Serpula,* lamellibranchs and belemnites.
Peach, B. N. and others 1910b, pp. 114, 186.
Geol. Surv. 71 ; Ord. Pop. 35.

**Kirkibost.** River at Kilmarie, 150 yds. N.W. of Kilmarie Lodge, and N.W. of this, a few yards W. of point where burn enters main stream from N.
Jurassic, Inferior Oolite, Group II, Lower *parkinsoni* zone, and Group I.
Crinoids and ostracods in Group II. Brachiopods and lamellibranchs in Group 1.
Peach, B. N. and others 1910b, p. 168.
Geol. Surv. 71 ; Ord. Pop. 35.

**Lusa.** Ob Lusa, 4 miles E.N.E. of Broadford.
Rhaetic, 8 ft. below Coral Limestone. Lamellibranchs, plant remains.
Peach, B. N. and others 1910b, pp. 94, 180.
Geol. Surv. 71 ; Ord. Pop. 35.

**Lusa.** Ob Lusa, 4 miles E.N.E. of Broadford.
Jurassic, Lower Lias, Broadford Beds, band beneath Coral Limestone.
Gastropods and lamellibranchs.
Peach, B. N. and others 1910b, pp. 99, 180-184.
Geol. Surv. 71 ; Ord. Pop. 35.

**Ord.** Shore of Loch Eishort, ½ mile N.N.E. of Ord.
Cambrian, Fucoid shales. Annelids and trilobites.
Peach, B. N. and others 1910b, pp. 68, 177-179.
Geol. Surv. 71 ; Ord. Pop. 35.

**Portree.** Rudha Sughar, 6 miles N. of Portree.
Jurassic, Inferior Oolite, *sowerbyi* and *humphriesianum* zones. Ammonites and lamellibranchs.
Geol. Surv. 81 ; Ord. Pop. 24.

**Rigg.** Loose blocks on the shore of the N. side of Bearreraig Bay.
Jurassic, Inferior Oolite, *murchisoni* to *parkinsoni* zones. Ammonites and belemnites.
Lee, G. W. 1920, pp. 49-50.
Geol. Surv. 81 ; Ord. Pop. 24.

**Rigg.** Coast ¾ mile S. of Rigg.
Jurassic, Inferior Oolite, *humphriesianum* zone. Lamellibranchs and cephalopods.
Lee, G. W. 1920, p. 50.
Geol. Surv. 81 ; Ord. Pop. 24.

**Sconser.** S. side of Loch Sligachan, W. of stream flowing from Leathad Dubh, 35-40 yds. N. of road bridge.
Jurassic, Lower Lias, Pabba Shales.. Brachiopods, lamellibranchs, gastropods and belemnites.
Peach, B. N. and others 1910b, pp. 111, 180-186.
Geol. Surv. 71 ; Ord. Pop. 35.

**Strathaird.** E. flank of Druim an Fhuarain Burn, on hillside W. of raised beach, 100 yds. S. of Faoilean, Strathaird.
Jurassic, Upper Lias, *bifrons* and *serpentinum* zones. Ammonites, belemnites and lamellibranchs.
Peach, B. N. and others 1910b, pp. 115, 187.
Geol. Surv. 71 ; Ord. Pop. 35.

**Strathaird.** S.W. shore of Loch Slapin, ½ mile N.E. of Dun Liath, at base of sandstone cliff at high water mark.
Jurassic, Upper Lias, *bifrons* and *serpentinum* zones. Ammonites, lamellibranchs and crinoids (*Pentacrinus*).
Peach, B. N. and others 1910b, pp. 115, 187.
Geol. Surv. 71 ; Ord. Pop. 35.

**Strathaird.** Abhuinn Cille Mhairs, main stream at point 50 yds. below fork of stream and waterfall.
Jurassic, Upper Oxford Clay, shales. Ammonites and belemnites.
Peach, B. N. and others 1910b, pp. 129-131, 190-191.
Geol. Surv. 71 ; Ord. Pop. 35.

**Strathaird.** Valley draining. S.E. between Ben Meabost and Ben Cleat.
Jurassic, Upper Oxford Clay, sandstone. Ammonites, lamellibranchs.
Peach, B. N. and others 1910b, pp. 130, 190-191.
Geol. Surv. 71 ; Ord. Pop. 35.

**Tokavaig.** Burn at head of wood, ¾ mile E. of Tokavaig.
Cambrian, Fucoid Shales. Trilobites and gastropods.
Peach, B. N. and others 1910b, pp. 68, 177-179.
Geol. Surv. 71 ; Ord. Pop. 35.

**Torran.** Allt Slapin at bend of stream, a few yards above crofters dyke.
Jurassic, Lower Lias. Brachiopods, lamellibranchs, belemnites.
Peach, B. N. and others 1910b, pp. 108, 180-185.
Geol. Surv. 71 ; Ord. Pop. 35.

**Torran.** Shore of Loch Slapin at Torran, 4½ miles S.W. of Broadford.
Cambrian, Durness Limestone. Gastropods and cephalopods.
Peach, B. N. and others 1910b, pp. 177-179.
Geol. Surv. 71 ; Ord. Pop. 35.

**Torran.** Allt an t-Sratha Bhig, about 1 mile from shore upstream from waterfall.
Jurassic, Lower Lias, Pabba Shales. Lamellibranchs, cephalopods.
Peach, B. N. and others 1910b, pp. 180-185.
Geol. Surv. 71 ; Ord. Pop. 35.

**Torran.** Allt an t-Sratha Bhig, Loch Slapin about ¾ mile from mouth of stream at a sharp double bend followed to N. by alluvial patch.
Jurassic, Lower Lias, Pabba Shales, *raricostatum* zone. Plant remains, crinoids (*Pentacrinus*), lamellibranchs, belemnites.
Peach, B. N. and others 1910b, pp. 180-185.
Geol. Surv. 71 ; Ord. Pop. 35.

## KINCARDINESHIRE

**Stonehaven.** Foreshore, just S. of pier at Cowie Harbour.
Silurian, Downtonian, almost vertical, striking N.E. to S.W. A 30 ft. band of " Volcanic Conglomerate " and tuff is succeeded seawards by 60 ft. of red sandstone, then by a few hundred feet of grey sandstones with bands of micaceous mudstones. The fossils occur mainly in the first and second of these bands. Arthropods (*Dictyocaris*) abundant. Type locality for the fishes *Traquairaspis campbelli*, *Phialaspis pococki* var. *cowiensis* snd *Hemitelaspis heintzi*. Eurypterids and myriapods also occur.
Campbell, R. 1913, p. 923. Westoll, T. S. 1945, p. 341. White, E. I. 1946, p. 207.
Geol. Surv. 67 ; Ord. Pop. 51.

## KINROSS

**Dollar.** In River Devon, 300 yds. above Vicar's Bridge, 1½ miles E. of Dollar.
Carboniferous, Upper Limestone Series, Vicar's Bridge Limestone. Plant remains and lamellibranchs.
Dinham, C. H. and Haldane, D. 1932, p. 109.
Geol. Surv. 39 ; Ord. Pop. 67.

**Dollar.** Rough Cleugh (tributary of Black Davon), S.S.W. of Wester Muirhead Farm, 3½ miles S.E. of Dollar.
Carboniferous, " Millstone Grit." Brachiopods, lamellibranchs and gastropods.
Dinham, C. H. and Haldane, D. 1932, p. 126.
Geol. Surv. 39 ; Ord. Pop. 67.

# KIRKCUDBRIGHT

**Arbigland.** On shore S. of Gardener's Cottage, 2¼ miles slightly N. of W. of mouth of River Nith.
Carboniferous, Calciferous Sandstone Series. Corals, brachiopods, lamellibranchs and gastropods.
Hill, D. 1937-1941, p. 19.
Geol. Surv. 6 ; Ord. Pop. 92.

**Balmaclellan.** Barend Burn, ½ mile N.E. of Barend Farmhouse, and upstream to waterfall, 4½ miles S.E. of Balmaclellan.
Silurian, Llandovery, Birkhill Shales. Graptolites.
Peach, B. N. and Horne, J. 1899, p. 161.
Geol. Surv. 9 ; Ord. Pop. 87.

**Castle Douglas.** Streamlet in a field N.W. of Mountskip Plantation, N. of Castle Douglas.
Ordovician, Caradoc, Glenkiln Shales. Graptolites.
Peach, B. N. and Horne H. 1899, p. 169.
Geol. Surv. 5 ; Ord. Pop. 92.

**Castle Douglas.** Near entrance and upstream on S. bank of Trowdale Glen, 4 miles N. of Castle Douglas.
Ordovician, Caradoc, Glenkiln Shales. Graptolites.
Peach, B. N. and Horne, J. 1899, pp. 164-167.
Geol. Surv. 5 ; Ord. Pop. 92.

**Castle Douglas.** Tottlehams Burn and fields S.W. of Corsehill, on S. side of fold on a knoll, about 150 yds. N. of E. end of Tottlehams Wood, 4½ miles slightly E. of N. of Castle Douglas.
Ordovician, Caradoc, Glenkiln-Hartfell Shales. Graptolites.
Peach, B. N. and Horne, J. 1899, pp. 167-169.
Geol. Surv. 5. Ord. Pop. 92.

**Castle Douglas.** In field and S. of Bellymack Farmhouse, ½ mile E. of Lawrieston.
Ordovician, Caradoc, Glenkiln-Hartfell Shales. Graptolites.
Peach, B. N. and Horne, J. 1899, p. 170.
Geol. Surv. 5 ; Ord. Pop. 92.

**Corsock.** Water of Urr, between Nether Glaisters and Crogs Tower, 1 mile N.W. of Corsock.
Silurian, Llandovery, Birkhill Shales. Graptolites.
Peach, B. N. and Horne, J. 1899, p. 160.
Geol. Surv. 9 ; Ord. Pop. 88.

**Corsock.** Croggs Burn (tributary of Urr Water) a few yards E. of crossing of Corsock-New Galloway Road, 2 miles N.W. of Corsock.
Silurian, Llandovery, Birkhill Shales. Graptolites.
Peach, B. N. and Horne, J. 1899, p. 161.
Geol. Surv. 9 ; Ord. Pop. 88.

**Dalry.** Section in Long Burn, ¼ mile N.E. of Stroampatrick Shepherd's House, 7½ miles N.N.E. of Dalry.
Ordovician, Caradoc, Glenkiln and Hartfell black shales. Graptolites.
Peach, B. N. and Horne, J. 1899, p. 343.
Geol. Surv. 9 ; Ord. Pop. 83.

**Dalry.** N. of mansion House of Dalshangen, 300 yds. from foot of Pulwhanity Burn on W. bank of Deugh Water.
Ordovician, Caradoc, Hartfell Group. Graptolites and brachiopods.
Peach, B. N. and Horne, J. 1899, p. 344.
Geol. Surv. 9 ; Ord. Pop. 83.

**Dalry.** Carroch Lane, N. of Culmark, 6 miles N.N.E. of Dalry.
Ordovician, Caradoc, Glenkiln-Hartfell Shales. Graptolites.
Peach, B. N. and Horne, J. 1899, p. 346.
Geol. Surv. 9 ; Ord. Pop. 83.

**Dundrennan.** Centre of bay W. of Raebeery Castle, E. side of Kirkcudbright Bay.
Silurian, Wenlock. Graptolites and cephalopods.
Peach, B. N. and Horne, J. 1899, p. 555.
Geol. Surv. 5 ; Ord. Pop. 92.

**Dunscore.** In a wood along Anchenhay Burn, ¼ mile N. of junction with Knarie Burn (a tributary of Urr water), 7¼ miles S.W. of Dunscore.
Silurian, Llandovery, Birkhill Shales. Graptolites.
Peach, B. N. and Horne, J. 1899, p. 160.
Geol. Surv. 9 ; Ord. Pop. 88.

**Kirkcudbright.** On shore S. of Balmae Haven, E. side of Kirkcudbright Bay.
Silurian, Wenlock. Graptolites, cephalopods and crustaceans.
Peach, B. N. and Horne, J. 1899, p. 553.
Geol. Surv. 5 ; Ord. Pop. 92.

**Kirkcudbright.** Shore immediately N. and S. of Witch Wifes Haven, E. side of Kirkcudbright Bay.
Silurian, Wenlock. Graptolites, cephalopods and crustaceans.
Peach, B. N. and Horne, J. 1899, p. 553.
Geol. Surv. 5 ; Ord. Pop. 92.

**Kirkcudbright.** Shore N. and S. of Torrs Point, E. side of Kirkcudbright Bay.
Silurian, Wenlock. Graptolites, cephalopods and crustaceans.
Peach, B. N. and Horne, J. 1899, p. 553.
Geol. Surv. 5 ; Ord. Pop. 92.

**Kirkcudbright.** Shore E. of boatman's house, Mulloch Bay, E. side of Kirkcudbright Bay.
Silurian, Wenlock. Graptolites.
Peach, B. N. and Horne, J. 1899, p. 556.
Geol. Surv. 5 ; Ord. Pop. 92.

**Kirkcudbright.** Immediately N. and S. of Long Robin, E. side of Kirkcudbright Bay.
Silurian, Wenlock. Graptolites.
Peach, B. N. and Horne, J. 1899, p. 552.
Geol. Surv. 5 ; Ord. Pop. 92.

**Kirkcudbright.** Little Balmae Farmhouse, 4 miles S.S.E. of Kirkcudbright.
Silurian, Wenlock, fine brecciated conglomerate. Corals, crinoids, brachiopods, trilobites, gastropods and lamellibranchs.
Peach, B. N. and Horne, J. 1899, p. 556.
Geol. Surv. 5 ; Ord. Pop. 92.

**Kirkcudbright.** Shore E. side of Howell Bay, E. side of Kirkcudbright Bay.
Silurian, Wenlock. Graptolites.
Peach, B. N. and Horne, J. 1899, p. 555.
Geol. Surv. 5 ; Ord. Pop. 92.

**Kirkcudbright.** Shore to S. of Ganger's Loop, E. side of Kirkcudbright Bay.
Silurian, Wenlock. Graptolites and cephalopods.
Geol. Surv. 5 ; Ord. Pop. 92.

**Lawrieston.** In stream 50 yds. N. of Dunnance Farm, and in a branch of it ¼ mile S.W. of farm, S.W. of Lawrieston, 5½ miles W.N.W. of Castle Douglas.
Silurian, Llandovery, Birkhill Shales. Graptolites.
Peach, B. N. and Horne, J. 1899, p. 170.
Geol. Surv. 5 ; Ord. Pop. 92.

**New Galloway.** Margree Burn, 6¼ miles N.N.E. of New Galloway ; also ¾ mile S. of Margree in burn at Regland shepherd's house.
Ordovician, Caradoc, Hartfell and Glenkiln Groups. Graptolites.
Peach, B. N. and Horne, J. 1899, pp. 349-350.
Geol. Surv. 9 ; Ord. Pop. 87.

**Parton.** Hensol House, in River Dee close to junction with River Ken, 7 miles N.W. of Castle Douglas.
Silurian, Llandovery, Birkhill Shales. Graptolites.
Peach, B. N. and Horne, J. 1899, pp. 170-171.
Geol. Surv. 5 ; Ord. Pop. 92.

**Southwick.** On shore W.S.W. of Southerness Point, 3¼ miles S.W. of River Nith.
Carboniferous, Calciferous Sandstone Series. Brachiopods and lamellibranchs.
Geol. Surv. 6 ; Ord. Pop. 92.

**Tynron.** Carlae Burn, 1½ miles E. of Manwhill shepherd's house.
Ordovician, Caradoc, Glenkiln-Hartfell black shales. Graptolites and brachiopods.
Peach, B. N. and Horne, J. 1899, p. 346.
Geol. Surv. 9 ; Ord. Pop. 84.

## LANARKSHIRE

**Abington.** Wandel Water at junction with Hawkwood Burn.
Ordovician, Caradoc (Glenkiln Black Shales), containing graptolites.
Peach, B. N. and Horne, J. 1899, p. 224.
Geol. Surv. 15 ; Ord. Pop. 79.

**Abington.** Birnock Burn, near head of Wandel Burn, 1 mile S.S.E. of N.W. corner of Geol. 1-inch Sheet 16.
Ordovician, Caradoc (Glenkiln-Hartfell Shales), containing graptolites.
Peach, B. N. and Horne, J. 1899, pp. 221-222.
Geol. Surv. 16 ; Ord. Pop. 79.

**Abington.** Rein Gill, near junction with Wandel Water, 3¼ miles N.E. of Abington.
Ordovician, Caradoc (Glenkiln Shales), containing graptolites and brachiopods.
Peach, B. N. and Horne, J. 1899, p. 223.
Geol. Surv. 15 ; Ord. Pop. 79.

**Abington.** Right bank of River Clyde at bridge, ½ mile above Wandel Mill.
Ordovician, Caradoc (Glenkiln Shales), containing graptolites.
Peach, B. N. and Horne, J. 1899, pp. 327-328.
Geol. Surv. 15 ; Ord. Pop. 79.

**Abington.** Wallace's Castle, Wandel Burn, 3 miles N.E. of Abington.
Ordovician, Caradoc (grey shales with limestone nodules) ; contain trilobites, brachiopods, gastropods, lamellibranchs and sponges.
Peach, B. N. and Horne, J. 1899, pp. 224-225.
Geol. Surv. 15 ; Ord. Pop. 79.

R

**Avonbank.** Hamilton High Parks ; a short deep gully on W. bank of River Avon a little N. of W. of Avonbank ; on both E. and W. sides of a N.-S. fault crossing the gully.

Carboniferous, Coal Measures (*similis-pulchra* zone ; Skipsey's Marine Band) ; yields plants, lamellibranchs, brachiopods and goniatites.

Clough, C. T. and others 1920, p. 100.
Geol. Surv. 23 ; Ord. Pop. 73.

**Bothwell.** Left bank of River Clyde, ¼ mile W. of Bothwell Bridge.

Carboniferous, Coal Measures (upper *similis-pulchra* or *phillipsi* zone) ; green shales in Barren Red Measures ; contain *Anthraconaia pruvosti* and *A. glotae.*

Weir, J. and Leitch, D. 1936, pp. 914 and 944-945.
Geol. Surv. 31 ; Ord. Pop. 73.

**Braidwood.** Fiddler Burn ; in gully on right bank below Fiddler Bridge and E.N.E. of Woodhall.

Carboniferous, Calciferous Sandstone Series (white shelly limestone above *Productus giganteus* Limestone) ; contains plants and brachiopods.

Hinxman, L. W. and others 1921, pp. 10-13.    Hill, D. 1937-1941, p. 21.
Geol. Surv. 23 ; Ord. Pop. 73.

**Braidwood.** In bed of Fiddlers Burn below fall, 15-20 yds. upstream from Sampsons Slingstone.

Carboniferous, Limestone Coal Group (Slingstone Limestone) ; contains brachiopods and lamellibranchs.

Hinxman, L. W. and others 1921, p. 34.
Geol. Surv. 23 ; Ord. Pop. 73.

**Carluke.** Bed of Fiddlers Burn at Nellfield ; also on left bank of burn under the farmhouse ; also ¼ mile N.E. of Nellfield ; also 1/12th mile E.S.E. of Nellfield.    1½ miles S.E. of Carluke.

Carboniferous, Calciferous Sandstone Series (Fiddler Shell Bed ; limestones and shales) ; containing brachiopods, corals, gastropods and echinoderms.

Hinxman, L. W. and others 1921, pp. 10-13.
Geol. Surv. 23 ; Ord. Pop. 73.

**Carluke.** In bed of Fulwood Burn, at point due W. of Birkenhead ; 3½ miles S.E. of Carluke.

Carboniferous, Calciferous Sandstone Series (*Productus giganteus* Limestone ) ; contains brachiopods and corals.

Hinxman, L. W. and others 1921, p. 14.
Geol. Surv. 23 ; Ord. Pop. 73.

**Carluke.** Thorn Quarry, 2 miles N.E. of Carluke.

Carboniferous, Lower Limestone Group (Main Limestone) ; contains brachiopods, lamellibranchs, trilobites, cephalopods and fish remains.

Hinxman, L. W. and others 1921, pp. 27-28.
Geol. Surv. 23 ; Ord. Pop. 73.

**Carluke.** Birkfield, 1 mile E.S.E. of Carluke ; quarry on left bank of Fiddlers Burn ; old quarry in spruce plantation on W. side of burn, 1/12th mile S. of Birkfield ; and old ironstone workings, 1/12th mile E. of Birkfield.

Carboniferous (shale with First Calmy Limestone) ; contains ostracods, productids and lamellibranchs.

Hinxman, L. W. and others 1921, p. 32.
Geol. Surv 23 ; Ord. Pop. 73.

**Carluke.** Hallcraig House, 1½ miles W. of Carluke ; cliff under the house and on left bank of Jocks Burn below house and also opposite to it ; on left bank of burn below Hallcraig Bridge.

Carboniferous, Lower Limestone Group (Top Hosie Limestone and First Kingshaw Limestone) ; contain plants, productids, *Lingula* and lamellibranchs.
Hinxman, L. W. and others 1921, pp. 31-33.
Geol. Surv. 23 ; Ord. Pop. 73.

**Carluke.** Maregill Burn ; bed of burn near Southbank and also 1/12th mile N. of Southbank, 1¾ miles S.S.W. of Carluke.
Carboniferous, Upper Limestone Group ; containing brachiopods, lamellibranchs and crinoids.
Hinxman, L. W. and others 1921, pp. 39-40.
Geol. Surv. 23 ; Ord. Pop. 73.

**Coalburn.** Poniel Water ; 20 yds., 34 yds., 40 yds., 66 yds. and 166 yds. up in small stream entering Poniel Water 333 yds. W. of Brackenside, Coalburn.
Carboniferous, Calciferous Sandstone Series ; containing corals, productids and gastropods.
Geol. Surv. 23 ; Ord. Pop. 79.

**Coalburn.** Poniel Water : in bank of stream (1) 158 yds. W. 22° N., (2) 240 yds. N. 40° W., (3) 170 yds. W., (4) 175 yds. W., (5) 285 yds. W., (6) 290 yds. W., (7) 385 yds. W., (8) 498 yds. W., (9) 600 yds. W., (10) 830 yds. W. of Brackenside, Brockley, Coalburn.
Carboniferous, Lower Limestone Series ; containing productids, orthotetids, bryozoa, cephalopods, crinoids, lamellibranchs, corals and trilobites.
Hill, D. 1937-1941, p. 21.
Geol. Surv. 23 ; Ord. Pop. 79.

**Dalserf.** Dalserf Burn ; (1) S. of the Clyde at Whinstone Linn, (2) N.E. of railway line, about ¼ mile N. of Netherburn, near outcrop of Upper Coal as shown on 1-inch map.
Carboniferous, Coal Measures (Kiltongue Musselband at base of *modiolaris* zone) ; contains plants and *Carbonicola*.
Hinxman, L. W. and others 1921, p. 94.
Geol. Surv. 23 ; Ord. Pop. 73.

**Douglas.** Amegalloch Burn, just above Townhead Cottage, 1 mile S. of Douglas.
Carboniferous, Coal Measures (*communis* zone, sandy sediments); containing partly decalcified, but otherwise well-preserved specimens of *Carbonicola crista-galli*, etc.
Weir, J. and Leitch, D. 1936, p. 716. MacLennan, R. M. 1946, p. 88.
Geol. Surv. 23 ; Ord. Pop. 79.

**Douglas.** Broadlea Burn, ½ mile W. of Douglas.
Carboniferous, Coal Measures (*modiolaris* and lower *similis-pulchra* zones) ; grey shale, roof of Four Foot Coal, 500 yds. upstream from Broadlea Cottage, contains *Anthracosia* and *Anthraconaia* of upper part of *modiolaris* zone.
Weir, J. and Leitch, D. 1936, p. 717.
Geol. Surv. 23 ; Ord. Pop. 79.

**Douglas.** Burnhouse Burn, ¼ mile E. of Douglas and 200-230 yds. upstream from road.
Carboniferous, Coal Measures (top of *modiolaris* zone and base of *similis-pulchra* zone) ; musselband with *Anthraconaia*, etc., above Three Foot Coal, 20-30 yds. downstream from waterfall : basal fauna of *similis-pulchra* zone. Also, on top of waterfall, grey shale above the Four Foot Coal containing *Anthracosia* and *Anthraconaia* of the upper part of *modiolaris* zone.
Weir, J. and Leitch, D. 1936, p. 717.
Geol. Surv. 23 ; Ord. Pop. 79.

**East Kilbride.** Arrotshole Farmhouse ; old quarry at the farmhouse and above it in bed of Kittock Water ; 1½ miles W. by N. of East Kilbride Church.

Carboniferous, Calciferous Sandstone Series, and Main Limestone of Lower Limestone Group ; containing brachiopods, plants, fish remains and ostracods.

Carruthers, R. G. and Dinham, C. H. 1917, p. 15.

Geol. Surv. 23 ; Ord. Pop. 72.

**East Kilbride.** Basket Farmhouse ; left bank of Calder Water nearly opposite farmhouse, and ⅛ mile N.W. of it ; at stream level in W. bank of Rotten Calder, between East Kilbride and Blantyre ; also on right bank of Rotten Calder, about ⅛ mile S.S.W. of Basket.

Carboniferous, Calciferous Sandstone Series ; containing brachiopods, lamellibranchs, plants and crustaceans.

Carruthers, R. G. and Dinham, C. H. 1917, pp. 5-10.

Geol. Surv. 23 ; Ord. Pop. 72.

**Glenboig.** Moulding Sand Quarry, 1/16th mile W. of Gain, about 1 mile N.N.E. of Glenboig railway station.

Carboniferous, Millstone Grit ; contains lamellibranchs, brachiopods and gastropods.

Clough, C. T. and others 1926, pp. 37-39.

Geol. Surv. 31 ; Ord. Pop. 73.

**Glenbuck.** Galawhistle Burn ; in small burn entering Galawhistle Burn, ¼ mile W. of High Monkshead, 1¼ miles N.N.W. of Glenbuck.

Carboniferous, Limestone Coal Group (Johnstone Shell Bed) ; Lower Limestones (Main Limestone) ; Calciferous Limestone Series ; contain brachiopods, corals, bryozoa, lamellibranchs and gastropods.

Geol. Surv. 23 ; Ord. Pop. 79.

**Glespin.** Carmacoup Burn ; 350 yds., 300 yds., 250 yds., 80 yds., 34 yds. and 20 yds. upstream from junction with small burn, entering from south at a point 667 yds. E. 15° S. of the N.W. corner of the 6-inch map.

Carboniferous, Lower Limestone Series ; contains brachiopods and corals.

Geol. Surv. 15 ; Ord. Pop. 79.

**Glespin.** Glentaggart Burn : (1) on lower side of road-bridge at Glentaggart House ; (2) ⅛ mile E.N.E. of house ; (3) scaur on right bank, 100-120 yds. upstream from Blackmire Burn ; (4) scaur on right bank, ⅓ mile upstream from junction with Glespin Burn ; and (5) left bank, 50-60 yds. upstream from coal worked at outcrop.

Carboniferous, Lower Limestone Series and (?) " Millstone Grit " ; the former contains corals, brachiopods and *Phillipsia,* and the latter plants.

Geol. Surv. 15 ; Ord. Pop. 79.

**Kennox** (Douglas). Kennox Water, right bank tributary, 500 yds. S. 23° E. of Kennox Farm.

Carboniferous, Coal Measures (*communis* zone) ; siltstones and shales exposed in right bank, the latter containing well-preserved solid shells of *Carbonicola* aff. *communis,* etc., and *Anthraconauta.*

Weir, J. and Leitch, D. 1936, p. 716 ; MacLennan, R. M. 1946, pp. 81-82.

Geol. Surv. 15 ; Ord. Pop. 79.

**Kennoxhead.** Kennox Water : (1) in bed of stream, 700 yds. E. 23° S. of Chapel Hill ; (2) high up on left bank, 600 yds. E. 32° S. of Chapel Hill ; (3) in sharp bend of stream, N. 38° W. of Kennox Hill and 250 yds. up from same bend. One mile E.N.E. of Kennoxhead.

Carboniferous, Upper and Lower Limestone series ; contain brachiopods, lamellibranchs, *Phillipsia* and corals.

Geol. Surv. 15 ; Ord. Pop. 79.

**Lamington.** In gully on hillside, ⅝ mile S. 23° E. of Hartside and in bed of burn, 1210 yds., 1310 yds. and 1320 yds. up from Hartside. 1½ miles S.W. of Lamington.

Ordovician, Caradoc, Glenkiln Shales ; contain graptolites and brachiopods.

Geol. Surv. 23 ; Ord. Pop. 79.

**Lanark.** Lee Burn : (1) N.N.W. of The Lee ; (2) ¼ mile E.N.E. of The Lee, right bank of burn, 100 yds. below main road ; (3) downstream from (2), left bank near water-level, between two little cascades. 3 miles N.W. of Lanark.

Carboniferous, Lower Limestone Series and Calciferous Sandstone Series ; contain brachiopods, lamellibranchs, gastropods and goniatites.

Hinxman, L. W. and others 1921, p.15.

Geol. Surv. 23 ; Ord. Pop. 73.

**Larkhall.** Stream nearly ¼ mile S.W. of crossroads at Birkenshaw, a few yards downstream from remains of old mill. 2 miles S. of Larkhall.

Carboniferous, Upper Limestone Series (Orchard Limestone) ; contains brachiopods, gastropods, cephalopods, lamellibranchs, corals and trilobites.

Hinxman, L. W. and others 1921, pp. 63-64.

Geol. Surv. 23 ; Ord. Pop. 73.

**Larkhall.** Left bank of Avon Water, at bottom of Ringsdale Castle cliff ; also 260 yds. S.E. of site of castle and ⅛ mile W.S.W. of Birkenshaw. 2 miles S. of Larkhall.

Carboniferous, Coal Measures (sandstone under Slatyband Ironstone) ; " Millstone Grit " ; Upper Limestone Series (Gair Limestone) ; contain plants, crinoids, brachiopods and lamellibranchs.

Hinxman, L. W. and others 1921, pp. 76-77.

Geol. Surv. 23 ; Ord. Pop. 73.

**Lesmahagow.** In Teiglum Burn, ¼ mile S.E. of and 3/16th mile W. of Kerse. 1½ miles N. of Lesmahagow.

Carboniferous, Lower Limestone Series ; and Calciferous Sandstone Series ; contain brachiopods and lamellibranchs.

Hinxman, L. W. and others 1921, p. 17.

Geol. Surv. 23 ; Ord. Pop. 79.

**Lesmahagow.** Birkwood Burn below Kypehall Bridge, 1¼ miles S. by E. of Blackwood station and 1½ miles N.N.W. of Lesmahagow.

Carboniferous, Lower Limestones ; contain lamellibranchs, productids and other brachiopods, corals, gastropods, cephalopods and bryozoa.

Hinxman, L. W. and others 1921, pp. 43-46.

Geol. Surv. 23 ; Ord. Pop. 79.

**Lesmahagow.** Nethan River ; right bank S. of Auchenheath House (first limestone N. of bridge at Burnfoot). 2¼ miles N. of Lesmahagow.

Carboniferous, Lower Limestone Series ; contains brachiopods, corals and gastropods.

Hinxman, L. W. and others 1921, pp. 42-43.

Geol. Surv. 23 ; Ord. Pop. 79.

**Lesmahagow.** In bank of River Nethan, 266 yds. N. of Old Stockbriggs and 383 yds. N. 12° E., 466 yds. N. 8° E. and 468 yds. N. 8° E. of Old Stockbriggs.

Carboniferous, Lower Limestone Series ; and Calciferous Sandstone Series ; contain productids and corals.

Geol. Surv. 23 ; Ord. Pop. 79.

**Lesmahagow.** In bed of River Nethan, 200 yds. W. 19° N. of Auchlochan ; in bank of river, 115 yds. N. of, 500 yds. W. 4° S. of, and 500 yds. W. 3° S. of Auchlochan, Lesmahagow.

Carboniferous, Upper and Lower Limestones ; contain brachiopods, corals, gastropods, bryozoa and crinoids.
Geol. Surv. 23 ; Ord. Pop. 79.

**Muirkirk.** In right bank of Slot Burn, tributary of Greenock Water, 200 yds. above ruins of Seggholm House. The locality is 3 miles W. of N. from Muirkirk.
Silurian, Downtonian or Ludlow ; 15 ft. of greenish-grey or brownish mudstones (division 9 of the Geological Survey account) contain *Dictyocaris, Ceratiocaris* and eurypterids not uncommon. Fishes include *Thelodus, Lanarkia, Birkenia, Lasanius* and *Ateleaspis* described by Traquair.
Peach, B. N. and Horne, J. 1899, p. 578. Traquair, R. H. 1899, 1905.
Geol. Surv. 23 ; Ord. Pop. 78.

**Stonehouse.** Cot Castle Farm ; about ⅛ mile N. of the farm on right bank of Avon Water, also upstream on opposite side, on N. side of fault ; 1¼ miles S.W. of Stonehouse.
Carboniferous, Lower Limestone Series and Calciferous Sandstone Series ; contain plants, brachiopods and lamellibranchs.
Hinxman, L. W. and others 1921, pp. 20-23.
Geol. Surv. 23 ; Ord. Pop. 73.

**Stonehouse.** Avon Water, near Avonholm, 1 mile S.W. of Stonehouse ; also above Avonholm, 1¼ miles S. by W. of Stonehouse.
Carboniferous, Lower Limestone Series ; contains brachiopods, lamellibranchs, crinoids and corals.
Hinxman, L. W. and others 1921, p. 65.
Geol. Surv. 23 ; Ord. Pop. 73.

**Stonehouse.** 270 yds. S.E. of Patrickholm, right bank of River Avon ; also 350 feet S.E. of Patrickholm on same bank ; also left bank of river on S.E. side of Patrickholm, on S. side of fault. 2 miles N. of Stonehouse.
Carboniferous, Upper Limestone Series (Orchard Limestone and Slatyband Ironstone) ; contain plants, brachiopods, corals, bryozoa and gastropods.
Hinxman, L. W. and others 1921, pp. 62-64.
Geol. Surv. 23 ; Ord. Pop. 73.

**Strathaven.** Darngaber Burn, E. of L.M. & S. Railway. Downstream from railway. 3 miles N. of Strathaven.
Carboniferous, Upper Limestone Series (Castlecary Limestone) ; contains brachiopods and plant remains.
Carruthers, R. G. and Dinham, C. H. 1917, p. 29.
Geol. Surv. 23 ; Ord. Pop. 73.

**Strathaven.** In bank of burn (1) 166 yds. W. 10° N., (2) 466 yds. W. 34° N., (3) 266 yds. W. 43° N., (4) 275 yds. W. 43° N., (5) 333 yds. W. 44° N. of West Ryelandside. 4 miles S.W. of Strathaven.
Carboniferous, Lower Limestone Series and Calciferous Sandstone Series ; contain brachiopods, corals and lamellibranchs.
Geol. Surv. 23 ; Ord. Pop. 78.

**Strathaven.** In bank and bed of burn, 500 yds. W. 19° N., 600 yds. W. 6° N. and 615 yds. W. 5° N. of Snabe. 5 miles S.W. of Strathaven.
Carboniferous, Lower Limestone Series and Calciferous Sandstone Series ; contain brachiopods and corals.
Geol. Surv. 23 ; Ord. Pop. 78.

**Tweedsmuir.** Cow Linn, 1½ miles from source of Fruid Water, N. of Hartfell, below foot of Black Cleuch.
Silurian, Llandovery Series (Lower Birkhill Shales) ; with graptolites.
Peach, B. N. and Horne, J. 1899, p. 142.
Geol. Surv. 16 ; Ord. Pop. 79.

**Waterloo.** Garriongill, deep gorge of Garrion Burn, ½ mile S. of Waterloo and ⅓ mile N. of Law Junction : (1) top of scarp below Jacob's Ladder ; (2) a few yards above pumping station ; (3) left bank, 30-40 yds. below footbridge and miner's path.

Carboniferous, Coal Measures (from Kiltongue Musselband to Upper Ell Coal, *modiolaris* and lower *similis-pulchra* zones) ; yield non-marine lamellibranchs, notably from the Kiltongue Musselband ; basal fauna of *modiolaris* zone at two exposures at E. end of Section.

Macgregor, M. 1913, pp. 279-290 ; Weir, J. and Leitch, D. 1936, pp. 708-714.

Geol. Surv. 23 ; Ord. Pop. 73.


# MIDLOTHIAN

**Bonnyrigg.** Viewfield Sandstone Quarry, Bonnyrigg.
Carboniferous, Lower Coal Measures ; contains plants.
Peach, B. N. and others 1910a, pp. 377-387.
Geol. Surv. 32 ; Ord. Pop. 74.

**Borthwick.** Middleton Limestone Quarries ; 6½ miles S.S.E. of Dalkeith.
Carboniferous, Lower Limestone Series ; contains foraminifera, echinoderms, bryozoans and brachiopods.
Peach, B. N. and others 1910a, pp. 380-405.
Geol. Surv. 32 ; Ord. Pop. 74.

**Carlops.** North Esk, near second rivulet, ⅓ mile above North Esk reservoir and ½ mile S.W. of this.
Silurian, Wenlock Shales ; contain sponges, corals, brachiopods and lamellibranchs.
Peach, B. N. and Horne, J. 1899, pp. 593-597.
Geol. Surv. 32 ; Ord. Pop. 74.

**Carlops.** Wetherlaw Linn ; from scar on W. bank of Esk, a few yards N. of Wetherlaw Linn Burn.
Silurian, Wenlock Series ; contains sponges, graptolites, corals, trilobites, brachiopods and molluscs.
Peach, B. N. and Horne, J. 1899, pp. 597-598.
Geol. Surv. 32 ; Ord. Pop. 74.

**Colinton.** Water of Leith, left bank, above Spylaw House.
Carboniferous, Calciferous Sandstone Series ; contains plants, cephalopods and lamellibranchs.
Peach, B. N. and others 1910a, pp. 375-405.
Geol. Surv. 32 ; Ord. Pop. 74.

**Dalkeith.** Mayfield Quarry, 2 miles S.E. of Dalkeith.
Carboniferous, Lower Limestone Series ; contains crinoids, annelids, ostracods, brachiopods, lamellibranchs, gastropods and fish.
Peach, B. N. and others 1910a, pp. 383-405.
Geol. Surv. 32 ; Ord. Pop. 74.

**Dalkeith.** Cousland Quarries, 3 miles N.E. of Dalkeith.
Carboniferous, Lower Limestone Series (No. 2 Limestone) ; contains foraminifera, echinoderms, arthropods, bryozoans, brachiopods, lamellibranchs, gastropods, cephalopods and fish.
Peach, B. N. and others 1910a, pp. 383-405.
Geol. Surv. 32 ; Ord. Pop. 74.

**Dalkeith.** Left bank, River North Esk, 600 yds. W. of Elginhaugh Bridge, 1 mile W.S.W. of Dalkeith.
Carboniferous, Coal Measures (*communis* zone, black parroty shales above Parrot Rough Coal) ; contain *Carbonicola pseudorobusta* ; fossils occur as red-stained flattened shells.
Weir, J. and Leitch, D. 1936, p. 732.
Geol. Surv. 32 ; Ord. Pop. 74.

**Edinburgh.** Craigleith Quarry, W. side of city of Edinburgh.
Carboniferous, Calciferous Sandstone Series (shales overlying sandstone) ; contain plants, annelids, lamellibranchs, gastropods, cephalopods, arthropods and fish.
Peach, B. N. and others 1910a, pp. 374-405.
Geol. Surv. 32 ; Ord. Pop. 74.

**Gilmerton.** Ferniehill Old Limestone Quarry, Gilmerton.
Carboniferous, Lower Limestone Series ; contains echinoderms, bryozoans, brachiopods, lamellibranchs and gastropods.
Peach, B. N. and others 1910a, pp. 376-405.
Geol. Surv. 32 ; Ord. Pop. 74.

**Gorebridge.** Blinkbonny Quarry ; 1 mile N.N.E. of Gorebridge.
Carboniferous, Lower Limestone Series (No. 3 Limestone) ; contains foraminifera, ostracods, bryozoans, brachiopods and molluscs.
Peach, B. N. and others 1910a, pp. 381-405.
Geol. Surv. 32 ; Ord. Pop. 74.

**Gorebridge.** Mansfield Quarry, 3 miles S.E. of Dalkeith.
Carboniferous, Lower Limestone Series ; contains brachiopods, lamellibranchs, cephalopods and gastropods.
Peach, B. N. and others 1910a, pp. 383-405.
Geol. Surv. 32 ; Ord. Pop. 74.

**Gorebridge.** Arniston Glen in steep slope on left bank 100-150 feet above stream (South Esk), 50 yds. upstream from wooden footbridge. ½ mile N.W. of Arniston Mains.
Carboniferous, " Millstone Grit " (lower part of " Millstone Grit " Marine Bed) ; contains brachiopods, lamellibranchs and crinoids.
Peach, B. N. and others 1910a, pp. 380-405.
Geol. Surv. 32 ; Ord. Pop. 74.

**Granton.** Wardie Shore between Trinity and E. side of Granton Harbour, Edinburgh.
Carboniferous, Calciferous Sandstone Series ; contains plants, fish, lamellibranchs and arthropods.
Peach, B. N. and others 1910a, pp. 374-405.
Geol. Surv. 32 ; Ord. Pop. 74.

**Heriot.** Corsehope, 1½ miles S. from Heriot station, W. side of valley of Gala Water, 250 yds. S. of Corsehope Burn.
Ordovician, Caradoc Series (Glenkiln shales and radiolarian cherts) ; the shales contain graptolites.
Peach, B. N. and Horne, J. 1899, p. 270.
Geol. Surv. 25 ; Ord. Pop. 74.

**Juniper Green.** Woodhall, Water of Leith, right bank at ford below weir near Juniper Green. 5 miles S.W. of Edinburgh.
Carboniferous, Calciferous Sandstone Series ; contains plants, molluscs, crustaceans and fish.
Peach, B. N. and others 1910a, pp. 375-405.
Geol. Surv. 32 ; Ord. Pop. 74.

**Loanhead.** Bilston Burn, left bank below Pathhead Farmhouse.
Carboniferous, Lower Limestone Series (shale in middle of the Bilston Burn Limestone) ; contains crinoids, brachiopods, lamellibranchs and gastropods.
Peach, B. N. and others 1910a, pp. 377-405.
Geol. Surv. 32 ; Ord. Pop. 74.

**Loanhead.** Bilston Burn, 1 mile S.W. of Loanhead, at Dryden.
Carboniferous, Lower Limestone Series (shale below Gilmerton Limestone) ; contains brachiopods and lamellibranchs.
Peach, B. N. and others 1910a, pp. 377-405.
Geol. Surv. 32 ; Ord. Pop. 74.

**Newtongrange.** D'Arcy Quarry, 1¾ miles E. of Newton Grange and 2½ miles S.E. of Dalkeith.
Carboniferous, Lower Limestone Series ; contains foraminifera, ostracods, brachiopods, gastropods, cephalopods and fish.
Peach, B. N. and others 1910a, pp. 383-405.
Geol. Surv. 32 ; Ord. Pop. 74.

**Pathhead.** Currielee No. 2 Quarry, right bank, 20-30 ft. above River Tyne, 4 miles S.E. of Dalkeith.
Carboniferous, Lower Limestone Series (No. 2 Limestone) ; contains bryozoans, brachiopods, lamellibranchs, gastropods and fish.
Peach, B. N. and others 1910a, pp. 383-405.
Geol. Surv. 32 ; Ord. Pop. 74.

**Penicuik.** Fullarton Limestone Quarries, 3½ miles S.E. of Penicuik.
Carboniferous, Lower Limestone Series ; contains foraminifera, crinoids, ostracods, bryozoans and brachiopods.
Peach, B. N. and others 1910a, pp. 379-405.
Geol. Surv. 32 ; Ord. Pop. 74.

**Penicuik.** Mount Lothian Old Limestone Quarries, 3 miles S.E. of Penicuik.
Carboniferous, Lower Limestone Series (No. 2, Limestone) ; contains foraminifera, crinoids, ostracods, bryozoans and brachiopods.
Peach, B. N. and others, 1910a, pp. 379-405.
Geol. Surv. 32 ; Ord. Pop. 74.

**Penicuik.** Cornton Burn, right bank opposite Cornton ; 2 miles S.W. of Penicuik.
Carboniferous, Upper Limestone Series ; contains crinoids, brachiopods, lamellibranchs and gastropods.
Peach, B. N. and others, 1910a, pp. 379-405.
Geol. Surv. 32 ; Ord. Pop. 74.

**Polton.** Bilston Burn near Polton.
Carboniferous, " Millstone Grit " ; contains brachiopods, lamellibranchs and gastropods.
Peach, B. N. and others 1910a, pp. 377-405.
Geol. Surv. 32 ; Ord. Pop. 74.

**Stow.** Lugate Water, ½ mile upstream from confluence with Ewes Water, 4¾ miles W.N.W. of Stow.
Silurian, Llandovery Series (Birkhill Shales) ; contain graptolites.
Peach, B. N. and Horne, J. 1899, p. 195.
Geol. Surv. 25 ; Ord. Pop. 74.

**Stow.** Ewes Water (Luggate Water) below Shepherd's house of Trously, 4¾ miles W. by S. of Stow.
Silurian, Llandovery Series ; contains graptolites.
Peach, B. N. and Horne, J. 1899, p. 196.
Geol. Surv. 25 ; Ord. Pop. 80.

**Straiton.** Burdiehouse Limestone Quarry, 4½ miles S.S.E. of Edinburgh.
Carboniferous, Calciferous Sandstone Series ; contains plants, annelids,
lamellibranchs and fish.
   Peach, B. N. and others, 1910a, pp. 376-405.
   Geol. Surv. 32 ; Ord. Pop. 74.

**Temple.** Esperston Limestone Quarries, 1¾ miles S.E. of Temple, 6½ miles
S. of Dalkeith.
Carboniferous, Lower Limestone Series ; contains arthropods, crinoids,
brachiopods, lamellibranchs, cephalopods and fish.
   Peach, B. N. and others, 1910a, pp. 380-405.
   Geol. Surv. 32 ; Ord. Pop. 74.


# MORAYSHIRE

**Elgin.** " Rosebrae " Quarry, 400 yds. N.N.E. of the crossroads on the
main Elgin-Forres road and 200 yds. E. of the third milestone from Elgin.
The quarry is now abandoned.
Devonian, Upper Old Red Sandstone (Rosebrae Beds) ; current-bedded
yellowish sandstones full of clay-galls ; several faults are seen, one of which
brings down a few feet of the basal soft sandstone (with numerous dreikanters)
of the Permian Cutties Hillock Beds. Fossil fish are scarce : *Holoptychius*
scales may occasionally be found, *Phyllolepis* occurs more rarely. This is the
type-locality of the Rosebrae Beds, and also of the important, and so far unique,
specimen of the long-nosed dipnoan fish *Rhynchodipterus elginensis* and of
*Bothriolepis cristata*.
   Traquair, R. H. 1895, p. 259.
   Geol. Surv. 95 ; Ord. Pop. 29.

**Longmorn Station.** Scaat Craig, a knoll (now rather obscured) in the
valley of the Longmorn Burn, 370 yds. S.W. of Whitewreath ; also 300 yds.
upstream, opposite the underway railway bridge.
Devonian, Upper Old Red Sandstone ; at Scaat Craig itself, red and
yellow crumbling pebbly sandstone ; at the upstream locality, soft yellow and
red sandstones. Equivalent of the Alves Beds. Fish remains, usually fragmentary and very friable ; especially *Holoptychius* scales and teeth, *Bothriolepis
major* and *Psammosteus*.
   Hinxman, L. W. and Grant Wilson, J. S. 1902, p. 63. Traquair, R. H.
1895, p.243.
   Geol. Surv. 95 ; Ord. Pop. 79.

**Lossiemouth.** Range of abandoned quarries almost immediately S.W. of
Lossiemouth station.
Triassic, Middle or Upper (light-coloured sandstone showing dune-bedding);
fossils now extremely scarce. The quarry has yielded numerous remains of
*Stagonolepis* ; *Telerpeton* and other reptiles are much less abundant.
   Geol. Surv. 95 ; Ord. Pop. 29.


# NAIRNSHIRE

**Nairn.** Kingsteps Quarry, along margin of 25 ft. raised beach, 1 mile E.
of Nairn.
Devonian, Upper Old Red Sandstone (Nairn Beds) ; extensive range of
quarries in greyish and reddish micaceous, relatively coarse-grained sandstones,
almost horizontal : fossil fishes, especially *Asterolepis maxima*, *Polyplocodus*,
etc. Much material of *Asterolepis* figured by Traquair, Mon. Pal. Soc.
   Horne, J. 1923, p. 81.
   Geol. Surv. 84 ; Ord. Pop. 28.

## PEEBLESSHIRE

**Baddinsgill.** Lyne Water, a few yards below Hareshaw Shepherd's house : 1 mile N. of Baddinsgill, near West Linton.
Silurian, Upper Ludlow Series ; contains trilobites, brachiopods and molluscs.
Peach, B. N. and Horne, J. 1899, pp. 601-602.
Geol. Surv. 24 ; Ord. Pop. 74.

**Broughton.** Glencotho Burn ; quarries near the burn, basin of Holms Water. 4½ miles S. by W. of Broughton.
Ordovician, Caradoc Series (Caradoc Limestone) ; contains crinoids, trilobites, brachiopods and molluscs.
Peach, B. N. and Horne, J. 1899, p. 258.
Geol. Surv. 24 ; Ord. Pop. 79.

**Broughton.** Quarries near Drummelzier, 2 miles S.E. of Broughton.
Ordovician, Caradoc Series (Caradoc Limestone) ; contains crinoids, trilobites and brachiopods.
Peach, B. N. and Horne, J. 1899, p. 257.
Geol. Surv. 24 ; Ord. Pop. 79-80.

**Carlops.** Old quarries E. of the village.
Carboniferous, Lower Limestone Series (limestone and overlying shales) ; fossils abundant in the shales including occasional crinoid cups and micro-crinoids and micro-fossils in general.
Peach, B. N. and others 1910a, pp. 379-405. Wright, J. 1932, p. 337.
Geol. Surv. 24 ; Ord. Pop. 74.

**Carlops.** South Mains ; old quarry, 300 yds. S.E. of South Mains, which is 1200 yds. S.S.E. by E. of Carlops.
Carboniferous, Lower (blaes below limestone) ; contain bryozoa, brachiopods, lamellibranchs and ostracods.
Geol. Surv. 24 ; Ord. Pop. 74.

**Culter.** Gair Gill (tributary of Culter Water, ½ mile S. of Snaip) ; at head of stream : 3½ miles S.S.W. of Biggar.
Ordovician, Caradoc Series (Glenkiln Black Shales) ; contain graptolites.
Peach, B. N. and Horne, J. 1899, p. 238.
Geol. Surv. 24 ; Ord. Pop. 79.

**Eddleston.** Cowie's Linn Burn (joins Eddleston Water 2½ miles N. of Eddleston station).
Ordovician, Caradoc Series (Glenkiln Shales) ; contain graptolites.
Peach, B. N. and Horne, J. 1899, pp. 252-253.
Geol. Surv. 24 ; Ord. Pop. 74.

**Eddleston.** Bowbeat Hill, near head of Leithen Water, 7 miles N.N.W. of Innerleithen.
Ordovician, Caradoc Series (Lower Hartfell black shales) ; contain graptolites.
Peach, B. N. and Horne, J. 1899, p. 264.
Geol. Surv. 24 ; Ord. Pop. 74.

**Eddleston.** In glen at Darn Hall, less than ½ mile W. of Eddleston station.
Ordovician, Caradoc Series (Lower Hartfell black shales) ; contain grapto-lites and brachiopods.
Peach, B. N. and Horne, J. 1899, p. 251.
Geol. Surv. 24 ; Ord. Pop. 74.

**Innerleithen.** Walker Burn, eastern branch, 200 yds. up, on slope of Glede Knowe ; 1 mile up from junction with the Tweed.
Silurian, Llandovery Series, Tarannon blue shales ; contain graptolites.
Peach, B. N. and Horne, J. 1899, p. 205.
Geol. Surv. 24 ; Ord. Pop. 80.

**Innerleithen.** Grieston Quarry ; 1¼ miles S.W. of Innerleithen.
Silurian, Llandovery Series, Tarannon shales ; contain graptolites.
Peach, B. N. and Horne, J. 1899, p. 206.
Geol. Surv. 24 ; Ord. Pop. 80.

**Innerleithen.** Leithen Water, opposite St. Ronan's Spinning Mill ;
½ mile N. of Innerleithen.
Silurian, Llandovery Series (Tarannon) ; contain graptolites in thin dark
bands.
Geol. Surv. 24 ; Ord. Pop. 80.

**Innerleithen.** Pirn Quarry ; ¾ mile E. of Innerleithen.
Silurian, Llandovery Series (Birkhill group) ; contain graptolites, cephalo-
pods and arthropods.
Peach, B. N. and Horne, J. 1899, pp. 192-193.
Geol. Surv. 24 ; Ord. Pop. 80.

**Leadburn.** In small burn, 400 yds. S.S.W. of Ridderlees and about 700 yds.
N. of Grassfield ; about 3½ miles S.W. of Leadburn.
Ordovician, Caradoc Series (Glenkiln Shales) ; contain graptolites and
brachiopods.
Peach, B. N. and Horne, J. 1899, p. 249.
Geol. Surv. 24 ; Ord. Pop. 80.

**Peebles.** Hamilton Hill, W. side of Eddleston Valley, about 1½ miles N.N.W.
of Peebles. Quarries on N.E. declivity.
Ordovician, Caradoc Series ; with graptolites in black shale and brachiopods
in limestone.
Peach, B. N. and Horne, J. 1899, pp. 259-260.
Geol. Surv. 24 ; Ord. Pop. 80.

**West Linton.** Whitfield Quarries, 270 yds. W. 30° N. of Deepsykehead ;
also 860 yds. N.W. by N. of the same place.
Carboniferous, Lower (blaes with limestones) ; contain corals, brachiopods,
lamellibranchs and gastropods.
Geol. Surv. 24 ; Ord. Pop. 74.

**West Linton.** Bents Quarry, Macbiehill, ¼ mile S. of Macbie Hill railway
station.
Carboniferous, Lower ; blaes containing brachiopods and foraminifera.
Geol. Surv. 24 ; Ord. Pop. 74.

**West Linton.** Rutherford Mains : (1) small stream below dam, 50 yds. N.
of Rutherford Mains ; (2) Burn just south of, and (3) 770 yds. S.S.W. of
Rutherford Mains.
Carboniferous, Lower ; blaes and limestone containing bryozoans, brachio-
pods and molluscs.
Geol. Surv. 24 ; Ord. Pop. 74.

**West Linton.** Deepsykehead, 900 yds. E. 5° S. of Deepsykehead in Cairn
Burn ; also 830 yds. E. by N. of the same place.
Carboniferous, Lower ; blaes up and downstream from limestone contain
brachiopods and lamellibranchs.
Geol. Surv. 24 ; Ord. Pop. 74.

**Wrae.** Wrae Quarries ; E. slope of Wrae Hill overlooking the Tweed.
3 miles S. of Broughton.
Ordovician, Caradoc Series (limestone and tuff) ; contain crinoids, trilo-
bites, brachiopods and cephalopods.
Peach, B. N. and Horne, J. 1899, pp. 255-257.
Geol. Surv. 24 ; Ord. Pop. 79.

## RENFREWSHIRE

**Barrhead.** Waukmill Glen, 1½ miles E.S.E. of Barrhead.
Carboniferous, Upper Limestone Series (shale above Lyoncross Cement-stone) ; contains lamellibranchs, echinoderms, cephalopods and gastropods.
Clough, C. T. (the late) and others 1925, p. 69.
Geol. Surv. 30 ; Ord. Pop. 72.

**Bridge of Weir.** Coalbog, right bank of River Gryfe, just above ford at Coalbog, near Bridge of Weir.
Carboniferous, ( ?) Blackbyre Limestone ; contains corals, brachiopods, lamellibranchs, fish remains and plants.
Hinxman, L. W. and others 1920, p. 17.
Geol. Surv. 30 ; Ord. Pop. 72.

**Bridge of Weir.** Gryfe Water, south of Goldenlee, Bridge of Weir.
Carboniferous (floor of Blackbyre Limestone) ; contains lamellibranchs.
Hinxman, L. W. and others 1920, p. 32.
Geol. Surv. 30 ; Ord. Pop. 72.

**Howwood.** Old quarries at Howwood, 2 miles S.W. of Johnstone ; and burn W. of Howwood, 2½ miles S.W. of Johnstone.
Carboniferous Limestone ; contains brachiopods, lamellibranchs, gastropods, cephalopods, trilobites and crinoids.
Hinxman, L. W. and others 1920.
Geol. Surv. 30 ; Ord. Pop. 72.

**Johnstone.** Black Cart Water, near Johnstone Bridge ; also opposite Warbowie, 2¼ miles S.W. of Johnstone.
Carboniferous Limestone (limestone and soft shales underlying limestone) ; contain brachiopods, crinoids and molluscs.
Hinxman, L. W. and others 1920.
Geol. Surv. 30 ; Ord. Pop. 72.

**Paisley.** Hawkhead Reservoir, about 2 miles S.E. of Paisley.
Carboniferous, Calciferous Sandstone Series (Hollybush Limestone) ; contains brachiopods and corals.
Hinxman, L. W. and others 1920, p. 13.
Geol. Surv. 30 ; Ord. Pop. 72.

**Paisley.** Old quarry, ¾ mile S.W. of Darnley, 4 miles S.S.E. of Paisley; also small burn at Darnley.
Carboniferous Limestone (beds just above the Calmy or Arden Limestone) contains brachiopods, gastropods and corals.
Hinxman, L. W. and others 1920, pp. 72-73.
Geol. Surv. 30 ; Ord. Pop. 72.

## ROSS AND CROMARTY

**Achneigie.** Allt Righ Iain, streamlet, 1 mile W. of Carn nam Feithean, 2 miles E.S.E. of Achneigie.
Cambrian, *Olenellus* Shale (fucoid beds); contain worm-casts, the doubtful mollusc *Salterella* and the trilobite *Olenellus*.
Peach, B. N. and others 1907, p. 412.
Geol. Surv. 92 ; Ord. Pop. 19.

**Applecross.** Allt Brengaireadch ; a little over ½ mile S.E. of Post Office and 100 yds. above the corner of the wood, base of right bank under over-hanging ledge ; also from blocks in bed of stream.
Jurassic, Lower Lias (Broadford Beds, oolitic limestone) ; contain lamellibranchs, gastropods, cephalopods and corals.
Lee, G. W. 1920, pp. 9-11.
Geol. Surv. 81 ; Ord. Pop. 25.

**Balintore.** Shore from ½ mile S. of Port-an-Righ (Cadhan Righ) to ½ mile N.E. of same.

Jurassic, Corallian, Oxford Clay, Kellaways Rock and Estuarine Series in descending sequence ; contain lamellibranchs, ammonites, belemnites and brachiopods.

Read, H. H. and others 1925, pp. 79, 81, 85, 99.

Geol. Surv. 94 ; Ord. Pop. 28.

**Cromarty.** Tidal foreshore, ¼ to ½ mile E. of Cromarty.

Devonian, Middle Old Red Sandstone (Cromarty fish-bed) ; greyish mudstones with limestone nodules containing numerous fishes, e.g., acanthodians, placoderms and crossopterygians ; a locality made famous by Hugh Miller.

Miller, Hugh 1841, etc.

Geol. Surv. 94 ; Ord. Pop. 28.

**Ethie.** Ethie shore at low tide, 3 miles S. of Cromarty (a small exposure).

Jurassic, Kimmeridge Series ; contain lamellibranchs, ammonites, belemnites and plants.

Read, H. H. and others 1925, pp. 114-115.

Geol. Surv. 94 ; Ord. Pop. 28.

**Kinlochewe.** Meall a' Ghuibhais : streamlet rising near Loch ra Mna' Bige on N. side, 1 mile S. of Loch Maree and 5¾ miles slightly N. of W. of Heights of Kinlochewe.

Cambrian, Fucoid Beds (*Olenellus* band) ; contains trilobites, especially *Olenellus*, and brachiopods.

Peach, B. N. and others 1907, p. 414.

Geol. Surv. 92 ; Ord. Pop. 26.


# ROXBURGHSHIRE

**Edgerston.** Jed Water at Doresford Camptown, 5 miles S.S.E. of Jedburgh.

Silurian, Wenlock Series ; shales containing graptolites and arthropods.

Peach, B. N. and Horne, J. 1899, p. 562.

Geol. Surv. 17 ; Ord. Pop. 86.

**Hownam.** Hindhope Burn, which drains N. slopes of Coquet Head, 10 miles S. of Morebattle.

Silurian, Wenlock Series ; shales with graptolites and cephalopods.

Peach, B. N. and Horne, J. 1899, pp. 562-563.

Geol. Surv. 18 ; Ord. Pop. 86.

**Langholm.** Archer Beck, 4½ miles S.E. of Langholm.

Carboniferous, Calciferous Sandstone Series ; contains brachiopods, lamellibranchs, corals, etc.

Peach, B. N. and Horne, J. 1903, pp. 847-848.

Geol. Surv. 11 ; Ord. Pop. 89.

**Larriston.** Larriston Burn, above its junction with Liddel, 5 or 6 miles N.E. of Newcastleton ; also from quarry, 6½ miles N.E. of Newcastleton.

Carboniferous, Calciferous Sandstone Series (Main Algal series) ; contain *Spirorbis*, *Ortonella*, brachiopods and ostracods.

Garwood, E. J. 1931, pp. 133-134, with map.

Geol. Surv. 11 ; Ord. Pop. 85.

**Newcastleton.** Liddel Water : in cliff opposite the manse about 2 miles above New Castleton.

Carboniferous, Calciferous Sandstone Series (Cementstone Group) ; contains worm-tubes (*Spirorbis*) and lamellibranchs (*Modiola*, etc.).

Peach, B. N. and Horne, J. 1903, pp. 841-842.

Geol. Surv. 11 ; Ord. Pop. 85.

**Newcastleton.** Kershope Burn, from a little below Kershope to near head of burn ; 3 miles S.E. of Newcastleton.
Carboniferous, Upper Calciferous Series (Lawston Linn Series) ; contains brachiopods, molluscs and plant remains.
Garwood, E. J. 1931, pp. 129-131 with map.
Geol. Surv. 11 ; Ord. Pop. 85.

**Newcastleton.** Upper part of Tweeden Burn, Liddel Water ; 1 mile S.E. of Newcastleton.
Carboniferous, Calciferous Sandstone Series ; contains brachiopods, molluscs and fish remains.
Peach, B. N. and Horne, J. 1903, pp. 848-849.
Geol. Surv. 11 ; Ord. Pop. 85.

**Newcastleton.** Harden Burn above Dikeraw, 3 miles N.E. of New Castleton.
Carboniferous, Calciferous Sandstone Series (main algal series) ; contains lamellibranchs, ostracods and plant remains.
Garwood, E. J. 1931, pp. 129-131, with map.
Geol. Surv. 11 ; Ord. Pop. 85.

**Newcastleton.** Lawston Linns, Liddel Water ; 4 miles S.S.W. of New Castleton.
Carboniferous, Calciferous Sandstone Series ; limestone and nodules in soft shales containing corals, brachiopods and lamellibranchs.
Peach, B. N. and Horne, J. 1903, pp. 847-848.
Geol. Surv. 11 ; Ord. Pop. 89.

**Penton.** Limestones and shales in bed and banks of the Liddel Water, below Penton Bridge.
Carboniferous, Lower Limestone Series ; fossils abundant, including a layer of crinoid crowns in shale overlying main limestone.
Peach, B. N. and Horne, J. 1903, p. 850 ; Wright, J. 1924.
Geol. Surv. 11 ; Ord. Pop. 89.

**Priesthaugh.** Priesthaugh Burn (joins Allan Water below Skelfhill), about 8½ miles S.S.W. of Hawick.
Silurian, Wenlock Shale Series ; contains graptolites, crustaceans, cephalopods and brachiopods.
Peach, B. N. and Horne, J. 1899, p. 560.
Geol. Surv. 17 ; Ord. Pop. 85.

**Riccarton.** Riccarton Junction ; from burn at the junction.
Silurian, Wenlock Shale Series ; contains graptolites and cephalopods.
Peach, B. N. and Horne, J. 1899, p. 561.
Geol. Surv. 17 ; Ord. Pop. 85.

**Riccarton.** Peel Burn, above Myredykes, about 4 miles slightly N. of E. of Riccarton Junction railway station.
Carboniferous, Calciferous Sandstone Series (Cementstone Group) ; contains lamellibranchs, brachiopods, fish, plants and algae.
Geol. Surv. 17 ; Ord. Pop. 86.

**Riccarton.** Thorlieshope Burn and old quarry, 8 miles N.E. of Newcastleton.
Carboniferous, Calciferous Sandstone Series (Cementstone Group) ; contains corals, echinoderms, ostracods, brachiopods, lamellibranchs and gastropods.
Peach, B. N. and Horne, J. 1903, pp. 842-843.
Geol. Surv. 11 ; Ord. Pop. 86.

**Riccarton.** Skelfhill Burn, in streamlet at head of burn (a tributary of the Allan Water), 6½ miles E.N.E. of Riccarton Junction and 9 miles S.S.W. of Hawick.
Silurian, Wenlock Shale Series ; contains graptolites and cephalopods.
Peach, B. N. and Horne, J. 1899, p. 560.
Geol. Surv. 17 ; Ord. Pop. 86.

**Stobs Castle.** Stobs Castle Gate at junction of a small tributary with Slitrig Water, 4 miles S. of Hawick.
Silurian, Wenlock Shale Series ; contains graptolites and arthropods.
Peach, B. N. and Horne, J. 1899, p. 559.
Geol. Surv. 17 ; Ord. Pop. 85.

**Stobs Castle.** Penchrise Burn S. of Stobs Castle, 5 miles S. of Hawick.
Silurian, Wenlock Shale Series ; contains graptolites and cephalopods.
Peach, B. N. and Horne, J. 1899, pp. 559-560.
Geol. Surv. 17 ; Ord. Pop. 85.

**Wolflee.** Kirn Cleuch, Hyndlee Burn, about 4 miles S. of Hobkirk.
Silurian, Wenlock Shale Series ; graptolites and cephalopods.
Peach, B. N. and Horne, J. 1899, p. 561.
Geol. Surv. 17 ; Ord. Pop. 86.


# SELKIRKSHIRE

**Chapelhope.** Berrybush Burn, 2¼ miles E.S.E. from road which crosses S. end of St. Mary's Loch.
Ordovician, Caradoc Series (Glenkiln Beds) ; contain graptolites.
Peach, B. N. and Horne, J. 1899, p. 119.
Geol. Surv. 25 ; Ord. Pop. 80.

**Clovenfords.** Hillend, ½ mile N. of Clovenfords, 6½ miles W. of Melrose.
Silurian, Llandovery Series (Tarannon Shales) ; contain graptolites and arthropods.
Peach, B. N. and Horne, J. 1899, p. 204.
Geol. Surv. 25 ; Ord. Pop. 80.

**Clovenfords,** ½ mile N.W. of Cadonfoot and ¼ mile N.W. of Cadonlee Farmhouse on N. side of Galashiels road, 7 miles W. of Melrose.
Silurian, Llandovery Series (Tarannon Shales) ; contain graptolites.
Peach, B. N. and Horne, J. 1899, p. 204.
Geol. Surv. 25 ; Ord. Pop. 80.

**Ettrickbridgend.** Ettrick Water : at foot of cliff below Manse, Ettrickbridgend, 9½ miles N.W. of Hawick.
Silurian, Llandovery Series (Birkhill Shales) ; contain graptolites.
Peach, B. N. and Horne, J. 1899, p. 128.
Geol. Surv. 17 ; Ord. Pop. 80.

**Ettrickbridgend.** River Ettrick near Kirkhope Farmhouse, 9½ miles N.W. of Hawick.
Ordovician, Caradoc Series (Lower Hartfell black shales) ; contain graptolites and brachiopods.
Peach, B. N. and Horne, J. 1899, pp. 121-128.
Geol. Surv. 17 ; Ord. Pop. 80.

**Galashiels.** Ladhope Burn at old bridge, 1 mile above Buckholmside, Galashiels.
Silurian, Llandovery Series (Tarannon ; blue shale) ; contains graptolites.
Peach, B. N. and Horne, J. 1899, p. 203.
Geol. Surv. 25 ; Ord. Pop. 80.

**Galashiels.** Allan Water, nearly opposite Avenel Plantation ; also S.W. of Plantation on Westa Hill, 1 mile E. of Galashiels.
Silurian, Llandovery Series (Tarannon) ; contains graptolites.
Peach, B. N. and Horne, J. 1899, p. 202.
Geol. Surv. 25 ; Ord. Pop. 80.

**Kirkhope.** River Ettrick : river section, cliff below the manse ; up the river from the Baillie Burn.
Silurian, Llandovery Series (Birkhill Shales) ; contain graptolites.
Peach, B. N. and Horne, J. 1899, p. 128.
Geol. Surv. 16 ; Ord. Pop. 80.

**Melrose.** Rhymers Glen, 1½ miles S.W. of Melrose.
Ordovician, Caradoc Series (Hartfell Shales) ; contain graptolites and brachiopods.
Peach, B. N. and Horne, J. 1899, pp. 190-191.
Geol. Surv. 25 ; Ord. Pop. 80.

**Melrose.** Coldshields Loch : S.E. margin, 2½ miles S.W. of Melrose.
Silurian, Llandovery Series (Lower Tarannon and Birkhill groups) ; contain graptolites.
Peach, B. N. and Horne, J. 1899, p. 191.
Geol. Surv. 25 ; Ord. Pop. 80.

**Melrose.** Packman's Burn (joins Leader Water 1 mile N. of Leaderfoot), from ⅓ mile W. of railway bridge to the bridge, 2 miles N.E. of Melrose.
Silurian, Llandovery Series (Tarannon Group) ; greywacke containing graptolites.
Peach, B. N. and Horne, J. 1899, p. 202.
Geol. Surv. 25 ; Ord. Pop. 80.

**Melrose.** Lindean Glen, N. bank downstream from farmhouse, 4 miles S.W. of Melrose.
Silurian, Llandovery Series (Birkhill Shale) ; contains graptolites.
Peach, B. N. and Horne, J. 1899, p. 192.
Geol. Surv. 25 ; Ord. Pop. 80.

**Yarrow.** Mountbenger Burn : near road in Vale of Yarrow, 3 miles N.E. from N.E. end of St. Mary's Loch.
Ordovician, Caradoc Series (Lower Hartfell black shales) ; contain graptolites and brachiopods.
Peach, B. N. and Horne, J. 1899, p. 113.
Geol. Surv. 16 ; Ord. Pop. 80.

# STIRLINGSHIRE

**Baldow** (Lennoxtown). Baldow Glen, 200 yds. W.S.W. and 400 yds. S.W. of Baldow House.
Carboniferous, Calciferous Sandstone Series (Craigenglen Beds : bone bed and lamellibranch bed, Blackhall Limestone, Neilson Shell-bed) ; contain brachiopods, lamellibranchs, gastropods, cephalopods, corals, entomostraca, plants and fish.
Hinxman, L. W. and others 1920, p. 76.
Geol. Surv. 30 ; Ord. Pop. 66.

**Denny.** River Carron, near Mill and above Mill, 1¼ miles W. of Denny ; also 1 mile W. of Denny.
Carboniferous, Upper Limestone Series ; contains gastropods, lamellibranchs, brachiopods and cephalopods.
Hinxman, L. W. and others 1917, p. 19.
Geol. Surv. 31 ; Ord. Pop. 67.

**Kilsyth.** Corrie Burn, W.N.W. of Cairnbog Farm, 2¼ miles W.N.W. of Kilsyth ; also 2 miles W.N.W. of Kilsyth.
Carboniferous, Lower Limestone Series ; contains plants, lamellibranchs, brachiopods and gastropods.
Robertson, T. and Haldane, D. 1937, fig 4, p. 17. Hill, D. 1937-1941, p. 23.
Geol. Surv. 31 ; Ord. Pop. 66.

**Larbert.** Torwood Glen : right bank of burn, 20 yds. and 50 yds. upstream from road bridge ; at point about ½ mile W. of Carbrook House ; at point where Roman Road crosses the stream, bed on right striking up and down stream : 2½ miles N.W. of Larbert.
Carboniferous, Millstone Grit Series ; contains brachiopods, gastropods and lamellibranchs.
Hinxman, L. W. and others, 1917, p. 38.
Geol. Surv. 31 ; Ord. Pop. 67.

**Lennoxtown.** Lower Glenwhapple, N.W. of ruins of Craigenglen Cottage, 300 yds. S.S.E. of Upper Carlstoun Steading, 1½ miles S.S.W. of Lennoxtown Church.
Carboniferous, Calciferous Sandstone Series (Craigenglen Beds, type-locality) ; contain gastropods, productids, lamellibranchs, cephalopods, bryozoans and ostracods.
Clough, C. T. and others 1925, p. 26.
Geol. Surv. 31 ; Ord. Pop. 66.

**Lennoxtown.** Burn a little below Bencloich Mill, ¼ mile N.E. of Lennoxtown.
Carboniferous Limestone ; soft grey shales containing brachiopods, lamellibranchs, cephalopods and gastropods.
Robertson, T. and Haldane, D. 1937, p. 14-15.
Geol. Surv. 31 ; Ord. Pop. 66.

**Lennoxtown.** Burn Rannie at Balgrochan, ½ mile N. of Lennoxtown.
Carboniferous Limestone ; dark shale below Main Limestone yields gastropods, brachiopods and lamellibranchs.
Robertson, T. and Haldane, D. 1937, p. 14. Clough, C. T. and others 1925, p. 41.
Geol. Surv. 31 ; Ord. Pop. 66.

**Lennoxtown.** Glenwynd, 1½ miles S.W. of Lennoxtown.
Carboniferous, Lower Limestone Series (blaes between Hurlet Limestone and Coal) ; contain cephalopods, lamellibranchs, brachiopods and crinoids.
Clough, C. T. and others 1925, p. 41.
Geol. Surv. 30 ; Ord. Pop. 66.

**Lennoxtown.** Old quarries near Glorat, 1 mile N.N.E. of Lennoxtown.
Carboniferous Limestone (limy shale resting on Main Limestone) ; contains trilobites, brachiopods, lamellibranchs, gastropods and cephalopods.
Robertson, T. and Haldane, D. 1937, p. 24.
Geol. Surv. 31 ; Ord. Pop. 66.

**Linlithgow.** Left bank of River Avon opposite Littlemill, 1½ miles N.W. of Linlithgow.
Carboniferous, Upper Limestone Series (Dykeneuk Limestone) ; contains productids, bryozoa, lamellibranchs, trilobites and gastropods.
Macgregor, M. and Haldane, D. 1933, p. 62.
Geol. Surv. 31 ; Ord. Pop. 67.

**Milton of Campsie,** ¼ and ⅛ of a mile E. of Shields Farmhouse and 1 mile N.E. of Milton of Campsie.

Carboniferous, Lower Limestone Series (Blackhall Limestones) ; contain brachiopods, gastropods, lamellibranchs, cephalopods and ostracods.
Clough, C. T. and others 1925, p. 42.
Geol. Surv. 31 ; Ord. Pop. 66.

**Milton of Campsie.** Second branch of Spouthead Burn (W. to E.), near junction with trap, near large fault and a few yards below stone fence ; 1 mile N. of Milton : also third branch of this burn, 1½ miles N. of Milton.
Carboniferous Limestone (Main = Hurlet Limestone) ; contains brachiopods, lamellibranchs, gastropods and plants.
Robertson, T. and Haldane, D. 1937.
Geol. Surv. 31 ; Ord. Pop. 66.

**Milton of Campsie.** Burnbrae Burn, downstream from boundary fault and at road leading from Shields Farm ; 1 mile N.N.E. of Milton of Campsie.
Carboniferous, Upper Limestone Series ; contains lamellibranchs, brachiopods and gastropods.
Geol. Surv. 31 ; Ord. Pop. 66.

**Murrayshall.** Touchadam ; in Bannock Burn at Touchadam Quarry, ⅔ of a mile N. of North Third Reservoir.
Carboniferous, Lower Limestone Series ; contains brachiopods, corals, goniatites, cephalopods, lamellibranchs and gastropods.
Dinham, C. H. and Haldane, D. 1932, pp. 21, 24.
Geol. Surv. 39 ; Ord. Pop. 67.

**Old Sauchie.** South Sauchie Craig, on E. side of North Third Reservoir.
Carboniferous, Lower Limestone Series ; contains productids and other brachiopods, and fish remains.
Dinham, C. H. and Haldane, D. 1932, pp. 25, 26, 32.
Geol. Surv. 39 ; Ord. Pop. 67.

**Stirling.** Todholes : S. of Todholes farmstead, Upper Bannock Burn, a mile S.W. of North Third Reservoir, 4 to 5 miles S.S.W. of Stirling.
Carboniferous, Lower Limestone Series ; contains brachiopods, corals, fish remains, lamellibranchs and cephalopods.
Dinham, C. H. and Haldane, D. 1932, pp. 21, 26, 28.
Geol. Surv. 39 ; Ord. Pop. 67.

## SUTHERLANDSHIRE

**Brora.** Lower Brora : on shore, 660 yds. S.W. of U.F. Church, Brora.
Jurassic, Oxford Clay ; contains lamellibranchs, belemnites, ammonites and gastropods.
Read, H. H. and others 1925, pp. 81-85.
Geol. Surv. 103 ; Ord. Pop. 21.

**Brora.** Northern bank of River Brora, ½ mile W. of Brora Coal Pit.
Jurassic, Oxford Clay ; contains belemnites, ammonites and lamellibranchs.
Read, H. H. and others 1925, pp. 83-85.
Geol. Surv. 103 ; Ord. Pop. 21.

**Brora.** Uppat Wood : road-metal quarry by roadside, 320 yds. S.W. of Uppat House.
Jurassic, Corallian Beds ; contains lamellibranchs, ammonites and *Serpula*.
Read, H. H. and others 1925, p. 95.
Geol. Surv. 103 ; Ord. Pop. 21.

**Brora.** In southern bank of River Brora, ½ mile N. 38° E. of Inverbrora.
Jurassic, Corallian Beds (Fascally Sandstone) ; contains lamellibranchs, ammonites, belemnites and gastropods.
Read, H. H. and others 1925, pp. 87-93.
Geol. Surv. 103 ; Ord. Pop. 21.

**Brora.** Ardassie Point : on shore, ½ mile due E. of Brora railway station. Jurassic, Corallian Beds; contains lamellibranchs, ammonites, belemnites and *Serpula*.
Read, H. H. and others 1925, pp. 96-99.
Geol. Surv. 103 ; Ord. Pop. 21.

**Clyneleish.** Clyneleish Quarry, Brora.
Jurassic, Corallian Beds and Oxford Clay ; contain *Serpula, Terebratula,* lamellibranchs and ammonites.
Read, H. H. and others 1925, pp. 90-94.
Geol. Surv. 103 ; Ord. Pop. 21.

**Durness.** Eilean nan Cas-Leac : middle island of group and island most S.E. of group : 4 miles N.W. of Durness.
Cambrian, Balnakiel Group ; contains gastropods and cephalopods.
Peach, B. N. and others 1907, p. 391.
Geol. Surv. 114 ; Ord. Pop. 9.

**Durness.** Coast section below the churchyard at Balnakiel Bay, Durness.
Cambrian (Upper), *Olenus* Series (limestones of the Balnakiel Stage V of the Durness Limestone Series) ; contain mainly cephalopods and gastropods.
Peach, B. N. and others 1907, pp. 379-391, 626.
Geol. Surv. 114 ; Ord. Pop. 9.

**Durness.** Natural exposures of limestone on Ach' a' Chorrain, 4 miles S.S.W. of Durness.
Cambrian (Upper), *Olenus* Series (limestone pavements of the Balnakiel Stage V of the Durness Limestone Series) ; contain primitive siliceous sponges, gastropods, and cephalopods.
Peach, B. N. and others 1907, pp. 379-391, 626.
Geol. Surv. 114 ; Ord. Pop. 9.

**Durness.** The rocky island, An Garbh Eilean, 4¾ miles E. of Cape Wrath and 5½ miles N.W. of Durness.
Cambrian (Upper), *Olenus* Series (limestones and dolomites of the Croisaphuil Stage VI of the Durness Limestone Series) ; contain gastropods, cephalopods and trilobites, weathered out on marine eroded surfaces.
Peach, B. N. and others 1907, pp. 379-391, 626.
Geol. Surv. 114 ; Ord. Pop. 9.

**Durness.** Limestone pavements, S. of Loch Croispol and E. of the N. end of Loch Borralie, 1 mile W.S.W. of Durness.
Cambrian (Upper), *Olenus* Series (limestones and dolomites of the Croisaphuil [Stage VI of the Durness Limestone Series]); contain gastropods and cephalopods weathered out on limestone pavements.
Peach, B. N. and others 1907, pp. 379-391, 626.
Geol. Surv. 114 ; Ord. Pop. 9.

**Golspie.** Shore ½ mile N.E. of Dunrobin Castle, 50 yds. E. of gate leading from Rifle Range to Dunrobin Grounds, Golspie.
Jurassic, Lower Lias ; contains brachiopods, lamellibranchs, ammonites, belemnites and gastropods.
Read, H. H. and others 1925, pp. 68-69.
Geol. Surv. 103 ; Ord. Pop. 21.

**Heilem.** An-t-Srón : about centre of E. shore of Loch Eireboll : 1 mile S. of Heilem.
Cambrian, Ghrudaidh Dolomite and Limestone, Fucoid beds, Serpulite Grit, and *Salterella* limestone ; contain *Serpulites*, worm-casts and fragments of trilobites (*Olenellus*).
Peach, B. N. and others 1907, pp. 482-483.
Geol. Surv. 114 ; Ord. Pop. 9.

**Helmsdale.** (1) shore, 666 yds. E. 24° N. of Navidale House ; (2) N. side of small bay, ½ mile E. 33° N. of Navidale House ; (3) N. side of Navidale Bay, Helmsdale.
Jurassic, Kimmeridge Beds ; contain lamellibranchs and ammonites.
Read, H. H. and others 1925, pp. 103-115.
Geol. Surv. 103 ; Ord. Pop. 17.

**Helmsdale.** (1) Shore, 260 yds. S. of Portgower ; (2) on shore below it, 165 yds. S. of well ; (3) shore, ½ mile, 710 yds. and 650 yds. S.W. of Portgower.
Jurassic, Kimmeridge Beds ; contains lamellibranchs, ammonites and gastropods.
Read, H. H. and others 1925, pp. 103-115.
Geol. Surv. 103 ; Ord. Pop. 17.

**Kintradwell.** Reefs on shore, 255 yds. E. 27° S. of, and 250 yds. E. 17° S. of, Picts Tower ; also on shore from mouth of small stream to a position 100 yds. to S. ; also on shore, 600 yds. S. 25° E. of Picts Tower, Brora.
Jurassic, Kimmeridge Beds ; contain brachiopods, lamellibranchs and ammonites.
Read, H. H. and others 1925, pp. 103-115.
Geol. Surv. 103 ; Ord. Pop. 17.

**Lothbeg.** Allt-na-Cuille : at cliff where railway crosses stream (Lower Kimmeridge Beds) ; also old quarry in bank of stream, 250 yds. up from railway, 4 miles N.E. of Brora (Corallian).
Jurassic, Lower Kimmeridge and Corallian Beds ; contain lamellibranchs, brachiopods, ammonites, gastropods, *Serpula* and *Cidaris*.
Read, H. H. and others 1925, pp. 104-106.
Geol. Surv. 103 ; Ord. Pop. 17.

**Wester Garty.** (1) Shore, 560 yds., 600 yds., 1130 yds. and 1246 yds. N.E. of Sron Rudha na Gavithe ; (2) shore at, and shore 330 yds. and 660 yds. S.W. of Sron Rudha na Gavithe : Wester Garty, Helmsdale.
Jurassic, Kimmeridgian Beds ; contain lamellibranchs, ammonites, brachiopods, *Serpula*, corals and gastropods.
Read, H. H. and others 1925, pp. 112-114.
Geol. Surv. 103 ; Ord. Pop. 17.

# WEST LOTHIAN

**Bathgate.** Petershill Quarry, 1 mile N.E. of Bathgate.
Carboniferous Limestone (shale and Bathgate Limestone) ; contain brachiopods, lamellibranchs, corals, bryozoans and annelids.
Macgregor, M. and Anderson, E. M. 1923, pp. 22-24. Hill, D. 1937-1941, pp. 20, 25.
Geol. Surv. 31 ; Ord. Pop. 73.

**Dalmeny.** Shore between Longcraigs Pier and the Forth Bridge.
Carboniferous, Calciferous Sandstone Series ; contains plants, lamellibranchs and fish.
Peach, B. N. and others 1910a, pp. 374-405.
Geol. Surv. 32 ; Ord. Pop. 73.

**Linlithgow.** Whitebaulks Quarry, 1½ miles S. of Linlithgow.
Carboniferous, Lower Limestone Series ; contains foraminifera, echinoderms, ostracods, gastropods and cephalopods.
Peach, B. N. and others 1910a, pp. 373-405.
Geol. Surv. 32 ; Ord. Pop. 73.

**Linlithgow.** Avon River : shale exposed in bed of right bank and on left bank of River Avon, about halfway between Avon Paper Mill and Linlithgow Bridge, 1½ miles W. of Linlithgow : and shale exposed on right bank of first burn on right of river, ½ mile E. of Kinneil Mill, 1½ miles N.W. of Linlithgow.
Carboniferous, Upper Limestone Series ; contains brachiopods, gastropods, bryozoans and lamellibranchs.
Macgregor, M. and Haldane, D. 1933, pp. 57-64.
Geol. Surv. 31 ; Ord. Pop. 73.


# WIGTOWN

**Cairnryan.** East shore of Loch Ryan, near Polymodie Burn, which joins the sea about 1¼ miles N. of Cairnryan.
Ordovician, Caradoc Series (Glenkiln division) ; contains graptolites.
Peach, B. N. and Horne, J. 1899, p. 416.
Geol. Surv. 3 ; Ord. Pop. 90.

**Colfin.** Colfin Glen, ½ mile up wooded glen, 3 miles S. of Stranraer.
Ordovician, Caradoc Series (Hartfell Shales) ; contain graptolites.
Peach, B. N. and Horne, J. 1899, pp. 408-409.
Geol. Surv. 3 ; Ord. Pop. 90.

**Drummore.** Clanyard Bay: N. side of bay, 2½ miles N.W. of Drummore.
Silurian, Llandovery Series (Birkhill Shales) ; contain graptolites.
Peach, B. N. and Horne, J. 1899, pp. 183-185.
Geol. Surv. 1 ; Ord. Pop. 90.

**Glenluce.** Camrie Burn (tributary of Luce, a mile above Glenluce) : W. bank, ½ mile N.N.W. of White Cairn Farmhouse, about 2 miles N. of Glenluce.
Ordovician, Caradoc Series (Glenkiln Shales) ; contain graptolites.
Peach, B. N. and Horne, J. 1899, pp. 392-393.
Geol. Surv. 4 ; Ord. Pop. 90.

**Glenluce.** Drumpail Burn, 400 yds. W.N.W. of Drumpail, 3 miles N. of Glenluce.
Ordovician, Caradoc Series (Hartfell Shales) ; contain graptolites.
Peach, B. N. and Horne, J. 1899, p. 394.
Geol. Surv. 3 ; Ord. Pop. 90.

**Glenluce.** Gabsnout Burn : 250 yds. above Glenluce road and in burn opposite Gabsnout Cottage ; 2 miles N. of Glenluce, 7¼ miles E. of Stranraer.
Ordovician, Caradoc Series (Lower Hartfell Shale) ; contains graptolites.
Peach, B. N. and Horne, J. 1899, pp. 393-394.
Geol. Surv. 3 ; Ord. Pop. 90.

**Glenluce.** In Gillespie Burn, about 400 yds. E. of Culroy Farmhouse, in a rocky gorge, W. of Castle Loch, Glenluce Parish, 4 miles S.E. of Glenluce.
Ordovician, Caradoc Series (Hartfell black shales) ; contain graptolites.
Peach, B. N. and Horne, J. 1899, p. 180.
Geol. Surv. 4 ; Ord. Pop. 90.

**Glenluce.** E. shore of Luce Bay, 1 mile S. of Glenluce, between the Fish House and the Crow's Nest.
Silurian, Llandovery Series (Tarannon group) ; contains graptolites.
Peach, B. N. and Horne, J. 1899, pp. 182-183.
Geol. Surv. 4 ; Ord. Pop. 90.

**Kirkcolm.** Dounan Bay, southern limit, cliff section on shore road, 4 miles W. of Kirkcolm.
Ordovician, Llandeilo-Caradoc ; contain graptolites.
Peach, B. N. and Horne, J. 1899, pp. 411-412.
Geol. Surv. 3 ; Ord. Pop. 90.

**Kirkcolm.** Portobello, small bay on W. coast, 4½ miles S.W. of Kirkcolm.
Ordovician, Llandeilo-Caradoc shales ; contain graptolites.
Peach, B. N. and Horne, J. 1899, p. 412.
Geol. Surv. 3 ; Ord. Pop. 90.

**Kirkcolm.** Craigoch Burn, 390 yds. N. 5° E. of Marslaugh, Kirkcolm.
Carboniferous, Coal Measures ; contain plants.
Geol. Surv. 3 ; Ord. Pop. 90.

**Kirkcowan.** Drumabrennan : at bend in Black Burn E. of footbridge and
N. of Drumabrennan Farmhouse, 7¼ miles N. of W. of Newton Stewart.
Ordovician, Llandeilo-Caradoc ; contain graptolites.
Peach, B. N. and Horne, J. 1899, pp. 391-392.
Geol. Surv. 4 ; Ord. Pop. 87.

**Mochrum.** S. of Water of Malzie on by-road to Crailloch Farmhouse,
½ mile W. of Low Glenling, 7 miles W.S.W. of Wigtown.
Ordovician, Caradoc Series (Glenkiln Shales) ; contain graptolites.
Peach, B. N. and Horne, J. 1899, pp. 177-178.
Geol. Surv. 4 ; Ord. Pop. 91.

**Newton Stewart.** ½ mile N. of Carseriggan Farmhouse, 6 miles W.N.W.
of Newton Stewart.
Ordovician, Llandeilo-Caradoc ; contain graptolites.
Peach, B. N. and Horne, J. 1899, p. 391.
Geol. Surv. 4 ; Ord. Pop. 87.

**Newton Stewart.** Penhill Burn (tributary of River Cree), N. bank, ½ mile
up, 2 miles N.N.E. of Newton Stewart.
Ordovician, Caradoc Series (Glenkiln-Hartfell shales) ; contain graptolites.
Peach, B. N. and Horne, J. 1899, pp. 172-173.
Geol. Surv. 4 ; Ord. Pop. 87.

**Newton Stewart.** River Cree, about 1 mile N. of Bridge of Cree, Newton
Stewart.
Ordovician, Caradoc Series (Glenkiln-Hartfell series) ; contain graptolites.
Peach, B. N. and Horne, J. 1899, pp. 172-173.
Geol. Surv. 4 ; Ord. Pop. 87.

**Newton Stewart.** Near head of burn about 1½ miles N.N.W. of Glassoch,
6¼ miles N.W. of Newton Stewart.
Ordovician, Caradoc Series (Hartfell Shales) ; contain graptolites.
Peach, B. N. and Horne, J. 1899, p. 391.
Geol. Surv. 4 ; Ord. Pop. 87.

**Port Patrick.** Morroch Bay : cliff and beach (at low tide), 1½ miles S.E.
of Port Patrick.
Ordovician, Caradoc Series (Glenkiln and Hartfell shales) ; contain
graptolites and brachiopods.
Peach, B. N. and Horne, J. 1899, pp. 401-408.
Geol. Surv. 3 ; Ord. Pop. 90.

**Port Patrick.** Portayew Bay : 100 yds. S. of centre of bay where burn
flows into sea, at base of cliff, 2 miles S. of Morroch Bay section, 3¼ miles
S. by E. of Port Patrick.
Ordovician, Caradoc Series (Hartfell Shales) ; contain graptolites.
Peach, B. N. and Horne, J. 1899, p. 409.
Geol. Surv. 3 ; Ord. Pop. 90.

**Stoneykirk.** Grennan Point : S. limit of Grennan Bay, 8 miles S.E. of
Port Patrick.
Silurian, Llandovery Series (Birkhill Shale) ; contains graptolites.
Peach, B. N. and Horne, J. 1899, pp. 186-187.
Geol. Surv. 3 ; Ord. Pop. 90.

**Stranraer.** Crailloch Burn, about 1 mile W.N.W. of Piltanton Burn, at bend of stream, 2 miles S.W. of Stranraer.
Ordovician, Caradoc Series (Glenkiln Series) ; contains graptolites.
Peach, B. N. and Horne, J. 1899, pp. 409-410.
Geol. Surv. 3 ; Ord. Pop. 90.

**Stranraer.** Innermessan : boulder clay near Innermessan, 2 miles N.E. of Stranraer.
Pleistocene, glacial deposits ; contain lamellibranchs, gastropods and foraminifera.
Geol. Surv. 3 ; Ord. Pop. 90.

**Whithorn.** Shore 400 yds. W. of Burrow Head and about 100 yds. W. from old ruined fort, 4 miles S.S.E. of Whithorn.
Silurian, Llandovery Series (Tarannon Group), and Wenlock Series ; contain graptolites, cephalopods and arthropods.
Peach, B. N. and Horne, J. 1899, pp. 551-552.
Geol. Surv. 2 ; Ord. Pop. 91.

**Whithorn.** Shore cliffs S. of Morrach, about 1 mile N.E. of Burrow Head.
Silurian, Wenlock Shale Series ; contains graptolites.
Peach, B. N. and Horne, J. 1899, pp. 551-552.
Geol. Surv. 2 ; Ord. Pop. 91.

**Whithorn.** Devil's Bridge : shore cliffs ¼ mile N.E. of Burrow Head, 4 miles S.S.E. of Whithorn.
Silurian, Wenlock Shale Series ; contains graptolites and cephalopods.
Peach, B. N. and Horne, J. 1899, pp. 551-552.
Geol. Surv. 2 ; Ord. Pop. 91.

**Wigtown.** Burn W.N.W. of Low Glenling, 6½ miles W.S.W. of Wigtown.
Ordovician, Caradoc Series (Glenkiln-Hartfell shales) ; contain graptolites.
Peach, B. N. and Horne, J. 1899, pp. 177-179.
Geol. Surv. 4 ; Ord. Pop. 91.

## LIST OF WORKS REFERRED TO

N.B.—Papers written jointly by more than two authors are referred to in the text as by the first author " and others." An asterisk indicates that the work includes plates of fossils.

AGASSIZ, L. 1844-1845. " Monographie des Poissons Fossiles du Vieux Grès Rouge ou Système Dévonien (Old Red Sandstone) des Iles Brittaniques et de Russie." Neuchatel.*

ALLAN, J. K. and KNOX, J. 1934. " The Economic Geology of the Fife Coalfields. Area II, Cowdenbeath and Central Fife." *Mem. Geol. Surv.*

ANDERSON, F. W. and PRINGLE, J. 1946. " On a Section of the Balclatchie Beds at Craighead Quarry, near Girvan, Ayrshire." *Geol. Mag.*, vol. lxxxiii, pp. 172-176.

BAILEY, E. B. and ANDERSON, E. M. 1925. " The Geology of Staffa, Iona and Western Mull." *Mem. Geol. Surv.*

—— and others. 1924. " Tertiary and Post-Tertiary Geology of Mull, Loch Aline and Oban." *Mem. Geol. Surv.*

BARRETT, H. H. and RICHEY, J. E. 1945. " The Economic Geology of the Canonbie Coalfield." · *Geol. Surv. Wartime Pamphlet*, No. 42.

BULMAN, O. M. B. 1944-1947. "A Monograph of the Caradoc (Balclatchie) Graptolites from Limestones in Laggan Burn, Ayrshire." *Palaeont. Soc.*

CAMPBELL, R. 1913. " The Geology of South-Eastern Kincardineshire." *Trans. Roy. Soc. Edin.*, vol. xlviii, pp. 923-960, with geol. map.

CARRUTHERS, R. G. and DINHAM, C. H. 1917. " The Economic Geology of the Central Coalfield of Scotland. Area VIII, East Kilbride and Quarter." *Mem. Geol. Surv.*

CLOUGH, C. T. and others. 1910. " The Geology of East Lothian." 2nd ed. *Mem. Geol. Surv.*

—— (the late) and others. 1920. " The Economic Geology of the Central Coalfield of Scotland. Area VII, Rutherglen, Hamilton and Wishaw." *Mem. Geol. Surv.*

—— (the late) and others. 1925. " The Geology of the Glasgow District." 2nd ed. *Mem. Geol. Surv.*

—— (the late) and others. 1926. " The Economic Geology of the Central Coalfield of Scotland. Area V, Glasgow East, Coatbridge and Airdrie." 2nd ed. *Mem. Geol. Surv.*

CRAMPTON, C. B. and CARRUTHERS, R. G. 1914. " The Geology of Caithness." *Mem. Geol. Surv.*

DINHAM, C. H. and HALDANE, D. 1932. " The Economic Geology of the Stirling and Clackmannan Coalfield." *Mem. Geol. Surv.*

FORSTER-COOPER, C. 1937. " The Middle Devonian Fish Fauna of Achanarras." *Trans. Roy. Soc. Edin.*, vol. lix, pp. 223-240.*

GARWOOD, E. J. 1931. " The Tuedian Beds of Northern Cumberland and Roxburghshire East of the Liddel Water." *Quart. Journ. Geol. Soc.*, vol. lxxxvii, pp. 97-159, with geol. map.*

GEIKIE, A. 1900. " The Geology of Central and Western Fife and Kinross." *Mem. Geol. Surv.*

——. 1902. " The Geology of Eastern Fife." *Mem. Geol. Surv.*

HALDANE, D. and ALLAN, J. K. 1931. " The Economic Geology of the Fife Coalfields. Area I, Dunfermline and West Fife." *Mem. Geol. Surv.*

HARKER, A. 1908. " The Geology of the Small Isles of Inverness-shire (Rum, Canna, Eigg, Muck, etc.)." *Mem. Geol. Surv.*

HARVIE BROWN, J. A. and BUCKLEY, T. E. 1895. (*See* TRAQUAIR, R. H. 1895.) "A Fauna of the Moray Basin." 2 vols. *Edinburgh.**

HEINTZ, A. 1938. " Notes on Arthrodira." *Norsk Geol. Tidsskrift,* vol. xviii, pp. 1-27.*

HICKLING, G. 1912. " On the Geology and Palaeontology of Forfarshire." *Proc. Geol. Assoc.,* vol. xxiii, pp. 302-311.

HILL, D. 1937-1941. "A Monograph on the Carboniferous Rugose Corals of Scotland." *Palaeont. Soc.**

HINXMAN, L. W. and GRANT WILSON, J. S. 1902. " The Geology of Lower Strathspey." *Mem. Geol. Surv.*

—— and others. 1917. " The Economic Geology of the Central Coalfield of Scotland. Area II." *Mem. Geol. Surv.*

—— and others. 1920. " The Economic Geology of the Central Coalfield of Scotland. Area IV, Paisley, Barrhead, Renfrew." *Mem. Geol. Surv.*

—— and others. 1921. " The Economic Geology of the Central Coalfield of Scotland. Area IX, Carluke, Strathaven and Larkhall." *Mem. Geol. Surv.*

HORNE, J. 1923. " The Geology of Lower Findhorn and Lower Strath Nairn." *Mem. Geol. Surv.*

KIDSTON, R. and LANG, W. H. 1917, 1920, 1921. " On Old Red Sandstone Plants showing Structure, from the Rhynie Chert Bed, Aberdeenshire." *Trans. Roy. Soc. Edin.,* vol. li, pp. 761-784 ; vol. lii, pp. 603-627, 643-650, 831-902.*

LAMONT, A. 1935. " The Drummock Group, Girvan ; a stratigraphical Revision, with Descriptions of New Fossils from the Lower Part of the Group." *Trans. Geol. Soc. Glasgow,* vol. xix, pp. 288-334, with geol. map.*

LEE, G. W. 1920. " The Mesozoic Rocks of Applecross, Raasay and North-East Skye." *Mem. Geol. Surv.*

—— and BAILEY, E. B. 1925. " The Pre-Tertiary Geology of Mull, Loch Aline and Oban." *Mem. Geol. Surv.*

—— and CROOKALL, R. 1930. *See* Richey, J. E. and others. 1930.

MACGREGOR, M. 1913. " The Garriongill Section at Overtown, near Wishaw." *Trans. Geol. Soc. Glasgow,* vol. xiv, pp. 279-290, with geol. map.

—— and ANDERSON, E. M. 1923. " The Economic Geology of the Central Coalfield of Scotland. Area VI, Bathgate, Wilsontown and Shotts." *Mem. Geol. Surv.*

—— and HALDANE, D. 1933. " The Economic Geology of the Central Coalfield. Area III, Bo'ness and Linlithgow." *Mem. Geol. Surv.*

MACLENNAN, R. M. 1946. " The Carbonicola Fauna of the Ovalis Zone in Scotland." *Trans. Geol. Soc. Glasgow,* vol. xxi, pp. 75-96.

MILLER, Hugh. 1841 (and later editions). " The Old Red Sandstone, or New Walks in an old Field." *Edinburgh.*

PEACH, B. N. and HORNE, J. 1899. " The Silurian Rocks of Britain. Vol. I. Scotland." *Mem. Geol. Surv.*

——. 1903. " The Canonbie Coalfield : its Geological Structure and Relations to the Carboniferous Rocks of the North of England and Central Scotland." *Trans. Roy. Soc. Edin.*, vol. xl, pp. 835-877, with geol. map.

—— and others. 1907. " The Geological Structure of the North-West Highlands of Scotland." *Mem. Geol. Surv.*

——. 1910a. " The Geology of the Neighbourhood of Edinburgh." *Mem. Geol. Surv.*

——. 1910b. " The Geology of Glenelg, Lochalsh and South-East part of Skye." *Mem. Geol. Surv.*

READ, H. H. 1923. " The Geology of the Country around Banff, Huntly and Turriff." *Mem. Geol. Surv.*

—— and others. 1925. " The Geology of the Country around Golspie, Sutherlandshire." *Mem. Geol. Surv.*

RICHEY, J. E. and THOMAS, H. H. 1930. " The Geology of Ardnamurchan, North-West Mull and Coll." *Mem. Geol. Surv.*

—— and others. 1930. " The Geology of North Ayrshire." *Mem. Geol. Surv.*

ROBERTSON, T. and HALDANE, D. 1937. " The Economic Geology of the Central Coalfield. Area I, Kilsyth and Kirkintilloch." *Mem. Geol. Surv.*

SCOURFIELD, D. J. 1926. " On a New Type of Crustacean from the Old Red Sandstone (Rhynie Chert Bed, Aberdeenshire)—*Lepidocaris rhyniensis*, gen. et sp. nov." *Phil. Trans. Roy. Soc.*, Ser. B, vol. 214, pp. 153-187.*

——. 1940. " The Oldest Known Fossil Insect." *Nature*, vol. cxlv, pp. 799-801.

SEDGWICK, A. and MURCHISON, R. I. 1829. " On the Structure and Relations of the Deposits contained between the Primary Rocks and the Oolitic Series in the North of Scotland." *Trans. Geol. Soc.*, Ser. 2, vol. iii, pp. 125-160.*

SIMPSON, J. B. and RICHEY, J. E. 1936. " The Geology of the Sanquhar Coalfield and adjacent Basin of Thornhill." *Mem. Geol. Surv.*

SPENCER, W. K. 1925. "A Monograph of the British Palaeozoic Asterozoa." Part VI. *Palaeont. Soc.*

STENSIÖ, E. A. 1932. " Cephalaspids of Great Britain." *Brit. Mus. (Nat. Hist.).*

TRAQUAIR, R. H. 1895 (in Harvie Brown, J. A. and Buckley, T. E.). " The Extinct Vertebrate Animals of the Moray Firth Area." (Vol. 2, pp. 235-285.).*

——. 1899. " Report on Fossil Fishes collected by the Geological Survey of Scotland in the Silurian Rocks of the South of Scotland." *Trans. Roy. Soc. Edin.*, vol. xxxix, pp. 827-864.*

——. 1905. " Supplementary Report on the Fossil Fishes collected by the Geological Survey of Scotland in the Upper Silurian Rocks of Scotland." *Trans. Roy. Soc. Edin.*, vol. xl, pp. 879-888.*

TRUEMAN, A. E. and WEIR, J. 1945-. "A Monograph of British Carboniferous Non-Marine Lamellibranchia." *Palaeont. Soc.*

TYRRELL, G. W. 1928. " The Geology of Arran." *Mem. Geol. Surv.*

WEIR, J. and LEITCH, D. 1936. " The Zonal Distribution of the Non-Marine Lamellibranchs in the Coal Measures of Scotland." *Trans. Roy. Soc. Edin.*, vol. lviii, pp. 697-751.*

WESTOLL, T. S. 1945. "A New Cephalaspid Fish from the Downtonian of Scotland, with Notes on the Structure and Classification of Ostracoderms." *Trans. Roy. Soc. Edin.*, vol. lxi, pp. 341-357.*

WHITE, E. I. 1946. " The Genus *Phialaspis* and the ' *Psammosteus* Limestones.' " *Quart. Journ. Geol. Soc.*, vol. ci, pp. 207-242.*

WRIGHT, J. 1920. " On Carboniferous Crinoids from Fife : with Notes on some Localities, and Provisional Lists of Species." *Trans. Geol. Soc. Glasgow*, vol. xvi, pp. 364-392.*

——. 1924. "A ' Woodocrinus ' Fauna from the Scottish Border." *Geol. Mag.*, vol. lxi, pp. 270-279.*

——. 1925. " Notes on the Occurrence of Crinoids in the Carboniferous Limestones of Scotland." *Trans. Geol. Soc. Edin.*, vol. xi, pp. 275-299.*

——. 1932. " The Scottish Species of *Allagecrinus*." *Geol. Mag.*, vol. lxix, pp. 337-366.*

——. 1939. " The Scottish Carboniferous Crinoidea." *Trans. Roy. Soc. Edin.*, vol. lx, pp. 1-78.*